THE STRUCTURE OF ATOMS AND MOLECULES

by V.

Translated from the Russian by G. Yankovsky

DOVER PUBLICATIONS, INC., NEW YORK

Published in Canada by General Publishing Company, Ltd., 30 Lesmill Road, Don Mills, Toronto, Ontario.

Published in the United Kingdom by Constable and Company, Ltd., 10 Orange Street, London W. C. 2.

This Dover edition, first published in 1965, is an unabridged and unaltered republication of the work first published by the Foreign Languages Publishing House, Moscow.

Library of Congress Catalog Card Number 65-26029

Manufactured in the United States of America

Dover Publications, Inc.
180 Varick Street
New York, N. Y. 10014

CONTENTS

Chapter 1

ELECTRONS AND QUANTA

Chapter 2

ATOMIC NUCLEUS

Chapter 9

ELECTRICAL AND MAGNETIC PROPERTIES OF ATOMS AND MOLECULES

Chapter 10

MOLECULAR CONSTANTS

CHAPTER 1

ELECTRONS AND QUANTA

1. The Elementary Electric Charge

Ions in solutions. Since the time of Davy and Faraday it has been known that atoms and molecules (and also fragments of molecules—radicals) may be either electrically neutral or possess electric charge, positive or negative. As far back as 1807, Davy came to the correct conclusion that electric charges can arise in the chemical interaction of molecules (in solution) or can be imparted to particles of matter when the latter undergoes chemical decomposition by electric current. In 1834 Faraday expressed the view that the electric conduction of solutions is due to the motion of these charged particles (which he called ions) in an electric field. Faraday distinguished between positively charged ions, or *cations*, and negatively charged ions, *anions*.

The laws of electrolysis discovered by Faraday provided the first experimental proof of the existence of an *elementary electric charge*, which was formulated most explicitly by Helmholtz in 1881 in his Faraday address: "If we accept the existence of atoms of elements, we cannot avoid the further corollary that electricity too — both positive and negative — is divided into definite elementary quantities, which behave like atoms of electricity."

The magnitude of this elementary quantity of electricity, or elementary charge, could be obtained from Faraday's laws. In accordance with these laws, the passage of a certain quantity of electricity through an electrolyte always causes the deposition, on the electrodes, of a strictly definite amount of the given element, different elements being deposited in amounts proportional to their *electrochemical equivalents*, that is, their atomic weights A divided by the valence of the given element V. Thus, 1 coul of electricity deposits from a solution of silver nitrate $q = 1.118$ mg (milligrams) of silver, from a solution of cupric salt 0.3292 mg of copper, and from a solution of ferric salt 0.1930 mg of iron. The electrochemical equivalents of these metals are 107.88, 31.77, and 18.62, respectively. Dividing the electrochemical equivalent of a given element by the appropriate value of q, we obtain the *Faraday constant* F; this is the number of coulombs of electricity that deposits a quantity of grams of the given element which is numerically equal to its electrochemical equivalent:

$$F = 96{,}500 \text{ coul.}$$

Since in this number of grams there are $\frac{N_A}{V}$ atoms of the given metal (N_A is the Avogadro number, which is 6.02×10^{23} atoms per gram atom), by dividing the Faraday constant (expressed in absolute electrostatic units) by the number of atoms $\frac{N_A}{V}$ we obtain the following expression for the charge of a single ion:

$$Q = V\frac{F}{N_A} \qquad (1.1)$$

From this formula it follows that the charge of an ion is an *integral multiple* (V-multiple) of a certain *minimum (elementary) charge:*

$$e = \frac{F}{N_A} = 4.82 \times 10^{-10} \text{ CGSE.}$$

Thus, the charge of an ion of silver Ag^{+} is equal to e, that of an ion of bivalent copper Cu^{++}, 2e, and of an ion of trivalent iron Fe^{+++}, 3e.

Ions in gases. Measurements of ion charges in gases have shown that in this case also the charge of the ion is an integral multiple of the elementary charge e which has the value given above. We shall pass over earlier attempts at an experimental determination of the charge of a gaseous ion by various workers and touch only on the experiments of Millikan (1910-16), in which the procedures of earlier investigators were considerably refined. In his first experiments, Millikan measured the rate of fall, in air, of individual water droplets formed through the condensation of supersaturated vapour on gaseous ions The presence of an electric charge Q on a liquid drop could be established by the change in rate of fall (or by change in the sign of the velocity) when an electric field was switched on. By appropriate choice of the magnitude of the field intensity E, it was possible to stop the drop in its fall when the electric force QE balanced the force of gravity, i. e., the weight of the drop mg (m is the mass of the drop and g is the acceleration of gravity).

Assuming that the Stokes law holds for a freely falling drop (in the absence of an electric field), we have

$$mg = 6\pi\eta r v \qquad (1.2)$$

where η is the viscosity factor of air, r is the radius of the drop, and v is its rate of fall. In the case of a stationary drop,

$$mg=QE. \tag{1.3}$$

Taking into account that $m=\frac{4}{3}\pi r^3\varrho$ (ϱ is the density of the drop) and eliminating r from equations (1.2) and (1.3), we see that simultaneous solution of these equations gives

$$Q=9\sqrt{2}\,\eta^{3/2}(g\varrho)^{-1/2}\frac{v^{\frac{3}{2}}}{E}. \tag{1.4}$$

Thus, by measuring the speed of a freely falling drop v and the intensity of the balancing field E, it was possible to determine the charge of the drop with the aid of η and ϱ, which are found from equation (1.4). By such measurements Millikan found that the charge of the drop and, hence, the charge of a gaseous ion (just as in the case of ions in solutions) is a magnitude which is a *multiple* of a certain minimum quantity e and which came out equal to $e=4.70\times10^{-10}$ CGSE; in other words, it coincided, within the limits of experimental error, with the elementary charge of an ion in solution.

In subsequent experiments, Millikan used droplets of oil. Besides, he introduced a correction for the Stokes law, which takes into account the effect of Brownian motion on the frictional force experienced by a falling droplet. The experiments were conducted at different air pressure. The elementary ionic charge obtained in these experiments was $e=4.774\times10^{-10}$ CGSE. The presently accepted value of the elementary electric charge is

$$e=(4.80217\pm0.00006)\times10^{-10}\ \text{CGSE}.$$

We may add that, applying a method similar to Millikan's, Ioffe, in 1912, measured the charge acquired by metal dust particles (suspended in air) through irradiation with ultraviolet light (photoelectric effect). In this case, too, the charge of a dust particle is an integral multiple of the elementary charge.

2. Specific Charge and Mass of an Electron

Cathode rays. Numerous investigations of ions in various gases show that the positive ions always have a mass comparable with the mass of the atoms and molecules of the given gas. In other words, these ions are positively charged gas molecules or fragments of molecules. In addition to ions with masses comparable with those of molecules and atoms, at low pressures there are observed negatively charged particles of mass thousands of times less than that of an atom. The existence of these particles, called *electrons*,* is evident from investigations of the so-called cathode rays, which are observed in electric discharges in gases at low pressures. One of the features of an electric discharge arising in a gas at pressures of several millimetres of mercury or less and at potential differences of thousands and tens of thousands of volts is luminescence of the gas, which is particularly intense near the cathode (negative luminescence). Measurements of the distribution of potential along the path of the discharge show that the potential drop (and, consequently, the electric force) is particularly great also near the cathode (cathode potential drop), where it can attain many hundreds of volts per centimetre (V/cm). When the gas pressure is reduced to hundredths of a millimetre of mercury and less, the negative glow (and also the glow in the remaining part of the discharge tube, which is called positive) disappears; in its place there appears a faintly luminescent beam from the cathode along the axis of the discharge tube—the cathode beam. Numerous experiments showed that this beam is actually a stream of negatively charged particles. It was likewise established that these particles are emitted by the surface of the metallic cathode as a result of its bombardment with positive ions that acquired high energies in the region of the cathode potential drop.

Specific electronic charge. Many scientists measured the deflection of cathode rays in electric and magnetic fields and determined the specific charge of the particles of the cathode beam (electrons), i.e., the ratio of the charge of the electron to its mass. In the very first experiments, J. J. Thomson (1897) established that the magnitude of the specific charge is independent of the material of the cathode and of the nature of the gas in the zone of discharge and that, consequently, the electron is some universal elementary particle which is a component of the atoms of all elements. In these experiments, it was also found that the quantity e/m (e is the absolute magnitude of the electronic charge, m is the electron mass) is about 10^7 CGSE. We shall not dwell on the peculiarities of various methods used to determine the specific electronic charge; by way of illustration, we take the Kaufmann method, which is the most precise.

---

* The term "electron" was proposed by Stoney in 1891 to designate an elementary electric charge of any sign. Later the name electron was given to a negatively charged particle of a definite (small) mass (see below). In 1932, the positively charged counterpart—positron—was discovered.

In Kaufmann's experiments, the cathode beam accelerated by the electric field of a discharge tube (direction x) entered a transverse magnetic field (direction y). According to the Biot-Savart law, each electron in the magnetic field is subjected to a force evH (where v is the speed of the electron and H is the magnetic-field intensity) which is normal to the direction of motion of the electrons and which deflects the cathode beam from its original direction (x). For small angles of deflection, the direction of magnetic force may be considered perpendicular to x (direction z), whence it follows that

$$m\frac{d^2z}{dt^2}=evH.$$

Taking into account that $v=v_0=\frac{dx}{dt}$ and integrating the foregoing equation, we get

$$z=\frac{1}{v_0}\frac{e}{m}\int_0^l dx\int_0^x H\,dx,$$

where l is the path length of the cathode beam in the magnetic field. On the basis of

$$\frac{mv_0^2}{2}=eV,$$

where V is the potential difference that accelerates the electrons, we obtain from the foregoing equation the following expression for the specific electronic charge:

$$\frac{e}{m}=\frac{2z^2V}{\left(\int_0^l dx\int_0^x H\,dx\right)^2}. \tag{2.1}$$

Measuring the quantities of equation (2.1), we obtain the specific electronic charge $\frac{e}{m}$. According to Kaufmann, $\frac{e}{m}=1.8\times10^7$ CGSE. This value is sufficiently close to the subsequently obtained and more precise value

$$\frac{e}{m}=(1.758896\pm0.000028)\times10^7\ \text{CGSE}.$$

Electronic mass. From this value of the specific electronic charge and the quantity e (p. 9), we obtain for the mass of the electron:

$$m=(0.910710\pm0.000022)\times10^{-27}\ \text{g}.$$

This is the so-called rest mass, the mass of a stationary electron or an electron moving with a velocity negligibly small in comparison to the velocity of light. * We denote the rest mass by m_0 and the mass of a moving electron by m; there is a definite relationship between these two masses. From the concept of an electron contracting in the direction of motion (Lorentz) and also from relativity theory (Einstein) we obtain the following expression for this relationship:

$$m = \frac{m_0}{\sqrt{1-\beta^2}}, \tag{2.2}$$

where $\beta = \frac{v}{c}$ is the ratio of electron velocity to the velocity of light.

The rest mass of an electron is approximately 2000 times less than that of an atom of hydrogen. The precise value of the ratio of the mass of an H atom, m_H, to the rest mass of an electron, m_0, is obtained from the mass of the H atom,

$$m_H = (1.673059 \pm 0.000080) \times 10^{-24} \text{ g},$$

and from the rest mass of the electron given above:

$$m_H : m_0 = 1837.093 \pm 0.044.$$

To summarise, the specific charge of an atomic ion of hydrogen (proton) is approximately 2000 times less than the specific electronic charge. The specific charge of all other ions is over 2000 times less than the specific electronic charge.

3. Thermionic emission

Thermionic current as a function of applied potential difference. It has been pointed out above that cathode rays arise as a result of electron emission by metals under bombardment of the metal surface with fast ions. In the above-mentioned experiments carried out by Ioffe, metallic dust particles emitted electrons (and were charged positively in the process) when illuminated with ultraviolet light. It will be noted that the first precise measurements of the specific charge of photoelectrons were made in experiments carried out by Kaufmann who obtained $e/m = 1.8 \times \times 10^7$ CGSE. Kaufmann likewise found the mass of the photoelectron to be a function of its velocity.

Metals are also capable of emitting electrons when heated. By placing two electrodes, one hot and one cold, in an evacuated

* The velocity of light *in vacuo* is $c = 299{,}790.0 \pm 0.7$ km/sec, or approximately 3×10^{10} cm/sec.

vessel and applying a potential difference between them, it is possible to measure the emission current from the heated electrode and also to convince oneself that this current is perceptible only when the hot electrode is at a negative potential (relative to the cold one), in other words, that the emission current is due to the ejection of negatively charged particles by the hot metal. A study of the emission current as a function of the potential difference permits determining the specific charge of these particles, which appears to coincide with the specific electronic charge.

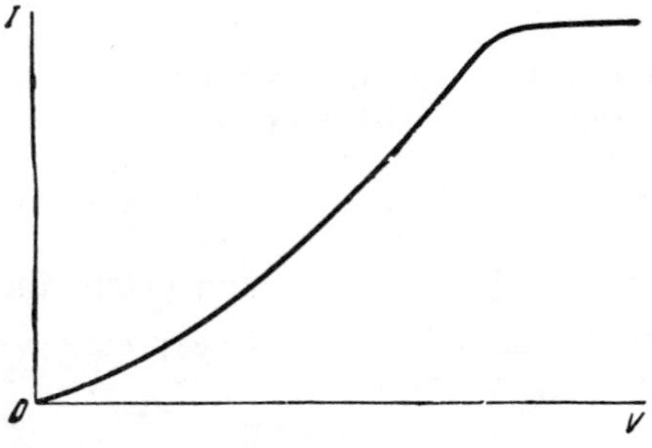

Fig. 1. The electron-emission current I as a function of potential difference V

An experimentally derived graph of the emission current versus applied potential difference is given in Fig. 1. It will be seen that the current at first increases with the potential difference faster than by the law of direct proportionality; then, at a certain potential difference, it reaches saturation, i.e., it ceases to be a function of V. This shape of the I vs. V curve may be explained as follows. The initial current increase is due to the fact that as V increases, more and more electrons emitted by the cathode reach the anode. The remaining electrons are returned to the cathode by the space charge near the cathode; and the lower V is, the greater the density of the space charge. At a certain potential difference the space charge disappears since all the electrons emitted by the cathode reach the anode. Obviously, if the temperature of the cathode remains constant, further rise in potential difference cannot increase the current because the number of emitted electrons is determined by the temperature (see below); for a constant temperature, it determines the observed maximum emission current (*saturation current*). If the temperature of the cathode is increased (at a constant potential difference) the saturation current rises.

For the ascending portion of the I vs. V curve in Fig. 1, the current I as a function of potential difference V may be given by a theoretical formula obtained on the basis of the foregoing reasoning and properly reflecting the I-V relationship. Considering a one-dimensional problem, i.e., taking both electrodes to be parallel planes, we shall have the following differential equation for a potential at a certain point at a distance x from the cathode, V_x:

$$\frac{d^2V_x}{dx^2} = -4\pi\varrho$$

(Poisson equation), where ϱ is the density of the space charge at point x; it is connected with the density of the emission current by the following relation:

$$i = \varrho v.$$

Here, the electron velocity v at point x may be expressed in terms of the potential V_x:

$$\frac{mv^2}{2} = eV_x,$$

or $v = \sqrt{2\frac{e}{m}V_x}$ (e and m are the charge and mass of the electron). Substituting this expression into the differential equation for V_x, we obtain

$$\frac{d^2V_x}{dx^2} = -4\pi i \sqrt{\frac{1}{2}\frac{m}{e}}\frac{1}{\sqrt{V_x}}.$$

Integrating this equation for the boundary conditions $V_x = 0$ and $\frac{dV_x}{dx} = 0$ at $x = 0$ (cathode) and $V_x = V$ at $x = d$ (anode) and solving the expression obtained for i, we find

$$i = \frac{\sqrt{2}}{9\pi}\sqrt{\frac{e}{m}}\frac{V^{3/2}}{d^2}. \tag{3.1}$$

In the case of a cylindrical design, when the cathode is a wire and the anode a cylinder of radius r (the cathode is situated on the axis of the cylinder), solution of the differential equation for the potential leads to the following formula:

$$i = \frac{2\sqrt{2}}{9}\sqrt{\frac{e}{m}}\frac{V^{3/2}}{r\beta^2} \tag{3.2}$$

where $\beta = \ln\frac{r}{a} - \frac{2}{5}\left(\ln\frac{r}{a}\right)^2 + \frac{11}{120}\left(\ln\frac{r}{a}\right)^3 - \frac{47}{3300}\left(\ln\frac{r}{a}\right)^4 + \ldots$
(a is the radius of the wire).

It will be seen that in both cases the emission current, for a given potential difference, is proportional to $\sqrt{\frac{e}{m}}$; this enables us, by measuring the magnitude of i for various V, to determine the specific electronic charge $\frac{e}{m}$. As a result of measurements of this kind, Langmuir obtained the value $\frac{e}{m}=1.775\times10^7$ electromagnetic units (emu), which is very close to the subsequently obtained more precise value (see p. 11).

Richardson's equation. According to equations (3.1) and (3.2), the emission current increases with the potential difference as $V^{3/2}$. As has already been pointed out, this rise ceases when all the electrons emitted by the hot cathode reach the anode. The emission current can then be computed as follows. Assuming the number of "free" electrons in each cubic centimetre of metal (conduction electrons) to be n and taking the Maxwellian distribution of electron velocities for the portion of electrons the velocities of which along the axis x, perpendicular to the surface of the cathode, are contained between $\dot{x}$ and $\dot{x}+d\dot{x}$, we will have

$$\frac{dn_{\dot{x}}}{n}=\frac{e^{-\frac{m\dot{x}^2}{2kT}}d\dot{x}}{\int\limits_{-\infty}^{+\infty}e^{-\frac{m\dot{x}^2}{2kT}}d\dot{x}}=\frac{e^{-\frac{m\dot{x}^2}{2kT}}d\dot{x}}{\sqrt{\frac{2\pi kT}{m}}}.$$

Due to the electron-retarding field on the surface of the metal, only those electrons moving in the positive direction of the x axis will be emitted whose energies exceed a certain value $e\varphi$, which is the *work function* for the removal of an electron from the metal and is characterised by the *contact potential* of the given metal φ. Thus, for the density of the saturation current at a certain temperature T we have

$$i=e\int\limits_{\dot{x}_0}^{\infty}\dot{x}\,dn_{\dot{x}},$$

where $\dot{x}_0$ is the minimum velocity at which electron emission is still possible; it is determined by the condition

$$\frac{m\dot{x}_0^2}{2}=e\varphi.$$

Substituting $dn_{\dot{x}}$ into the expression for i and performing integration, we obtain the following expression for the density of the saturation current:

$$i=en\sqrt{\frac{kT}{2\pi m}}\,e^{-\frac{e\varphi}{kT}}. \qquad (3.3)$$

Equation (3.3) is called *Richardson's equation*.

Experiments carried out by Richardson and other workers showed that this equation gives a correct description of the saturation current as a function of temperature. For instance, in a graphical representation of $\ln \frac{i}{\sqrt{T}}$ as a function of $\frac{1}{T}$ we obtain a straight line corresponding to equation (3.3); whence follows the constancy of φ (for the given metal). At the same time, experiments show that the values of "free"-electron density in the metal as computed from the pre-exponential factor in equation (3.3) do not accord with the conventional concepts of identity of the number of "free" and valence electrons of a given metal. Thus, for example, for a tungsten cathode Richardson obtained $n_e = 9.9 \times 10^{20}$ electrons per cm^3 (for tungsten, Richardson found $\varphi = 4.25$ V). Yet, when computing the number of atoms of tungsten in one cubic centimetre of metal from the formula

$$n_{at} = N_A \frac{\varrho}{A} \tag{3.4}$$

(ϱ is the density of tungsten equal to 19.1, A is its atomic weight, 184.0), we find $n_{at} = 6.24 \times 10^{22}$ atoms per cm^3, which is some 60 times that of n_e. Without going into the reasons for this discrepancy, let it be noted that it precludes any possibility of directly determining the electronic charge on the basis of Richardson's equation (3.3).

Field-induced electron emission. The electronic charge may be obtained from data on the ejection of electrons from metal by an electric field. Sufficiently strong electric fields give rise to a number of phenomena (unipolar conduction of plate-point contact, vacuum breakdown) which are due to field-induced electron emission. Increased thermionic emission is likewise observed in strong electric fields. As was shown by Schottky, when the electric field is sufficiently strong, the Richardson equation for saturation current (3.3), which we shall rewrite in the following simplified form

$$i = i_0 e^{-\frac{e\varphi}{kT}}, \tag{3.3'}$$

converts to the following equation:

$$i = i_0 e^{-\frac{e\varphi - \sqrt{e^3 E}}{kT}}, \tag{3.5}$$

where E is the electric-field gradient.

From Schottky's equation it follows that at constant temperature the quantity $\ln (i/i_0)$ must be a linear function of the square root of the field gradient; the slope tangent of the straight line

$\ln(i/i_0)$, $\sqrt{E}$ must be equal to $e^{3/2}/kT$. This regularity was corroborated by the experiments of Bruins carried out at high temperatures (1580° K and above) with a tungsten cathode in the form of a 0.02-mm-thick wire. Bruins' data for the electronic charge give $e=4.84\times10^{-10}$ CGSE, which, within experimental error, coincides with the later obtained precise value (see p. 9).

4. Black-Body Radiation

The laws of thermal radiation. In 1859, Kirchhoff demonstrated thermodynamically that at a constant temperature the quantity of radiant energy within a certain closed cavity and representing a spectral interval from λ to $\lambda+d\lambda$, is independent of the walls of the cavity. Denoting the spectral density of this universal radiation, called black-body radiation, by ϱ_λ (the quantity of radiant energy of wavelength λ in unit volume), *Kirchhoff's law*, which expresses this property of ideal black-body radiation, may be written as

$$\varrho_\lambda d\lambda = F(\lambda, T)\, d\lambda, \tag{4.1}$$

where $F(\lambda, T)$ is a certain universal function of the wavelength and temperature.

This function was later (1893) specified by Wien. On the basis of thermodynamics and the electromagnetic theory of light he obtained the following expression for the spectral density of ideal black-body radiation:

$$\varrho_\lambda = \lambda^{-5} f(\lambda T) \tag{4.2}$$

(*Wien's law*). In accordance with the experimental fact that at each given temperature the density of thermal radiation (which always, to a greater or lesser degree, approaches black-body radiation) has a *maximum* at a specific wavelength λ_{max}, from (4.2) we obtain an unambiguous relationship between λ_{max} and T. Indeed, from the condition of the maximum of ϱ_λ $\left(\frac{d\varrho_\lambda}{d\lambda}=0\right)$ we find $5f(\lambda_{max}T)=\lambda_{max}\times Tf'(\lambda_{max}T)$, whence it follows that

$$\lambda_{max} T = \text{const.} \tag{4.3}$$

This relationship, which expresses *Wien's displacement law*, was obtained independently in that same year of 1893 by Golitsyn.

From Wien's law (4.2) there also follows another important law that expresses the dependence of the total density of black-body radiation upon its temperature. This law was earlier established experimentally by Stefan (1879) and theoretically by Boltzmann (1884) and is called the *Stefan-Boltzmann law*. Computing the total density of radiation,

$$u=\int_0^\infty \varrho_\lambda d\lambda=\int_0^\infty \lambda^{-5} f(\lambda,T)\, d\lambda,$$

we obtain the Stefan-Boltzmann law in the form

$$u=\sigma T^4 \tag{4.4}$$

where

$$\sigma=\int_0^\infty \frac{f(\xi)d\xi}{\xi^5} \quad \text{and} \qquad \xi=\lambda T.$$

The spectral density of black-body radiation inside a certain closed cavity may be computed in yet another way. Since in this case we are speaking of the energy of an electromagnetic field within the cavity under consideration, which field (on the assumption that the walls of the cavity are ideal reflectors of light) may be represented as a system of standing electromagnetic waves, the energy of this system may be computed as the product of the number of degrees of freedom of the system by the mean energy of one degree of freedom. Assuming the number of degrees of freedom (this number is equal to that of the natural oscillations of the system) over the range of wavelengths from λ to $\lambda+d\lambda$ to be proportional to the volume of the cavity V and to the magnitude of this range, $\varphi(\lambda)\, Vd\lambda$, we must, for reasons of dimensionality (in view of the fact that the number of degrees of freedom is a dimensionless quantity), set the function $\varphi(\lambda)$ proportional to λ^{-4}. Since a precise computation yields $\varphi\lambda=\frac{8\pi}{\lambda^4}$, for the number of degrees of freedom we shall have

$$\varphi(\lambda)\, Vd\lambda=8\pi V\lambda^{-4}d\lambda.$$

Further, designating the mean energy of one degree of freedom by $\bar{\varepsilon}$, we get

$$\varrho_\lambda d\lambda=8\pi\lambda^{-4}\bar{\varepsilon}d\lambda \tag{4.5}$$

or, passing from λ to ν and noting that $\varrho_\lambda d\lambda=-\varrho_\nu d\nu$, $\nu=\frac{c}{\lambda}$ and $d\lambda=-\frac{c}{\nu^2}d\nu$ (where c is the velocity of light), we find

$$\varrho_\nu d\nu=8\pi\frac{\nu^2}{c^3}\bar{\varepsilon}d\nu. \tag{4.6}$$

Identifying each degree of freedom of the system with some *oscillator* and taking the energy distribution between the oscillators to obey the Boltzmann law, we have, for the portion of oscillators possessing energy ε,

$$\frac{N(\varepsilon)}{N} = Ae^{-\frac{\varepsilon}{kT}} \tag{4.7}$$

(N is the total number of oscillators), whence, for the mean energy per oscillator, we obtain

$$\bar{\varepsilon} = \frac{\int\limits_0^\infty \varepsilon N(\varepsilon)\,d\varepsilon}{\int\limits_0^\infty N(\varepsilon)\,d\varepsilon} = \frac{\int\limits_0^\infty \varepsilon e^{-\frac{\varepsilon}{kT}}\,d\varepsilon}{\int\limits_0^\infty e^{-\frac{\varepsilon}{kT}}\,d\varepsilon} = kT. \tag{4.8}$$

Substituting $\bar{\varepsilon} = kT$ into (4.5), we find

$$\varrho_\lambda = 8\pi\lambda^{-4}kT. \tag{4.9}$$

Equation (4.9) is called the *Rayleigh-Jeans equation* and is readily seen to be a particular expression of Wien's law (4.2) that is obtained from the latter when $f(\lambda T) = 8\pi k\lambda T$.

According to this equation, the dependence of the spectral density of black-body radiation upon the wavelength should be expressed by a function that monotonically increases with diminishing wavelength (as $1/\lambda^4$) and tends to ∞ when $\lambda \to 0$. This relationship between ϱ_λ and λ is in sharp contradiction with experiment (particularly in the region of medium and short wavelengths). As has been noted, in actuality, at a certain wavelength λ_{max}, ϱ_λ passes through a maximum; as λ decreases further, ϱ_λ diminishes and approaches zero when $\lambda \to 0$. The variation of ϱ_λ with wavelength according to Rayleigh-Jeans and the experimentally observed relationship between ϱ_λ and λ are given in Fig. 2, where the

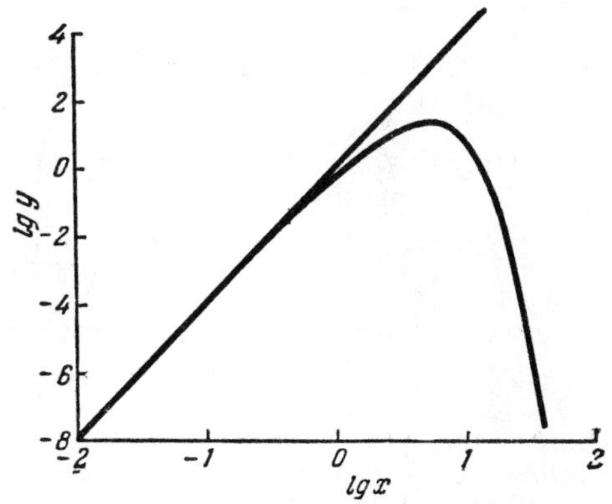

Fig. 2. The spectral density of black-body radiation $\varrho\lambda$ (which is proportional to y) versus the wavelength (which is inversely proportional to x). The straight line is log $\varrho\lambda$ as a function of $1/\lambda$ (after Rayleigh-Jeans)

vertical axis is the logarithm of y, which is proportional to ϱ_λ, and the horizontal axis is the logarithm of x, which is proportional to $1/\lambda$

Light quanta. A way out of the impasse of classical physics and the thermodynamics of radiation was given by Planck in 1900. He reasoned that the energy of each of the oscillators representing electromagnetic radiation can take on only *discrete* values that are *integral multiples* of some quantity ε_0 which is the *energy quantum*: $\varepsilon = n\varepsilon_0$ $(n=0, 1, 2, 3, \ldots)$.

Assuming Boltzmann energy distribution of the oscillators when computing the mean energy of an oscillator, we can again take advantage of equation (4.7); here, however, we replace the integrals in expression (4.8) by summations in accordance with the quantum hypothesis:

$$\bar{\varepsilon} = \frac{\sum\limits_{n=0}^{n=\infty} n\varepsilon_0 e^{-\frac{n\varepsilon_0}{kT}}}{\sum\limits_{n=0}^{n=\infty} e^{-\frac{n\varepsilon_0}{kT}}} = \varepsilon_0 \left(e^{-\frac{\varepsilon_0}{kT}} + e^{-\frac{2\varepsilon_0}{kT}} + e^{-\frac{3\varepsilon_0}{kT}} + \ldots\right) = \frac{\varepsilon_0}{e^{\frac{\varepsilon}{kT}} - 1}. \quad (4.10)$$

Substituting (4.10) into equation (4.6), we obtain for the spectral density of black-body radiation the expression

$$\varrho_\nu = 8\pi \frac{\nu^2}{c^3} \frac{\varepsilon_0}{e^{\frac{\varepsilon_0}{kT}} - 1}.$$

Comparing this formula with the expression of Wien's law (4.2), which, when passing from λ to ν, may be written as

$$\varrho_\nu = \nu^3 \chi\left(\frac{\nu}{T}\right), \quad (4.2')$$

we see that both formulas can agree only on the condition that

$$\varepsilon_0 = h\nu \quad (4.11)$$

where the proportionality factor h is a universal constant (*Planck's constant*) with the dimensions of energy multiplied by time. From (4.11), the expression for ϱ_ν assumes the form

$$\varrho_\nu = \frac{8\pi\nu^2}{c^3} \frac{h\nu}{e^{\frac{h\nu}{kT}} - 1}. \quad (4.12)$$

Formula (4.12) is called the *Planck radiation formula*.

It will readily be seen that in the region of low frequencies (long waves) that satisfy the condition $h\nu \ll kT$, the Planck formula passes into the Rayleigh-Jeans equation, which, in terms of ν, takes the form

$$\varrho_\nu = 8\pi \frac{\nu^2}{c^3} kT. \tag{4.9'}$$

Indeed, in this case or under the identical condition $\varepsilon_0 \ll kT$, expanding the function $e^{\frac{\varepsilon_0}{kT}} = 1 + \frac{\varepsilon_0}{kT} + \ldots$ in a series and confining ourselves to the first two terms of the expansion, we obtain from (4.10) $\bar{\varepsilon} = kT$, which is the result earlier established by means of the classical formula (4.8). This accounts for the fact that in the region of long wavelengths the Rayleigh-Jeans equation is confirmed experimentally (see Fig. 2).

In the limiting case of high frequencies that satisfy the condition $h\nu \gg kT$, the Planck formula (4.12) may be written in the form

$$\varrho_\nu = \frac{8\pi h \nu^3}{c^3} e^{-\frac{h\nu}{kT}}, \tag{4.13}$$

or in the form

$$\varrho_\lambda = c_1 \lambda^{-5} e^{-\frac{c_2}{\lambda T}}, \tag{4.13'}$$

where $c_1 = 8\pi ch$ and $c_2 = \frac{hc}{k}$. Equation 4.13) coincides with the equation proposed by Wien in 1896 that correctly describes the variation of ϱ_λ with wavelength in the range of short wavelengths.

Rewriting the Planck formula (4.12) in the form

$$\varrho_\lambda = c_1 \lambda^{-5} \frac{1}{e^{\frac{c_2}{\lambda T}} - 1}, \tag{4.12'}$$

we obtain the following equation from the condition of maximum density of radiation:

$$\frac{x_{max}}{5} + e^{-x_{max}} = 1,$$

where $x_{max} = \frac{hc}{k\lambda_{max} T} = \frac{c_2}{\lambda_{max} T}$. A graphical solution of this equation yields $x_{max} = 4.965$ and, hence,

$$\lambda_{max} T = \frac{1}{4.965} \frac{hc}{k} = \text{const}.$$

Substituting here the experimentally obtained value of $\lambda_{max} T = = \text{const} = 0.288$ cm deg and the values of the constants

$c=3\times 10^{10}$ cm/sec and $k=1.38\times 10^{-16}$ erg deg^{-1}, we obtain for the Planck constant $h=6.58\times 10^{-27}$ erg sec.

In exactly the same way, from equation (4.12′) for the constant of the Stefan-Boltzmann law σ (4.4) we obtain the expression $\left(x=\frac{c_2}{\lambda T}\right)$:

$$\sigma=\frac{c_1}{c_2^4}\int_0^\infty \frac{x^3dx}{e^x-1}=\frac{8\pi k^4}{h^3c^3}\int_0^\infty \frac{x^3dx}{e^x-1}.$$

Evaluating the integral $\int_0^\infty \frac{x^3dx}{e^x-1}$ graphically, we find 6.494. Substituting this number together with the experimental value of the constant $\sigma=7.64\times 10^{-15}$ erg cm^{-3} deg^{-4} and the values of the constants c and k into the preceding expression, for Planck's constant we find $h=6.52\times 10^{-27}$ erg sec.

It may be noted that there are also other possibilities of an experimental determination of the constant h. Spectroscopic measurements are the most accurate. At present, the most precise value is

$$h=(6.62363\pm 0.00016)\times 10^{-27} \text{ erg sec.}$$

5. The Photoelectric Effect

Photoelectrons. The quantum hypothesis proved fruitful in interpreting a number of other phenomena, including the *photoelectric effect*, which consists in the emission of electrons by metals (and other bodies) when the latter are irradiated with light of sufficiently short wavelengths. As early as 1887, Hertz noticed that when the electrodes of a spark gap are irradiated with ultraviolet light the discharge sets in at a lower voltage. As Hallwachs established in 1888, a drop in the discharge voltage is due to the appearance of electrically charged particles emitted by the cathode as a result of illumination. This phenomenon was subjected to a quantitative study by Stoletov (1888-90), who found that the magnitude of the photoelectric current is *strictly proportional to the intensity* of the light absorbed by the cathode. The next step in the study of the photoelectric effect was made by Lenard, who showed that the charged particles emitted by the cathode under illumination are *electrons* (1899). In addition, Lenard found (1902) that the emission of electrons from the metal is possible only at a frequency of the light that exceeds a *certain minimal value* ν_0, and the energy of the ejected electrons (photoelectrons) increases with *increasing difference* $\nu-\nu_0$ and is *independent of the intensity of the light*, which (in accord with the law established by Stoletov) determines only the number of photoelectrons (the magnitude of the photoelectric current).

Interpretation of these regularities on the basis of the wave theory of light encounters insuperable difficulties. Indeed, if we consider the photoelectric effect as the result of the effect of the electromagnetic field of the wave on the electrons in the metal, it is impossible to account either for the existence of a threshold frequency or for the fact that the energy of the photoelectrons is independent of the light intensity. All the regularities involved in the photoelectric effect were interpreted quantitatively on the basis of the quantum theory formulated by Einstein in 1905.

Quantum theory of the photoelectric effect. Einstein, in a certain sense, revived the corpuscular theory of light and proceeded from the concept of light as a stream of *light quanta*, or *photons*, each of which has an energy $h\nu$. When light is absorbed by a metal, each quantum interacts with *one* electron only. On the basis of this reasoning, the law of conservation of energy, as applied to a single elementary photoelectric event, is expressed as follows:

$$h\nu = h\nu_0 + \frac{mv^2}{2}, \tag{5.1}$$

where ν_0 is the limiting (minimum) photon energy that corresponds to the threshold of the photoeffect and is the work done in ejecting an electron from the metal, and $\frac{mv^2}{2}$ is the kinetic energy of a photoelectron. Equation (5.1) expresses *Einstein's photoelectric law.*

It will readily be seen that all the foregoing regularities of the photoelectric effect follow directly from theory. Indeed, since the intensity of monochromatic light (light of a certain frequency) is proportional to the number of light quanta, and the number of quanta absorbed by the metal is equal to the number of photoelectrons (when $\nu > \nu_0$), the latter must be proportional to the intensity of the absorbed light, as was verified by experiment. Further, from Einstein's law it follows that electron emission is possible only under the condition that $\nu > \nu_0$, when the photon energy is equal to or greater than the electronic work function, which is the energy needed to remove an electron from the metal. Finally, from (5.1) and also in accord with experiment, the energy of the photoelectrons increases with the difference $\nu - \nu_0$ and is independent of the light intensity, or of the number of absorbed quanta.

Einstein's law was subjected to a comprehensive quantitative investigation. Millikan (1916), measuring the maximum energy of the photoelectrons of lithium, sodium, and potassium at various wavelengths by the retarding-field method, found that the quantity $\frac{mv^2}{2}$ is a linear function of the frequency difference $\nu - \nu_0$, in accord with the Einstein law (5.1). From the slope of the straight lines obtained for the Planck constant, he found $h = 6.56 \times 10^{-27}$ erg sec. This value is in good agreement with the precise value (see p. 22) and is indicative of the high degree of accuracy of the Einstein law. Lukirsky and Prilezhayev (1926) carried out particularly detailed and extremely accurate quantitative studies of the photoelectric effect in the case of aluminium, nickel, copper, zinc, silver, cadmium, tin, platinum, and lead. The value of h as measured by these workers came out to 6.55×10^{-27} erg sec.

Moreover, the intersection of the line representing the photoelectron energy as a function of frequency difference $\nu - \nu_0$ with the frequency axis yields the magnitude of the work needed to remove an electron from the metal $h\nu_0$ (a correction must be introduced for the contact difference of potential). For example, from the threshold frequencies thus determined and as found by Millikan ($\nu_0 = 4.39 \times 10^{14}$ sec^{-1} for sodium and $\nu_0 = 5.70 \times 10^{14}$ sec^{-1} for lithium), we obtain the electronic work functions $h\nu_0 = 1.814$ eV (Na) and $h\nu_0 = 2.355$ eV (Li).

In principle, the work function for removal of an electron from a metal computed from the threshold of the photoelectric effect should coincide with the magnitude of $e\varphi$ found from the temperature dependence of thermionic emission (see p. 15). In reality, such coincidence is a rare occurrence because of the extreme sensitivity of the work function value to the state of the metal surface (for instance, to the presence of minute impurities), which is complicated by the different conditions under which the photoelectric and thermionic processes occur (low and high temperatures).

The photoelectric effect is observed not only in the illumination of metals (solid or liquid) but also in the case of solid or liquid non-metals and gases. In the latter case we are obviously dealing with the removal of electrons from the atoms and molecules of the gas, which is *ionisation* of atoms and molecules (*photoionisation*). Designating the work needed to remove an electron from an atom by eI (I is the *ionisation potential*) and noting that eI corresponds to the work needed to remove an electron from the metal $h\nu_0$, we rewrite formula (5.1) as

$$h\nu = eI + \frac{mv^2}{2}. \tag{5.2}$$

From (5.2) it follows that, like the long-wavelength threshold of the photoelectric effect $\left(\lambda=\frac{c}{\nu_0}\right)$, there should be a long-wavelength *threshold of photoionisation* defined by the equality

$$h\nu=h\nu_0=eI. \tag{5.3}$$

The photoionisation of gases (and vapours) is detected by the appearance of photoelectrons due to irradiation:

$$h\nu+A=A^{+}+e \tag{5.4}$$

(where A is an atom or molecule, A^{+} is a positive ion formed by photoionisation, and e is a photoelectron), and also by the presence of a *continuous absorption spectrum** associated with the (5.4) process. Such a spectrum was, for example, observed by Kuhn (1932) in sodium vapour at wavelengths $\lambda<\lambda_0=2412$ A. The wavelength λ_0, which corresponds to the long-wavelength boundary of the continuous absorption of light by sodium vapour, obviously corresponds likewise to the long-wavelength threshold of photoionisation as determined by formula (5.3). Substituting into this formula the frequency ν_0 that corresponds to this wavelength, we find $I=5.138$ V for the ionisation potential of sodium.

Continuous spectra associated with the photoionisation of atoms are also observed in the case of X-rays (see below, p. 142).

It may further be noted that, recently, cases have been reported of the photodetachment of an electron from a negative ion, that is, processes of the type

$$h\nu+X^{-}=X+e. \tag{5.5}$$

A determination of the long-wavelength boundary of the (5.5) process enables one to find the *electron affinity* of an atom (or molecule) X, $E=h\nu_0$, which is the energy released in the formation of an X^{-} ion from a neutral particle X and an electron.

6. Compton Effect

One of the most convincing proofs of the existence of light quanta was given by Compton in 1923. Studying the scattering of X-rays by graphite, Compton found that in addition to the ordinary scattering known as far back as the time of Roentgen and occurring without any change in the wavelength, there is a

* Continuous spectra are those containing all possible wavelengths (in a broad spectral interval).

type of scattering in which the wavelength of the scattered rays is *increased* as compared with the initial wavelength. This phenomenon became known as *Compton scattering* or the *Compton effect*.

The theory of this effect was given by Compton and also Debye on the basis of the Einstein theory of photons. In photon scattering, the observed decrease in photon energy (which corresponds to an increase in wavelength) indicated a certain loss of energy; this was naturally associated with the interaction of a photon with one of the electrons in the atoms of the scattering substance. Denoting the frequency of the photons undergoing scattering (prior to scattering by ν and after scattering through a certain angle φ, by ν_φ), the law of conservation of energy as applied to the process of Compton scattering may be written as

$$h\nu = h\nu_\varphi + eI + K, \qquad (6.1)$$

where eI is the work performed to remove an electron from an atom of the scattering substance and K is the kinetic energy of the "Compton electron". However, since the X-ray quanta are usually three orders of magnitude in excess of the ionisation energy of the atom,* eI in equation (6.1) may be disregarded, as if the scattering electron were free. Thus, considering Compton scattering of a photon as its interaction with a free electron, whose velocity prior to collision is negligibly small compared with that after, the equation of conservation of energy may be rewritten as

$$h\nu = h\nu_\varphi + K. \qquad (6.2)$$

In the Compton and Debye theory, photon scattering on a free electron is interpreted as the collision of *elastic spheres*, i.e., it is taken that both energy and momenta are exchanged in the scattering process. Taking advantage of the relation of equivalence of mass and energy,

$$E = Mc^2 \qquad (6.3)$$

we obtain $M_{ph} = \frac{h\nu}{c^2}$ for the mass of the photon M_{ph} and, consequently,

$$g_{ph} = \frac{h_\nu}{c} \qquad (6.4)$$

for its momentum.

---

* In Compton's experiments on the scattering of X-rays on graphite, use was made of rays with wavelength $\lambda = 0.712\,605$ A, to which there corresponds a quantum energy $h\nu = 17{,}395$ eV. Since the ionisation energy of a carbon atom is $eI = 11.217$ eV, in this case we have $\frac{h\nu}{eI} = 1550$.

Then, assuming that the velocity of the Compton electron may be rather high and taking into account, in this connection, the dependence of electron mass on the velocity of the particle, we have, for the kinetic energy and momentum of the electron,

$$K = mc^2\left(\frac{1}{\sqrt{1-\beta^2}} - 1\right) \tag{6.5}$$

and

$$g_e = \frac{mv}{\sqrt{1-\beta^2}} = \frac{mc\beta}{\sqrt{1-\beta^2}}. \tag{6.6}$$

Here, $\beta = \frac{v}{c}$ and m is the electron rest mass.

To every photon scattered through an angle φ there corresponds a Compton electron *(recoil electron)* flying at a certain

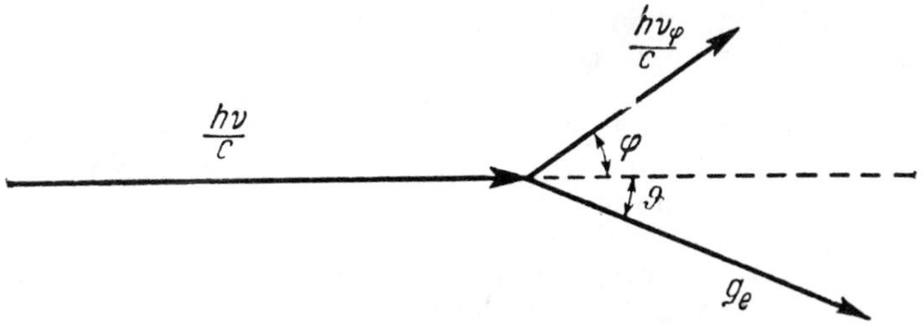

Fig. 3. Compton scattering of a photon

angle ϑ to the incident photon (Fig. 3). Substituting (6.5) into (6.2) and writing the law of conservation for projections of the momenta of photon and electron on the initial direction of the photon and on that perpendicular to it, we get

$$h\nu = h\nu_\varphi + mc^2\left(\frac{1}{\sqrt{1-\beta^2}} - 1\right), \tag{6.7}$$

$$\frac{h\nu}{c} = \frac{mc\beta}{\sqrt{1-\beta^2}}\cos\vartheta + \frac{h\nu_\varphi}{c}\cos\varphi, \tag{6.8}$$

$$0 = \frac{mc\beta}{\sqrt{1-\beta^2}}\sin\vartheta + \frac{h\nu_\varphi}{c} + \sin\varphi. \tag{6.9}$$

Considering the angle φ given, we have three unknown quantities, ν_φ, ϑ and β, which may be evaluated from the three equations (6.7), (6.8) and (6.9).

Eliminating ϑ and β, we find

$$\frac{\nu_\varphi}{\nu} = \frac{1}{1+\alpha(1-\cos\varphi)} = \frac{1}{1+2\alpha\sin^2\frac{\varphi}{2}},$$

where

$$\alpha = \frac{h\nu}{mc^2} = \frac{h}{mc\lambda}.$$

Passing from ν to λ, we rewrite the latter expression in the form

$$\frac{\lambda_\varphi}{\lambda} = 1 + 2\alpha \sin^2 \frac{\varphi}{2}$$

and, substituting the value of α, as

$$\lambda_\varphi - \lambda = \Delta\lambda = \frac{2h}{mc} \sin^2 \frac{\varphi}{2}. \quad (6.10)$$

As may be seen from expression (6.10), which is called *Compton's formula*, the change in wavelength in Compton scattering through a given angle φ is independent of the original wavelength. Numerous experiments both by Compton and by other investigators confirmed the correctness of this result and also the dependence, which follows from the Compton formula, of the magnitude of $\Delta\lambda$ upon the scattering angle. It will be noted that in accordance with formula (6.10) the wavelength of rays scattered in the direction of original propagation ($\varphi = 0$) remains constant. The change in wavelength is a maximum for $\varphi = 180°$, when it is $\Delta\lambda = \frac{2h}{mc} = 0.0485$ Angstrom units.

Simultaneous solution of equations (6.7), (6.8), and (6.9) leads to the following relationship between the scattering angles φ and ϑ for the photons and Compton electrons:

$$\tan\vartheta = -\frac{1}{1+\alpha} \frac{1}{\tan\frac{\varphi}{2}}. \quad (6.11)$$

From equation (6.11) it follows that the Compton electrons fly only forwards. Let us show this for the case of small α ($\alpha \ll 1$), that is, for quanta, the energy of which $h\nu$ is small compared with the energy mc^2, which is equivalent to the electronic rest mass ($mc^2 = 0.51$ MeV). In this case, equation (6.11) takes the form $\tan\vartheta = -\cot\frac{\varphi}{2}$, whence we find $\vartheta = \frac{\varphi}{2} - 90°$. From the latter relation it follows that the values of angle φ 0°, 90°, 180°, 270° and 360° correspond to the values of angle ϑ —90°, —45°, 0°, 45°, and 90°; that is, angle ϑ lies in the fourth and first quadrants.

Let us also compute the kinetic energy of the recoil electrons K (6.5) as a function of the scattering angle. Taking advantage of (6.10), we obtain from (6.7)

$$\frac{K}{h\nu}=\frac{2\alpha\sin^2\frac{\varphi}{2}}{1+2\alpha\sin^2\frac{\varphi}{2}}. \tag{6.12}$$

From (6.12) it follows that when $\varphi=0°$, $K=0$. K increases with the angle φ, and at $\varphi=180°$ reaches a maximum:

$$\frac{K}{h\nu}=\frac{2\alpha}{1+2\alpha}. \tag{6.13}$$

It will be noted that $\vartheta=0°$ corresponds to $\varphi=180°$ (see above). Consequently, recoil electrons moving in the direction of the incident photon have maximum energy, which is small for small α, increases with α, that is, with the energy of initial quanta and at sufficiently large values of $h\nu$ it becomes practically equal to $h\nu\left(\frac{K}{h\nu}\approx 1\right)$.

The Compton effect is observed in the scattering not only of X-rays, but gamma rays as well. The first investigations of this effect were likewise carried out by Compton, who studied the scattering of the γ-rays of RaC on aluminium and paraffin ($\lambda=0.022$A, $h\nu=0.563$ MeV).

These and subsequent experiments with various wavelengths and various scattering substances likewise confirmed the validity of the Compton formula in the case of γ-rays.

Important for investigations of the energy of recoil electrons resulting from the scattering of γ-rays is a method due to Skobeltsyn, which consists in measuring the radius of curvature of the electron tracks observed in a Wilson cloud chamber situated in a magnetic field.

The distinguishing feature of the Compton effect in the case of γ-rays is that the spectrum of γ-rays scattered by light elements exhibits only a displaced line (λ_φ), whereas the spectrum of scattered X-rays exhibits, as a rule, both displaced and initial (λ) lines. According to Compton, this is due to the fact that atoms have strongly bound electrons, which cannot be considered as free, and, moreover, can be torn out of the atom only by γ-rays, which are harder (of shorter wavelengths) than X-rays. For this reason, the scattering of X-rays on these electrons is ordinary (non-Compton) scattering that occurs without any change in wavelength.

For this same reason, visible light, the quanta of which have energies less than the ionisation potential of any atom, does not exhibit the Compton effect.

It may be added that a refined theory of the Compton effect was subsequently developed. It corroborated the results of the elementary Compton-Debye theory and also permitted evaluating the probability of the scattering process (for various ν and φ), which cannot be done within the framework of the elementary theory.

7. Wave-Particle Duality

Wave and corpuscular optics. The history of modern optics is in large measure a history of the struggle of two theories: the corpuscular and wave theories of light. The corpuscular theory, which represents light as a stream of particles (corpuscles), is usually attributed to Newton, although Newton himself made use of both the corpuscular view (which he frequently preferred) and the wave concept.* Almost at the same time that Newton formulated the corpuscular theory (1672), Huygens (1678), in his "Traité de la lumière", formulated the wave theory of light.** According to Huygens' views, which held their ground in physics for 140 years, light consists of longitudinal oscillations of an "ethereal matter" undergoing propagation in space with a certain finite velocity. Using a principle (Huygens' principle) which he formulated for the construction of the front of a propagating light wave, Huygens gave a clear explanation of the laws of reflection and refraction of light. However, Huygens' wave theory did not consider either the phenomenon of diffraction of light then known or the Newton rings; also absent was the concept of wavelength. Thus, this theory was actually confined to geometrical optics and did not deal with the phenomena of physical optics. The fact that the corpuscular theory of light prevailed throughout the eighteenth century is to be explained by the incompleteness of the Huygens theory and also by the absence of any significant discoveries in physical optics.

The first blow to the corpuscular theory was dealt in 1801 by Young, who introduced the concept of the interference of light, which is alien to this theory, and explained the Newton rings on the basis of this concept. At the same time, Young found a way of determining the length of light waves (by means of the Newton rings). In 1809 Malus discovered the polarisation of light; this led Young to the idea of the transversality of light oscil-

* Descartes (1630) was one of Newton's most immediate predecessors who adhered to the corpuscular view.

** Prior to Huygens, wave concepts on the nature of light were developed by Hooke (1665).

lations (1817), which was further developed in the experiments of Fresnel and Arago (1819), who showed that rays polarised at right angles do not interfere. An important role in establishing the wave theory of light was played by the diffraction theory of Fresnel (1818) based on the Huygens principle and the interference of light waves. The wave theory was brought to completion by Maxwell's electromagnetic theory of light (1865), which became generally recognised through the experiments of Hertz (1888) with electromagnetic waves. Due to the successes of the wave theory, by the start of the twentieth century the corpuscular theory of light was practically abandoned.

However, in this century it was revived on the basis of new discoveries in physics; first among them is the discovery of the photoelectric effect and of quanta of radiant energy. We have already pointed out (Sec. 5) that all the experimentally established regularities of the photoelectric effect could not be accounted for on the basis of the wave theory of light and were fully interpreted only by means of the photon theory (Einstein, 1905). Later (1923), this same theory made possible a brilliant interpretation of the Compton effect (Sec. 6).

As has already been pointed out (pp. 20 and 23), the photon theory did not confine itself to recognising Planck's postulate of the quantum nature of absorption and emission of light by advancing the concept of light quanta, the quantum nature of light; in the photon theory, light quanta (or photons) are endowed with corpuscular properties: a definite energy ($h\nu$), velocity (c), mass $\left(\frac{h\nu}{c^2}\right)$, and momentum $\left(\frac{h\nu}{c}\right)$.

The photon theory, or the corpuscular theory of light, which described such phenomena as the photoelectric effect and the Compton effect that could not be accounted for on the basis of the wave theory of light, proved (in turn) to be helpless in explaining a broad range of optical phenomena, first of all the interference and diffraction of light, which are readily understood in terms of wave concepts. Thus, the wave theory concepts should by no means be rejected as a consequence of the successes of the photon theory. The bulk of information concerning the properties of light compels us to recognise that light possesses both corpuscular and wave properties, but in certain phenomena corpuscular properties predominate, in others, wave properties. Furthermore, manifestation of the properties is frequently dependent upon the conditions under which the given optical phenomenon occurs. For example, the wave properties of light are most evident when the waves are propagated in a confined space having dimensions commensurable with the wavelength. To illustrate, a beam of parallel rays passing through a slit, the width of which is large compared to the wavelength, obeys the laws of geometrical optics (rectilinear propagation of light), and in this case the propagation of light in space is equally well described on the basis of wave and corpuscular concepts. When a beam of parallel rays passes through a narrow slit, we have diffraction of light (Fraunhofer diffraction), which is characteristic of wave optics. For this reason, to observe the interference of X-rays, one has to make use of a diffraction grating with a constant of the order of 1Å, that is, of the order of wavelength of X-rays. Such gratings, it will be recalled, are crystals characterised by crystal-lattice parameters (the distances between crystal planes) precisely of this order of magnitude.

One of the expressions of *wave-particle duality*, i.e., the duality of properties underlying the nature of light, is the existence of a direct relationship between the corpuscular and wave characteristics of light. Thus, according to Planck's relation (4.11) the photon energy $h\nu$, which is a corpuscular characteristic of light, is associated with its wave characteristic (the frequency of light oscillations). In the same way, the momentum of the photon $g_{ph}=\frac{h\nu}{c}$ (6.4) turns out to be connected with the length of the light waves $\lambda=\frac{c}{\nu}$ by the relation

$$\lambda=\frac{h}{g} \tag{7.1}$$

(here, the subscript "ph" is omitted).

Wave properties of particles. In 1924, de Broglie extended the wave-particle parallelism of optics to electrons, atoms, and molecules, correlating with the motion of each particle a certain wave that characterises its wave properties. De Broglie connected this wavelength with the momentum of the particle $g=mv$ (where v is the velocity and m the mass of the particle) establishing a relation similar to formula (7.1):

$$\lambda=\frac{h}{g}=\frac{h}{mv}\,. \tag{7.2}$$

This formula became known as the *de Broglie relation*.

Proceeding from the de Broglie theory, Elsasser (1925) concluded that when electrons pass through a crystal they should, like X-rays, exhibit the phenomena of interference and diffraction. Expressing the kinetic energy of the electron in terms of the potential difference V that accelerates the electron beam,

$$\frac{mv^2}{2}=eV$$

or

$$mv = \sqrt{2meV},$$

we obtain, from known values of charge and mass of the electron and on the basis of the de Broglie relation (7.2),

$$\lambda = \sqrt{\frac{150.5}{V}}\ \text{A (V in volts)}.$$

From this expression it follows that an electron of energy 150 eV is characterised by a wavelength of 1A. Consequently, such electrons should exhibit properties similar to the properties of

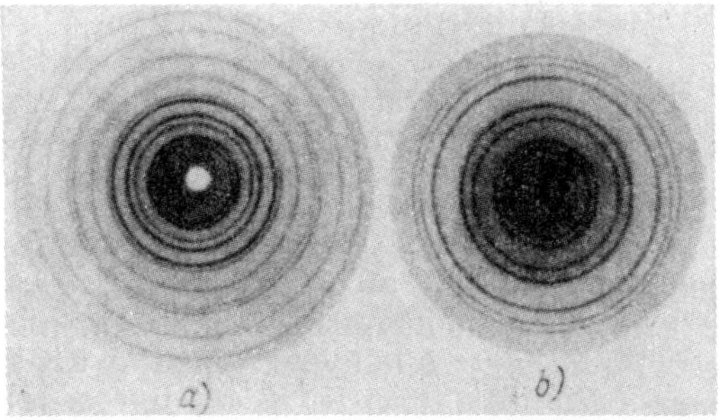

Fig. 4. Diffraction patterns obtained in the scattering, by silver, of a) X-rays of wavelength 0.71A and b) electrons of energy corresponding to the de Broglie wavelength, 0.645 A (after Wierl)

light waves of wavelength $\lambda = 1$A. The diffraction of electrons as predicted by Elsasser is one of the manifestations of these wave properties. Electron diffraction was detected in the experiments of Davisson and Germer (1927) and in the later experiments of Thomson, Wierl, Shalnikov, and others.

Stern (1929) and Johnson (1931) also established the diffraction of atoms of helium and hydrogen and molecules of hydrogen.

Electron diffraction is similar to the diffraction of X-rays. When a beam of X-rays passes through a layer of some substance, one can observe, on a screen placed in the path of the rays scattered by this substance, a peculiar pattern due to interference of the scattered rays. When the scattering substance has a microcrystalline structure, this pattern represents a system of concentric rings. An *X-ray photograph* obtained by Wierl for the scattering of X-rays of wavelength $\lambda = 0.71$ A by silver foil is shown in Fig. 4a. Fig. 4b is an electron diffraction pattern obtained by

Wierl in the scattering of a 36 keV electron beam by the same substance. Computing the momentum of the electron from the formula

$$g = \frac{mc\beta}{\sqrt{1-\beta^2}} = \sqrt{2meV + \frac{e^2V^2}{c^2}}$$

which follows from equations (6.5) and (6.6) for $K = eV$, and substituting g into formula (7.2), we find $\lambda = 0.0645$ A for the de Broglie wavelength. The close resemblance of both diffraction patterns shown in Fig. 4a and b indicates that both the scattering of electrons and the scattering of X-rays obey the laws of wave optics. In other words, electrons must possess both corpuscular and wave properties.

We may add that in 1925 Goudsmit and Uhlenbeck demonstrated that the electron should have, in addition to an electric charge, *an angular momentum* and *a magnetic moment*. In connection with an attempt (which was unsuccessful) to interpret this electron property as due to rotation about its axis, the angular momentum of the electron came to be known as spin. Spin proved to be an extremely important property of the electron, one of prime significance for the physical interpretation of Mendeleyev's Periodic Law, and also for explaining many physical (magnetic, optic, etc.) and chemical properties of matter as well as for the theory of the structure of atoms and molecules and for solid-state theory.

The development of our concepts of the electron, beginning with its discovery at the end of last century, is a brilliant illustration of the thesis of dialectical materialism that the universe is inexhaustible. Indeed, at first the electron was conceived of as a particle (corpuscle) with a definite electric charge and mass. Let us provisionally attribute to the electron the shape of a sphere of radius a with an electric charge distributed uniformly over its volume and let us compute the electrostatic energy of this sphere $E = \frac{2}{3}\frac{e^2}{a}$. Now, on the basis of the equivalence of mass and energy (6.3), we obtain an expression for the radius of the electron:

$$a = \frac{2}{3}\frac{e^2}{mc^2}. \qquad (7.3)$$

From this expression it follows that $a = 2 \times 10^{-13}$ cm.

It seemed that this picture of the electron was exhaustive and final. But new discoveries showed that the particle concept of the electron did not by far exhaust all its properties and, consequently, was one-sided. The electron was discovered to have wave properties; then the spin was discovered. The properties of the electron proved to be immeasurably richer than the properties of a corpuscle. In the light of these data, Lenin's words on the inexhaustibility of the electron (1908) are truly prophetic: "...dialectical materialism insists on the transient, relative, and approximate character of all these stages in the cognition of nature by man's progressing science. The electron is just as inexhaustible as the atom."

CHAPTER 2

ATOMIC NUCLEUS

8. Nuclear Charge

Scattering of α-particles. The universality of the electron, whose properties are reflected in diverse properties of matter, leaves no doubt that electrons are fundamental structural elements of atoms and molecules. As for the positive charge of the atom, it was assumed in one of the first atomic models* proposed by J. J. Thomson in 1903 that it is distributed throughout the body of the atom. On this model, the atom is a positively charged sphere with a radius equal to that of the atom, i.e., of size of the order of 10^{-8} cm = 1 A.** The electrons are retained within the atom by the attraction of the positive space charge.

This model, however, did not face up to the facts. A correct picture of the positive charge of the atom was obtained in experiments carried out by Rutherford and his colleagues on the scattering of α-particles by various substances (1911). These experiments demonstrated that fast α-particles produced in radioactive disintegration pass through matter and readily penetrate into atoms. The regularities observed are simply and effectively accounted for on the basis of the following model. When α-particles approach an atom they experience a repulsive force which is inversely proportional to the square of the distance (Coulomb's law) and is the cause of the scattering of the α-particles. The ease with which α-particles penetrate deep into the atom indicates that the bulk of the atomic mass is concentrated in its central part, or *nucleus*, the dimensions of which are negligible

* The first electrical model of the atom was proposed by Ampere (1825), who considered that the periphery of the atom had a charge opposite that of its central part. According to Ampere, the hydrogen atom had a positive charge and its peripheral part, a negative charge.

** An idea of the size of an atom may be obtained by computing the volume V per atom of a solid body. Thus, from the density of solid sodium, $\varrho = 0.971$ g/cm^3 and its atomic weight, $A = 23.00$, we find the number of atoms per cm^3 of the metal: $n = \frac{\varrho N_A}{A}$, where N_A is Avogadro's number equal to $(6.02402 \pm 0.00017) \times 10^{23}$ and, consequently, the volume $V = (2r)^3 = 39 \cdot 4 \times 10^{-24}$ cm^3, whence we obtain the radius of a sodium atom: $r = 1.7 \times 10^{-8}$ cm.

(see below) when compared with those of the atom. Now from the presence of a Coulomb repulsive force it follows that the atomic nucleus, like the α-particle, * has a positive electric charge. Assuming the nuclear charge of the scattering atom equal to Ze, where e is the elementary charge (the absolute magnitude of the electron charge), we obtain for the force of mutual repulsion of the nucleus and α-particle

$$f=\frac{2e^2Z}{r^2},$$

where r is the distance between the centres of the α-particle and the atom (nucleus).

A simple calculation shows that given this law of interaction of the nucleus and an α-particle, the portion of α-particles $\frac{dN}{N}$ scattered through an angle ϑ (ϑ is the angle between the direction of the scattered α-particles and their original direction) within the solid angle $d\Omega=2\pi \sin\vartheta d\vartheta$ is expressed by the formula

$$\frac{dN}{N}=nd\left(\frac{Ze^2}{mv^2}\right)^2\frac{d\Omega}{\sin 4\frac{\vartheta}{2}}, \tag{8.1}$$

which was first derived by Rutherford and is called the *Rutherford formula*. Here, n denotes the number of atoms in unit volume of the scattering material, d is the thickness of the scattering layer, m, the mass, and v, the velocity of the α-particles.

In the experiments of Rutherford and his colleagues, Rutherford's formula was quantitatively verified by counting the scintillations produced when each α-particle impinged on a fluorescent screen placed behind the scatterer (metallic foil) at a certain distance R from it. It is convenient to alter equation (8.1) as applied to this experimental set-up. The area of the screen on which the α-particles that are scattered at angles lying between ϑ and $\vartheta+d\vartheta$ impinge is, obviously, $dS=R^2d\Omega$. Denoting the number of α-particles scattered through an angle ϑ and impinging on 1 cm^2 of screen surface in 1 sec by N_1 (ϑ), we will have $N_1=\frac{dN}{dS}=\frac{1}{R^2}\frac{dN}{d\Omega}$ and, consequently,

$$\frac{N_1\vartheta}{N}=\frac{nd}{R^2}\left(\frac{Ze^2}{mv^2}\right)^2\sin^{-4}\frac{\vartheta}{2}. \tag{8.2}$$

* As early as 1903, in experiments with α-particle deflection in a magnetic field, Rutherford found that the ratio of charge to mass in α-particles corresponds to doubly charged positive ions of helium He^{++}. Somewhat later (1909), Rutherford and Royds obtained spectroscopic evidence for the complete identity of the α-particle and He^{++}.

Verification of the Rutherford formula with respect to dependence of the number of scattered α-particles on the scattering angle ϑ and also on the velocity (energy) of the α-particles and the thickness of the scatterer showed that in the case of elements heavier than copper ($Z=29$) it yields quantitative agreement with experiment for all α-particle velocities right up to maximum, equal to $\frac{1}{15}c$, and for all scattering angles (see below, Sec. 9). Whence it followed that in the case of heavy elements the interaction of an α-particle with a nucleus obeys Coulomb's law.

The principal significance of this formula lies in the fact that, on the basis of α-particle scattering experiments, it permits determining the charge of the atomic nuclei of the scattering material. The first experiments carried out by Chadwick yielded the following nuclear charge Z: 29.3 (Cu), 43.3 (Ag), and 77.4 (Pt), which, within measurement error, coincides with the numbers of these elements in the Periodic Table, namely, 29, 47 and 78, respectively. From these and also the latest experiments, it followed that the nuclear charge Z is always equal to the number of the element N in the Periodic Table. Since the positive charges are ordinarily associated with a mass equal to or greater than that of the hydrogen atom, and insofar as the absence of such masses in the atom outside its nucleus followed from α-particle scattering experiments, one can conclude from the equality $Z=N$ that the positive charge of the atom is totally concentrated in its nucleus and is equal to Ne. Since under ordinary conditions atoms are electrically neutral, it follows that the number of electrons in any atom is likewise equal to the number of the given element in the Periodic Table.

Scattering of X-rays. The same result is obtained also in X-ray scattering experiments. If we denote the energy of the primary rays by P, the energy of the rays scattered by unit volume of the scattering material, by S, then the scattering factor that characterises the scattering ability of the given material may be defined as

$$s=\frac{S}{P}$$

or, referring scattering to unit mass, as

$$s'=\frac{s}{\varrho}$$

where ϱ is the density of the scattering material equal to $\varrho=m_H An$ (n is the number of atoms in unit volume, m_H is the mass of the hydrogen atom, and A is the atomic weight of the scattering material). From classical electrodynamics the following expression is obtained for the specific scattering factor s′:

$$s' = \frac{8\pi}{3} \frac{e^4 N_A}{m^2 c^4} \frac{Z}{A} = 0.40 \frac{Z}{A}. \qquad (8.3)$$

Thus, an experimental determination of the scattering factor s′ enables us, on the basis of equation (8.3), to find the ratio $\frac{Z}{A}$ and, hence, the charge of the nucleus Z. The measurements of Barkla and others demonstrated that for all the elements they studied (with $A < 27$) s′ is close to 0.2, whence it follows that

$$\frac{Z}{A} = \frac{0.2}{0.4} = \frac{1}{2};$$

that is, in the case of light elements the nuclear charge is equal to one-half the atomic weight. And since the atomic number and the atomic weight of these elements are, approximately, in the same ratio, the result obtained may be considered a corroboration of the foregoing conclusion that the nuclear charge and, hence, the number of electrons in the atom is equal to the number of the element in the Periodic Table.

Thus, the hydrogen atom (first in the Periodic Table) has one electron, the helium atom, two, lithium, three, etc. The atom of the ninety-second element — uranium — has 92 electrons. It may be added that the α-particle, which has a positive charge of 2, is identical with the nucleus of the helium atom; this was established experimentally by Rutherford (see p. 37). In the same way, the proton, with its charge +1 and mass close to the mass of the hydrogen atom, turns out to be the nucleus of this atom.

9. Size of the Nucleus

When α-particles traverse a substance, they are both scattered (the characteristic sharp break in their trajectories) and *slowed down* without any change in direction of motion, as a result of which their path length in matter is finite. This difference in the type of α-particle trajectories is very clearly shown in cloud-chamber photographs (Fig. 5). In large measure, α-particles lose speed due to ionisation of the atoms which they encounter. This ionisation is evident from the increase in electrical conductivity and by the appearance of visible *tracks* of α-particles in a cloud chamber due to condensation of water vapour on the ions along the path of the α-particle. Cloud-chamber photographs show that in most cases the α-particle trajectories are straight-line, while those with a sharp break (which occur when an α-particle interacts with an atomic nucleus) are very rare. This fact in itself is sufficient for one to conclude that the size of the nucleus is small compared with that of the atom.

Fig. 5. Alpha-particle paths in helium (stereoscopic photo). Among the many rectilinear tracks, there is one which ends in a double fork caused by the flight of a deflected α-particle and a helium atom that underwent impact (after Rutherford and Chadwick)

The same conclusion is also drawn from the fact that Coulomb's law (which assumes point charges) is very well fulfilled in the scattering of α-particles at sufficiently large angles, when the distances between the α-particles and the nucleus are considerably less than the size of the atom.

Let us calculate the minimum distance between an α-particle and a nucleus (r_{min}) that corresponds to a certain impact parameter p (Fig. 6). In polar coordinates (r, φ), the laws of conservation of energy and angular momentum for an α-particle-nucleus system are written as

$$\frac{m}{2}(\dot{r}^2 + r^2\dot{\varphi}^2) + \frac{2e^2Z}{r} = \frac{mv^2}{2}, \quad mr^2\dot{\varphi} = mvp,$$

where $\dot{r} = \frac{dr}{dt}$, $\dot{\varphi} = \frac{d\varphi}{dt}$ and $\frac{mv^2}{2}$ is the energy of an α-particle at an infinite distance from the nucleus. From these equations we obtain

$$\frac{m}{2}\left(\dot{r}^2 + \frac{v^2p^2}{r^2}\right) + \frac{2e^2Z}{r} = \frac{mv^2}{2}.$$

When $r=r_{min}$, $\dot{r}=0$, and the preceding equation is rewritten as

$$\frac{m}{2}\frac{v^2p^2}{r_{min}^2}+\frac{2e^2Z}{r_{min}}=\frac{mv^2}{2}.$$

Solving this equation for r_{min}, we find

$$r_{min}=\frac{2e^2Z}{mv^2}\left(1+\sqrt{1+\left(\frac{mv^2}{2e^2Z}\right)^2p^2}\right). \tag{9.1}$$

Whence it is seen that for given Z and $\frac{mv^2}{2}$, r_{min} diminishes with decreasing impact parameter p, and for $p=0$ (central impact) it assumes the least possible value

$$r_{min}=\frac{4e^2Z}{mv^2}. \tag{9.1a}$$

Rewriting this expression in the form

$$\frac{2e^2Z}{r_{min}}=\frac{mv^2}{2} \tag{9.2}$$

we see that in the case of a central impact at a distance of closest approach of the α-particle to the nucleus, the potential

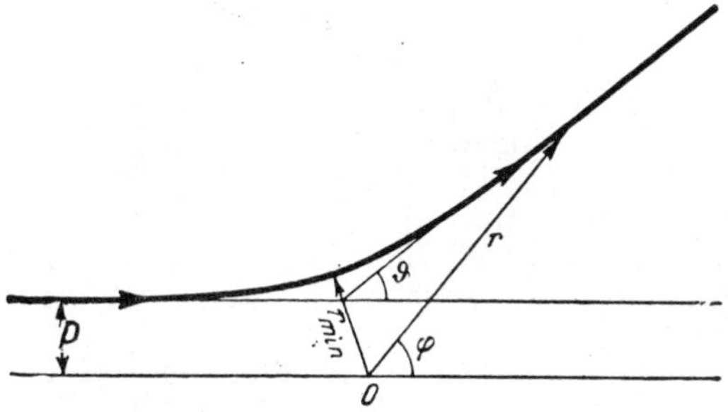

Fig. 6. The scattering of an α-particle by a nucleus.

energy of their Coulomb repulsion is equal to the original kinetic energy of the α-particle.

When $p=0$ the scattering angle ϑ (see Fig. 6) is, obviously, 180°. Since for sufficiently large p the scattering angle may be arbitrarily small, it is clear that there should be a direct relationship between the scattering angle and the impact parameter and, consequently, between ϑ and r_{min}. Indeed, in polar coordinates the equation of an α-particle trajectory in the nuclear field is of the form

$$\frac{p}{r} = \sin\varphi - \frac{2e^2Z}{mv^2p}(1+\cos\varphi).$$

Since at $r=\infty$ the angle φ should equal the scattering angle (see Fig. 6), from this equation we obtain

$$p = \frac{2e^2Z}{mv^2}\cot\frac{\vartheta}{2}. \quad (9.3)$$

Which is the relationship between p and ϑ that is needed.

Substituting (9.3) into (9.1), we obtain the following relation between r_{min} and ϑ:

$$r_{min} = \frac{2e^2Z}{mv^2}\frac{1+\sin\frac{\vartheta}{2}}{\sin\frac{\vartheta}{2}}. \quad (9.4)$$

From (9.4) it is seen that r_{min} has the smallest value for a scattering angle $\vartheta = 180°$; this value satisfies relation (9.2).

The distance of closest approach of the α-particle to a nucleus is, obviously, the upper limit of the nuclear radius (more precisely, the sum of the radii of the nucleus and the α-particle). To compute r_{min} we can take advantage of (9.4). Since, on the basis of experiments in the scattering of the α-particles of RaC by gold, formula (8.2) is fulfilled even for scattering angles as large as 150°, whence follows the validity of (9.4), let us compute, by means of this formula, the value of r_{min} that corresponds to $\vartheta = 150°$. Substituting into (9.4) $\vartheta = 150°$, $Z = 79$, and the velocity of RaC α-particles $v = 1.992 \times 10^9$ cm/sec, we find $r_{min} = 2.8 \times 10^{-12}$ cm, the atomic radius being 1.8×10^{-8} cm. Thus, it may be concluded that the size of the nucleus of an atom of gold should be less than the size of the atom by a factor exceeding 6000.

We can also obtain an approximate picture of the dimensions of the atomic nuclei of heavy elements from the following reasoning. From experiment it is known that only the nuclei of relatively light elements can be artificially decomposed through bombardment by α-particles (see below). This may be attributed to the strong Coulomb repulsion between the nucleus of a heavy atom (large Z) and the α-particle, as a result of which the latter cannot approach the nucleus to a distance at which a nuclear reaction could occur. Having in view a central impact, we find, by means of formula (9.1) for the α-particles of RaC, $r_{min} = 0.35 \times 10^{-13}$ Z cm, which for lead ($Z = 82$) yields $r_{min} = 2.9 \times 10^{-12}$ cm. Consequently, as in the case of gold, we may state that the radius of an atom of lead must be less than 3×10^{-12} cm.

More exact data on the dimensions of the atomic nucleus are given by investigations of the so-called *anomalous scattering* of α-particles. As has been pointed out (p. 37), the Rutherford formula (8.2) is strictly fulfilled only in the case of heavy elements, whence we concluded that in this case the field of the nucleus does not differ from a Coulomb field at the minimal distances of α-particle approach to the nucleus. But in the case of light nuclei ($Z < 29$) at large scattering angles we observe anomalous scattering of α-particles, which is evident from the discrepancy between the measured number of scattered α-particles and the number computed from equation (8.2). This discrepency is particularly great in the case of hydrogen and helium where the observed number of scattered α-particles is 10 to 20 times that calculated from the Rutherford formula. The reason for anoma lous scattering should be sought in the deviation of the nuclear field from a Coulomb field; this becomes perceptible at small values of r_{min} that correspond to small Z and large scattering angles. Recent investigations have shown that the deviation is due to superimposition of *forces of attraction* on the Coulomb force of repulsion, the action of the attractive forces being independent of the charge of the particles and rapidly falling off with distance between the particles (see below). Identifying the range of these forces with the *radius of the nucleus* a, we can determine the magnitude of a as the distance between an α-particle and the nucleus at which normal α-particle scattering passes into anomalous scattering. Accordingly, $r_{min} = a$ is obtained from equation (9.4).

Studies of anomalous scattering show that the magnitude of a increases with Z and may be expressed approximately by the empirical formula

$$a = 2 \times 10^{-13} \sqrt[3]{Z}. \qquad (9.5)$$

Thus, the radius of an atomic nucleus is of the order of 10^{-13} — 10^{-12} cm. Another empirical formula for the nuclear radius is

$$a = 1.45 \times 10^{-13} \sqrt[3]{A} \qquad (9.6)$$

where A is the atomic weight *(mass number)* of the given element.

It may be noted that the distribution of electricity and mass in the atom, as established on the basis of α-particle experiments, led to the planetary model of the atom with the nucleus as the "sun" situated at the centre, and the electrons as "planets" revolving round the nucleus. This model was proposed by Rutherford (1911) and subsequently utilised by Bohr as the basis of his atomic theory.

10. Radioactive Transformations of the Elements

Radioactive families. Radioactivity was discovered by Becquerel in 1896. The existence of radioactive elements, that is, of elements that convert into other, lighter, elements with the emission of α-particles (α-active elements) and of elements that convert into adjacent elements with the ejection of β-particles (β-active elements) is irrefutable proof of the complex structure of atomic nuclei. This tendency to spontaneous disintegration is especially characteristic of heavy elements and accounts for the relative instability of their nuclei. The degree of stability of the nucleus of a given element is characterised by its *half-life* $T_{\frac{1}{2}}$, which is the time during which one-hal of the initial quantity of the element disintegrates (decays). Measurements of the magnitude of $T_{\frac{1}{2}}$ are based on an analysis of *activity curves* of radioactive substances. These are curves that give the radiation intensity as a function of time. The difficulties of this analysis lie in the fact that, ordinarily, one has to deal not with a single radioactive element, but with a more or less complex mixture consisting of the original element and its decay products.

The decay of each element (and, hence, its activity) obeys a "monomolecular" law

$$-\frac{dn}{dt}=\lambda n \tag{10.1}$$

where n is the number of atoms (concentration) of the element at a time t, and λ is the *decay constant* of the element. Integrating equation (10.1), we obtain

$$n=n_0e^{-\lambda t} \tag{10.2}$$

where n_0 denotes the concentration of the element at time $t=0$

For the case of a chain of radioactive transformations

$$n_1\longrightarrow n_2\longrightarrow n_3\longrightarrow \ldots \longrightarrow n_i\longrightarrow \ldots$$

we have a system of differential equations

$$\frac{dn_1}{dt}=-\lambda_1 n_1,$$

$$\frac{dn_2}{dt}=\lambda_1 n_1-\lambda_2 n_2,$$

$$\frac{dn_3}{dt} = \lambda_2 n_2 - \lambda_3 n_3$$

. . . .

$$\frac{dn_i}{dt} = \lambda_{i-1} n_{i-1} - \lambda_i n_i,$$

. . . .

The overall activity I measured by some instrument (for example, an ionisation chamber) is in this case expressed by the equation

$$I = k_1 \lambda_1 n_1 + k_2 \lambda_2 n_2 + \ldots + k_i \lambda_i n_i + \ldots,$$

where the coefficients k_i account for the susceptibility of the instrument to the radiation of the element. By integrating the foregoing system of equations it can be shown that I as a function of time is a sum of terms, each of which is proportional to the respective function $e^{-\lambda_i t}$.

Thus, in the simplest case of a chain of two elements, $n_1 \longrightarrow n_2$, integration of the two differential equations yields

$$I = k_1 \lambda_1 n_1^0 \left[\left(1 - \frac{k_2}{k_1} \frac{\lambda_2}{\lambda_1 - \lambda_2} \right) e^{-\lambda_1 t} + \frac{k_2}{k_1} \frac{\lambda_2}{\lambda_1 - \lambda_2} e^{-\lambda_2 t} \right]$$

We see that already in the very simplest case the activity I is a composite function of time. However, over definite time intervals, namely, when the conditions $t \gg 1/\lambda_2$ and $\lambda_1 t \gtrapprox 1$, or $t \gg 1/\lambda_1$ and $\lambda_2 t \gtrapprox 1$ are fulfilled, the magnitude of I will be proportional to $e^{-\lambda_1 t}$ and, accordingly, to $e^{-\lambda_2 t}$. Within these time intervals we will have lnI as a linear function of time. It is from the slopes of the corresponding straight-line sections of the curve lnI, t (one for small t and the other for large t) that the decay constants λ_1 and λ_2 can be determined. It is thus possible to find the values of the decay constants also for chains involving more than two elements. In the case of long chains or close values of λ, the complex mixture of elements should be separated into simpler mixtures.

The decay constant of every element is connected with its half-life by the following relation:

$$T_{\frac{1}{2}} = \frac{\ln 2}{\lambda}. \qquad (10.3)$$

As a result of the painstaking work of scientists, the half-lives of practically all the known radioactive elements have been determined.

To illustrate, we give the half-lives of a chain of radioactive transformations beginning with the α-decay of radium and ending in the formation of nonradioactive lead RaC^{206} (as a result of the α-decay of polonium Po^{210} and also the β-decay of the thallium isotope RaE^{206}). Notice the branching of the chain, for example, when RaC passes into RaD. It is due to the fact that RaC is capable both of α- and β-decay (of the RaC nuclei undergoing transformation, only 0.04% undergo α-decay and 99.96% experience β-transformation).

Transformation scheme of radium and its decay products

Ra_{88} Fr_{87} Rn_{86} At_{85} Po_{84} Bi_{83} Pb_{82} Tl_{81}

$Ra^{226} \xrightarrow{\alpha} Rn^{222} \xrightarrow{\alpha} RaA^{218} \xrightarrow{\alpha} RaB^{214}$

1620 yrs 3.825 days $\beta\swarrow$ 3.05 min $\beta\swarrow$ 26.8 min

$At^{218} \xrightarrow{\alpha} RaC^{214} \xrightarrow{\alpha} RaC''^{210}$

3 sec $\beta\swarrow$ 19.7 min $\beta\swarrow$ 1.32 min

$RaC'^{214} \xrightarrow{\alpha} RaD^{210}$

1.5×10^{-4} sec $\beta\swarrow$ 22 yrs

$RaE^{210} \xrightarrow{\alpha} RaE''^{206}$

$\beta\swarrow$ 5 days $\beta\swarrow$ 4.23 min

$Po^{210} \xrightarrow{\alpha} RaG^{206}$

138.4 days (stable)

The elements of this chain of transformations form part of a *series*, or *family*, of radioactive substances called the *uranium series*; it is characterised by mass numbers $A=4n+2$ (where n is an integer). Of the naturally occurring radioactive elements, two other analogous series have been established: the *thorium series* described by mass numbers $A=4n$ and the *actinium series* with $A=4n+3$. Later, it was shown that the artificially obtained new radioactive elements (see below) form a fourth, missing, series, which is sometimes called the *neptunium series* characterised by mass numbers $A=4n+1$.

Since the charge of an α-particle is equal to two elementary charges, its ejection causes the charge of the nucleus of the element to diminish by two units. The resulting new element is shifted *two columns to the left* in the Periodic Table relative to the original element. A new element produced by a single β-decay is shifted *one column to the right* of the original element, thus corresponding to an increase in the nuclear charge and, consequently, in the atomic number by unity. This is the essence of the radioactive *displacement law of Fajans and Soddy* (1911-13).

From this law it follows that an element which has lost one α- and two β-particles in succession returns to its original place in the Periodic Table. Such, for example, is lead RaG^{206}_{82} in the foregoing scheme of radioactive transformations. It is obtained from RaD^{210}_{82} as a result of the emission, by the latter, of two β- and one α-particle.* We thus have two elements, RaG^{206}_{82} and RaD^{210}_{82}, occupying one and the same place in the Periodic Table; consequently, they are chemically identical but have different atomic weights, since the ejection of a single α-particle involves a decrease in atomic weight by 4.

Isotopes. Elements with the same atomic number and, for this reason, with identical nuclear charge and number of electrons but with different atomic weights are called *isotopes*. This term was introduced in 1910 by Soddy, who, in order to account for the fact that even at that time the number of known radioactive elements exceeded the number of places in the Periodic Table, presumed the existence of varieties of radioactive elements that differ in atomic weight (mass number) and in radioactivity, but have identical chemical properties ** and, consequently, occupy the same place in the Periodic Table. Soddy called these varieties isotopes, which is in full accord with later concepts of chemical elements (that the atomic number and not the atomic weight is the chief characteristic of an element).

Scientists at first inclined to the view that isotopism is found only in radioactive elements and is associated with radioactive transformations. However, already in 1912, J. J. Thomson, while studying the deflection of a beam of neon ions in electric and magnetic fields parallel to each other and perpendicular to the direction of flight of the ions, demonstrated that there are two varieties or two isotopes of this element possessing mass numbers 20 and 22. *** The fundamental significance of this discovery was that it proved that stable elements too could have isotopes.

The method of measuring the masses of gaseous ions in an ion beam (first used by J. J. Thomson) was considerably refined by

---

* Here, as in the foregoing scheme of radioactive transformations, the superscript of the symbol of the chemical element denotes the mass number (A), the subscript, the atomic number (Z).

** Earlier still, Butlerov (1881) and Crookes (1886) believed in the existence of varieties of a chemical element differing by mass.

*** Later, a third stable isotope of neon with mass number 21 was discovered. The percentage content of isotopes 20, 21, and 22 in natural neon is 90.00%, 0.27%, 9.73%, respectively. Neon's atomic weight is 20.18.

Aston, who in 1919 devised an instrument known as the mass spectrograph. In Aston's mass spectrograph, the ion beam first enters an electric field perpendicular to it and is dispersed into a spectrum, the slower ions being deflected more than those with higher velocities. The ions then enter a magnetic field perpendicular to the electric field and to the direction of motion of the ions. This field deflects them in a direction opposite to that produced by the electric field. Besides, the magnetic field focuses ions of different velocities but identical masses on a certain plane. When ions with different masses (or, to be more precise, with different charge-to-mass ratios) are present, we obtain, in the focal plane, a number of images of the slit (which separates out the original beam) in the form of lines similar to optical spectral lines. The *mass spectrum* is photographed by placing a photographic plate in the focal plane.

Aston's mass spectrograph was subsequently refined considerably. Then came mass spectrometers with electrical and not photographic recording. Most common at present is the mass spectrometer in which a magnetic analyser admits ions with very slightly divergent velocities (monoenergetic ions), thus dispensing with a deflecting electric field. In a uniform magnetic field, the ions move in circular paths, the radii of which are defined from the condition of equality of the magnetic force evH acting on the ion (e and v are charge and velocity of the ion, H is the magnetic field intensity) and the centrifugal force mv^2/r. Expressing the kinetic energy of the ion in terms of the ion-accelerating potential difference, $mv^2/2=eV$ (where m is the ion mass and V the potential difference), we obtain, from the preceding formula,

$$\frac{m}{e}=\frac{1}{2}\frac{H^2r^2}{V}. \tag{10.4}$$

Thus, given H and V, a definite radius of the circular path corresponds to ions characterised by a definite m/e value. In mass spectrometers with r fixed and determined by the position of the respective slits, H or V are varied, and ions of one kind or another are directed into the slit of the receiver. The mass spectrum thus obtained is usually registered by means of a self-recording instrument.

The principle of the mass spectrometer that utilises monoenergetic ions was proposed by Dempster (1918),* who first applied it in 1921 to study the isotopic composition of alkaline metals by analysing positive ions emitted by the heated salts of

* This principle was still earlier utilised by Classen to devise an instrument which he used to measure the specific electronic charge (1907).

these elements. In 1924, a mass spectrometer of the same design was used by Kondratyev and Semyonov to study the action of electrons on the molecules of alkali-halogen salts.

The principal significance of the mass-spectrographic investigations carried out by Aston and later by Dempster, Bainbridge and others lies in the fact that the isotopes of a large number of elements were discovered. This was proof of the universality of isotopism. Some of the isotopes were discovered spectroscopically. Finally, a large number of radioactive isotopes were discovered by radiochemical methods. The number of isotopes discovered every year increased especially after 1939 with the discovery of the fission of atomic nuclei (see below). Whereas in 1938 the number of known isotopes of all the elements was 260, in 1946 it was 630, and in 1957, over 1300. This gives an average of 13 isotopes per element.

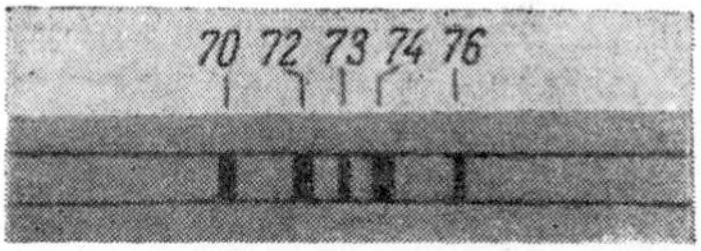

Fig. 7. Mass spectrum of germanium (after Bainbridge)

Fig. 7 is a mass spectrum of germanium (obtained by Bainbridge) containing five lines, which correspond to isotopes 70, 72, 73, 74, and 76. The different intensity of the lines is due to different isotope abundances, which may be determined by measuring ion currents that correspond to ions of different masses. The following percentages of abundance were thus obtained for the five isotopes of germanium: 21.2 (70); 27.3 (72); 7.9 (73); 37.1 (74); and 6.5 (76). All these isotopes, like the majority of isotopes detected by mass-spectrometric methods, are stable. In addition, there are eight radioactive isotopes of germanium with masses 66, 67, 68, 69, 71, 75, 77 and 78.

In connection with the isotopic composition of elements, we note the following very essential circumstance. The atomic weights of many elements in the Periodic Table differ greatly from whole numbers. For instance, the atomic weight of chlorine is 35.456. With the discovery of chlorine isotopes it became clear that its fractional atomic weight is due to the simple fact that this element is a mixture of two stable isotopes with atomic weights 35 (Cl^{35}) and 37 (Cl^{37}), and the measured atomic weight of chlorine is, therefore, a mean value of these two. At one time it was thought possible to explain the deviations of atomic weights from whole numbers in this manner, and it was believed that the atomic weights of the pure isotopes are in all cases strict integers. However, accurate measurements of the atomic masses showed that the deviations of atomic weights from integral values represent very specific quantities. To illustrate, the atomic weights of the above-mentioned stable isotopes of chlorine turned out equal to 34.98004 ± 0.00005 and 36.97766 ± 0.00005. As we shall see later on (Sec. 13), these deviations play a very significant role in the theory of the atomic nucleus.

At present the atomic weights of over 600 isotopes have been measured with great accuracy. Naturally, the atomic weights of the light isotopes have been measured with particularly high absolute accuracy. The atomic weights of all known isotopes of elements from hydrogen to neon are given in Table 1.

Table 1

Atomic weights (masses) of the isotopes of light elements

Isotope	Mass	Isotope	Mass	Isotope	Mass	Isotope	Mass
H^1	1.008146	Be^7	7.019153	C^{14}	14.007698	O^{18}	18.004888
H^2	2.014741	Be^8	8.007849	C^{15}	15.0141	O^{19}	19.0092
H^3	3.017003	Be^9	9.015042	N^{12}	12.02280	F^{17}	17.007496
He^3	3.016983	Be^{10}	10.016717	N^{13}	13.009877	F^{18}	18.006683
He^4	4.003877	B^9	9.016192	N^{14}	14.007531	F^{19}	19.004454
He^5	5.01390	B^{10}	10.016118	N^{15}	15.004877	F^{20}	20.00635
He^6	6.02083	B^{11}	11.012796	N^{16}	16.01124	Ne^{19}	19.007951
Li^5	5.01379	B^{12}	12.018172	N^{17}	17.01632	Ne^{20}	19.998798
Li^6	6.017028	C^{10}	10.02034	O^{14}	14.01305	Ne^{21}	21.000525
Li^7	7.018225	C^{11}	11.014931	O^{15}	15.007782	Ne^{22}	21.998336
Li^8	8.025026	C^{12}	12.003817	O^{16}	16.000000	Ne^{23}	23.001722
Li^9	9.03007	C^{13}	13.007488	O^{17}	17.004536		

It will be noted that in Table 1 the unit of atomic weight is 1/16 the atomic weight of the oxygen isotope O^{16}. This unit is called the *physical* unit of atomic weight in contrast to the *chemical* unit, which is equal to 1/16 the atomic weight of oxygen. Since the abundance of oxygen isotopes corresponds to the following percentage content: 99.76 (O^{16}), 0.04 (O^{17}), and 0.20 (O^{18}), it is easy to show that the physical unit of atomic weight is 0.0273 % less than the chemical unit.

The mass values given in Table 1 are the relative masses (atomic weights) of isotopes M and are connected with the absolute masses of the corresponding atoms m (expressed in grams) by the relation

$$m = \frac{M}{N_A} \tag{10.5}$$

where N_A is Avogadro's number, which corresponds to the physical unit of atomic weight, and $N_A = (6.02566 \pm 0.00016) \times 10^{23}$ (the value of N_A that corresponds to the chemical unit of atomic weight is $(6.02402 \pm 0.00017) \times 10^{23}$).

11. Artificial Nuclear Disintegration

Nuclear reactions. Exceedingly fruitful investigations into the artificial splitting of nuclei that opened a new era in nuclear physics began with the experiments of Rutherford (1919), who succeeded in demonstrating that the bombardment of nitrogen (and also a number of other elements) with RaC-emitted α-particles gives rise to fast H-particles (protons) which result from interaction of the α-particle with the target nucleus. That this is precisely the origin of H-particles is obvious from the following. First of all, measurements show that the velocities of these H-particles considerably exceed those that can be acquired by an H-atom nucleus in an elastic collision with an α-particle. What is more, the kinetic energy of the H-particles produced in the bombardment of aluminium turns out greater than that of the bombarding α-particles. Finally, the detection of H-particles flying in a direction opposite to that of the α-particles is cogent proof that there can be no other source of H-particles except the interaction of the α-particle with the target nucleus. All these observations may be interpreted as follows: under the influence of the perturbing action of the α-particle there is a rearrangement of the nucleus accompanied by the ejection of a proton. A more detailed picture of the mechanism of this process is given by the experiments of Blackett (1925), who studied the process of disintegration of a nitrogen nucleus by means of a cloud chamber. In addition to the straight α-particle tracks, Blackett photographed *forked* tracks that represented the path of an α-particle prior to its collision with a nitrogen nucleus and the paths of the products of interaction between an α-particle and an N^{14} nucleus. Fig. 8 shows one of the photographs obtained by Blackett. It will be seen that one of the paths ends in a *double fork*. The left-hand (long) branch of the fork is the path of an H-particle that has formed. The fact that there are only two (and not three) branches shows that

Fig. 8. Paths of α-particles in nitrogen (after Blackett). The fork represents the tracks of an H-particle (fine line on the left) and an O^{17} nucleus (heavy line to the right)

the α-particle and the nucleus, which has lost an H-particle, cease to exist as independent nuclei after the collision and merge to form the nucleus of a *new* element, which originates simultaneously with the ejection of the H-particle. In Fig. 8, the second, shorter branch of the fork is precisely the path of the nucleus of this new element. Thus, the process under examination may be represented by the following equation, similar to conventional chemical equations:

$$He_2^4 + N_7^{14} = O_8^{17} + H_1^1.$$

Here it is taken that the oxygen isotope O^{17} is the product of this *nuclear reaction* along with the H-particle. This conclusion follows of necessity from the laws of conservation of mass (mass number) and nuclear charge.

Later, Rutherford and Chadwick discovered similar reactions of α-particles with the nuclei of B, F, Na, Mg, Al, Si, P, S, Cl, and K. All these reactions result in the production of a proton and a new element which in the Periodic Table follows the bombarded element. Subsequently, the list of reactions of this type was considerably extended. The general formula for these reactions may be written as

$$He_2^4 + X_Z^A = Y_{Z+1}^{A+3} + H_1^1.$$

The conservation of mass and nuclear charge in such transformations is ensured by equality of the sums of the subscripts and superscripts on the left side of the equation ($4+A$ and $2+Z$) to the corresponding ones on the right side ($A+3+1$ and $Z+1+1$).

We note that reactions of this type are customarily denoted by the symbol $Z^A(\alpha, p)(Z+1)^{A+3}$, or, more simply still, (α, p).

Neutron. A study of the reactions of α-particles with the nuclei of light elements led Chadwick to the discovery of the *neutron* (1932), which is a particle with mass close to that of the proton and with zero charge. Neutrons were found to be produced by α-particle bombardment of Li, Be, B, F, Ne, and other elements.

Characteristic of neutron radiation is its great penetrating power due to the low absorption coefficient of neutrons in matter. Since neutrons cannot ionise atoms and molecules, various indirect methods are used to detect them. One is based on the observation of recoil nuclei, which are fast atoms produced in elastic collisions of a neutron with the nucleus of some atom. Recoil nuclei are readily detected by the ionisation they produce in an ionisation chamber or cloud chamber or else by activation of nuclear emulsion due to recoil nuclei: after the emulsion is developed, there appears a chain of grains (track) which can be seen under a microscope and represents the path of the recoil nucleus. This is similar to the chain of droplets that makes the path of a fast ion visible in the Wilson cloud chamber.

As follows from the theory of collision of elastic spheres, the energy conveyed from one sphere to another during a collision is particularly great when they have the same mass. When a moving sphere collides head-on with a stationary one of the same mass, the entire energy of the former is transmitted to the latter. For this reason, fast recoil atoms are especially readily formed in the passage of neutrons through hydrogen-containing substances (for example, paraffin), the atoms of which, as has been pointed out, have mass close to that of the neutron. This accounts, in particular, for the sharp increase in current when paraffin is introduced into an ionisation chamber that has been neutron-irradiated. The current increase was discovered by Curie and Joliot and correctly interpreted by them as due to the appearance of fast protons (recoil protons).

The general formula of a neutron-producing nuclear reaction with an α-particle may be written as

$$\alpha_2^4 + X_Z^A = Y_{Z+2}^{A+3} + n_0^1$$

where n is the neutron. This reaction may also be written as $Z^A(\alpha,\ n)(Z+2)^{A+3}$ or as $(\alpha,\ n)$.

The interaction between an α-particle and a nucleus is not the only source of neutrons. Neutrons are produced in the bombardment of various nuclei by protons and deuterons (the nuclei of heavy hydrogen H^2, or deuterium, D), and also in a number of other reactions (see below). The use of particles which possess less charge and are lighter than the α-particle has certain advantages. First of all, the smaller the charge of the bombarding particle, the closer it approaches the nucleus for a given kinetic energy (see Eq. (9.1a)) and, consequently, the more readily it interacts with the nucleus. Further, as follows from the theory of α-decay (Sec. 15), the probability of penetration of fast particles into a nucleus increases radically with decreasing mass of the particles. Finally, of no small importance is the possibility of obtaining powerful beams of protons and deuterons artificially in modern high-voltage ion accelerators.

One of the common "natural" sources of neutrons is a radium-beryllium source* in which the neutrons are obtained in the reaction

$$\alpha_2^4 + Be_4^9 = C_6^{12} + n_0^1.$$

---

* A mixture of radium-salt powders (usually $RaBr_2$) and metallic beryllium sealed in a copper or glass ampoule.

The neutron yield of a source with 1 gram of radium is 10^7 neutrons per second. This is practically the limit for natural neutron sources in which the α-particles are produced by radium decay, because of the comparatively low activity as well as the high cost of this element. In contrast to the natural sources of α-radiation, the possibilities of obtaining powerful ion beams artificially are almost unlimited.

The first nuclear reaction investigated by means of artificially obtained fast particles was that of a proton with a Li^7 nucleus,

$$H_1^1 + Li_3^7 = 2\,He_2^4,$$

discovered by Cockroft and Walton (1932). This reaction is peculiar in that it can be accomplished at comparatively low proton energies because of the ease with which a proton can penetrate a lithium nucleus (see above). In the first Cockroft-Walton experiments, the proton energy was 600 keV; however, it was later found that the reaction is observed even at 10 keV.

Two α-particles are also produced in a deuteron reaction with a light lithium isotope:

$$D_1^2 + Li_3^6 = 2\,He_2^4.$$

We may add that, as shown by special cloud-chamber experiments, both α-particles fly apart in accord with the law of conservation of momentum.

In addition to these and similar reactions of the (p, α) and (d, α) types, other proton and deuteron reactions were discovered, for instance, (p, n) and (d, n). The following is an illustration of the (p, n) type:

$$p_1^1 + Li_3^7 = Be_4^7 + n_0^1,$$

which is analogous to the α-particle reaction that had been observed:

$$\alpha_2^4 + Li_3^7 = B_5^{10} + n_0^1.$$

The following can serve to illustrate the (d, n) type reaction:

$$d_1^2 + D_1^2 = He_2^3 + n_0^1$$

and

$$d_1^2 + T_1^3 = He_2^4 + n_0^1,$$

which have found application in sources of monoenergetic neutrons.

Further, it is well to note that neutrons can also originate in the interaction of a γ-photon and a nucleus. Reactions of this type, called *photonuclear reactions* are symbolised as (γ, n); one of numerous cases of this type is the reaction

$$Be_4^9 + \gamma = Be_4^8 + n_0^1$$

established by the appearance of neutrons when beryllium is irradiated with gamma rays. It has been shown that the minimum γ-photon energy required for this reaction is 1.662 ± 0.003 MeV. Obviously, this energy may be interpreted as the binding energy (strength) of the neutron in the Be^9 nucleus. Another case of this type of reaction is

$$D_1^2 + \gamma = H_1^1 + n_0^1.$$

The protons produced in this reaction were detected directly in a cloud chamber. The neutron-proton binding energy in a deuterium nucleus, which is equal to the minimum energy of the γ-photon that caused the reaction, is 2.227 ± 0.003 MeV. Both the (γ, n) reactions and also certain other reactions of this type are used to produce monoenergetic neutrons.

Finally, it should be pointed out that neutrons are likewise obtained in nuclear fission reactions, which are considered below (Sec. 17).

A large number of neutron-induced reactions are known at present. These reactions are characterised by a high probability of occurrence, in particular at negligibly low neutron energies, for example, when induced by *thermal neutrons*, that is, by neutrons of energy equal to the mean thermal energy of the translational motion of molecules at a given temperature 3/2 kT, where k is the Boltzmann constant equal to $(1.38020 \pm 0.00007) \times \times 10^{-16}$ erg deg^{-1} (T is absolute temperature). The comparative ease with which neutron reactions develop stems from the advantage that neutrons have over charged particles in that there is no nuclear repulsion and the neutrons readily penetrate into the nuclei. The following are examples of neutron nuclear reactions:

$$n_0^1 + B_5^{10} = Li_3^7 + \alpha_2^4,$$
$$n_0^1 + B_5^{10} = Be_4^9 + d_1^2,$$
$$n_0^1 + S_{16}^{32} = P_{15}^{32} + p_1^1,$$
$$n_0^1 + Mn_{25}^{55} = Mn_{25}^{56} + \gamma.$$

These reactions correspond to types (n, α), (n, d), (n, p), and (n, γ), respectively, and are the reverse reactions of the above-considered types (α, n), (d, n), (p, n), and (γ, n).

It will be noted that some of these pairs of reactions were studied independently, for example, $n_0^1 + B_5^{10} = Li_3^7 + \alpha_2^4$ and $\alpha_2^4 + Li_3^7 = B_5^{10} + n_0^1$. Also studied was the *capture reaction*

$$n_0^1 + H_1^1 = D_1^2 + \gamma,$$

which is the reverse of the foregoing photonuclear reaction that consisted in the splitting of a deuteron into a proton and neutron by a γ-photon. Measurements of the energies of gamma photons emitted in the formation of a deuteron from a proton and neutron yielded 2.23 MeV, which, within experimental error, coincides with the above-mentioned limiting energy of γ-photons that induce a direct reaction (2.227 ± 0.003 MeV). It may be added that for the capture cross-section (σ_c) a value $\sigma_c = 0.325 \times 10^{-24}$ cm² was obtained from measurements of the mean lifetime of thermal neutrons in water; this time is determined by their disappearance due to capture by protons of the water. The capture cross-section determines the probability of this process and enters into the expression for its velocity $-\frac{d(n)}{dt} = \sigma_c u(H)(n)$, where u is the mean velocity of relative motion of the neutron and proton, and (n) and (H) are their concentrations. Putting the quantity σ_c equal to $\pi(a_p + a_n)^2$, we obtain 3.2×10^{-13} cm for the sum of the effective radii of the proton and neutron $a_p + a_n$; considering the radii of these particles to be the same, we find $a_p = 1.6 \times 10^{-13}$ cm. The effective radius of the proton thus found turns out close to that of a as computed from equation (9.6), from which for $A = 1$ it follows that $a = 1.45 \times 10^{-13}$ cm. Whence it may be concluded that the capture of a neutron by a proton occurs practically in every collision.

Positron. Artificially produced nuclear reactions (like natural radioactive transformations) very often lead to the formation of new radioactive elements or new radioactive isotopes of the initial element. Before considering the question of the nature of activity of artificial radioactive elements we must examine an extremely important discovery, the discovery of the positron made by Anderson (1932) when studying cosmic rays with a cloud chamber in a magnetic field. From the character of the track of the particle in the magnetic field it followed that the positron has a mass equal that of the electron and an equal and opposite electric charge. It is interesting to note that four years before the discovery of the positron its existence had been predicted by Dirac (1928) on the basis of an equation of motion of superfast electrons which he derived (Dirac equation).

In the same year of 1932, Blackett and Occhialini showed that when cosmic rays traverse matter they frequently give rise to *showers*, which are streams of particles that consist half of electrons and half of positrons, both having roughly the same speeds.

Further, Blackett and Occhialini (1933) and other investigators found that positrons could also originate from γ-photons on the condition that the energy of the latter exceeds 1.02 MeV. In this case, the electron and positron (*pair*) are produced simultaneously. For example, an electron-positron pair was produced by the γ-photons of RaC of energy 1.8 MeV, while in the case of the γ-photons of Po of energy 0.8 MeV this phenomenon was not observed. The existence of a limiting energy for γ-photons (1.02 MeV) follows directly from the law of conservation of energy. Indeed, computing the energy of an electron on the basis of the relation of equivalence of mass and energy (6.5),

$$E_e = \frac{mc^2}{\sqrt{1-\beta^2}} = K + mc^2$$

(K is the kinetic energy of the electron, m its rest mass and $\beta = v/c$, where v is the velocity of the electron), we find $E_e = K + 0.51$ MeV, or in the limiting case of sufficiently slow electrons ($\beta^2 \ll 1$ and, consequently, $K \approx 0$) $E_e = 0.51$ MeV.* Assuming the energy of the positron to be equal to that of the electron (in view of the equality of their masses) $E_p = E_e$, for the limiting energy of a γ-photon capable of converting into an electron-positron pair we find $E_{\gamma\,\mathrm{lim}} = E_e + E_p = 1.02$ MeV. Fig. 9 shows the generation of an electron-positron pair in a cloud-chamber photograph.

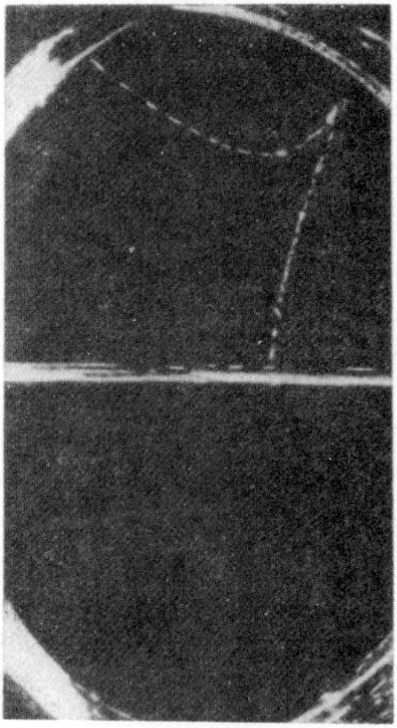

Fig. 9. Electron-positron pair production in the gas of a cloud chamber under irradiation with hard γ-radiation. The magnetic field deflects the two particles in different directions, thus indicating unlike charges

* The exact energy corresponding to the rest mass of an electron is 0.510969 ± 0.000009 MeV.

Also detected was a process which is the reverse of the transformation of a γ-photon into an electron-positron pair, i. e., the conversion of an electron and positron into γ-photons (two or three). This process is known as *annihilation* of an electron-positron pair.

As has already been pointed out, the artificial transformation of elements frequently gives rise to new radioactive nuclei. While studying nuclear reactions induced by bombardment of various elements with α-particles, Curie and Joliot (1934) found that in certain cases the new radioactive nuclei produced in such reactions *emit positrons*. Such nuclei were called positron- or β^+-active (in contrast to electron- or β^--active nuclei that emit β-particles, or electrons). Later it was found that positron activity is an extremely common phenomenon. Approximately two-thirds of artificially obtained radioactive isotopes are electron-active, the remaining third having positron activity. It was also found that positrons are likewise present, in small quantities, in the radiation of natural radioactive substances. However, in this case they arise as a result of secondary nuclear reactions that lead to the formation of positron-active isotopes.

In β^+-decay, the nuclear charge diminishes by unity, and the new element precedes the initial element in the Periodic Table. Thus, if the process of electron decay is represented by the scheme

$$Z^A = (Z+1)^A + \beta^-$$

or, correspondingly, by the symbol $Z^A\,(\beta^-)\,(Z+1)^A$, then positron decay must be represented by the scheme

$$Z^A = (Z-1)^A + \beta^+$$

or

$$Z^A\,(\beta^+)\,(Z-1)^A.$$

Positron decay is not the only possible mode of spontaneous transformation of an active nucleus, as a result of which its charge is diminished by unity. Another, similar, process, which is known as *electron* capture or *K-capture* was discovered in 1938 by Alvarez. This process consists in the spontaneous transition of one of the electrons of the atom into the nucleus. This reduces the nuclear charge by unity. Here, like in positron decay, the result is one of the isotopes of the element preceding the initial one in the Periodic Table. Despite the fact that both of these processes lead to one and the same final nucleus (from one and the same initial nucleus) they are easily distinguished experimentally because the atom of the element that is produced as a result of electron capture is in an *excited state*, that is, in a state with enhanced internal energy. This energy is radiated in the form of X-rays (see Sec. 21), which indicate whether the case is one of electron capture or not. Electron capture may be represented by the scheme

$$Z^A + e^- = (Z-1)^A.$$

Symbolically, this process is designated as $Z^A(K)(Z-1)^A$.

Both processes—positron decay and electron capture—are sometimes observed for one and the same nucleus. To illustrate, the radioactive isotope of manganese Mn_{25}^{52} (half-life, 6.5 days) in five cases out of one hundred undergoes positron decay and in 95 cases, electron capture, converting into a stable isotope of chromium, Cr_{24}^{52}. This dual transformation into the same final nucleus has likewise been established for V^{48}, Cu^{61}, Zn^{65} and a number of other nuclei.

It is interesting to note that there are cases of triple conversion. The radioactive isotope of copper Cu_{29}^{64} (half-life, 12.8 hours) is converted into the nickel isotope Ni_{28}^{64} via positron decay or electron capture and then, by means of electron decay, into the zinc isotope Zn_{30}^{64}. Similarly, the isotope Cl_{17}^{36} is converted in the following reactions: Cl (β^+) S, Cl (K) S and Cl (β^-) Ar.

It should, however, be noted that cases where a nucleus is inclined both to positron (or electron capture) and to electron decay are rather rare; usually, each given unstable nucleus is subject to one characteristic type of spontaneous transformation. The following variation in activity is observed for the isotopes of an element as the ratio of the mass number A to the nuclear charge Z increases: β^+ active isotopes, stable isotopes, β^--active isotopes. Obviously related to this regularity is the following: nuclear reactions consisting in the addition of a neutron to the nucleus of the initial element, for example, the reaction $n_0^1 + F_9^{19} = F_9^{20} + \gamma$ or $d_1^2 + Li_3^7 = Li_3^8 + p_1^1$ yield the β^--active isotopes F_9^{20} and Li_3^8, whereas reactions involving loss of a neutron by the initial nucleus, for example, $n_0^1 + F_9^{19} = F_9^{18} + 2n_0^1$ or $d_1^2 + B_5^{10} = C_6^{11} + n_0^1$, yield β^+-active isotopes (F_9^{18} and C_6^{11}). These and similar regularities are very important for the problem of the structure of atomic nuclei (see Secs. 12, 13, 14).

12. Structure of the Atomic Nucleus

Proton-neutron theory of the nucleus. The foregoing facts are obvious indications of the great complexity of the structure of atomic nuclei. This raises the question of the nature of the particles that make up the nucleus. Before the discovery of the neutron, the nuclei of all elements were generally considered to consist of protons and electrons (the proton-electron theory of the nucleus).

This view was based primarily on the fact that atomic weights are, practically, integers; this had become obvious after the discovery of isotopes and had made it possible, due to the smallness of the electron mass as compared with the proton mass, to express the mass of any nucleus as a multiple of the proton mass. The proton-electron hypothesis goes back to the views of Prout (1815), who, in view of the integrality of atomic weights, considered that the atoms of all elements consisted of hydrogen atoms.

The presence of protons in atomic nuclei likewise followed directly from experiments in the artificial splitting of nuclei. The emission of protons (H-particles) by nuclei subjected to α-particle bombardment was established in these experiments. β-radioactivity — electron emission by the nuclei of radioactive elements—likewise appeared to be irrefutable proof of the existence of electrons in the nucleus.

Moreover, electrons were needed in the nucleus to strengthen it, since positively charged particles alone (protons) could not ensure the high stability of the atomic nucleus.

The α-particles emitted by α-active elements were regarded as secondary structural elements of the nucleus consisting of the basic, primary, units — four protons and two electrons. The non-elementary nature of the α-particle is obvious from a number of nuclear reactions that indicate the possibility of destruction and creation of an α-particle, for instance,

$$p_1^1 + Li_3^7 = 2\alpha_2^4$$

or

$$d_1^2 + T_1^3 = \alpha_2^4 + n_0^1.$$

However, the assumption of electrons in the nucleus encountered unsurmountable difficulties in explaining certain things and was dropped as not being true to fact.

One of the chief objections to the presence of electrons in the atomic nucleus is the following. As will be shown in the next chapter, the electron (irrespective of whether it is in the free state or is bound in an atom) possesses a specific *angular momentum—spin*—and a *magnetic moment* proportional to it. In electron interactions, both the magnetic moments and angular momenta combine according to a definite law and form a certain total (resultant) magnetic moment and a total (resultant) angular momentum of the system. And, according to the law of addition of momenta, the resultant spin of a system consisting of N electrons will have one of the following values (in units of $\hbar = h/2\pi$): 1/2 N, 1/2 N—1, 1/2 N—2, ..., 1/2 or 0, depending on whether the number N is odd or even.

From this it follows, in particular, that when the number of electrons is odd, the resultant spin cannot be less than the spin of one electron (equal to 1/2 in the accepted system of units). Obviously, the same is true for the magnetic moment of the system.

Like the electron, the proton also has angular momentum (spin) and magnetic moment, and the spin of the proton is *equal* to that of the electron, while its magnetic moment is three orders of magnitude *less* than the magnetic moment of the electron. For this reason, if we assume that the nucleus is built up of protons and electrons, we would have to expect that nuclei with an odd number of electrons and an odd total number of particles should have odd spin and a magnetic moment not less than of the order of the magnetic moment of the electron.

Such are all nuclei of even mass number A and odd atomic number (nuclear charge), for example, the nuclei of Li_3^6 and N_7^{14}, since for them the number of electrons, equal to A—Z, will always be odd. Thus, for Li_3^6 the number of electrons is $A-Z=3$ and the number of protons and electrons $2A-Z=9$. Consequently, the total spin of the nucleus in this case should be 9/2, 7/2, 3/2 or 1/2, whereas experiment yields a spin of 1. For an N_7^{14} nucleus, we have, respectively, $A-Z=7$ and $2A-Z=21$, which again gives a half-integral total spin (21/2, 19/2, 17/2, 15/2, 13/2, 11/2, 9/2, 7/2, 5/2, 3/2, and 1/2). But in this case, too, experiment gives a whole number, 1. The same discrepancy is observed in respect to the magnetic moments of Li_3^6 and N_7^{14}. Due to the odd number of electrons (3 and 7), these should have values of the order of the magnetic moment of the electron. In actuality, however, the magnetic moments of the nuclei are in all cases, including those of Li^6 and N^{14}, several orders of magnitude *less* than the electronic moment.

These facts in themselves are sufficient for rejecting the hypothesis of nuclear electrons, which is contradicted by a series of other facts as well.

All these difficulties disappear if we assume that nuclei are built up of *protons* and *neutrons* instead of protons and electrons. This idea, first expressed by Chadwick in 1932, was developed in the works of Heisenberg, Tamm, and Ivanenko that appeared in the same year. A detailed study of the new model of the nucleus showed that it is in excellent agreement with experiment and, apparently, is the only correct one.

On the proton-neutron theory, the nucleus with mass number A and charge Z contains Z protons, which determine its charge, and A — Z neutrons. Thus, the deuterium nucleus D_1^2 contains, one proton and one neutron, the helium nucleus He_2^4, two protons and two neutrons, the lithium nucleus Li_3^6, three protons and three neutrons, the flourine nucleus F_9^{19}, 9 protons and 10 neutrons etc. The presence of neutrons in the nucleus follows directly in part from the foregoing reactions and also from an enormous number of other nuclear reactions that have been studied, for instance, from neutron capture reactions and the corresponding reverse photonuclear reactions, and also from reactions (n, 2n), which involve capture and emission of neutrons by nuclei. Since by independent experiments it was established that neutrons, like protons, have spins of 1/2 (in units of $\hbar$), the coincidence of one of the calculated values of spin with the measured value can likewise be regarded as experimental proof of the presence of neutrons in atomic nuclei. For example, from the rule of addition of spins we obtain integral values 1 and 0 for the spin of a deuteron (D), the first of which coincides with the experimental value (1); for the spin of a triton (T), the values 3/2 and 1/2 (experimental, 1/2), for He^4, 2, 1, and 0 (experimental, 0), for Li^6, 3, 2, 1 and 0 (experimental, 1), for Li^7, 7/2, 5/2, 3/2, and 1/2 (experimental, 3/2), etc.

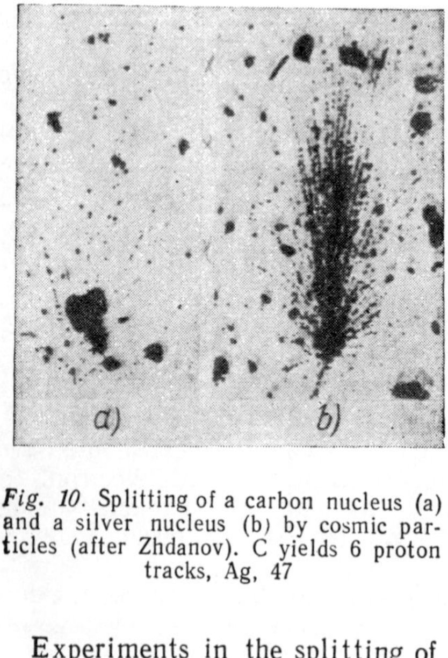

Fig. 10. Splitting of a carbon nucleus (a) and a silver nucleus (b) by cosmic particles (after Zhdanov). C yields 6 proton tracks, Ag, 47

Experiments in the splitting of atomic nuclei with fast cosmic particles give one of the most vivid proofs of the correctness of the proton-neutron theory of the nucleus. Due to their very high energies, which run into thousands of millions of electron-volts (GeV, or BeV), cosmic-ray particles are capable of breaking up an atomic nucleus into all its component particles.

Fig. 10a and b shows two pictures of such a break-up of carbon and silver nuclei. The pictures were obtained with nuclear emulsions. Only proton tracks are recorded since only protons possess ionising power and, hence, display photographic action. The first photograph (Fig. 10a) reveals six proton tracks, and according to the proton-neutron theory, the carbon nucleus C^{12} actually contains six protons (and six neutrons).

Fig. 10b (the disintegration of an Ag_{47} nucleus, which contains 47 protons) shows 47 such tracks. It will be noted that if the proton-electron hypotheses were valid, 12 tracks would be expected in the first case and 107-109 tracks in the second.

Nuclear transformations accompanied by the emission of α-particles show that two protons and two neutrons tend to form a stable complex — He_2^4 nuclei, which are readily formed in the process of nuclear transformation and, possibly, even exist as a "whole" in certain nuclei. In the latter case, the α-particles should exist in the nucleus as independent structural units. This point of view, which finds expression in the so-called *α-model* of the nucleus (in this model, the nucleus, at least for all light elements with A a multiple of 4, consists of α-particles), is somewhat corroborated in investigations of the photodisintegration of C^{12} and O^{16} nuclei by hard γ-photons. The "photographs" obtained by the photoemulsion technique occasionally reveal α-particle tracks emanating from a single point ("stars"), which point to a single source of all the α-particles forming the star. For example, when C^{12} is irradiated with γ-photons of energy of tens of MeV, we observe three-pronged stars whose origin must be associated with the reaction

$$\gamma + C_6^{12} = 3\alpha_2^4.$$

The irradiation of O^{16} nuclei reveals four-pronged stars (the process is $\gamma + O_8^{16} = 4\alpha_2^4$).

It may be that phenomenon of α-decay, which is so widespread among the heavy elements,* and also observed cases of α-particle emission in nuclear fission ** should likewise be regarded as an indication of a more or less separate existence of He_2^4 groups in nuclei.

The foregoing data, of course, do not in any way affect the conclusion (p. 60) concerning the nonelementary nature of

* For the lighter elements, α-activity has been established in samarium Sm_{62}^{128}, which has a half-life of 1.4×10^{11} years.

** It has been found, in the fission of U^{235}, that an α-particle is ejected in one out of 220 cases, a proton, in one out of 5000.

α-particles. To the foregoing facts that demonstrate the possibility of creation and destruction of α-particles, we may add the following. The detection of protons (by means of photoemulsion techniques) in the irradiation of helium with hard γ-photons testifies to the possibility of the photo-dissociation of He nuclei. In exactly the same way, observations of two-pronged stars produced by 90-MeV-neutron irradiation revealed the following processes of destruction of He^4 nuclei: in 47 cases out of 90, He^4 nuclei decayed into p + t, in 18, into d + t, in 14, into p + d (+ n), in 10, into d + d, and in one case, into p + p (+ 2n). The relatively low probability of the latter type of decay is undoubtedly due to the fact that it requires the greatest energy.

Theory of β-decay. After eliminating the difficulties from the hypothesis of nuclear electrons, the proton-neutron theory of the nucleus encountered new difficulties. The chief one was the necessity of interpreting the β-decay of nuclei, that is to say, the emission of electrons by nuclei which do not contain electrons. It must be stressed here that in β-decay the electrons are emitted by the nuclei. This follows directly from the attendant increase in the nuclear charge (displacement law). It should also be noted that the hypothesis of nuclear electrons does not eliminate the difficulties involved in the discovery of positron nuclear decay.

Overcoming the difficulties of the theory of β-decay involves the problem of the *nature* of the proton and the neutron. According to the theory of Heisenberg and Majorana (Sec. 14), the interaction of protons and neutrons (which ensures the stability of the atomic nucleus) presumes that an *exchange* of electric charge is possible between these particles. If the proton is considered the elementary particle and the neutron is regarded as a complex particle consisting of a proton and an electron, then the electron will be the exchanged charge. But if the neutron is considered the elementary particle and the proton is regarded as consisting of a neutron and a positron, then the positron will be this charge.

A proper solution to the problem of the elementary nature of the proton and the neutron proceeds from the concept that both the proton and the neutron designate two different states of *one and the same particle*, which we shall call the *nucleon*, or *heavy particle* (to distinguish it from the *light* particles: electron and positron). This is the underlying concept of the present theory of β-decay (Fermi, 1934). On this theory, β-decay is regarded as the transition of a nucleon from one state into another accompanied by the emission of an electron (β^--decay) or a positron (β^+-decay), just like the transition of an atom from one energy state to another is attended by the emission of a light quantum, or photon. Obviously, an electron is ejected in the transition of a nucleon from the neutron to the proton state ($n \to p$), while a positron is ejected in the reverse transition ($p \to n$). In other words, β-decay of a nucleus may be regarded as some sort of *generation* of a light particle in the same sense as we speak of the production of a photon when it is emitted by an atom.

The production of an electron or positron in β-decay is the result of a change in the internal energy of the nucleus. Earlier (p. 57) we learned of another case of the production of light particles at the expense of the energy of γ-radiation. In this case, an electron-positron pair is always produced, for otherwise the law of conservation of electricity would be violated and also the law of conservation of angular momentum. A more detailed consideration of the process of production of a β-particle in the β-decay of an atomic nucleus shows that in this case, too, there must be a simultaneous generation of a *pair* of light particles.

Above all, we are led to this conclusion by general theoretical reasoning based on the conservation laws. Indeed, the law of conservation of electricity is fulfilled here, because when a β-particle is ejected by the nucleus, the charge of the latter changes by a corresponding magnitude. However, a β-particle has angular momentum (spin) in addition to charge. For this reason, according to the law of conservation of angular momentum, simultaneously with the ejection of a β-particle together with its spin, there must arise, in the nucleus, an angular momentum equal in magnitude to the spin of the β-particle (but opposite in direction). But, as has already been pointed out, the angular momentum of the nucleus is determined by the mass number, and since the mass number in β-decay remains unchanged, it likewise must remain constant. The only way out of this difficulty is to assume that a *second* light particle (with spin equal but opposite in direction to that of the β-particle) is emitted by the nucleus together with the β-particle.

This second particle should not have any electric charge, otherwise the radioactive displacement law will not hold. Such a particle—the *neutrino*—was introduced by Pauli in 1933 in connection with yet another grave difficulty that was encountered in the theory of β-decay. This difficulty is connected with the energy or the spectrum of β-radiation. While the nuclei-ejected α-particles always have a strictly definite kinetic energy (or, to be more precise, a set of several discrete values of energy) characteristic of each given nucleus, the electrons and positrons produced in β^-- or β^+-decay of the nucleus have all kinds of velocities ranging from zero to a certain maximum value characteristic of the given nucleus v_{max} (a continuous spectrum of velocities). On the assumption that in β-decay the nucleus ejects only one light particle (electron or positron), the existence of a continuous spectrum of β-radiation appears as an unresolvable riddle. Indeed, since in this process the energy of the nucleus varies by a strictly definite discrete magnitude, all the β-particles that it ejects should have identical velocities; but this is not borne out by experiment.

The introduction of the neutrino eliminates this contradiction, since the energy liberated in β-decay is now distributed between two particles: a β-particle and the neutrino. Thus, the Pauli hypothesis at one stroke eliminates both of the above difficulties in the theoretical interpretation of the phenomenon of β-decay.

Repeated attempts were made to detect the neutrino and obtain more information about its nature. Most of these attempts were aimed at detecting the neutrino when it was formed in β-decay or electron capture. One of the trends in this research is to measure the energy of the recoil nuclei that appear in electron capture. The first measurements of this kind were made by Allen (1942), who showed that the energy of a Li^7 nucleus produced in the process $Be^7 + e = Li^7 + \nu$ (where ν is a neutrino), is close to the computed value if it is assumed that the rest mass of the neutrino is zero. Later, on the basis of measurements of the energy distribution of electrons in the β-spectrum of tritium (the reaction $T^3 = He^3 + e + \nu$), a value of the order of 0.001 of the electron mass was obtained for the upper limit of the rest mass of the neutrino. Attempts were also made to detect free neutrinos. For instance, positron radiation was recorded and attributed to the interaction of neutrinos (emerging from an atomic reactor) with protons; the process is $\nu + p = n + \beta^+$. The magnitude of the observed effect also yielded the effective cross-section for this process, which (in agreement with theoretical calculations) proved to be of the order of 10^{-43} cm^2. Comparing this value with the one above (p. 56) for the effective cross-section of the process $n + p = d + \gamma$, we see that the probability of a neutrino-proton reaction is 3×10^{18} times less than that of the neutron-proton reaction.

Summarising, we find that the principal structural elements of atomic nuclei are exclusively heavy particles—protons and neutrons (nucleons). There is also the question of the forces that bind nucleons together and ensure the great strength of nuclei. It will be considered in Sec. 14.

13. Dynamics of the Atomic Nucleus

Energetics of nuclear transformations. Up till now, when considering various transformations of atomic nuclei, both spontaneous (α- and β-decay, electron capture) and those produced by some form of radiation (nuclear reactions produced by α-particles, protons, deuterons, neutrons, photonuclear reactions), we hardly at all touched on the energy aspect of these phenomena. This aspect comes to the fore when we deal with the forces that bind the separate components of the nucleus into a whole. Without speaking of the nature of these forces, we nevertheless have no doubt that they are forces of attraction. Consequently, in the formation of a nucleus of protons and neutrons, a definite energy *(the binding energy of the nucleus)* must be released, like the heat of atomisation of molecules, that is, the energy released in the formation of a molecule out of its component atoms. Obviously, the released energy corresponds to the decrease in the energy of the system; in other words, it is equal to the difference between the energy of the isolated protons and neutrons and the energy of the nucleus. According to the relationship of the equivalence of energy and mass,

$$E = mc^2,$$

a decrease in the energy of the nucleus should be attended by a decrease in its mass as compared with the mass of the separate protons and neutrons. Therefore, as the measure of the energy (thermal) effect of the reaction of formation of a nucleus out of its components, or as the measure of the binding energy of the nucleus, we can take the difference between the mass of the separately taken component protons and neutrons of the nucleus and the mass of the nucleus (Δm). Denoting the mass of a nucleus consisting of Z protons and A—Z neutrons by m, and the masses of the proton and neutron, by m_p and m_n, respectively, we obtain

$$\Delta m = Zm_p + (A - Z)\, m_n - m. \qquad (13.1)$$

The binding energy of the nucleus will, accordingly, be

$$\Delta E = \Delta mc^2. \qquad (13.2)$$

Since the binding energy of a nucleus, like the energy effects of nuclear reactions, is usually expressed in MeV, we must determine the energy equivalent of unit mass. Taking 1/16 of the mass of an oxygen atom for the unit of mass $\Delta m_1 = \frac{m_O}{16} = \frac{1}{N_A}$

$\left(\text{inasmuch as } m_O = \frac{16}{N_A}\right)$, and substituting this quantity into equation (13.2), we have

$$\Delta E_1 = \frac{c^2}{N_A}.$$

Numerical substitution gives $\Delta E_1 = 1.4915 \times 10^{-3}$ erg or, since 1 eV $= 1.602 \times 10^{-12}$ erg,

$$\Delta E_1 = 931.16 \text{ MeV}.$$

The possibility of expressing energy effects in terms of the mass of the nucleus and its component particles shows how important are measurements of atomic masses in determining the degree of stability of nuclei and, in the final analysis, in clarifying the nature of the interaction forces of the component parts of the nucleus. On the basis of known atomic masses we can compute both the energy effects of various nuclear reactions and the binding energies of the nuclei. As we have seen, to do this we must know the mass of the neutron.

One of the methods of determining the mass of the neutron is to compute the balance of energy in certain nuclear reactions involving nuclear disintegration. This method was first applied by Chadwick and Goldhaber, and also by Feather for γ-fission of a deuterium nucleus (deuteron). These authors have shown that when deuterium is irradiated with γ-rays of ThC″ (the quanta have an energy of 2.616 MeV), the deuterons disintegrate into protons and neutrons. The energy balance of this reaction is written as

$$\gamma = (m_p + m_n - m_d)\, c^2 + K,$$

where m_d is the mass of the deuteron and K is the total kinetic energy of the proton and neutron. By measuring the kinetic energy of the proton and considering it equal to the neutron energy (as the masses of the two particles are nearly the same), one can determine from this equality the binding energy of the proton and the neutron in the deuteron, i.e., the quantity $\Delta m = m_p + m_n - m_d$. It turns out equal to 2.2 MeV, or 0.0024 unit of mass. Substituting into the expression for Δm the values $m_p = 1.0081$ and $m_d = 2.0147$ (see Table 1), we find $m_n = 0.0024 + 2.0147 - 1.0081 = 1.0090$. The latest and more accurate measurements of the neutron mass give

$$m_n = 1.008985 \pm 0.000002.$$

We shall use this value of neutron mass in our subsequent computations.

By computing the magnitude of Δm (13.1)—which characterises the nuclear binding energy—from known values of mass of the given nucleus m, m_p, and m_n and dividing this value by the number of nucleons A, we obtain the binding energy (in units of atomic mass) per nucleon. This quantity may be called the *specific binding energy* of the nucleus δm. These quantities (multiplied by 1000 for convenience) for the stable isotopes of light elements (from deuterium to neon) are represented graphically in Fig. 11.* It will be seen that the curve of specific binding

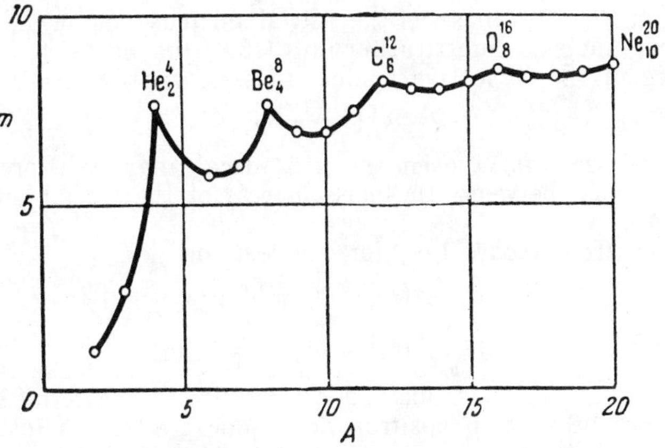

Fig. 11. Specific binding energy of light nuclei

energies has maxima for isotopes with values of A that are multiples of 4 and, in addition, that contain equal quantities of protons and neutrons. From this it may be concluded that the nuclei of such isotopes are extremely stable. It may be noted that this was one of the reasons for supposing that such nuclei are built up of α-particles (the α-model of the nucleus).

Energies of nuclear reactions. Both the binding energy and the specific binding energy characterise the stability of the nucleus against disintegration into protons and neutrons. These quantities could also be used to compute the energies of nuclear reactions. But in this case it is more convenient to use a quantity called the *mass defect*; it is equal to the difference between the mass of the nucleus and the mass number A,

$$\Delta = m - A, \tag{13.3}$$

* Here, only one nonstable isotope was used—beryllium Be^8, which disintegrates into two α-particles (see below).

or a quantity obtained from it, $\delta = \Delta/A$, called the *coefficient of nuclear packing*. For convenience sake, the quantities Δ and δ may be multiplied by 1000.

Let us consider the reaction of β-decay. The energy of electron decay, i.e., that of the reaction

$$Z^A = (Z+1)^A + \beta^- + \nu$$

(where ν is a neutrino), is expressed by the formula

$$Q = c^2 (m_Z - m_{Z+1}), \tag{13.4}$$

where m_z is the mass of the initial nucleus and m_{Z+1} that of the final nucleus. Substituting into (13.4) the mass defects (13.3) in place of the respective nuclear masses, we obtain

$$Q = c^2 (\Delta_Z - \Delta_{Z+1}). \tag{13.5}$$

Thus, we see that the energy of β^--decay may be expressed as the difference between the mass defects of the initial and final nuclei.*

For positron decay, i.e., for the reaction

$$Z^A = (Z-1)^A + \beta^+ + \nu,$$

we get

$$Q = c^2 (m_Z - m_{Z-1}) + 2c^2 m_e \tag{13.6}$$

where m_e is the rest mass of the electron. The term $2c^2 m_e$ is introduced because in positron decay one electron is lost simultaneously with a positron, since the atom of the new element no longer contains Z electrons but $Z-1$ electrons.** Thus, on the whole, we have a loss of mass equal to $2m_e$. Expressing Q (13.6) in terms of the mass defects, we obtain

$$Q = c^2 (\Delta_Z - \Delta_{Z-1}) + 2c^2 m_e. \tag{13.7}$$

We note that the quantity $2c^2 m_e$ is equal to 1.02194 MeV, or 0.0010975 atomic mass (physical units of atomic weight).

Stable and unstable isobaric nuclei. From the point of view of nuclear stability, which is extremely important for the theory of the atomic nucleus and for the periodic system of

---

* It is easy to show that the quantity Q is expressed in terms of the binding energy ΔE_Z and ΔE_{Z+1} by the following formula

$$Q = (\Delta E_{Z+1} - \Delta E_Z) + c^2 (m_n - m_p).$$

It will be noted that to the quantity $m_n - m_p = 0.0008389$ there corresponds an energy 0.782 MeV.

** We must remember that the quantities m are the masses (atomic weights) of the atoms, and not of the nuclei, which means they include the masses of the electrons as well.

isotopes, it is interesting to consider the so-called *isobaric nuclei* (*isobars*), which are nuclei with different charges but the same mass numbers. Table 2 gives some of the isobaric nuclei found among the light elements. The fifth column gives the activity of the unstable nuclei and their half-lives, the sixth column, differences in the mass defects of active and stable isobars (in mass units multiplied by 1000) $\Delta^x - \Delta$.

In Table 2 we note the positron activity (β^+) of all nuclei (with the exception of He^3) containing a surplus number of protons as compared with the number of neutrons. This indicates instability of such nuclei. Some authors associate this with the mutual repulsion of protons. The F_9^{18} nucleus is unstable despite the equal number of protons and neutrons; and this goes for all subsequent nuclei containing an equal number of protons and neutrons, with the exception of Mg_{12}^{24}, Si_{14}^{28}, S_{16}^{32}, Ar_{18}^{36} and Ca_{20}^{40}, which have even Z. Ca_{20}^{40} is the last stable isotope in the group of nuclei under consideration. It is important to point out that for nuclei with the same number of protons and neutrons but with odd Z, the series of stable nuclei comes to an end with the N_7^{14} nucleus. Now nuclei with $Z > 7$ are either radioactive or are simply undetectable due to their low stability, like nuclei with sufficiently large even Z. Whence we may conclude that nuclei with odd Z are less stable than nuclei with even Z. This conclusion likewise follows from the curve of specific binding energy of light nuclei shown in Fig. 11: the minima of this curve correspond to nuclei with odd Z: Li_3^6, B_5^{10}, N_7^{14}.

In accordance with the reduced stability of nuclei with excess protons, the mass of β^+-active nuclei comes out greater than that of the corresponding isobaric stable nuclei. Here, the greater the mass difference (and, hence, the difference in mass defects), the shorter the half-life (Table 2) and, hence, the greater the probability of radioactive transformation of an unstable nucleus. On the Fermi theory, the radioactive transformation of these nuclei is regarded as a transition of a heavy particle of the nucleus from the proton to the neutron state, which results in a nucleus of an appropriate stable isobar:

$$C_6^{10} \longrightarrow B_5^{10},\ C_6^{11} \longrightarrow B_5^{11},\ N_7^{12} \longrightarrow C_6^{12},\ N_7^{13} \longrightarrow C_6^{13},\ O_8^{14} \longrightarrow N_7^{14},\ O_8^{15} \longrightarrow N_7^{15},$$
$$F_9^{17} \longrightarrow O_8^{17},\ F_9^{18} \longrightarrow O_8^{18},\ Ne_{10}^{19} \longrightarrow F_9^{19}.$$

Also unstable are isobars with two surplus neutrons (see Table 2), with the exception of O_8^{18} and Ne_{10}^{22} and tritium, which is unstable even with the single surplus neutron. From the

Table 2

Mass-defect differences and the activity of isobaric nuclei

Nucleus	A	Z	A − Z	Activity, $T_{1/2}$	$(\Delta^* - \Delta)\cdot 10^3$	Nucleus	A	Z	A − Z	Activity, $T_{1/2}$	$(\Delta^* - \Delta)\cdot 10^3$
T_1^3	3	1	2	β^-, 12.46 yrs	0.02	C_6^{14}	14	6	8	β^-, 5670 yrs	0.17
He_2^3	3	2	1			N_7^{14}	14	7	7		
He_2^6	6	2	4	β^-, 0.85 sec	3.79	O_8^{14}	14	8	6	β^+, 76.5 sec	5.52
Li_3^6	6	3	3			C_6^{15}	15	6	9	β^-	9.2
Li_3^7	7	3	4			N_7^{15}	15	7	8		
Be_4^7	7	4	3	K-capture 52.9 days	0.93	O_8^{15}	15	8	7	β^+, 118 sec	2.90
Li_3^9	9	3	6	β^-	15.03	N_7^{16}	16	7	9	β^-, 7.35 sec	11.24
Be_4^9	9	4	5			O_8^{16}	16	8	8		
Be_4^{10}	10	4	6	β^-, $2.6\cdot 10^6$ yrs	0.60	N_7^{17}	17	7	10	β^-, 4.14 sec	11.79
B_5^{10}	10	5	5			O_8^{17}	17	8	9		
C_6^{10}	10	6	4	β^+, 19.1 sec	4.22	F_9^{17}	17	9	8	β^+, 66 sec	2.96
B_5^{11}	11	5	6			O_8^{18}	18	8	10		
C_6^{11}	11	6	5	β^+, 20.4 min	2.14	F_9^{18}	18	9	9	β^+, 107 min	1.79
B_5^{12}	12	5	7	β^-, 0.027 sec	14.36	O_8^{19}	19	8	11	β^-, 27.0 sec	4.8
C_6^{12}	12	6	6			F_9^{19}	19	9	10		
N_7^{12}	12	7	5	β^+, 0.0125 sec	18.98	Ne_{10}^{19}	19	10	9	β^+, 18.2 sec	3.50
C_6^{13}	13	6	7			F_9^{20}	20	9	11	β^-, 12 sec	7.55
N_7^{13}	13	7	6	β^+, 9.93 min.	2.39	Ne_{10}^{20}	20	10	10		

sixth column of Table 2 it is seen that the nuclei of all these isobars have an appreciable excess of energy over the corresponding stable isobar, and, via electron emission (β^-activity; one nucleon converts from the neutron to the proton state), they are transformed into the nucleus of the stable partner:

$$He_2^6 \rightarrow Li_3^6,\ Li_3^9 \rightarrow Be_4^9,\ Be_4^{10} \rightarrow B_5^{10},\ B_5^{12} \rightarrow C_6^{12},\ C_6^{14} \rightarrow N_7^{14},$$

$$C_6^{15} \rightarrow N_7^{15},\ N_7^{16} \rightarrow O_8^{16},\ N_7^{17} \rightarrow O_8^{17},\ O_8^{19} \rightarrow F_9^{19},\ F_9^{20} \rightarrow Ne_{10}^{20}.$$

We note that both in the case of β^-- and β^+-active nuclei the half-life is directly (but in the inverse sense) dependent on the mass difference of isobaric nuclei.

Whereas nuclei with even Z and an excess of two (or more) neutrons are stable beginning with O_8^{18} nuclei (see above), in the case of odd Z the first stable nucleus with excess neutrons (in this case, three neutrons) is that of Cl_{17}^{37}. Again there is a greater stability of nuclei with even Z over those with odd Z.

From data on the masses of isobaric elements it follows that the masses of isobars for each mass number A lie on a smooth curve with a pronounced minimum,* depending on the difference between the number of neutrons and the number of protons in the nucleus. A stable isobar is one with least mass; obviously, the values of the numbers of protons and neutrons corresponding to a minimum in the curve are those "optimum" values which, for a given number of nucleons A, ensure greatest stability of the nucleus. Electron-active nuclei result from an excess of neutrons over those with optimum values, positron-active nuclei result from a neutron deficiency.

As Z increases, the number of neutrons both in stable nuclei and in the nuclei of radioactive isotopes more and more exceeds the number of protons. Towards the end of the Periodic Table, the nuclei of heavy elements contain approximately two protons to three neutrons. For the nucleus of gold Au_{79}^{197} we have $\frac{(A-Z)}{Z} = \frac{118}{79}$, for the nucleus of bismuth Bi_{83}^{209}, $\frac{126}{83}$, etc. From the point of view of Coulomb interaction of protons, the stabilising action of such "diluting" with neutrons may be accounted for by the increasing size of the nucleus and, consequently, the greater mean distance between protons, in other words, by the decreasing forces of mutual repulsion of the protons.

It will readily be seen that such an explanation does not contradict the fact of the existence of a stability threshold of an

* In the case of isobars with an even number of protons and neutrons (even-even nuclei) and with an odd number of both (odd-odd nuclei), we have two such curves: for even-even and odd-odd isobars.

element, which finds expression in the fact that all heavy elements beginning with polonium ($Z=84$) are radioactive, i.e., they have unstable nuclei. Indeed, since in this case it is a question of the α-activity of heavy nuclei, one should expect that nuclear stability should significantly involve other factors in addition to the stabilising action of "neutron dilution". Here, one of these factors is undoubtedly the energy of the reaction:

$$X_Z^A = Y_{Z-2}^{A-4} + He_2^4$$

where X is the initial and Y the final nucleus. The influence of this factor is clearly seen when considering Fig. 12, which gives the energy of α-decay computed from the formula

$$Q=(m_X - m_Y - m_{He})\,c^2 \quad (13.8)$$

from the masses of atoms X, Y and He^4 for the following isotopes: stable — Hg_{80}^{200}, Hg_{80}^{202}, Tl_{81}^{203}, Pb_{82}^{204}, Pb_{82}^{206}, Pb_{82}^{207}, Pb_{82}^{208}, Bi_{83}^{209}, and α-active—Bi_{83}^{211} (AcC), Po_{84}^{210}, Rn_{86}^{222}, Ra_{88}^{226}, Th_{90}^{232}, U_{92}^{238}. From Fig. 12 it is seen that near the stability threshold (element 83, bismuth, is the last stable element), when passing to heavy elements there is a sharp increase in the energy of α-decay; this increase points to a direct relationship between the stability of the nucleus with respect to α-decay (or the probability of α-decay) and the energy effect of this reaction.

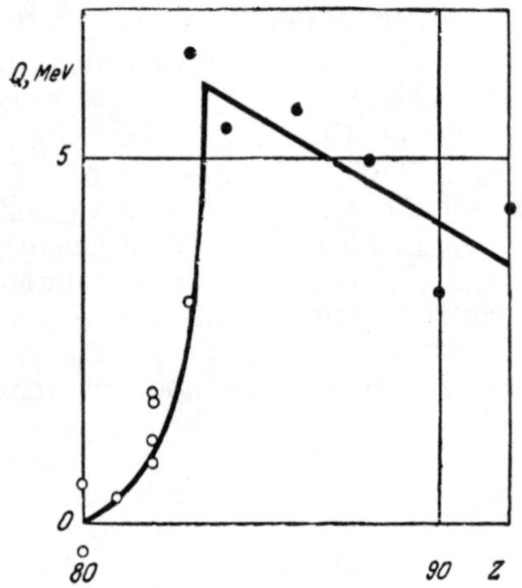

Fig. 12. Reaction energy of α-decay in heavy elements

14. Nuclear Forces

Properties of nuclear forces. In connection with the question of the size of atomic nuclei we have already (p. 43) spoken of the existence of special nuclear forces of attraction operating between the nuclear particles at distances close to the sum of the radii of these particles and falling off rapidly with distance. The magnitude of these forces may be judged by the binding energy of nuclei, which is many orders of magnitude greater than the energy of the chemical bonds in molecules. Indeed, comparing the binding energy of the proton and neutron in a deuteron, which is 2.23 MeV, with the energy of chemical coupling of a proton and H atom in a molecular ion of hydrogen H_2^+, which is 2.65 eV, we see that the former quantity exceeds the latter by six orders of magnitude. At distances of the order of nuclear dimensions, nuclear forces also exceed the electrical forces of Coulomb interaction of charged particles. For example, assuming that the difference in the binding energies of two isobaric nuclei, tritium T_1^3 and the light isotope of helium He_2^3, $8.49-7.73=0.76$ MeV, is due to the energy of mutual repulsion of protons in the He^3 nucleus, on the basis of the Coulomb law we have

$$\frac{e}{r}=0.76 \text{ MeV},$$

whence we get $r=1.9\times 10^{-13}$ cm for the distance between protons in the He^3 nucleus. Since this number practically coincides with the deuteron radius $a=1.8\times 10^{-13}$ cm computed from formula (9.6), which should be close to the distance between proton and neutron and, hence, also between two protons in the nucleus, we can compare directly the above obtained value of the energy of Coulomb interaction between two protons with the energy of nuclear interaction of proton and neutron in a deuteron. From this comparison it follows that at a distance equal to the radius of the deuteron, the force of nuclear attraction is $\frac{2.23}{0.76}=3$ times that of Coulomb attraction.

From this calculation it also follows that the forces of nuclear attraction between proton and neutron should be the same as between proton and proton or between neutron and neutron, that is to say, these forces are *independent of the electric charge* of the nucleon. This extremely important conclusion is also supported by other data, for instance, the results of studies in the scattering of protons and neutrons by protons.

Further, from the conclusion of the small range of nuclear forces it follows that the nucleons should interact only with their immediate neighbours in the nucleus. This conclusion is corroborated by the following data that refer to nuclear binding energy. Let us first consider the nuclei D_1^2, T_1^3, He_2^3, and He_2^4, for which we may assume direct contact between all nucleons. In this case, the number of bonds between each pair of nucleons in the nucleus is expressed by the formula $1/2\,A(A-1)$, from which we have 1 for D^2, 3 for T^3 and He^3, and 6 for He^4. Considering all bonds equivalent and disregarding Coulomb repulsion of protons, we must conclude that the separate binding energies in the above nuclei should approximately be in the ratio of 1:2:2:3. Computing from the nuclear masses the corresponding values of specific binding energy, we obtain 1.11; 2.83; 2.58, and 7.08 MeV; these figures are in the ratio 0.8:2.0:1.9:5.0, which approximately corresponds to that obtained "theoretically". It must be pointed out that one cannot expect complete coincidence because, for one thing, the dependence of nuclear forces on nucleon spin is disregarded (see below). We note that one of the consequences of this dependence is the particularly great strength of the two proton-two neutron system (the He^4 nucleus), which is manifested in its high binding energy. *

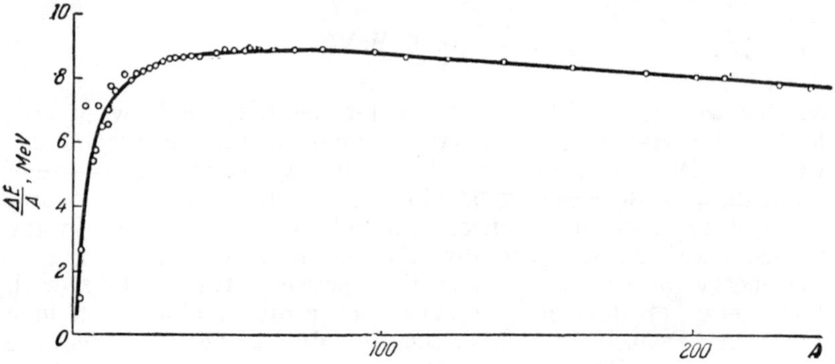

Fig. 13. Specific nucleus binding energy as a function of mass number A

Associated with the short range of nuclear forces is also the approximate constancy of the specific binding energy observed in all stable isotopes, with the exception of the first ten isotopes of the lightest elements, as may be seen from the curve of specific binding energy (expressed in MeV) versus mass number given in Fig. 13. Near $A=10$, δE attains 7.0 MeV, then passes through a flat maximum at $A=50-60$, which corresponds to $\delta E=8.8$ and with further increase in A it begins to decline slowly approaching 7.6 MeV near $A=240$. The approximate constancy of the specific binding energy finds a simple explanation in the fact that given a sufficiently large number of nucleons in the nucleus, each nucleon will be in direct con-

* A manifestation of the great stability of the α-particle may also be found in the instability of the He_2^5 nucleus against $(\alpha+n)$-decay, the Li_3^5 nucleus against $(\alpha+p)$-decay, Be_4^8, against 2α-decay, and B_5^9, against $(2\alpha+p)$-decay.

tact only with a limited number of surrounding nucleons; as a result, the expression $1/2\,A(A-1)$ for the binding energy of a nucleus, which expression presupposes the interaction of each nucleon with all the other nucleons in the nucleus, cannot be valid even approximately. From the approximate constancy of the specific binding energy it follows that the binding energy of the nucleus must be proportional to the number of nucleons A in the given nucleus. On the other hand, according to equation (9.6), we have $A \sim a^3$, whence it follows that the binding energy ΔE must be approximately proportional to the volume of the nucleus $4/3\,\pi a^3$.

It will be noted that similar relations occur in the case of a liquid drop, the energy of which is also proportional to its volume; this is due to the rapid decrease in the forces of mutual attraction of molecules with distance, as a result of which each molecule interacts only with its immediate neighbours. This analogy led to the liquid-drop model of the atomic nucleus, which was developed by Frenkel and Niels Bohr and which proved extremely fruitful in the interpretation of a variety of nuclear properties, and above all the fission of heavy nuclei (see below).

The liquid-drop model of the nucleus was utilised by Weizsäcker for computing the binding energy of atomic nuclei. The formula he derived for the specific binding energy is*

$$\delta E = \frac{\Delta E}{A} = \alpha - \beta\frac{(N-Z)^2}{A^2} - \gamma A^{-\frac{1}{3}} - \varkappa Z^2 A^{-\frac{4}{3}} \qquad (14.1)$$

where α, β, γ, and $\varkappa$ are constants. The first two terms in (14.1) express the portion of energy due to nuclear forces and reflect the experimental fact that in the case of light nuclei, when Coulomb repulsion of protons plays a comparatively slight lore, the stablest nuclei are those containing an equal number of protons and neutrons. The quantity α is the energy of nuclear interaction when $N=Z$. The symmetrical shape of the function $\frac{(N-Z)^2}{A^2}$ is in accord with the fact that the nuclear forces are independent of the nucleon charge.

The term $\gamma A^{-\frac{1}{3}}$ in formula (14.1) corresponds to the surface energy of a liquid drop and expresses the simple fact that the

* The binding energy is usually normalised so that the energy of a nucleus divided into nucleons at infinite recession is assumed equal to zero. Given this normalisation, the energy of the nucleus, being (in absolute magnitude) equal to the binding energy, will obviously be negative and equal to $-\Delta E$ due to the fact that energy is liberated when a nucleus is formed out of nucleons.

nucleons on the surface of the nucleus are more weakly bound than those inside the nucleus; this leads to a reduction in the mean binding energy of the nucleons in the nucleus. The surface energy of the nucleus, considered as a liquid drop, is, obviously, proportional to the magnitude of the surface, that is, to the square of the radius of the nucleus. Whence, because of (9.6), we have, for the portion of specific binding energy due to "surface tension", a quantity proportional to $\frac{A^{2/3}}{A} = A^{-1/3}$.

Finally, the last term in (14.1) expresses the energy of Coulomb repulsion of protons. Considering the nucleus as a uniformly charged sphere of radius a, possessing a charge Ze, we will have $\frac{3}{5}\frac{(Ze)^2}{a}$ for the energy of Coulomb repulsion of protons, or, using expression (9.6) and putting the numerical factor equal to a_0, we get $\frac{3\,(Ze)^2 A^{-4/3}}{5a_0}$ for the specific energy. From this expression it follows that the constant $\varkappa$, which is equal to $\frac{3}{5}\frac{e^2}{a_0}$, may be computed directly, since the quantities e and a_0 are known. Substituting $e = 4.8 \times 10^{-10}$ CGSE and $a_0 = 1.45 \times 10^{-13}$ cm, we find $\varkappa = 0.6$ MeV. The remaining constants are selected empirically on the basis of experimentally known binding energies of nuclei. The curve in Fig. 13 is plotted from equation (14.1) by means of the following empirical constants: $\alpha = 14.7$, $\beta = 20.5$, $\gamma = 15.4$ and the earlier obtained constant $\varkappa = 0.6$. As may be seen from this plot, the experimental values of the specific binding energy (open circles) fall well enough on the curve, with the exception of the initial portion of the curve where the liquid drop model of the nucleus, which presumes a sufficiently large number of nucleons in the nucleus, is inapplicable.

Nature of nuclear forces. From the foregoing, very incomplete, consideration of experimental facts we obtained some idea of the properties of nuclear forces without considering the *nature* of these forces. The present approach to the far-from-solved problem of nuclear forces starts from certain features of similarity between the properties of nuclear and chemical (valence) forces. Both rapidly fall off with distance, are independent of the charge of the interacting particles, but depend upon their spin, and are capable of *saturation*. The saturation capacity of chemical forces is exhibited, for example, in the fact that an atom of oxygen is capable of adding only one or two atoms of hydrogen to form the stable molecules HO and H_2O, there being no such molecules as H_3O, H_4O, etc. In exactly the same way, one proton can bind only one or two neutrons (in the nuclei of D_1^2 and T_1^3), and a neutron can bind not more than two protons (in a He_2^3 nucleus). This similarity of chemical and nuclear forces suggested the solution of the latter problem to be sought along the same lines that led to the solution of the problem of chemical forces.

The latter problem was solved by means of quantum mechanics. This will be considered in the necessary detail in Chapter 7. Here we shall confine ourselves only to concepts underlying one of the approximate quantum mechanical methods of molecule analysis and used in broad outline for a quantum-mechanical interpretation of nucleon interaction.

Within the framework of these concepts, the approximate solution of a chemical problem can start from a consideration of two (or several) conceivable states of the molecule (that occur at large distances between nuclei). We take a molecular ion of hydrogen H_2^+ as the simplest molecule; when evaluating its energy, account is taken of the states that correspond to the following two configurations of the H_2^+ molecule:

$$H^+ - H \text{ and } H - H^+.$$

Transition from a state corresponding to one configuration to a state corresponding to the second configuration is obviously possible as transition of an electron from the nucleus with which it is bound in the H atom to the other, bare, nucleus. Since the electron changes its positive partner, this and similar processes are generally called *exchange* processes. As a result of continual exchange, which symbolically may be represented as $H \rightleftharpoons H^+$ or $H \rightleftharpoons p$ (p stands for proton), there arises a state of the H_2^+ ion which may be regarded as the result of the superposition of two states that correspond to the foregoing configurations. Computation of the energy of this state shows that electric forces of attraction develop between the particles that make up the molecule. These forces are called *exchange forces*.

The interaction of neutral particles, for example, atoms of H in the H_2 molecule, may likewise be regarded from the viewpoint of superposition of states. In this case, too, the exchange forces ensure the molecule a high stability. These forces fall off rapidly with distance, in the simplest case approximately in accord with the law $e^{-\frac{C}{r}}$ (where C is a constant). One of the distinguishing features of exchange forces is their dependence upon the mutual orientation of the electron spins. In particular, it turns out that for anti-parallel orientation of spins, H atoms attract to form a stable H_2 molecule, while for parallel orientation they repulse and no molecule is formed (see Ch. 7).

According to the Heisenberg-Majorana theory, a superposition of states similar to that which occurs in the chemical interaction of atoms may also be invoked to describe particle interaction in a system consisting of protons and neutrons, that is to say, in an atomic nucleus. For instance, by analogy with the H_2^+ ion, the state of a deuteron may be symbolically represented as $n \rightleftarrows p$. Continuing the analogy, we may assume that exchange interaction occurs also between two protons or two neutrons (in the latter case, the H_2 molecule is the chemical analogy); this, to some extent, accounts for the fact that nuclear forces are independent of the nature of the interacting nucleons. It may also be noted that this analogy goes still further in that the nuclear forces, like chemical exchange forces, depend upon the direction of spin. A cogent experimental proof of the dependence of nuclear forces on orientation of spins is the observed difference in cross-sections for slow-neutron scattering on two modifications of hydrogen — ortho- and parahydrogen (see Sec. 36); it was found that at 20° K the cross-section for neutrons scattering on molecules of parahydrogen (the spins of both protons are anti-parallel) is approximately 30 times the cross-section for scattering on molecules of orthohydrogen (proton spins are parallel).

It was originally supposed that underlying the exchange interaction of nucleons is the emission of a β-particle and a neutrino by a single nucleon and absorption of these particles by another one, similar to the exchange interaction of an H atom with a proton, where one may speak of the emission of an electron by an H atom and of its absorption by a proton (with the formation of a neutral H atom). However, a quantitative evaluation of the forces arising in the exchange of a β-particle and a neutrino carried out by Tamm and others showed that these forces are many orders of magnitude weaker than nuclear forces.

As far as quantitative agreement between theory and experiment is concerned, we may also, apparently, consider a second attempt to reveal the nature of nuclear forces that was made by Yukawa (1935) to be just as groundless. He started from the premise that the exchange interaction of nucleons is effected by means of particles heavier than electrons but lighter than protons. Particles of this kind with mass about 200 electron masses were discovered in 1937 with the Wilson cloud chamber in cosmic radiation by Anderson, who called them *mesons*. Later it was shown (Williams, 1940) that mesons have a short lifetime and decay (depending on the sign of their charge) with the emission of an electron or positron (and, obviously, a neutrino). Subsequently, Powell (1947) succeeded in proving that the source of these mesons, called μ-mesons (μ^+- and μ^--mesons), are particles with mass about 300 electron masses, or π-mesons, which are also present in cosmic radiation and which decay with the emission of a μ-meson and a neutrino: $\pi^+ \rightarrow \mu^+ + \nu$ and $\pi^- \rightarrow \mu^- + \nu$. Later, π-mesons were likewise obtained in the laboratory. Also discovered were neutral π-mesons (π°) that arise in collisions of fast protons with nuclei; later, they were discovered in cosmic radiation as well.

In contrast to μ-mesons, which interact very weakly with nuclei π-mesons are strongly absorbed by the latter, whence it follows that the forces acting between mesons and nucleons are particularly great in the case of π-mesons. This suggested that exchange interaction between nucleons is accomplished by means of π-mesons, and the underlying principle of this interaction is the emission and absorption of π-mesons. However, as has been pointed out above, all attempts at a quantitative interpretation of nuclear forces from the point of view of meson theory have failed. For this reason, the meson theory concept of nuclear forces cannot, at present, be considered substantiated to any extent.

Yet there can hardly be any doubt about the exchange nature of nucleon interaction. For one thing, exchange interaction of neutrons and protons readily explains the results of experiments in the scattering of fast neutrons (energy of the order of 100 MeV) by protons, where a large number of fast protons was detected moving in the direction of motion of the neutrons. It was shown that the appearance of so many fast neutrons cannot be due to simple elastic scattering of neutrons and that these protons are due to an exchange of charge, i.e., the transformation, into a proton, of a neutron moving past a proton at a sufficiently small distance, and of this proton into a neutron.

We may add that the β-activity of nuclei is interpreted as the decay of a meson, at the instant of its emission by a nuclear nucleon, into an electron or positron and a neutrino. Insofar as the conversion of a proton into a neutron (with the emission of a positron and neutrino) requires energy, this process is accomplished only in the nucleus, accounting for the β^+-activity of nuclei. Now the transformation of a neutron into a proton, which takes place with release of energy, can also occur in the free state. In the latter case, the process $n \rightarrow p + \beta^- + \nu$ is accompanied by the release of 0.782 MeV of energy in the form of the maximum energy of emitted electrons; and the neutron is characterised by a half-life of 12.8 minutes.

Subatomic particles. The problem of the nature of nuclear forces is closely connected with that of the nature and interaction of subatomic particles that have been discovered in recent years during cosmic-ray investigations and in part obtained artificially by bombardment of various targets with protons of several BeV accelerated in proton synchrotrons. There is now hardly any doubt left that the solution of the problem of the nature of nuclear forces is to be sought in studies of subatomic particles. Without going into details we will confine ourselves to an enumeration of presently known particles and some of their properties.

First of all we note that these particles include also the corresponding *antiparticles*: positron (antielectron), antiproton, antineutron, etc. Some of these antiparticles were first predicted theoretically and only later discovered experimentally. Thus, on the Dirac theory of the electron there exists a particle with the same mass as that of the electron but with opposite (positive) electric charge. The positron turned out to be just such a particle. In exactly the same way, on the Dirac theory, the proton and neutron should likewise have antiparticles. The antiproton (with proton mass but negative charge) was first discovered in the laboratory by Chamberlain, Segré, Wiegand, and Ypsilantis in 1955 through an analysis of the masses of negative particles produced in the bombardment of a copper target with fast protons ($K_p > 4$ BeV). The antineutron, which differs from the neutron by the sign of its spin, was discovered in 1956.

All presently known subatomic particles may be divided into the following four groups. Group one includes heavy particles of mass equal to or greater than that of the nucleon (proton, neutron) and also the corresponding antiparticles. The heaviest known subatomic particle is the Ξ-particle with a rest mass of 2585 electron masses (m_e). The Ξ-particle has a lifetime $\tau = 10^{-10} - 10^{-9}$ sec, after which it decays into a Λ-particle (see below) and a negative pion (π-meson). Then there is the Σ-particle, which is known in the form of a positive particle (Σ^+) of mass 2325 m_e and $\tau = 7 \times 10^{-10}$ sec that decays into a proton and a neutral pion (π°) or into a neutron and positive pion (π^+); in the form of a negative particle (Σ^-) of mass 2341 m_e and $\tau = 1.5 \times 10^{-10}$ sec that decays into a neutron and a negative pion (π^-); and in the form of a neutral particle (Σ°) of mass 2324 m_e that decays into a Λ-particle and a photon.

Finally, the group of heavy subatomic particles includes the proton, the neutron, and the Λ-particle (the latter is known only in the form of a neutral particle, Λ°). The Λ°-particle has a mass of 2182 m_e, a lifetime $\tau = 2.7 \times 10^{-10}$ sec and decays into a proton and a negative pion or into a neutron and a neutral pion.

The next group is composed of particles with mass less than that of a nucleon but greater than that of a muon (μ-meson). These include the K-meson and pion. The K-meson is known in the form of a positive (K^+) and negative (K^-) particles of mass 966.5 m_e and $\tau = 1.2 \times 10^{-8}$ sec, and a neutral particle (K°) of mass 965 m_e and $\tau = 1 \times 10^{-10}$ sec (anti-K° has a lifetime between 3×10^{-8} and 10^{-6} sec). The K-meson undergoes many types of decay: into a muon and neutrino (or antineutrino), into two or three pions, into a muon, pion and neutrino (antineutrino), and into an electron (positron), antineutrino (neutrino) and pion. Pions existing in the form of a positive (π^+), negative (π^-), and neutral (π°) particles have mass 273.2 m_e (π^+ and π^-) and 264.2 m_e (π°) and lifetime 2.6×10^{-8} sec (π^+ and π^-) and 10^{-16} to 10^{-15} sec (π°). The π^+-particle decays into a positive muon (μ^+) and a neutrino, π^-, into a negative muon (μ^-) and an antineutrino, and π°, into two photons.

The third group of subatomic particles includes the muon, electron, and neutrino and their antiparticles. The muon has a mass of 206.7 m_e; after a lifetime of 2.2×10^{-6} sec it decays into an electron (positron), neutrino, and antineutrino.

Finally, the last, fourth, group is the photon with its rest mass of zero. The photon, like the proton, electron and neutrino, is stable.

15. The α-Decay of Nuclei

Potential barrier of a nucleus. Due to the rapid decline of nuclear forces with distance, a positively charged particle (for example, a proton or α-particle) will experience diminishing attraction near the surface of the nucleus when receding from the latter, and at a certain distance a the forces of attraction will be balanced by the Coulomb force of repulsion, which will become predominant at $r > a$. From this it follows that the internal part of the nucleus is separated from the outer space by a certain *potential barrier*. The curve of nuclear potential $U(r)$ for an α-particle as a function of its distance from the centre of the nucleus is given schematically in Fig. 14.

It must be noted that if something in the nature of separate groups consisting of two protons and two neutrons do exist in nuclei, these groups, by virtue of the interaction of each nucleon with all of its immediate neighbours in the nucleus (due to the close packing of nuclei), may be identified with α-particles only in a very approximate manner. It is in this sense that in future we shall speak of the penetration of α-particles into a nucleus, of their existence there, and their ejection from the nucleus. According to Frenkel, isolation of a group of two protons and two neutrons, i.e., the formation of an α-particle in nuclear α-decay occurs in the course of decay, just as the formation of NaCl molecules takes place during their evaporation

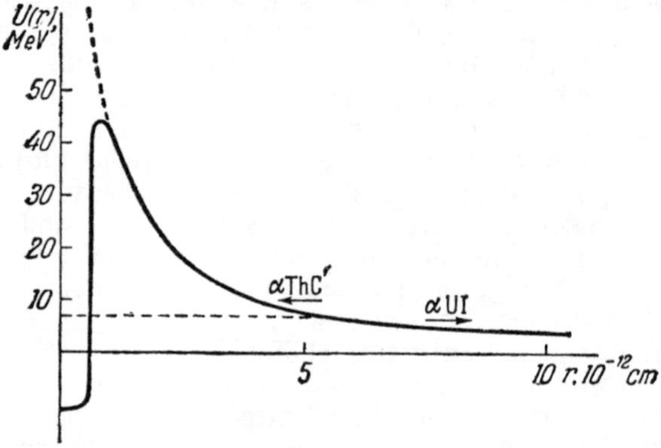

Fig. 14 Nuclear potential for α-particle

from the crystal or from a melt of sodium chloride in which the sodium and chlorine are present in the form of Na^+ and Cl^- ions.

The potential barrier is the barrier that prevents penetration of a charged particle into the nucleus. By measuring the minimum charged-particle velocities at which interaction with the nucleus (and, hence, penetration) is possible, we can form some idea of the height of the potential barrier of the nucleus undergoing bombardment. This height is measured by the distance of the top point of the barrier from the energy level that corresponds to infinite recession of the bombarding particle from the nucleus. For example, from the fact that the reaction $He_2^4 + N_7^{14} = O_8^{17} + H_1^1$ is accomplished for any values of energy of the α-particles exceeding 4.0 MeV, it may be concluded that the height of the potential barrier of a nitrogen nucleus for an α-particle is approximately 4.0 MeV. Analogously, we obtain the height of the potential barrier of an aluminium nucleus at 6.8 MeV.

It is also possible to evaluate the height of the potential barrier as follows. As has already been pointed out (p. 43), from experiments in the anomalous scattering of α-particles by various nuclei we obtain for the radius of the nucleus a the expression

$$a = a_0 \sqrt[3]{Z}$$

where $a = 2 \times 10^{-13}$ cm. Since the quantity a determines the distance from the centre of the nucleus at which the nuclear field differs perceptibly from the Coulomb field (according to Fig. 14, this can occur only close to the top point of the potential barrier), the height of the barrier (for this nucleus) may be found as

$$U_{max} = \frac{2e^2Z}{a}, \tag{15.1}$$

whence, on the basis of equation (9.5), we obtain

$$U_{max} = 1.44Z^{2/3} \text{ MeV}. \tag{15.2}$$

However, the height of the potential barrier is far from being the only criterion that determines the possibility of nuclear transformation involving charged particles. The following examples will elucidate this. Earlier, from the possibility of a reaction of the nuclei of nitrogen and aluminium with α-particles having energy in excess of a certain limiting value, we concluded that the height of the potential barrier of these nuclei approximately corresponds to the appropriate limiting values of energy of the α-particles (4.0 and 6.8 MeV). These values of barrier heights also turn out close to those computed from formula (15.2), 5.3 and 8.0 MeV, whence it may be concluded that in this case we are not far from the truth. It would, therefore, seem that the penetration of an α-particle into the nucleus (which is a prerequisite to a nuclear reaction) at α-particle energies less than the height of the potential barrier of the given nucleus should be absolutely excluded. However, experiment shows that in a number of cases the reaction nevertheless takes place, even though this condition is not fulfilled, as long as the energies of the α-particles have *strictly definite* values (though lower barrier heights). For example, in the case of aluminium (Al_{13}^{27}), which, as we have seen, has a potential barrier of 6.8 MeV, in addition to α-particles with energies that satisfy the condition $mv^2/2 \geqslant 6.8$ MeV, there have been found *discrete groups* of α-particles with energies 4.00, 4.49, 4.86, 5.25, 5.75, and 6.61 MeV that are capable of entering into the reaction $He_2^4 + Al_{13}^{27} = Si_{14}^{30} + H_1^1$. For a reason which will be given below, these and analogous cases are called *resonance penetration* of α-particles into the nucleus. It follows from the existence of resonance penetration that α-particles can enter the nucleus not only by passing *over* the potential barrier, but also by penetrating *through* the barrier.

In classical mechanics, processes of this kind are out of the question because they are associated with passage through a field of negative kinetic energies (imaginary velocities). On the contrary, wave mechanics, which describes the motion of a particle as a certain wave process, permits such processes and attributes to them a probability different from zero. According to the wave theory, α-particles with kinetic energy less than the height of the potential barrier are reflected from the barrier when colliding with the nucleus, though a small portion of them have a chance of penetrating the nucleus through the barrier. In wave mechanics, such processes are known as *tunnel* processes.

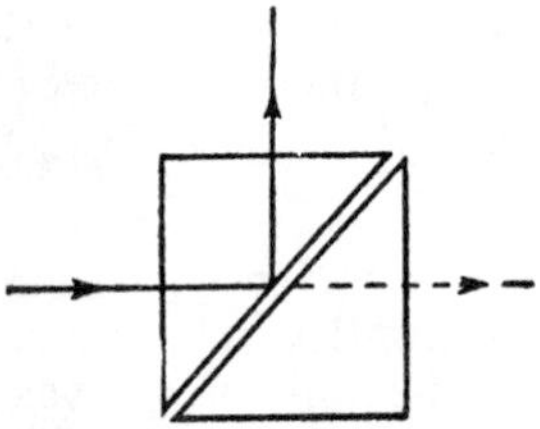

Fig. 15. Path of ray in total internal reflection.

An analogy may be found in optics. We know that in the case of total internal reflection, in addition to the reflected wave (which carries off most of the energy of the incident light) there is a wave of low intensity, which is refracted at the interface and penetrates into the second medium. This analogy will be still more complete if we consider reflection and refraction of waves in a system of two rectangular prisms as shown in Fig. 15. Denoting the distance between the adjacent planes of the two prisms by d, we can consider the following two limiting cases: the case when d is great in comparison to the wavelength λ, and the case of $d \ll \lambda$, which corresponds to practically complete contact of the prisms. In the former case, the intensity of the refracted wave passing from the first prism into the second will be practically zero, that is, we will observe total internal reflection. But in the latter case, due to the practical absence of a reflecting surface, the wave will pass unimpeded from the first into the second prism. Whence it is seen that for $d \approx \lambda$ there will be an intermediate case, when the intensities of both waves (reflected and refracted — the latter passing into the second prism) will be finite. The finite probability of penetration of α-particles into the nucleus at an energy less than the height of the potential barrier corresponds precisely to this case, the role of d being played by the width of the potential barrier, which is measured by the distance between two points of the potential curve, these two points corresponding to the same energy and being situated on opposite sides of the top point of the barrier.

The necessity of assuming tunnel penetration of α-particles through the potential barrier becomes particularly obvious if we turn to a detailed consideration of the phenomenon of natural α-decay. Indeed, we saw that the height of the potential barrier may be expressed by formula (15.1) to a rather high degree of accuracy. For uranium ($Z=92$), this formula gives $U_{max}=29$ MeV. Therefore, if α-particles left the uranium nucleus by surmounting the potential barrier, their kinetic energy after ejection from the nucleus, determined in this case by

$$\frac{mv^2}{2}=\int_a^\infty \frac{2e^2Z}{r^2}\,dr=\frac{2e^2Z}{a}\,(=U),$$

should come to about 29 MeV. Yet experiment shows that the energy of the uranium-emitted α-particles is only 4.21 MeV, i.e., considerably less than the height of the potential barrier. The situation is similar for all other α-active elements. Thus the only path of α-particles in α-decay of nuclei is tunnel penetration through the potential barrier of the nucleus.

This conclusion follows also from general reasoning about nuclear stability. Indeed, if only particles of sufficiently high energy can leave the nucleus over the barrier, the nuclei of α-active elements should be absolutely unstable; but this contradicts the finite and, frequently, very small probability of α-decay. This reasoning, therefore, leads to the conclusion that a *specific energy level* (or *levels*) *below* the top point of the potential barrier should correspond to α-particles in the nucleus. Due to the possibility of tunnel penetration through the barrier, an α-particle will always have a certain probability λ of leaving the nucleus without inducement by any external force, in particular, without energy being supplied. In this process, the number of nuclei decaying in unit time will, obviously, be equal to

$$-\frac{dn}{dt}=\lambda n$$

where n is the concentration of radioactive matter at time t; thus we obtain an empirical law of radioactive decay (10.1). The character of this law expresses the basic fact that radioactive decay follows the laws of probability, the decay constant λ being interpreted as the probability of decay.

Theory of α-decay of nuclei. The theory of radioactive decay of atomic nuclei was given by Gamow (1928) and Gurney and Condon (1928). Fundamental to this theory are the above-described concepts concerning tunnel penetration through the energy barrier. This penetration is one of the manifestations of the wave properties of matter. As we have seen, the occurrence of tunnel processes logically follows from the entire assemblage of experimental data that refer to α-decay of atomic nuclei.

When computing the constant of α-decay, Gamow proceeded from a simplified view of the shape of the potential barrier, assuming the potential energy of the α-particle to be constant (U_0) when $r \leqslant a$ and expressed by the formula

$$U(r) = \frac{2(Z-2)e^2}{r}$$

which corresponds to Coulomb interaction of the residual nucleus and the α-particle when $r \geqslant a$. Here, $U(a) = 2(Z-2)e^2/a > U_0$. The expression Gamow obtained for the decay constant λ is of the form

$$\lambda = \frac{8\pi h}{ma^2} e^{-\frac{2\sqrt{2m}}{h}\int_a^{r^*}\sqrt{\frac{2(Z-2)e^2}{r} - E}\,dr} \tag{15.3}$$

where E is the α-particle energy (equal to $mv^2/2$) and

$$r^* = \frac{2(Z-2)e^2}{E}$$

is the distance separating the centre of the nucleus from the point on the outer portion of the potential-energy curve that corresponds to $U = E$. In corpuscular interpretation, expression (15.3) is the product of the frequency of oscillations of an α-particle in the nucleus, or the number of its impacts per second against the barrier, by the probability of penetrating through the barrier.

Integrating the expression obtained and expanding it in a series of powers of the small quantity a/r^*, we obtain from (15.3)

$$\lambda = \frac{8\pi h}{ma^2} e^{\frac{4e\sqrt{m}}{h}\sqrt{(Z-2)a} - \frac{4\pi e^2(Z-2)}{hv}}. \tag{15.4}$$

This expression, rewritten in the form

$$\ln \lambda = A - \frac{B}{v}, \tag{15.5}$$

where

$$A = \ln \frac{8\pi h}{ma^2} + \frac{4e\sqrt{m}}{h}\sqrt{(Z-2)a}$$

and

$$B = \frac{4\pi e^2}{h}(Z-2),$$

corresponds to the empirical relation between the constant of α-decay and the α-particle path length,

$$\ln R = \alpha \ln \lambda + \beta, \quad (15.6)$$

established by Geiger and Nuttall as early as 1912. This relationship, or the *Geiger-Nuttall law*, may, with the aid of the empirical formula

$$R = Cv^3 \quad (15.7)$$

found by Geiger and connecting the path length of the α-particles with their velocity,* also be written as

$$\ln \lambda = A' + B' \ln v. \quad (15.8)$$

The values of ln λ for the naturally radioactive elements of the uranium series are given in Fig. 16 as a function of the logarithm of energy of α-particles E, which is a linear function of lnv (crosses) and also of $E^{-1/2}$, which is proportional to 1/v (open circles). We see that, to a sufficient degree of approximation, both cases yield a straight line and that the empirical formula (15.8) and the Gamow formula (15.5) both convey very well the dependence of λ on v over the entire range of values of λ and v. The Geiger-Nuttall law is thus theoretically substantiated.

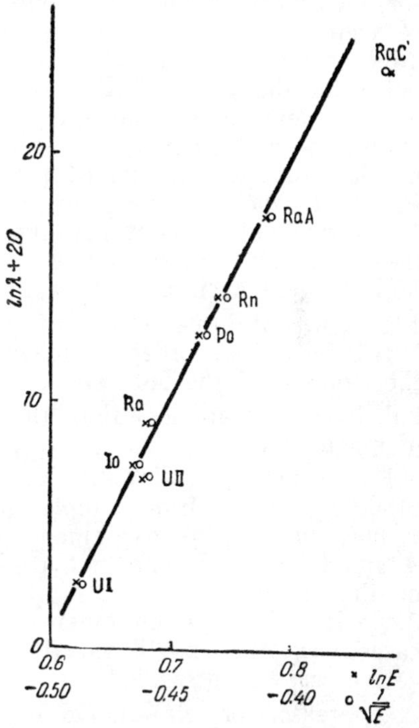

Fig. 16. Relationship between the constant of α-decay of nuclei and the energy of α-particles

* Formula (15.7), which underlies one of the important methods of determining α-particle energy (from their path length R) is derivable also theoretically from the following simple reasoning. Taking the energy lost by an α-particle per unit length of its path in a stopping medium to be proportional to the time the α-particle is near the molecules encountered on its way, and, consequently, inversely proportional to the velocity of the α-particle, we can put

$$\frac{dv^2}{dx} = \frac{2}{3C}\frac{1}{v}.$$

Integrating this equation, we obtain $Cv^3\Big|_0^v = x\Big|_0^R$, i. e., $R = Cv^3$.

It should, however, be pointed out that when utilising data for artificially obtained α-active isotopes even within the limits of a single radioactive series, there is a considerable spread of dots, though the general tendency towards a concentration of dots near the Geiger-Nuttall line is retained. Particularly great are the deviations from this straight line in the case of the transuranium elements, i.e., elements with nuclear charge greater than that of uranium ($Z=92$), which was the last element* in the Periodic Table prior to the discovery of the artificial transformation of elements. For example, on the basis of the measured values of α-particle energies E of two isotopes of the 96th element curium Cm_{96}^{238} and Cm_{96}^{242}, from the straight line in Fig. 16 we obtain values of half-lives that are less than the observed half-lives by five orders of magnitude. In exactly the same way, the isotopes of the 98th element californium Cf_{98}^{246} and Cf_{98}^{250} show half-lives that are less than the observed ones by 7 to 8 orders of magnitude.

From the point of view of the theory of α-decay, these and other deviations from simple monotonic dependence of λ upon v may in part be explained by the fact that the quantities A and B in (15.5) are not constants, due to their dependence on the radius and charge of the nucleus. According to Gamow, deviations from a monotonic relationship should be observed in cases when the smooth variation of a and v in the given radioactive series is disrupted.

One reason for relation (15.5) not being fulfilled may possibly be its insufficient accuracy due to the approximate character both of its theoretical calculation and of the theory itself, which assumes the existence of individual α-particles in the nucleus, whereas in reality these particles are, apparently, formed in the nucleus (from protons and neutrons) only in the course of α-decay.

---

* The transuranium elements are ordinarily obtained by bombardment of heavy elements with multiply charged ions of high energy needed to overcome the Coulomb barrier. Thus, for example, isotopes of the 99th element einsteinium Es_{99}^{246} and Es_{99}^{247} were obtained by bombarding uranium-238 with ions of nitrogen N^{++++++} of energy about 100 MeV in the reactions $U_{92}^{238}(N_7^{14}, 6n)Es_{99}^{246}$ and $U_{92}^{238}(N_7^{14}, 5n)Es_{99}^{247}$. Element 101, mendelevium, was obtained in the bombardment of einsteinium-253 by 41-MeV α-particles in the reaction $Es_{99}^{253}(\alpha, n)Mv_{101}^{256}$. Mendelevium-256 has a half-life of about 30 min and converts into element 100, fermium, by electron capture. Element 102, nobelium, was obtained by bombarding curium ($Z=96$) by C^{13} ions. Element 103, lawrencium, was recently obtained by bombarding californium ($Z=98$) with B^{10} and B^{11} ions.

16. Nuclear Energy Levels

Nuclear energy levels and the spectra of α-, β-, and γ-rays. The presence of definite discrete energy levels of the atomic nucleus (p. 87) postulated in the theory of α-decay follows directly from the fact that α-rays are *monoenergetic*. Measurements of the velocities of α-particles emitted by a given nucleus show that all α-particles fall into *separate groups*, each of which is characterised by a certain velocity that is constant for the given group. In such cases, one usually speaks of the *fine structure* of α-spectra. For example, in the α-spectrum of ThC, which converts into ThC″ with the emission of an α-particle, are observed five groups of α-particles with energies 6.0930, 6.0537, 5.7709, 5.6283, and 5.6095 MeV.* The existence of these discrete groups of α-particles indicates that the nuclei in α-decay are in various discrete energy states. Denoting the energy of the initial and final nuclei by ε_i^0 and ε_f respectively, on the basis of the law of conservation of energy, we will have

$$\varepsilon_i^0 - \varepsilon_f = \frac{mv_{if}^2}{2} + \frac{MV_{if}^2}{2} = \frac{m+M}{M}\frac{mv_{if}^2}{2}, \tag{16.1}$$

where $mv_{if}^2/2$ is the energy of an α-particle belonging to a given group of α-particles, and $MV_{if}^2/2$ is the energy of the final nucleus *(recoil nucleus)*. The quantity $\varepsilon_i^0 - \varepsilon_f$ is called the *energy of α-decay*. Substituting into equality (16.1), in place of $mv_{if}^2/2$, the foregoing values of α-particle energy and $m/M = 1/52$, we obtain for the decay energy the following values: 6.2103, 6.1703, 5.8819, 5.7366, and 5.7175 MeV. Since, with rare exceptions (see below), in the α-decay of atomic nuclei the disintegrating nucleus is in a state with least energy (we shall call it the *ground* or *normal state*), which is the case also in the α-decay of a ThC nucleus, we can put $\varepsilon_i^0 = \varepsilon_0^0 = \text{const}$. Thus, the existence of various discrete groups in the α-spectrum in this and similar cases is due to the fact that the final nucleus (ThC″) appears in *different* energy states. Putting the energy of the ground state of the ThC″ nucleus $\varepsilon_0 = 0$, we obtain from the differences of the foregoing decay energies for the remaining four levels: $\varepsilon_1 = 0.0400$, $\varepsilon_2 = 0.3284$, $\varepsilon_3 = 0.4737$, and $\varepsilon_4 = 0.4928$ MeV.

This *energy-level diagram* of the ThC″ nucleus is shown in Fig. 17. The correctness of this scheme is confirmed by the

* If resolution is weak, these five groups of α-particles are recorded as a single monoenergetic group with a certain mean (weighted) energy.

γ-spectrum observed in the decay of ThC. The discrete character of this spectrum, which consists of separate lines, shows that here the γ-radiation is due to transitions of the excited nucleus from one set of discrete energy states to another set. Identifying these states with the energy levels obtained above of the ThC″ nucleus, one should expect that the energy of the observed

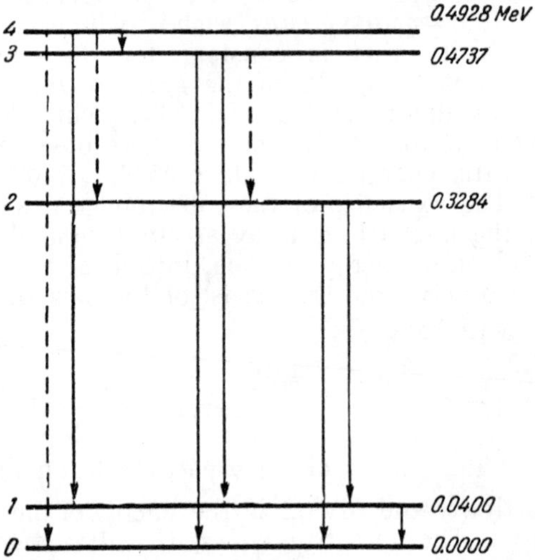

Fig. 17. Energy levels of ThC″ nucleus (in MeV)

γ-photons ($\gamma = h\nu$) will be equal to the energy differences of the corresponding levels, because from the law of conservation of energy we have *

$$\varepsilon_f - \varepsilon_{f'} = \gamma_{ff'} = h\nu_{ff'}. \qquad (16.2)$$

In Table 3 the differences $\varepsilon_f - \varepsilon_{f'}$ computed from the above-obtained values of ε_f are compared with the γ-photon energy. It is seen that six out of ten differences (within measurement error, which in the case of γ-rays comes to $1^{\circ}/_{0}$) coincides with the corresponding γ-quanta energies. As we shall see below (Ch. 5), by virtue of the so-called *selection rules* the number of possible transitions between different energy levels always proves to be *greater* than the number of actually observed transitions, i.e., than the number of lines in the spectrum of the given element.

* A type (16.2) relation was first used by J. J. Thomson in 1912 to explain the structure of the characteristic spectrum of X-rays (see below, p. 143).

Table 3

Energy levels and γ-spectra of THC″ nucleus

Energy difference, MeV	γ-quanta, MeV
$\varepsilon_4 - \varepsilon_3 = 0.0191$	—
$\varepsilon_4 - \varepsilon_2 = 0.1644$	—
$\varepsilon_4 - \varepsilon_1 = 0.4528$	0.4511
$\varepsilon_4 - \varepsilon_0 = 0.4928$	—
$\varepsilon_3 - \varepsilon_2 = 0.1453$	—
$\varepsilon_3 - \varepsilon_1 = 0.4337$	0.4317
$\varepsilon_3 - \varepsilon_0 = 0.4737$	0.4709
$\varepsilon_2 - \varepsilon_1 = 0.2884$	0.2869
$\varepsilon_2 - \varepsilon_0 = 0.3284$	0.3267
$\varepsilon_1 - \varepsilon_0 = 0.0400$	0.03995

Thus, from the foregoing it follows that excited ThC″ nuclei which appear in the α-decay of ThC pass into the ground state with the emission of γ-photons. The pattern is practically the same in all other cases of γ-decay. Such is the origin of γ-radiation attending the α-decay of nuclei.

Sometimes cases are observed in α-decay when a part (usually insignificant) of the initial nuclei is also in one of the excited states. In such cases, in addition to α-particles of energy ordinarily between 4 and 8 MeV, there are observed so-called *long-range α-particles* with energy exceeding 8 MeV. For instance, in the α-spectrum of ThC, in addition to an intense basic group of α-particles we find three exceedingly weak groups with energies $K = 8.776$, 9.491, and 10.542 MeV. Computing from these values the appropriate decay energies, $\varepsilon_i^0 - \varepsilon_f = 8.942$, 9.670, and 10.741 MeV and attributing the least of the values obtained to transition from the ground level of the ThC nucleus, we have for the levels of this nucleus: $\varepsilon_0 = 0$, $\varepsilon_1 = 0.728$, and $\varepsilon_2 = 1.799$ MeV. The reliability of these values follows from the fact that the differences $\varepsilon_1 - \varepsilon_0$ and $\varepsilon_2 - \varepsilon_0$ practically coincide with the energies of ThC γ-photons, 0.726 and 1.802 MeV. The general scheme of the transformation, $\text{ThC} \xrightarrow{\beta} \text{ThC}' \xrightarrow{\alpha} \text{ThD (Pb)}$, is given in Fig. 18, in which the transitions accompanied by γ-radiation (γ-transitions) are shown by wavy arrows.

Excited nuclei also appear in β-decay and electron capture, in the bombardment of nuclei with fast neutrons, protons, α- and other charged particles (inelastic collisions), and also in various nuclear reactions. By way of illustration, Fig. 19 gives the β-decay scheme of Mn_{25}^{56}. Here, we see three β-spectra with maximum energies 0.75, 1.04, and 2.81 MeV, whence it follows that the electron decay of Mn^{56} yields at least three different energy states of the final nucleus Fe^{56}_{26}. A parallel investigation of the γ-spectrum, which contains three lines with quantum energies 0.822, 1.77, and 2.06 MeV, leads to the decay scheme given in Fig. 19. Similar schemes have been established for nearly all β-active nuclei. Finally, Fig. 20 gives the energy levels of an O^{16} nucleus as obtained in various reactions.

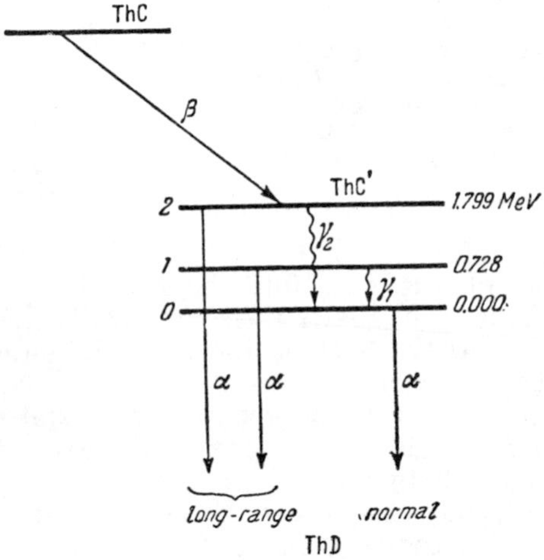

Fig. 18. Radioactive transformation $ThC \xrightarrow{\beta} ThC' \xrightarrow{\alpha} ThD\ (Pb)$

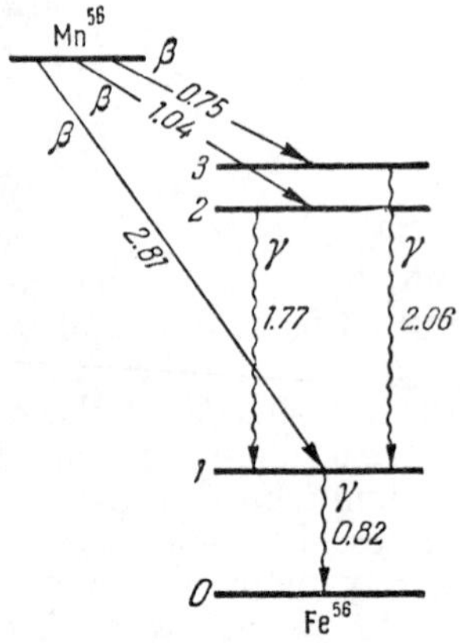

Fig. 19. Beta-decay of Mn^{56}_{25} The energy differences are given in MeV

Mean lifetime of excited nuclei. To various excited states of the nucleus there correspond different *mean lifetimes* (τ), which determine the probability of β- or γ-transition into a state with less energy* and which are reflected in the intensity of the corresponding spectrum.** Without touching on the question of the nature of the internal factors that determine the probability of the various nuclear transitions, we note here only the extremely

* The mean lifetime is usually determined as a reciprocal to the transition probability or the decay constant $\lambda: \tau = 1/\lambda$. The half-life $T_{1/2}$ and τ are connected by the following obvious relation: $T_{1/2} = \tau \ln 2$.

** In the vast majority of cases, the probability of transition of an excited nucleus to a lower state with α-particle emission is appreciably less than the probability of γ-transition to the same state. For this reason, excited nuclei, the lifetimes of which are determined by the probability of α-transition, are extremely rare. These include the emission of long-range α-particles by certain nuclei.

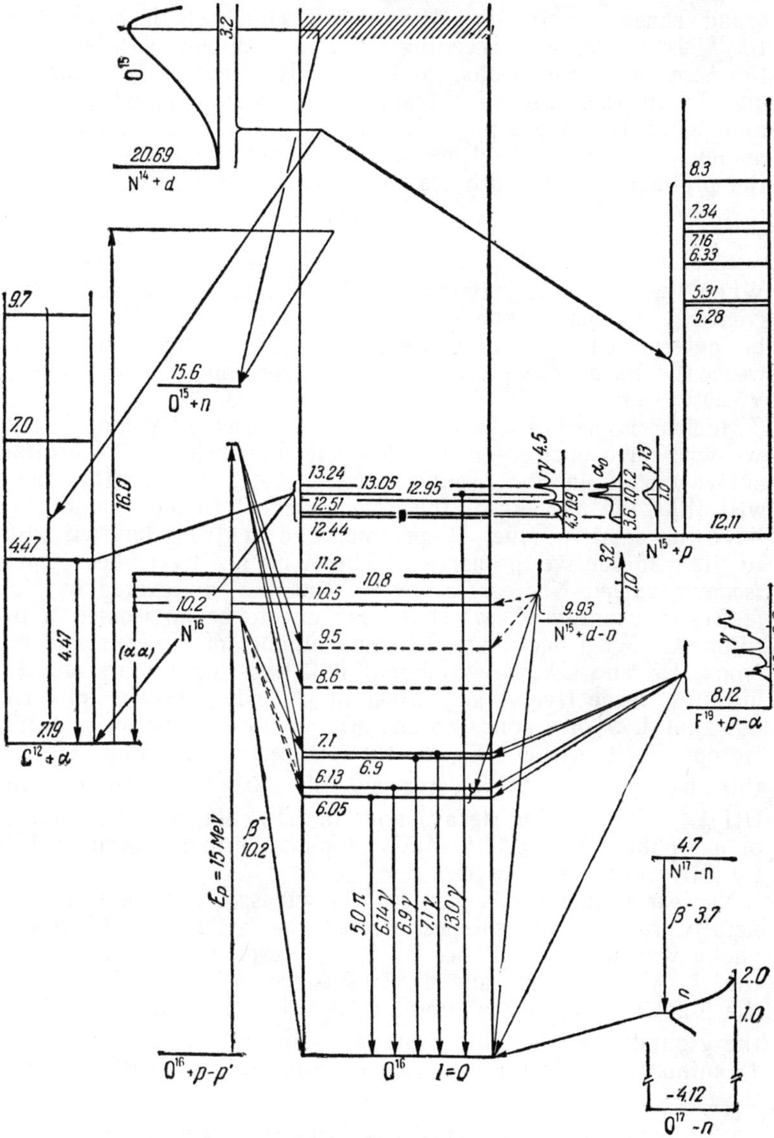

Fig. 20. Energy levels of O^{16} nucleus obtained from various reactions (after Hornyak, Lauritsen, Morrison and Fowler)

broad range covered by the quantity τ, which varies from 10^{-12} sec to values exceeding minutes and tens of minutes* in the case of γ-transitions, and from 10^{-2} sec to 10^{9} years and more** in the case of β-transitions. Obviously, when both γ- and β-transitions are possible from a given level of an excited nucleus, the mean lifetime will be determined by the sum of the probabilities of both transitions $\lambda=\lambda_\gamma+\lambda_\beta$:

$$\tau=\frac{1}{\lambda}. \qquad (16.3)$$

When the probability of one of the transitions is considerably greater than that of the other, the mean lifetime will, obviously, be determined by the greater probability. Thus, when $\lambda_\gamma \gg \lambda_\beta$ we will have $\tau=1/\lambda_\gamma=\tau_\gamma$ and, accordingly, when $\lambda_\gamma \ll \lambda_\beta$, $\tau=1/\lambda_\beta=\tau_\beta$

Nuclear isomerism. In the case of a sufficiently long lifetime we will have excited *metastable* nuclei that behave like ordinary active nuclei in the ground energy state. The excited nuclei will (like the nucleus of the given element in the ground state) have the same number of protons and neutrons but will differ in its radioactive properties. These nuclei have been called *isomeric nuclei*. Nuclear isomerism was first discovered by Hahn (1921) in uranium Z, which turned out to be an isomer of uranium X_2. With one and the same number of protons and neutrons, UZ and UX_2 have different half-lives (6.69 hours and 1.22 minutes, respectively) and different β- and γ-spectra. It turned out that UZ corresponds to the ground state of the protactinium isotope Pa^{234}_{91}, while UX_2, to the excited (metastable) state of this isotope; in 99.85 cases out of 100, UX_2 converts into UII (U^{234}_{92}) by electron decay, and, in 0.15 case, with the emission of a γ-photon ($\gamma=0.394$ MeV) it passes into the ground state, i.e., it "converts" into UZ.

Nuclear isomerism is particularly widespread among the artificially radioactive isotopes. Here, the existence of isomeric nuclei was first established by I. V. Kurchatov, B. V. Kurchatov, L. V. Mysovsky and L. I. Rusinov (1935) in the case of the β-active isotopes of bromine Br^{80}_{35}. It was demonstrated that the ground state of this isotope is a state with a half-life of 18 minutes, while the excited metastable nucleus Br^{80} has a half-

* As an exception, unusually long lifetimes have been obtained for all known isotopes of tellurium with odd mass number: from 1.75 days for Te^{131} to 200 days for Te^{121}.

** For example, for K^{40} and Rb^{87} τ is, respectively, 1.75×10^{9} and 109×10^{9} years, and for Re^{187}, 8400×10^{9} years.

life of 4.4. hours and passes into the ground state by emission of two successive γ-photons of energy 0.049 and 0.037 MeV.

During the past 20 years a large number of cases of nuclear isomerism have been discovered. The number of isomeric nuclei with short lifetimes is especially great.

Nuclear excitation in inelastic collisions with neutrons and charged particles. The excitation of atomic nuclei by bombardment with fast particles is the simplest case of an inelastic collision.* This excitation will be detected by changes in the spectra of the bombarding particles and also by the γ-radiation of the excited nuclei. For example, in the inelastic scattering, by magnesium, of monoenergetic neutrons with initial energy 2.5 MeV, the spectrum of scattered neutrons exhibits a new group (in addition to the given group) of neutrons with energy 1.1. MeV, whence for the excitation energy of the magnesium nucleus it follows that $\varepsilon = 1.4$ MeV. This same value is also obtained from experiments in the inelastic scattering of protons. The approximate value thus obtained of the excitation energy of a magnesium nucleus is in good agreement with the value of one of the two γ-photons observed in the γ-spectrum of the reaction $Na_{11}^{24}(\beta^-)Mg_{12}^{24}$: 1.380 and 2.758 MeV. That this spectrum belongs to the magnesium-24 nucleus is obvious from the following calculation. Since special experiments have shown that these γ-photons are emitted in succession (in a *cascade*), we should obtain the energy of the β-decay of Na^{24} by summing the energy of these photons with the maximum energy of the β-particles of Na^{24}. This summation gives $Q = 5.528$ MeV, which is in good agreement with the value 5.555 ± 0.035 MeV obtained from the known masses of the atoms Na^{24} and Mg^{24}.

In exactly the same way, the excitation level of the Li_3^7 nucleus $\varepsilon = 0.480$ MeV is obtained both from the γ-spectrum observed in the inelastic scattering of protons and α-particles by lithium-7, i.e., in the processes $Li^7(p, p')Li^7$ and $Li^7(\alpha, \alpha')Li^7$, and in the following reactions: $Be^7(K)Li^7$ from the γ-spectrum, $B^{10}(n, \alpha)Li^7$ from the α- and γ-spectra, $Be^9(d, \alpha)Li^7$ from the α- and γ-spectra, and $Li^6(d, p)Li^7$ from the γ-spectrum and the proton spectrum.

In the foregoing nuclear reactions that lead to the excitation of the Li^7 nucleus, the final nucleus is excited. Also widespread are cases when, in the course of a nuclear reaction of the types

* The inelastic collision of a fast particle x with a nucleus Y, which leads to excitation of the latter, is usually denoted by the symbol $Y(x, x')Y'$, where x' is the particle x that suffered inelastic collision. This process may be regarded as a particular case of the nuclear reaction $Y(x, y)X$.

considered, an *intermediate nucleus* is excited that corresponds to a certain transition state of the system on its way from the initial to the final state. Let us consider the general case of the reaction $A+a=B+b$, where A is the initial and B the final nucleus, a is the bombarding particle and b is the particle formed as a result of the reaction. This reaction, which symbolically may also be written as A (a, b) B, embraces all types of particle interaction with a nucleus, including elastic ($b=a$) and inelastic ($b=a'$) impacts and all possible nuclear reactions that lead to the formation of a new element or a new isotope of the initial element. When $b=\gamma$ (photon) we have a reaction of particle capture, and when $a=\gamma$, we have a photonuclear reaction. In all these cases, according to views most clearly stated by Bohr (1936, 1938), when a particle a penetrates into the nucleus,* which is a system of many bodies (nucleons), its energy is distributed among all the nuclear particles. This leads to a *complex*, or *intermediate*, *nucleus* which has a greater or lesser degree of stability characterised by a certain mean lifetime τ. The magnitude of τ is determined by the probability of such a redistribution of energy in the complex nucleus that results in a certain nuclear process becoming possible. Depending on the nature of this redistribution of energy and its concentration on a given particle, the latter can escape from the nucleus.

Thus, according to Bohr, every nuclear process should be represented as a double transition: initial state of the system $(A+a) \xrightarrow{I}$ complex nucleus $(C) \xrightarrow{II}$ final state of the system $(B+b)$. We note that in the case of α-decay the initial nucleus can be considered as a complex nucleus, since here the disintegration into a new nucleus and an α-particle takes place without any external force.

Due to the finite lifetime of a complex nucleus τ, it (like any other nucleus) can have definite energy levels, which may be detected by the appearance of specific *(resonance)* peaks on a curve of cross-section or probability of reaction versus the energy of the bombarding particle. A resonance peak of this kind is seen in Fig. 21, which gives the curve of neutron yield in the reaction Be_4^9 (p, n) B_5^9 for various proton energies. Another case are the curves of cross-sections of the reaction Al_{13}^{27} (p, α) Mg_{12}^{24} and the reverse reaction Mg_{12}^{24} (α, p) Al_{13}^{27} given in Fig. 22. For

* An exception to this mechanism are the deuteron reactions (d, n) and (d, p), which are accomplished in such manner that, due to a small binding energy, the deuteron (even near the surface of the nucleus) splits into a proton and neutron, one of which is absorbed by the nucleus and the other remains free.

these reactions, from the law of conservation of energy, we have

$$Q+K_r=\varepsilon_r+K_c$$

where Q is the formation energy of the complex (intermediate) nucleus, which in the cases given above is the nucleus B_5^{10} and, respectively, Si_{14}^{28}; this energy is computed from the following formula:

$$Q=c^2(m_a+m_A-m_{A+a})$$

(m_a is the mass of the bombarding particle, m_A is the mass of nucleus A, and m_{A+a} is the mass of the complex nucleus); K_r is the energy of the bombarding particle at resonance maximum, K_c is the kinetic energy of the complex nucleus equal to the kinetic energy of the centre of gravity of the system, and ε_r is the excitation energy of the complex nucleus. From the law of conservation of momentum it follows that $K_c=\frac{m_a}{m_{A+a}}K_r$. Substituting K_c into the preceding formula, we get

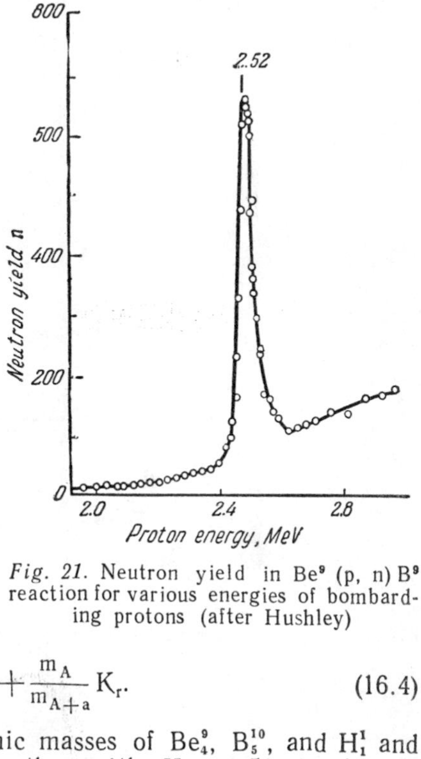

Fig. 21. Neutron yield in Be^9 (p, n) B^9 reaction for various energies of bombarding protons (after Hushley)

$$\varepsilon_r=Q+\frac{m_A}{m_{A+a}}K_r. \tag{16.4}$$

Computing Q from the atomic masses of Be_4^9, B_5^{10}, and H_1^1 and substituting this quantity together with $K_r=2.52$ MeV into (16.4), we find $\varepsilon=8.86$ MeV for the excitation energy of the B_5^{10} nucleus in the reaction Be_4^9 (p, n) B_5^9. In the same way, from the values of K_r that correspond to the four most intensive peaks on the curves of Fig. 22, we obtain for the excitation energy of the nucleus Si_{14}^{28}, $\varepsilon=2.755$, 2.931, 3.002, and 3.280 MeV.

Fig. 22 also illustrates one of the few sufficiently investigated cases of two nuclear reactions that proceed in both directions. Considering two such reactions (in the general case, $A+a\rightarrow B+b$ and $B+b\rightarrow A+a$) it should be concluded, on the basis of the statistical principle of detailed balancing, that both

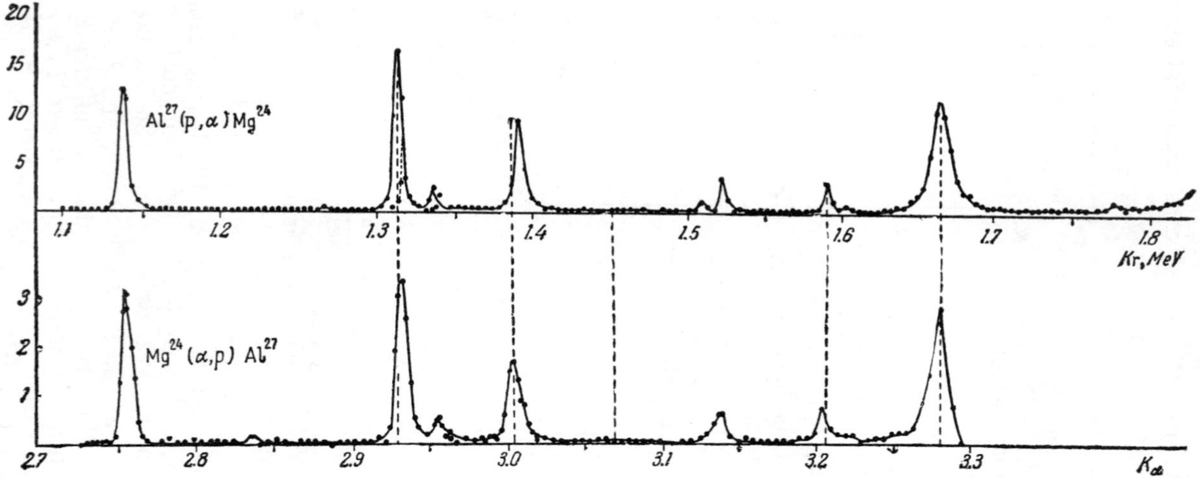

Fig. 22. Cross-sections for reaction Al^{27} (p, α) Mg^{24} and the inverse reaction Mg^{24} (α, p) Al^{27} for various energies of the bombarding particles (after Kaufmann, Goldberg, Koester and Mooring)

reactions must proceed via *one and the same* complex nucleus. It may, therefore, be expected that the cross-sections of the direct and reverse reactions will be in a definite ratio. Indeed, a consideration of statistical equilibrium $A + a \rightleftarrows C \rightleftarrows B + b$ leads to the following formula:

$$\frac{\sigma_{ab}(v_a)}{\sigma_{ba}(v_b)} = \frac{\lambda_a^2}{\lambda_b^2}, \tag{16.5}$$

where σ_{ab} and σ_{ba} are the effective cross-sections of the direct and reverse reactions, λ_a and λ_b are the de Broglie wavelengths a and b; the velocities of these particles are connected by a definite relationship derived from conservation laws. For example, for the centre of gravity of the system, i.e., in coordinates fixed in the complex nucleus, this relationship is of the form $\frac{m_a v_a^2}{2} + Q = \frac{m_b v_b^2}{2}$ (Q is the energy of the reaction). On the basis of (16.5), we should expect parallelism in the course of the direct and reverse reactions; this is clearly obvious from the curves in Fig. 22. We note that in this figure the energy scale of α-particles (reverse reaction) is displaced relative to the scale of proton energy (direct reaction) to such a degree that there is a coincidence of peaks corresponding to identical excitation energies of the Si_{14}^{28} nucleus. The energy thus obtained of the reaction $Al^{27} + H^1 = Mg^{24} + He^4, Q = 1.613 \pm 0.003$ MeV, coincides, within error limits, with that computed from the masses, $Q = 1.594 \pm 0.045$ MeV.

The lower curve of Fig. 22 relating to the reaction Mg^{24} (α, p) Al^{27} may be regarded as associated with the penetration of α-particles into the magnesium nucleus. We see that in this case the reaction has a pronounced resonance character. It is therefore natural to consider that the earlier mentioned (p. 85) resonance penetration of α-particles into nuclei is of the same nature. It should be pointed out that a connection between the resonance effects and the energy levels of the nucleus in α-particle interaction with the nucleus was pointed to by Gamow and Gurney, who theoretically found that the probability of tunnel penetration of an α-particle into a nucleus greatly increases when the α-particle energy coincides with that of some nuclear level (we are here dealing with the levels of a complex nucleus, i.e., a nucleus formed from an initial nucleus and an α-particle). It is this enhanced probability of penetration of α-particles (and also other charged particles) into the nucleus that explains the possibility of such nuclear reactions proceeding at a measurable rate.

Breit-Wigner formulas. The resonance character of the cross-sections for nuclear reactions (including the scattering of fast particles by nuclei) is to a certain extent similar to absorption and scattering of light by atoms and molecules. This analogy was first noted by Breit and Wigner (1936). Underlying it is the possibility of regarding the absorption and scattering of particles by a nucleus (and also the absorption and scattering of light by atomic systems) as a two-stage process. By quantum-mechanical treatment of the problem of finding the cross-sections for nuclear reactions associated with the absorption and scattering of fast particles, Breit and Wigner derived formulas that resembled those for optical dispersion, which express the refraction index and the absorption coefficient of light as functions of the wavelength or the frequency. Accordingly, the Breit-Wigner formulas involve the energies and velocities of the particles.*

By way of illustrating the Breit-Wigner formulas we give the following relation:

$$\sigma = \sigma_r \frac{\Gamma^2 \left(\frac{K_r}{K}\right)^{1/2}}{4(K - K_r)^2 + \Gamma^2}, \tag{16.6}$$

which expresses the *total* effective cross-section for neutron interaction with the nucleus, i.e., a cross-section that corresponds to the overall probability of absorption and scattering of a neutron. In (16.6), K is the energy of the bombarding neutrons, K_r is the energy at the point of resonance, σ_r is the appropriate (maximum) cross-section, and Γ is a constant that determines the width of the resonance peak. From (16.6) it is seen that for low-energy neutrons ($K \ll K_r$) the total neutron cross-section first diminishes (approximately like $1/v$) with increasing neutron velocity, then begins to increase, reaching a maximum value (σ_r) at the point of resonance ($K = K_r$), after which it again decreases.

Verification of the Breit-Wigner formulas by experiment shows that they are in good agreement with data referring to various reactions. We note that when there are closely situated levels in a given energy range of the bombarding particles, the single-term formula of type (16.6) is replaced by a sum of terms of type (16.6), just as in optics for the complex structure of an absorption spectrum.

---

* It will be recalled that the velocity and kinetic energy of particles are connected with the de Broglie wavelength by the following relation:

$$\lambda = \frac{h}{mv} = \frac{h}{\sqrt{2mK}}.$$

17. Fission of Heavy Nuclei

Fission reaction of atomic nuclei. The above-considered reactions do not exhaust all types of nuclear reactions. So far we have hardly touched on an exceedingly important reaction — *the fission reaction* — with the discovery of which practical use of the enormous reserves of energy concentrated in atomic nuclei became possible. Soon after the discovery of the neutron it was noted (Fermi, 1934) that when uranium is irradiated with neutrons, a large number of new electron-active nuclei are produced that may be detected by their different half-lives, which did not coincide with those of any of the then known radioactive elements; and so the search was first begun in the direction of transuranium elements and also the isotopes of known radioactive elements. However, chemical separation together with β-analysis yielded irrefutable proof that the products of transformation of neutron-irradiated uranium contain elements located in the *middle* of the Periodic Table. This fact was first established by Hahn and Strassmann (1938) who demonstrated chemically that one of the products of transformation of uranium, which at first was believed to be an isotope of radium (Ra_{88}), is actually barium (Ba_{56}). It is interesting to note that somewhat earlier I. Curie and Savitch identified lanthanum (La_{57}) in the products of uranium transformation, but (in spite of the data of their own chemical studies) they considered it an isotope of actinium (Ac_{89}). The identity of this product with lanthanum was later confirmed by Hahn and Strassmann, who, in addition, identified in the products of uranium transformation a new β-active substance with a half-life 3.5 hours and the properties of a rare-earth element, and demonstrated that it was not actinium. As was later established by Curie and Savitch (1939), this substance is an isotope of lanthanum (La_{57}^{141}). These new facts were correctly interpreted by Meitner who presumed that the excited uranium nucleus which arises due to the capture of a neutron * *splits* into two fragments with commensurable masses, which is reminiscent of the fission of living cells. For this reason, Meitner and Frisch called the new nuclear reaction a *fission reaction*. According to computations based on the liquid-drop model of the nucleus, a charged nucleus with $Z = 100$ should become unstable due to the predominance of Coulomb repulsion over the forces of attraction.

---

* The capture of a neutron by a nucleus of uranium-235 releases an energy of 6.0 MeV, by a uranium-238 nucleus, 5.7 MeV.

The fragments produced in nuclear fission have various masses. Thus, from the curve, shown in Fig. 23, of the yield of fission fragments of uranium-235 as a function of their masses it is seen that the masses of the fragments range from 70 to 160 (in units of atomic weight) and the most probable is nonsymmetric fission with the mass ratio of fragments ~ 2:3.

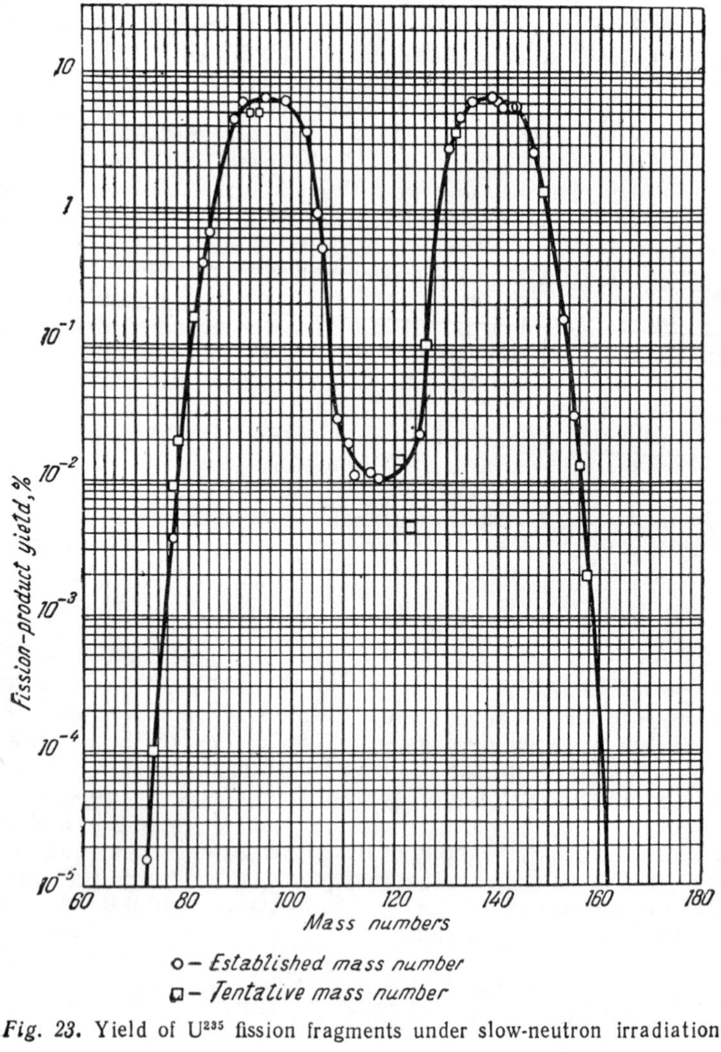

Fig. 23. Yield of U^{235} fission fragments under slow-neutron irradiation

Also very great is the diversity of elements in the fission fragments, which fact, like the diversity of fragment masses, is to be explained by the fortuitous nature of the nuclear fission process. Here, naturally, the proton-neutron ratio in the fragments is maintained approximately as it was in the uranium nucleus, three neutrons to two protons. Whence it follows that the nuclear charges of the fragments must be in the same ratio as their masses, this means that the most probable ratio is $Z_1:Z_2=2:3$, which is in good agreement with experiment.

Due to the fact that the number of neutrons in the nuclei of fission fragments of uranium is far in excess of the number of neutrons in the stable isotopes of elements with the appropriate atomic numbers, all fragments are electron-active. For example, let a uranium-235 nucleus fission according to the following scheme:

$$U_{92}^{235} \rightarrow Sr_{38}^{95} + Xe_{54}^{139}.$$

Since the heaviest stable isotopes of strontium and xenon are Sr_{38}^{88} and Xe_{54}^{136}, it is seen that the strontium isotope produced as a fission fragment contains seven extra neutrons, while the xenon isotope contains three. By successive electron emission the fission fragments convert to stable isotopes of elements with greater Z. Thus arise chains of β^--transformations, an example of which is the following:

$$Te_{52}^{135} \xrightarrow{\beta^-;\ 2\ \text{sec}} I_{53}^{135} \xrightarrow{\beta^-;\ 6.7\ \text{hrs}} Xe_{54}^{135} \xrightarrow{\beta^-;\ 9.2\ \text{hrs}} Cs_{55}^{135} \xrightarrow{\beta^-;\ 2.5\times10^{6}\ \text{yrs}} Ba_{56}^{135}.$$

We note the regular increase in half-life as we approach a stable isobar; this indicates an increasing stability of the nucleus.

Likewise attributable to an excess of neutrons in the fission fragments and in their transformation products is the fact that nuclear fission is always attended by *neutron emission*. Special experiments have shown that 2 to 3 neutrons are emitted in each nuclear fission event of uranium. These neutrons, which are apparently emitted by short-lived fragments (τ less than 10^{-14} sec), are called *fission neutrons*. Fission neutrons have a continuous energy spectrum with a maximum at about 0.7-0.8. MeV extending up to 12 MeV and more. Along with these neutrons that are ejected from the nucleus practically at the instant of fission, there are also so-called *delayed neutrons* emitted by the fission products after the lapse of a considerable time interval following the formation of the fragments. The half-lives corresponding to separate groups of delayed neutrons range from 0.05 sec to 120 min, those less than a minute being predominant. The total number of delayed neutrons, however, is small and comes out to only 0.755% of the number of fission neutrons (for U^{235}).

The large number of chains of β^--transformations of various fission fragments and also the secondary reactions involving both fission neutrons and delayed neutrons create, in the fissioning material, a great diversity of active and nonactive nuclei. In the case of uranium, for instance, over 300 different active fission products have been recorded.

In rare instances, an α-particle or a particle (nucleus) of greater mass is ejected together with the two fission fragments (ternary fission). In the fission of uranium-235 by thermal neutrons there is an average of one α-particle per 220 fission events and one proton per 5000.

Measurements show that in the fission of uranium about 170 MeV energy is released, the major portion of which is originally in the form of the kinetic energy of the fission fragments.* A value close to this one is obtained if it is taken that all the energy of the reaction is concentrated in the fragments and that its source is Coulomb repulsion of the fragments. Thus, assuming $Z_1=37$ and $Z_2=55$ $(Z_1:Z_2=2:3)$ and computing the distances between the fragment nuclei (at the instant of their formation) from formula (9.5) as the sum of the radii of these nuclei, $r=a_1+a_2=14.3\times10^{-13}$ cm, we obtain

$$U=\frac{37\times55\,(4.8)^2\times10^{-20}}{14.3\times10^{-13}\times1.6\times10^{-6}}=205\text{ MeV}$$

A value that practically coincides with this one is obtained as follows. From the curve of binding energy of atomic nuclei (Fig. 13), it follows that the binding energy per nucleon (specific binding energy) in the range of atomic weights $A=95$–140 (corresponding to $Z=37$-55) is 8.5 MeV and diminishes to 7.6 MeV at the end of the Periodic Table. Hence, for the energy released in the fission of uranium-235 we find $U=(8.5-7.6)\times236=$ $=212$ MeV.

Due to the high energy, the fission fragments are strongly ionising. For this reason, when using an ionisation chamber it is easy to distinguish the fission process from other nuclear processes by the powerful surges of current. Due to the high ionisation density and the considerable path lengths of the fragments,** the fission process may also be photographed with a Wilson

* A calorimetric determination of the kinetic energy of the fragments of uranium-235 fission by thermal neutrons yields 166 ± 2 MeV (which is in excellent agreement with the measurement data obtained by other methods).

** Uranium fission fragments in air at atmospheric pressure have a path length of 2 to 2.5 cm.

cloud chamber or by the method of nuclear emulsions. Fig. 24 is a photograph of the tracks of fragments in a cloud chamber obtained as follows: a thin layer of uranium (in the form of UO_3) was deposited on a 1-micron-thick aluminium foil; the foil was placed in a cloud chamber and irradiated with neutrons. The result was a picture of fission as shown in Fig. 24.

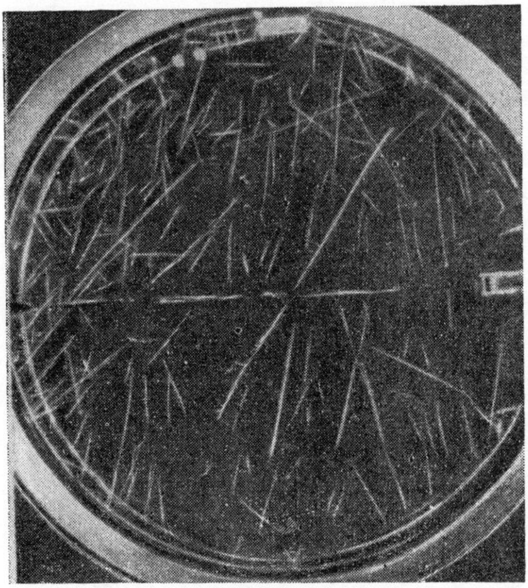

Fig. 24. Tracks of uranium fission fragments in Wilson cloud chamber

Uranium is not the only element that is fissionable under the action of neutrons. Thorium and all the transuranium elements have this property. Some isotopes fission even upon the capture of thermal neutrons. These are U_{92}^{232}, U_{92}^{233}, U_{92}^{235}, Pu_{94}^{239}, Am_{95}^{241}, Am_{95}^{242}, Am_{95}^{243}, etc. Other isotopes have been found to have a *fission threshold*, which is the minimum neutron energy for which fission occurs. For Np_{93}^{237} the fission threshold is 0.25 MeV, for U_{92}^{234} 0.28 MeV, for Pa_{92}^{231} 0.45 MeV, U_{92}^{238} 0.92 MeV, Th_{90}^{232} 1.05 MeV, and so forth. Nuclear fission may be initiated not only by neutrons but by fast charged particles and γ-photons (*photofission*). Thus, it has been found that uranium and thorium fission under the action of deuterons of energy $K \geqslant 8$ MeV. The photofission threshold (the minimum energy of γ-photons) is approximately 5.4 MeV for Th^{232}_{90}, 5 3 MeV for U^{235}_{92}, 5.1 MeV for U^{238}_{92}, etc.

The nuclei of heavy elements are capable, however, of fissioning not only under the action of external factors (irradiation

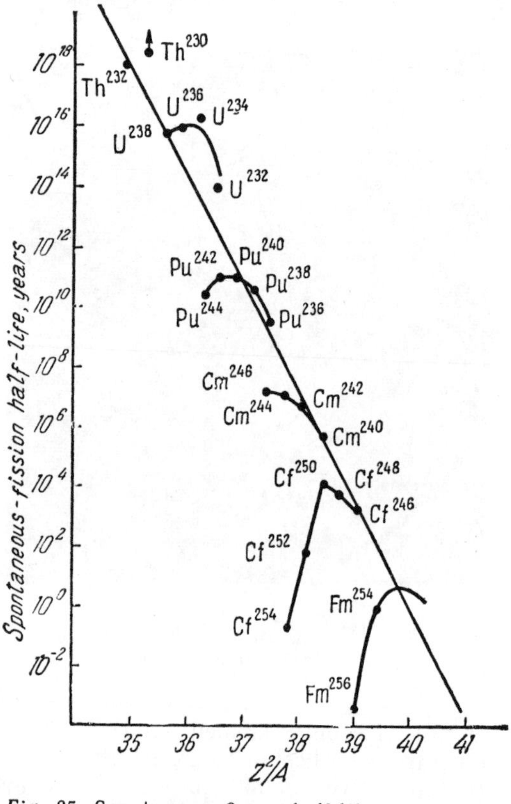

Fig. 25. Spontaneous-fission half-life as a function of Z^2/A (after Ghiorso).

with neutrons, γ-photons, or charged particles) but also, to a greater or lesser degree, spontaneously. *Spontaneous fission* of atomic nuclei was discovered by Flerov and Petrzhak in 1940. The appropriate half-life of uranium came out to 3×10^{15} years (more precise measurements give $T_{1/2} = 8.0 \times 10^{15}$ years). Later, spontaneous fission was established for a large number of nuclei. Fig. 25 gives the half-lives for spontaneous fission of elements beginning with thorium and ending with element 100 (fermium) as a function of Z^2/A. We see that as this parameter increases, the half-life exhibits a sharp decrease (almost linear): while for Th^{232}_{90} ($Z^2/A=34.91$) it is 1.4×10^{18} years, for Fm^{254}_{100} ($Z^2/A=39.37$) it is only half a year. The significance of this dependence of $\ln T_{1/2}$ on the parameter Z^2/A (Fig. 25) will be clarified below.

Let us now consider reactions of *superfast particles*, i.e., particles of several hundred MeV and more (up to thousands of millions of electron-volts), with nuclei. When nuclei are bombarded with neutrons, protons, deuterons, or α-particles of such energies, fission is observed not only in the case of uranium and thorium, but also Bi_{83}, Pb_{82}, Tl_{81}, Hg_{80}, Au_{79}, Pt_{78}, Ta_{73}, and other lighter elements. A number of peculiarities in fission reactions initiated by superfast particles, for example, different products from those produced in fission with slow particles, frequently observed stable isotopes among the primary fission products, etc., suggests that nuclear fission is in this case preceded by the emission of a large number of neutrons. This assumption is also confirmed by the fact that the sum of the masses of nuclei that arise with the greatest probability is considerably less than the mass of the initial nucleus. Thus, the fission of a nucleus by superfast particles is to be visualised as a three-stage process (in contrast to the two-stage process in the case of uranium fission with slow neutrons. $n+U^{235}_{92}\xrightarrow{I}U^{236}_{92}\xrightarrow{II}$ fission fragments. The fission of bismuth with superfast deuterons may serve as a probable instance of the three-stage fission process: $d+Bi^{209}_{83}\xrightarrow{I}$ $Po^{211}_{84}\xrightarrow{II}Po^{199}_{84}+12n\xrightarrow{III}$ fission fragments, or Bi^{209}_{83} (d, 12n) $Po^{199}_{84}\longrightarrow$ fragments.

The three-stage mechanism of nuclear fission by superfast particles follows from the views of Serber, who regards the collision of a superfast particle with a nucleus as a collision with a *single* nucleon. When this collision occurs near the centre of the nucleus, then as a result of subsequent secondary collisions of the struck nucleon and of the bombarding particle itself, the energy of the latter is distributed among a large number of nucleons. This produces a peculiar state of the nucleus, which Serber calls the "boiling nucleus"; due to its large store of energy, a "boiling nucleus" is capable of emitting ("evaporating") a large number of nucleons. However, since the escape of protons from the nucleus involves surmounting a high potential barrier, the evaporating nucleons must be mainly neutrons; this leads to the second stage of the three-stage fission mechanism. The third stage of the fission process sets in as a result of increasing density of the positive charge of the nucleus making it unstable against fission.

It should be expected that with increasing energy of the superfast particles, and, hence, also the energy of the "boiling nucleus" under bombardment, the predominance of the number of evaporating neutrons over the number of protons will tend to diminish. This is corroborated by bombarding nuclei with superfast protons of energy 2.2 GeV (or BeV). From measurements of the effective cross-sections of formation of various products it follows that the fission of a heavy nucleus (Bi, Pb, etc.) in this case becomes relatively less probable and gives way to the process of *deep splitting* or *spallation of the nucleus*, i.e., the ejection of a large number of nucleons (neutrons and protons), which in some cases reaches 60. It is obviously the loss of a large number of nucleons that makes fission of the nucleus a less probable process than spallation.

Theory of nuclear fission. A pictorial view of the fission process of heavy nuclei is given by the liquid-drop model of the nucleus. According to concepts developed by Frenkel (1939) and Bohr and Wheeler (1939), an external factor acting on the nuleus (for example, the capture of a neutron by the nucleus) gives rise to a comparatively long-lived (excited) complex with excess energy. The excitation energy of this complex is distributed statistically (like the thermal energy of a body having a large number of degrees of freedom). As a result of accidental fluctuations it can bring about oscillations similar to those of a liquid sphere. In a heavy nucleus with a large number of protons, the electrostatic forces of repulsion, which counteract the stabilising action of the forces of attraction, make the oscillations unsteady and cause disintegration (fission) of the nucleus into two smaller nuclei that correspond to an energetically more suitable state of the system.

Frenkel, Bohr and Wheeler also gave a mathematical theory of nuclear fission based on the liquid-drop model of the nucleus. Let us first consider the fission process from the point of view of its energy balance. Since the portion of energy due to nuclear forces is proportional to the number of nucleons, which practically remains constant when a nucleus fissions, we may disregard the first two terms in equation (14.1) when computing the energy change in the fission process. Thus, with an accuracy to within the constant term, we may represent the nuclear energy prior to fission in the following form:

$$-\Delta E = \gamma A^{2/3} + \varkappa Z^2 A^{-1/3},$$

or, introducing the radius of the nucleus $a = a_0 A^{1/3}$, in the form

$$-\Delta E = \gamma \left(\frac{a}{a_0}\right)^2 + \varkappa \frac{a_0}{a} Z^2. \tag{17.1}$$

Further, regarding (for the sake of simplicity) the nucleus as dividing into two identical fragments, we will have $Z_1 = Z_2 = \frac{Z}{2}$ and $a_1 = a_2 = \frac{a}{\sqrt[3]{2}}$ $\left(\text{inasmuch as } \frac{4}{3}\pi a^3 = \frac{4}{3}\pi a_1^3 + \frac{4}{3}\pi a_2^3\right)$, whence, for the fragment energy, we get

$$-\Delta E_1 - \Delta E_2 = \gamma \left(\frac{a}{a_0}\right)^2 2^{1/3} + \varkappa \frac{a_0}{a} Z^2 2^{-2/3}. \tag{17.2}$$

On the basis of (17.1) and (17.2), the equation of the energy balance of the fission process is written as

$$Q = \Delta E_1 + \Delta E_2 - \Delta E = \gamma \left(\frac{a}{a_0}\right)^2 (1 - 2^{1/3}) + \varkappa \frac{a_0}{a} Z^2 (1 - 2^{-2/3}). \tag{17.3}$$

Energywise, fission becomes possible at $Q \geqslant 0$. Thus, equating (17.3) to zero, we obtain the energy condition for the possibility of fission:

$$\frac{\varkappa}{\gamma} \left(\frac{a_0}{a}\right)^3 Z^2 = \frac{2^{1/3} - 1}{1 - 2^{-2/3}} = 0.70 \tag{17.4}$$

or, since $\left(\frac{a}{a_0}\right)^3 = A$,

$$\frac{Z^2}{A} = 0.70 \frac{\gamma}{\varkappa}. \tag{17.5}$$

Substituting into (17.5) $\gamma = 15.4$ and $\varkappa = 0.6$ (see p. 78) for the critical value of the parameter Z^2/A, which determines the possibility of fission from the viewpoint of the energy balance of the fissioning nucleus, we obtain $(Z^2/A)_{cr} = 18$. Putting $Z = A/2$ approximately, we find $A_{cr} = 72$ for the critical atomic weight. This means that fission is possible already in the range of medium atomic weights. The fact that in reality fission is observed only in the case of heavy nuclei is to be attributed to the insufficiency of the fission energy condition by itself, for, due to the existence of a potential barrier (the penetrability of which is small for heavy fission fragments), an additional condition must be fulfilled for fission to occur. The essence of this condition is that the fissioning nucleus must possess a certain excess energy, called the *activation energy* in analogy with the activation energy of chemical reactions. *

The problem of the activation energy of nuclear fission was investigated by Frenkel, Bohr and Wheeler, and others. Here we shall confine ourselves to a consideration of only a few of the results obtained. As follows from (17.5), from the viewpoint of energy, fission is possible when the electrostatic energy of the nucleus $\varkappa Z^2 A^{-1/3}$ amounts to 70% or more of its surface energy $\gamma A^{2/3}$. On the other hand, it was found that the activation energy is zero (i.e., the nucleus is absolutely unstable against fission) when the electrostatic energy of the nucleus is double its surface energy. The condition of absolute instability of a nucleus against fission may thus be written as

$$\frac{Z^2}{A} = 2\frac{\gamma}{\varkappa} = 50. \tag{17.6}$$

It may be noted that, according to the latest and most precise calculations, the instability condition is expressed by the formula

$$\frac{Z^2}{A} = 46. \tag{17.6a}$$

Comparing the number 46 with the value of the parameter Z^2/A for all known fissionable nuclei (including also spontaneously fissionable nuclei), it becomes clear that in all cases Z^2/A is less than 46. For example, for the nuclei Th_{90}^{232}, U_{92}^{235}, Fm_{100}^{254}, Z^2/A is 35.0, 36.0, 39.4, respectively. For the first two nuclei, the minimum energy of γ-rays that causes photofission is 5.40 and 5.31 MeV, respectively. Obviously, these numbers can be identified with the activation energy values of fission of Th_{90}^{232} and U_{92}^{235}. We may add that the activation energy of fission of the nucleus U_{92}^{235} may likewise be computed from the fission threshold of the nucleus U_{92}^{234} as a result of the capture of a neutron (0.28 MeV) and the binding energy of a neutron in the nucleus U_{92}^{235} (4.9 MeV), whence the value of activation energy is found to be 5.2 MeV. Within measurement error, this value coincides with the threshold of photofission of U_{92}^{235} (5.3 MeV). Thus we see that whereas for a hypothetical nucleus with the parameter $Z^2/A = 46$ the activation energy is zero, reduction of this parameter to 35-36 yields activation energy values that exceed 5 MeV.

* For instance, due to the existence of an energy potential barrier, the chemical reaction $N_2O = N_2 + O$ requires an energy of 60 kcal/mol at a reaction heat $Q = -39.5$ kcal/mol. The reaction $D + H_2 = DH + H$ proceeds with an activation energy of 7 kcal/mol at $Q = 0$.

Calculations made on the basis of the liquid-drop model of the nucleus show that the activation energy of fission increases as Z diminishes or as A increases; in other words, as the parameter Z^2/A decreases, retaining an approximately constant value for constant Z^2/A. Thus, there is a correspondence between the activation energies 0.5, 1, 3, 5, and 10 MeV and the values of the Z^2/A parameter close to 42.5, 41.0, 38.5, 36.5, and 34.0, respectively.

A correlation of computations and experimental data reveals satisfactory agreement between theory and experiment. Certain irregularities observed in the relationship of activation energy versus Z^2/A are, apparently, due to the fact that the liquid-drop model of the nucleus does not take into account quantum effects, as, for instance, the dependence of nuclear forces upon nucleon spins, which affects the size of the nucleus.

If the energy of a nucleus is less than that corresponding to its activated state, the oscillations that arise due to fluctuations of energy will be quasi-periodic, corresponding to specific energy levels of the nucleus. However, in this case, too, nuclear fission can still occur due to the probability (though small, it is still finite) of the tunnel effect. This is precisely the mechanism of spontaneous nuclear fission.

From the liquid-drop model of the nucleus we may obtain an expression for the probability of spontaneous fission in the form

$$\lambda = \nu P \tag{17.7}$$

where ν is the frequency of nuclear oscillations, of the order of 10^{21} sec^{-1}, and P is the probability of tunnel penetration, or the "transparency" of the potential barrier. We note the close similarity of (17.7) and (15.3) obtained from the theory of α-decay. P increases with diminishing difference in the energy corresponding to the top point of the potential barrier and the energy of the nucleus, i.e., with increasing Z^2/A. Whence we get the half-life as a function of the parameter Z^2/A in spontaneous fission (Fig. 25). Here, as in the case of artificial fission, the slight spread of dots about the curve in Fig. 25 is due to the influence of factors not taken into account by the simple liquid-drop model of the nucleus.

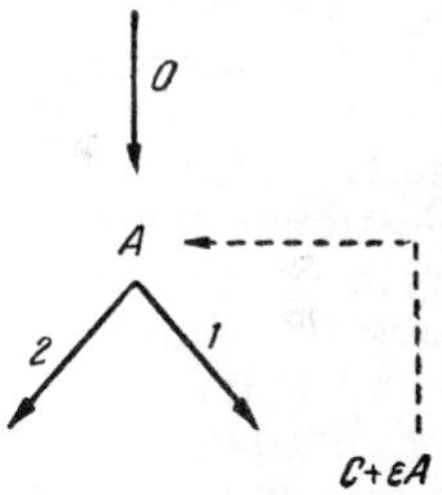

Fig. 26. Scheme of a chain reaction

From (17.7) it follows that for $P = 1$ (this occurs when the nuclear energy corresponds to the top point of the potential barrier, i.e., when the activation energy of fission is zero) the decay constant is of the order of 10^{21} sec^{-1} and, consequently, the half-life is of the order of 10^{-21} sec or 10^{-28} year. This is the half-life of an ideal nucleus that is absolutely unstable against fission.

Nuclear chain reaction. According to present-day views advanced and substantiated in the works of Semyonov (1928-34), a *chemical chain reaction* occurs with the participation of active particles or centres in the form of free atoms and radicals. The chief peculiarity of a chain reaction, that distinguishes it from non-chain reactions, is its continual regeneration of active centres, as a result of which the appearance of each active centre is accompanied by a large number of recurring links. The number of these links, or the length of the chain, together with the rate of generation of active centres is what determines the rate of the chain reaction.

A chain reaction may be represented diagrammatically as shown in Fig. 26 (A is an active centre, C is a reaction product). The arrow 0 indicates formation of an active centre as a result of thermal motion or some external agent, for instance, irradiation in the case of photochemical reactions. Arrow 1 denotes the set of processes that lead to the formation of a reaction product. Active centres are formed simultaneously (the number of these is ε per molecule of the product C). The quantity ε is called the *regeneration factor*, or the *active-centre multiplication factor*. Thus, according to the diagram, the chain reaction itself is an additional source of active centres (in Fig. 26 this is depicted by the dashed arrow). Finally, arrow 2 denotes the set of processes that lead to the disappearance of active centres (to chain termination).

Denoting the rate of generation of active centres (this corresponds to arrow 0) by W_0 and the probability that as a result of the reactions of a single active centre a reaction product C will be formed, by α, we can express the rate of a steady-state chain reaction W, i.e., the number of molecules C formed in unit time, by $W=(W_0+\varepsilon W)\alpha$, from which it follows that

$$W=W_0\frac{\alpha}{1-\varepsilon\alpha}. \tag{17.8}$$

As may be seen from (17.8), the rate of a chain reaction remains finite as long as $\varepsilon\alpha<1$, and increases beyond all bounds as $\varepsilon\alpha$ approaches 1. We note that at $\alpha<1$, i.e., when the chains terminate, the probability of which is obviously $\beta=1-\alpha$, an infinitely high rate of the reaction is possible only if $\varepsilon>1$. Using Semyonov's terminology, this case corresponds to *branched* chain reactions.

Let us now consider a nonsteady-state reaction. In Semyonov's theory, this problem is solved as follows. Designating the concentration of active centres at a certain time t by N, the specific rate of the reaction, i.e., the rate of the reaction referred to a single active centre, by $v_1 = W/N$, and the specific rate of disappearance of active centres by v_2, we write the kinetic equation of the reaction in the form

$$\frac{dN}{dt} = W_0 - (v_1 + v_2) N + \varepsilon v_1 N = W_0 - (v_1 + v_2)(1 - \varepsilon\alpha) N,$$

since, by definition, the probability of chain propagation is $\alpha = v_1/(v_1 + v_2)$. Integrating this equation for the boundary condition $N = 0$ at $t = 0$, we find

$$N = \frac{1 - e^{-(v_1+v_2)(1-\varepsilon\alpha)t}}{(v_1 + v_2)(1 - \varepsilon\alpha)} W_0,$$

whence, for the reaction rate at t, it follows that

$$W = v_1 N = \frac{\alpha W_0}{1 - \varepsilon\alpha} [1 - e^{-(v_1+v_2)(1-\varepsilon\alpha)t}]. \tag{17.9}$$

From (17.9) it is seen that a steady-state reaction, that is, one that proceeds at a constant rate, is possible only when $\varepsilon\alpha < 1$. Indeed, in this case, for sufficiently large t, $(t > 1/(v_1 + v_2)(1 - \varepsilon\alpha))$, when the second term in square brackets is negligibly small, (17.8) — the rate of a steady-state reaction — is obtained from (17.9). But in the case of $\varepsilon\alpha > 1$, given sufficiently large t, $(t > 1/(v_1 + v_2)(\varepsilon\alpha - 1))$, expression (17.9) passes into

$$W = \frac{W_0 v_1}{\varphi} e^{\varphi t}, \tag{17.10}$$

where $\varphi = (v_1 + v_2)(\varepsilon\alpha - 1)$. We see that in this case the rate of the reaction increases exponentially with time (*Semyonov's law*) tending to become large beyond all bounds. An immeasurably high reaction rate obviously corresponds to an *explosion*. According to Semyonov, the self-acceleration of the reaction as expressed by (17.10) is characteristic of branched chain reactions, i.e., of reactions with $\varepsilon > 1$.

It will be readily seen that the foregoing elementary kinetic theory of chemical chain reactions is applicable also to nuclear fission reactions. Indeed, inasmuch as the bombardment of heavy nuclei (and in the case of such nuclei as, for instance, U_{92}^{235} or Pu_{14}^{239}, the capture of thermal neutrons) causes fission accompanied by the emission of fission neutrons (plus delayed neutrons), the number of which is 2 or 3 ($\varepsilon > 1$) per fission event, a branched chain reaction is obviously possible in this case in which the neutrons play the role of active centres. The possibility of this reaction was first pointed out by Zeldovich and Khariton in 1939.

Having in view a nuclear chain reaction, let us clarify the meaning of the kinetic quantities W_O, v_1, and v_2 that enter into equations (17.9) and (17.10). The quantity W_O is the rate of production of neutrons in a mass of fissionable material. In the absence of neutron irradiation from without, this quantity is determined mainly by the rate of spontaneous fission of the given substance. For example, in the case of natural uranium, the isotopic composition of which is U^{238} — 99.274%, U^{235} — 0.720%, and U^{234} — 0.006%, and the rate of spontaneous fission 6.9 (U^{238}), 0.3 (U^{235}), and < 9 (U^{234}) fissions per kg/sec, we find that in one kilogram of this element there occur, on the average 6.85 fission events per second.* Since each fission event of uranium-238, which makes up the bulk of natural uranium, yields an average of 2.2 ($\pm$0.3) fission neutrons, we obtain $W_O = 15$ neutrons kg^{-1} sec^{-1}.**

In the case of a nuclear chain reaction, v_1 represents the specific rate of the fission reaction expressed by the product

$$v_1^{(x)} = \sigma_{fis}^{(x)} v N^{(x)}$$

where $\sigma_{fis}^{(x)}$ is the fission cross-section, v is the neutron velocity, and $N^{(x)}$ is the concentration of fissionable isotope of a given sort (x), i.e., the number of its nuclei in 1 cm^3 of the substance. As has already been pointed out (p. 107), only comparatively fast neutrons ($K > 0.9$ MeV) can fission uranium-238. This is due to a fission threshold. In this case, the fission cross-section increases from a value close to zero at $K = 0.9$ MeV; near $K = 2$ MeV it reaches 0.6×10^{-24} cm^2, and varies but slightly with increasing neutron energy. In contrast to uranium-238, the fission cross-section of uranium-235 is 500×10^{-24} cm^2 already for thermal neutrons. It decreases (as $1/v$) with increasing neutron energy and approaches a constant value of 1.5×10^{-24} cm^2. From these data it follows that with respect to neutron fission, uranium-235 is appreciably more active than uranium-238.** For this reason, in practice we use uranium *enriched* with the 235 isotope. It may be noted that plutonium-239, which is obtained in nuclear reac-

* Under ordinary conditions, fission processes due to cosmic radiation contribute a small portion (about 10%) to neutron production.

** Due to the small percentage of the uranium-234 isotope in natural uranium, it does not play any appreciable part in a uranium-fission chain reaction.

tors (see below), has the same properties as uranium-235 (with respect to fission).

Since about 75% of the fission neutrons have energies above the fission threshold of U^{238} (0.92 MeV), a uranium chain reaction proceeds with the participation of both isotopes (235 and 238). However, due to energy loss in inelastic collisions with nuclei, the fast neutrons become incapable of fissioning uranium-238, which thus drops out of the game. Moreover, at low neutron energies (about 7 eV) uranium-238 avidly absorbs neutrons without fission: the cross-section for neutron capture by a U^{238} nucleus has a resonance maximum at this energy (resonance capture) that corresponds to $\sigma_{cap} = 5000 \times 10^{-24}$ cm^2. The capture, by uranium-238, of neutrons, the energy of which is less than the fission threshold, thus leads to chain termination.

This, however, is not the sole cause of chain termination. The neutrons can also be absorbed by impurity nuclei in the uranium. In addition, the chain may terminate due to a neutron escaping from the fissile material. All these causes of chain termination determine the specific rate of neutron loss v_2.

A nuclear chain reaction may be accelerated either by raising v_1 or by reducing v_2. Besides increasing the percentage of the 235 isotope in the case of uranium, the rate of the fission reaction can also be increased by changing v_1 through the addition of *moderators*. The usual moderators are either deuterium in the form of heavy water D_2O, which does not absorb neutrons and which, due to the fact that its mass is close to the neutron mass, has a strong moderating action, or carbon (in the form of graphite) whose nuclei, like those of oxygen, are poor absorbers of neutrons. As a result of rapid moderation * the neutrons jump across the dangerous region of resonance capture by uranium-238 nuclei (7eV) and become thermal, in which state they are particularly capable of fissioning uranium-235 nuclei.

Speeding the chain reaction by acting on v_2 is accomplished by careful purification of the fissile mass and the moderator of neutron-absorbing impurities and also by increasing the mass (volume) of the materials so as to reduce the probability of neutron loss from the mass. In addition, a good effect is attained through the use of *reflectors*, which likewise reduce the probability of neutron loss. Neutron loss by escape is relatively large in the case of a small volume of fissile material. For this reason, every substance has a definite *critical size* or *critical mass* char-

* It may be shown that, for example, a neutron with an initial energy of 1 MeV becomes thermal after experiencing an average of 21 collisions with deuterium nuclei. Assuming the energy of a thermal neutron to be $K = 3/2\ kT$, at $T = 273°K$, we obtain $K = 1/30$ eV.

acterised by the fact that for dimensions or mass less than these values, a nuclear chain reaction will be an exceedingly slow steady-state reaction, whereas for dimensions and mass above critical the reaction is self-accelerating (according to the Semyonov law) and ends in an explosion.

By changing ν_2 it is possible to regulate the rate of a nuclear chain reaction. In nuclear reactions, this regulation is done by means of cadmium rods introduced into the mass of fissile material. Due to strong resonance absorption of neutrons by cadmium (in the energy region of 0.180 eV), which at resonance maximum has a capture cross-section of 7800×10^{-24} cm^2 (the cadmium isotope responsible for resonance capture is cadmium-113 and makes up 12.3% of natural cadmium; its cross-section is $63,400 \times 10^{-24}$ cm^2), the concentration of neutrons in the reactor is sharply reduced in the presence of cadmium rods, and this, consequently, slows down the chain reaction. The reaction rate is controlled simply by inserting cadmium rods into the reactor or pulling them out.

We note that the capture of slow neutrons by uranium-238 brings about the following chain of transformations:

$$n + U^{238}_{92} \xrightarrow{\gamma} U^{239}_{92} \xrightarrow{\beta^-;\ 23\ \text{min}} Np^{239}_{93} \xrightarrow{\beta^-,\ 2.3\ \text{days}} Pu^{239}_{94}.$$

As already pointed out, the Pu^{239} thus produced is capable of fissioning upon the capture of slow neutrons, just like uranium-235, and for this reason is a valuable nuclear chain "fuel". The difference in chemical properties of uranium and plutonium makes it possible to separate these elements by ordinary chemical methods and, consequently, to separate with relative ease the Pu^{239} from the used-up "fuel" of uranium reactors (piles). Plutonium-239 is α-active and has a half-life of 2.44×10^4 years. Its half-life with respect to spontaneous fission is 5.5×10^{15} years.

18. Thermonuclear Reactions

Fission chain reactions of heavy nuclei are not the only source of nuclear energy. Another source are thermonuclear reactions that occur in stars and are accomplished under terrestrial conditions — so far, unfortunately, only in hydrogen bombs. These reactions that involve protons and the nuclei of certain light elements (see below) become possible due to the very high temperatures in stellar interiors which, according to astrophysical data, range up to several tens of millions of degrees. Although at such temperatures the mean kinetic energy of the nuclei is only a few keV, i.e., far from that required to surmount the potential barrier, the height of which in the case of light nuclei is of the order of 1 MeV, the possibility of tunnel penetration considerably reduces their activation energy. For instance, above we saw (p. 54) that the reaction $H_1^1 + Li_3^7 = 2He_2^4$ is observed already at proton energies of $K = 10$ keV, whereas by computing the height of the potential barrier from the approximate expression

$$U_{max} = 0.77 \frac{Z}{1 + \sqrt[3]{Z}} \text{ MeV},$$

which is similar to equation (15.2), we find $U_{max} = 0.9$ MeV. Besides, at any temperature a noticeable portion of the nuclei has energies substantially higher than the mean energy at that temperature $\varepsilon = 3/2\,kT$; assuming a Maxwellian distribution of nuclear velocities it is not difficult to compute from the formula

$$\frac{dN}{N} = \frac{2}{\sqrt{\pi}} (kT)^{-3/2} e^{-\frac{\varepsilon}{kT}} \sqrt{\varepsilon}\, d\varepsilon$$

(dN is the number of particles of energy within the range between ε and $\varepsilon + d\varepsilon$, N is the total number of particles) that 1% of the nuclei has an energy six times that of the mean energy.

Taking into account the large abundance of hydrogen in stars and also the large binding energy of the helium nucleus (see Fig. 11) it is natural to assume that the chief source of stellar energy is the reaction of the formation of helium from hydrogen:

$$4H \rightarrow He,$$

the energy of which amounts to 5.9×10^{11} cal/gm-atom of helium.* We will show that this energy is quite sufficient to maintain the high temperature of a star, our sun for example, for a very long period of time. Indeed, since hydrogen makes up about 30% of the solar mass, which totals 5.5×10^{33} gm, the amount of hydrogen in the sun is 2×10^{33} gm, or 2×10^{33} gm-atoms. From this we find the energy that would be released if all the hydrogen in the sun were converted to helium:

$$\frac{5.9 \times 10^{11} \times 2 \times 10^{33}}{4} \approx 3 \times 10^{44} \text{ calories}.$$

We can also compute the quantity of energy radiated by the sun. Since each square centimetre of surface of the earth normal to the sun's rays (the distance of earth from sun being 1.5×10^8 km)

* Here we disregard the energy released in the annihilation of two positrons emitted in the synthesis of helium out of hydrogen.

receives 1.5 calories of radiant energy per minute, the total amount of energy radiated by the sun in one second comes out to

$$4\pi(1.5\times10^{13})^2\frac{1.5}{60}\approx7\times10^{25}\text{ cal sec}^{-1}.$$

Dividing by this number the reserves of nuclear solar energy contained in hydrogen atoms, we find the time during which this energy may be radiated (we take the radiation intensity to remain constant in time):

$$\frac{3\times10^{44}}{7\times10^{25}}\approx4\times10^{18}\text{ sec}\approx10^{11}\text{ years.}$$

Since the age of the sun is put at approximately 5×10^9 years, a comparison with the computed age shows that up to now the sun has used up roughly only one-twentieth of its store of energy.

The specific nuclear reactions underlying the synthesis of helium from hydrogen were, in the main, suggested by Weizsäcker (1938) and Bethe (1939). Calculating the half-life of various nuclear reactions (that is, the time during which half of the nuclei react) by extrapolation of known cross-sections of these reactions to high temperatures, Bethe demonstrated that the synthesis of helium could proceed in two chains of reactions: the *hydrogen-hydrogen cycle* and the *carbon-nitrogen cycle*. The latest researches have confirmed and improved upon this conclusion. It has been found that the hydrogen-hydrogen cycle plays the main part in stars cooler than the sun, while the carbon-nitrogen cycle is dominant in the hotter stars.

The hydrogen-hydrogen cycle is presently viewed as the following set of nuclear reactions:

$$2H\rightarrow D+\beta^+\ (1.4\times10^{10}\text{ years});$$
$$H+D\rightarrow He^3\ (5.7\text{ sec});$$
$$He^3+He^3\rightarrow He^4+2H\ (10^6\text{ years}).$$

Doubling the number of first and second reactions and summing, we obtain an equation of the total (overall) reaction $4H\rightarrow He^4+2\beta^+$. The time during which the reaction develops is given after each reaction. It will be seen that the slowest reaction is that of the formation of deuterium from hydrogen — of the order of 10^{10} years. Comparing this with the above-computed period of energy radiation latent in hydrogen ($\sim10^{11}$ years), we see that this figure is, however, sufficiently small for the hydrogen-hydrogen cycle to be accomplished. We note that the foregoing reaction times have been computed for a temperature of 13×10^6 degrees Kelvin, which is taken as the temperature at the centre of the sun.

The carbon-nitrogen cycle embraces the following reactions:

$$H + C^{12} \longrightarrow N^{13}\ (1.3 \times 10^7\ \text{years});$$
$$N^{13} \longrightarrow C^{13} + \beta^+\ (7\ \text{min});$$
$$H + C^{13} \longrightarrow N^{14}\ (2.7 \times 10^6\ \text{years});$$
$$H + N^{14} \longrightarrow O^{15}\ (3.2 \times 10^8\ \text{years});$$
$$O^{15} \longrightarrow N^{15} + \beta^+\ (82\ \text{sec});$$
$$H + N^{15} \longrightarrow C^{12} + He^4\ (1.1 \times 10^5\ \text{years}).$$

As in the hydrogen-hydrogen cycle, summing these reactions yields $4H \longrightarrow He^4 + 2\beta^+$. It will be noticed that in this cycle carbon-12 plays a part similar to that of catalysts in chemical reactions: it enters into the reaction at the start and again forms (is regenerated) at the end of the cycle. The reaction times are, as before, computed for a temperature of 13×10^6 °K.

CHAPTER 3

ELECTRONIC STRUCTURE OF ATOMS

19. Ionisation Potentials and Groups of Electrons in Atoms

Ionisation potentials of atoms. The entire assemblage of experimentally known physical and chemical properties of atoms shows that each atom consists of a positively charged part — the nucleus — and electrons, the number of which in a neutral atom is equal to the atomic number of the given element in Mendeleyev's Periodic Table.

If one or several electrons are removed from an atom, the result is a positive ion, for example, N^+, N^{++}, N^{+++}, etc. The energy necessary for ionisation may be imparted to the atom by the impact of a fast particle (say, an electron) or it may be absorbed by the atom in the form of a quantum of light (photon). In the former case (*ionisation by collision*), we will consider the process of ionisation as collision of elastic spheres, one of which represents the atom and is stationary; it will then be seen that on the basis of the laws of conservation of energy and momentum

$$K_0 = eI + K_c, \quad \sqrt{mK_0} = \sqrt{(m+M)\,K_c},$$

where K_0 is the minimum energy of the bombarding particle required to ionise the atom, m is its mass, M is the mass of the atom, K_c is the energy of the centre of gravity of the colliding system, and eI is the energy for ejection of the electron from the atom (I is the ionisation potential of the atom), we will have

$$K_0 = \frac{M}{m+M}\,eI. \qquad (19.1)$$

If the bombarding particle is an electron, then, since $m/M \leqslant 1/1840$, its mass m may be disregarded as compared to the atomic mass; hence, the minimum energy of the ionising electron is practically equal to the ionisation energy of the atom: $K_0 = eI$. It is thus possible, by subjecting atoms to the bombardment of fast electrons and by measuring the quantity of ions (the ionic current i) for various values of energy K of the bombarding electrons and by extrapolation of the i (K) curve to zero, to find K_0 and, consequently, I. This is usually the method applied to measure ionisation potentials. The energy is imparted to the bombarding electrons by an electric field, and for this reason K is expressed in electron-volts. It should, however, be pointed out that the error of measurement of ionisation potentials by this method is rarely less than 1%. Therefore, the spectroscopic method (see below) is resorted to when greater accuracy is required. It ensures much higher accuracy than the electron-impact method.

In the case of photoionisation of an atom, the energy of the ionising photon $h\nu$ and the ionisation potential are connected by the following relation:

$$h\nu = eI + K$$

where K is the energy of the electron ejected from the atom. It will be seen from this expression that there should be a certain minimum frequency ν_0, defined by the equality $h\nu_0 = eI$ $(K=0)$ and corresponding to the threshold that separates the region of photoionisation $(\nu > \nu_0)$ from that where photoionisation is energetically impossible $(\nu < \nu_0)$. The frequency ν_0 may be called the *threshold frequency* of photoionisation (or the photoelectric effect). The most precise values of ν_0 are obtained from investigations of atomic spectra.

The ionisation potentials I (in volts) for various elements are given in Fig. 27 (the horizontal axis is the atomic number Z of the element). From Fig. 27 it follows that the inert gases have maximum values of ionisation potentials while the alkaline elements have minimum values. As will be shown below, this fact and also the periodicity in values of I revealed by Fig. 27, which repeats the periodicity of the chemical properties (see below), reflect peculiarities in the structure of the electronic shells of atoms.

Electron affinity. The atoms of certain elements are capable of adding extra electrons thus forming negative ions, such, for example, are the ions H^-, O^-, F^-. The energy released in the formation of a negative ion out of a neutral atom and an electron, i. e., the energy of the process $A + e = A^-$ (A is the atom, e, the electron) is called *electron affinity*. The values of electron affinity E for certain atoms are (in eV): 0.71 (H), 3.62 (F), 3.78 (Cl), 3.56 (Br), 3.18 (I), 1.48 (O), 2.07 (S).

It will be noted that affinity for two (or more) electrons, i.e., the energy of formation of a doubly charged (or multiply charged) negative ion out of an atom and two (or more) electrons is always negative. In the formation of the O^{--} ion out of $O+2e$, for instance, about 7 eV is expended, while the S^{--} ion (out of $S+2e$) requires about 3.5 eV. Consequently, an electric system consisting of a nucleus and $Z+k$ electrons, i.e., a

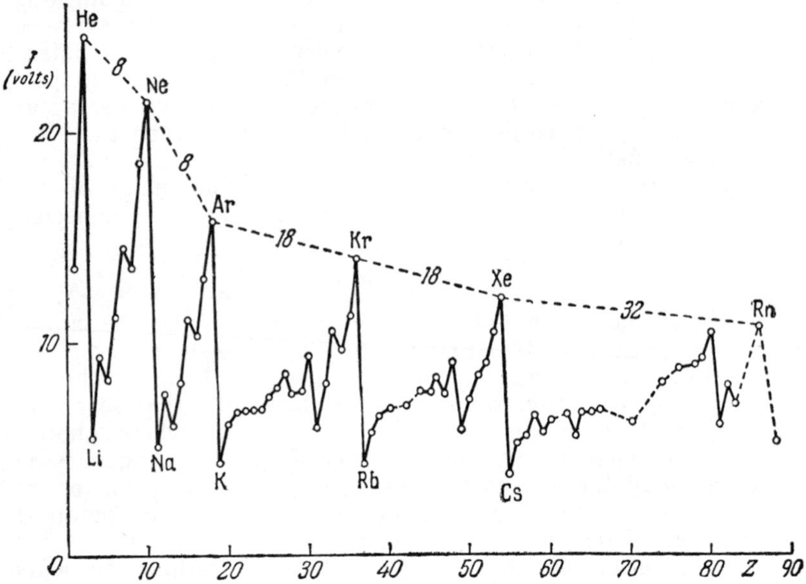

Fig. 27. Ionisation potentials of a number of elements

negative ion A^{-k}, is always unstable at $k>1$ and must disintegrate, with the release of energy, into an ion A^- and $k-1$ electrons or into a neutral atom A and k electrons. Experiment shows that the halogen atoms have the greatest electron affinity. As we shall see further on, this fact, which indicates that the electron shells of halogen ions X^- are extremely stable, is also due to peculiarities in the structure of the electronic shells of the atom. It will be noted that the electron affinity together with the ionisation potential are important quantitative characteristics of *electronegativity*, which plays an important part in the structure of molecules (see below, p. 298).

Electron groups. As one electron after another is removed from an atom, the charge of the remaining part of the atom (the *atomic core*) increases, and, consequently, there is an increase in the attraction of electrons by the atomic core. For this reason, the consecutive removal of electrons from an atom requires more and more energy. Designating the minimum energy required to remove one (the first) electron from the atom, by eI_1, the second, by eI_2, the third, by eI_3, etc., we will have $I_1 < I_2 < I_3 \ldots$. The number of different values of I_i (ionisation potentials) of each element is obviously equal to the corresponding atomic number Z. Note that the quantities I_i may be obtained from the minimum values of energy of the bombarding electrons, which energy is needed to convert the ions $A^{+(i-1)}$ into the ions A^{+i} (cf. above). The appearance of ions of a given sign may, in this case, be established mass-spectroscopically. However, precise values of ionisation potentials are obtained, as has already been pointed out, from atomic spectra.

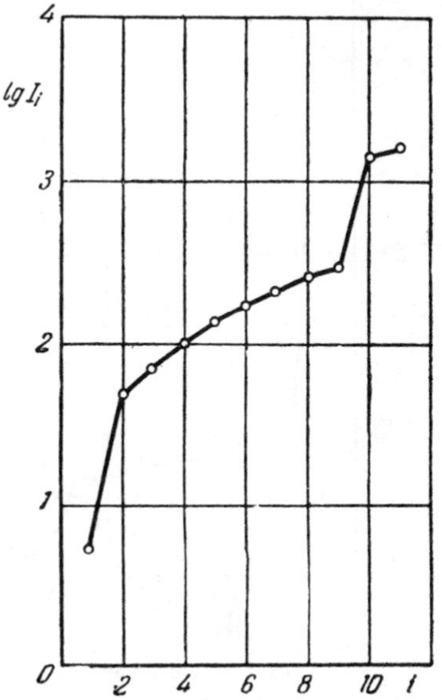

Fig. 28. The ionisation potentials (log I_i) of all eleven electrons of the sodium atom

A consideration of the quantities I_i for one and the same element shows that increase in I_i with the number of electrons removed i is not smooth, but exhibits sharp discontinuities at definite values of i. This relationship between I_i and i indicates that the electrons in an atom are distributed in discrete energy *groups*, or *layers*, characterised by different binding strength of the electrons. By way of illustration, let us examine the relationship between the ionisation potentials I_i of a sodium atom, found on the basis of spectral data, and the various ions of this element, $Na^{+(i-1)}$. I_1 is obviously the ionisation potential of the neutral atom Na, I_2 is the ionisation potential of the ion Na^+, I_3, that of the ion Na^{++}, etc. In Fig. 28, log I_i is represented as a function of i. The curve shows that the ionisation potential of sodium and its ions has two discontinuities: the first in the transition from the atom Na ($i=1$) to the ion Na^+ ($i=2$) and the second in the transition from the ion Na^{+8} ($i=9$) to the ion Na^{+9} ($i=10$). From this it follows that the first electron in the sodium atom is considerably more weakly bound than the remaining 10 electrons, of which 8, in turn, are bound appreciably more weakly than the last two. Consequently, the 11 electrons of sodium are distributed into three groups: a two-electron group of the most firmly bound electrons, an eight-electron group, and a group containing one electron, the most mobile one. This distribution of electrons into groups stands out prominently if the quantity i/I_i is represented as a function of i, as in Fig. 29.

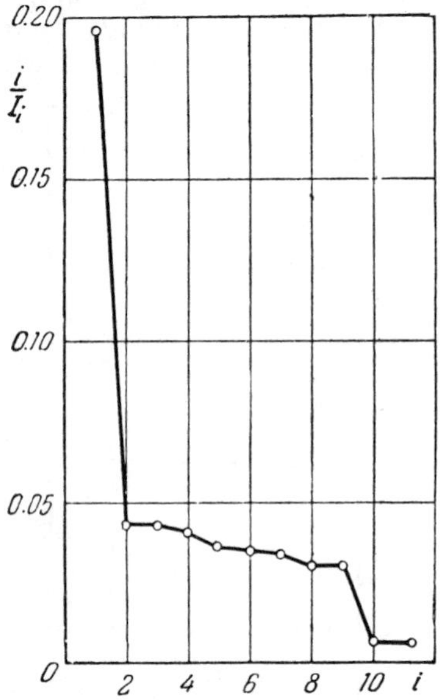

Fig. 29. Distribution of sodium-atom electrons into three groups.

This graph may be interpreted as follows. Assuming (approximately) total screening of the nuclear charge Ze by the surrounding electrons, that is, assuming that the electron being removed is acted upon by a point charge, the magnitude of which is determined by the nuclear charge minus the total charge of all remaining $Z-i$ electrons — the charge $Ze-(Z-i)e=ie$ — the ionisation potentials I_i may be represented by the formula *

$$I_i=\frac{ie}{2r} \tag{19.2}$$

where r is a certain mean distance of the removed electron from the nucleus. From this formula it follows that the quantities i/I_i must approximately vary as the mean distance r. Therefore, on the basis of Fig. 29, it may be concluded that the first electron of the sodium atom is in a layer farthest from the nucleus; in the next, deeper, layer there are 8 electrons, and, finally, in the layer closest to the nucleus there are two most firmly bound electrons. The electron of the outer layer may be called the *outer* electron, the remaining, the *inner* electrons.

* Assuming that the electrons revolve about the nucleus in circular orbits, and that the centrifugal force mv^2/r is balanced by the force of Coulomb attraction to the nucleus ie^2/r^2 (see below, Sec. 22), we obtain for the kinetic energy of the electron $K=mv^2/2=ie^2/2r$, so that the total energy of the electron is

$$E=\frac{ie^2}{2r}-\frac{ie^2}{r}=-\frac{ie^2}{2r}.$$

The energy for removal of an electron from the atom (eI_i) is equal to the energy E with sign reversed, whence we get formula (19.2).

Comparing the first and second ionisation potentials of the remaining alkaline elements (Table 4), we are convinced of a discontinuity (a change in ionisation potential by a factor of 14 to 6) when going from I_1 to I_2 (a thing that is not observed in the case of the greater part of the remaining elements where the quantity $I_2:I_1$ does not exceed 2-3). From this we may conclude that a common feature of all alkaline elements is the presence of *one* outer electron. This single electron gives the atoms

Table 4

First (I_1) and second (I_2) ionisation potentials of alkaline elements (in volts)

Ionisation potentials \ Elements	Li	Na	K	Rb	Cs
I_1	5.36	5.11	4.32	4.16	3.87
I_2	75.26	47.07	31.7	27.3	23.4

of the alkaline elements a certain similarity to the hydrogen atom with its one electron ($Z=1$). This is manifested in a similarity of physical and chemical properties of these atoms and the hydrogen atom (see Sec. 20).

Table 5 contains all the known ionisation potentials of the elements of the second period (from Li to Ne). Here, the stepped line indicates discontinuities that separate relatively weakly bound electrons from the most firmly bound inner electrons. From Table 5 it follows that all the elements represented in it have the same number (*two*) of such electrons with varying numbers of remaining electrons. And so we see that these two electrons form a strong *closed* group maintained throughout the second period. Investigations into the structure of the atomic clouds of the heavier elements show that this group persists also in the elements of the subsequent periods. It is first formed in helium ($Z=2$), both electrons of which belong to this group; this is evident from a comparison of the ionisation potentials of helium: $I_1=24.47$ V and $I_2=54.14$ V (no discontinuity). It is with the closed character of this group that the chemical inertness of helium is connected.

A similar closed group is formed by eight electrons of neon (which are outer with respect to the two most firmly bound in-

Table 5

Ionisation potentials of elements of the second period

Ionisation potentials \ Elements	Li	Be	B	C	N	O	F	Ne
I_1	5.36	9.28	8.25	11.20	14.46	13.55	18.6	21.47
I_2	75.26	18.12	25.00	24.26	29.44	34.94	34.81	40.91
I_3	121.84	153.11	37.74	47.64	47.20	54.63	62.35	63.3
I_4	—	216.63	258.03	64.17	72.04	77.03	86.72	(97)
I_5	—	—	338.53	390.02	97.40	113.30	—	—
I_6	—	—	—	487.55	549.08	137.42	156.37	—
I_7	—	—	—	—	663.73	735.22	184.26	—
I_8	—	—	—	—	—	867.09	—	—
I_9	—	—	—	—	—	—	1097.66	—
I_{10}	—	—	—	—	—	—	—	1355.48

ner electrons). This follows both from the chemical inertness of neon and from the fact that the element following neon, sodium, has not 9 but one outer electron (see above), magnesium, not 10 but 2, etc. The eight-electron closed group that takes shape in neon is maintained in all subsequent elements (like the earlier considered two-electron group).

20. Periodic System of Elements

The layer-like, group structure of atomic clouds is most clearly expressed in the recurrence of the chemical properties of the elements. This recurrence is expressed by Mendeleyev's periodic law. The periodic system of the elements is the most cogent and irrefutable proof of the existence of discrete groups in the electron clouds of atoms of all the elements. The recurring similarity of chemical properties of analogous elements is a direct indication of the identical structure of the outer electron layer of these elements and the closed character of the inner electron groups.

Diverse facts involving chemical and also certain physical properties of the elements indicate that a basic, if not exceptional, role in the chemistry of atoms is played by the *outer* electrons. The capacity for substitution (in various chemical compounds) of one atom for another that differs greatly from the former in atomic weight, atomic number, and, hence, in the total number of electrons, etc., together with a similarity in the chemical and physical properties of the resulting compounds (for instance, LiCl and KCl, NaCl and NaI, etc.) undoubtedly indicate that not all the electrons of these atoms, but only a certain very small part of them, participate in the formation of chemical compounds. We have already seen that all analog elements in the group of alkaline elements have one outer, or, as it may be called, *valence* electron. Elements of the second group (alkaline-earth elements) have two outer (valence) electrons, etc. Halogen atoms (seventh group) have seven outer electrons. The conclusion that the chemical properties of an atom are due to its outer electrons is likewise corroborated by studies of *X-ray spectra* of one and the same element in its different compounds. In this way it is shown that these spectra exhibit relatively slight change in the transition from the pure element to its compound. And since X-rays are associated precisely with the inner and most firmly bound electrons in the atom (see below), this constancy of X-ray spectra must be regarded as direct proof that the chemical properties of an atom are only very slightly dependent on the inner electrons. In contrast to X-ray spectra, optical spectra, which are associated with the outer, mobile electrons, undergo such changes that, as a rule, the spectrum of the compound has nothing in common with the spectra of the component elements.

Let us make a brief examination of Mendeleyev's Periodic Table (Table 6) from the viewpoint of the electronic structure of the atoms. The hydrogen atom, which occupies first place in this table, has only one electron ($Z=1$). This is likewise suggested by hydrogen having only one ionisation potential ($I_H = 13.60$ eV). The next element after hydrogen is helium with two electrons forming a closed two-electron group (see p. 127). It has already been pointed out that the inertness of helium is connected with the particular stability of this group.

The next element, lithium, is univalent.* By attributing this to the presence in the lithium atom of one outer electron, we obtain confirmation of the conclusion drawn from a consideration of the ionisation potentials of lithium that its three electrons are distributed in two groups: the inner, two-electron, group and the outer group with one electron. The isolated state of the outer electron of lithium confirms the conclusion about the closed character of the electron shell of the helium atom.

* Here we have in mind the so-called negative valence, or valence with respect to fluorine, which is determined by the number of fluorine atoms (or half the number of oxygen atoms) bound by the given atom in a saturated state (see Sec. 34); for example, the existence of LiF (but not LiF_2, etc.) indicates that lithium is univalent.

The elements that follow lithium-beryllium, boron, carbon, nitrogen, oxygen and fluorine — are chemically active, but the tenth element, neon, is inert. If we associate chemical inertness with the closed character of the outer electronic shell of the atom, we must conclude that none of the elements from lithium to fluorine has a closed outer shell; this shell closes only when an eighth electron is added (as in neon).

Earlier, proceeding from a consideration of the ionisation potentials of sodium, we came to the conclusion that ten out of its eleven electrons form two closed groups (the two- and eight-electron groups), while the eleventh electron is outside these groups. This fact, and also the presence of similar closed groups in the elements that follow sodium, confirm the conclusion about the closed nature of the outer eight-electron group of neon. Another indication of the closed eight-electron shell is the great electron affinity of the fluorine atom and, consequently, the high stability of the F^- ion, which finds expression, for one thing, in the fact that the F atom is more active chemically than the F^- ion.

From the chemical activity of all elements following sodium and ending with fluorine it follows that their outer electrons, like the eleventh electron of sodium, enter into a third, unclosed electron group. The same number of electrons in the outer unclosed electron group of elements of the second and third periods is the reason why sodium is the chemical analog of lithium, magnesium is the chemical analog of beryllium, aluminium the analog of boron, silicon of carbon, phosphorus of nitrogen, sulphur of oxygen, and chlorine of fluorine. This analogy is not confined solely to a similarity of chemical properties. As a rule, elements belonging to the same group have similar structures of optical spectra, similar magnetic properties, etc.

In the element following chlorine, argon, the third electron group has 8 electrons and again we have an inert element. However, a consideration of the chemical and other properties of the heavier elements that follow argon shows that only the first two groups retain the two and eight electrons, respectively, throughout the Periodic Table. The third electron group undergoes subsequent essential changes: beginning with scandium and ending with copper, this group builds up to 18 electrons and, up to the transuranium elements, remains an 18-electron group. The consequent irregularity in the filling of the electron groups finds expression in a number of chemical and physical anomalies observed in the elements from scandium to copper. The 29 electrons of the copper atom are distributed as follows: 28 form three closed groups (two-, eight-, and eighteen-electron groups), the 29th, outer, electron belongs to a new, fourth group.

MENDELEYEV'S PERIODIC SYSTEM OF THE ELEMENTS

PERIODS	Groups of Elements										
	I	II	III	IV	V	VI	VII	VIII			0
1	1H Hydro- gen 1.0080										2He Helium 4.003
2	3Li Lithium 6.940	4Be Bery- llium 9.02	5B Boron 10.82	6C Carbon 12.010	7N Nitrogen 14.008	8O Oxygen 16.0000	9F Fluorine 19.000				10Ne Neon 20.183
3	11Na Sodium 22.997	12Mg Magne- sium 24.32	13Al Alumi- nium 26.97	14Si Silicon 28.06	15P Phospho- rus 30.98	16S Sulphur 32.06	17Cl Chlorine 35.457				18Ar Argon 39.944
4	19K Potas- sium 39.096	20Ca Calcium 40.08	21Sc Scan- dium 45.10	22Ti Titanium 47.90	23V Vanadi- um 50.95	24Cr Chromi- um 52.01	25Mn Manga- nese 54.93	26Fe iron 55.85	27Co Cobalt 58.94	28Ni Nickel 58.69	
	29Cu Copper 63.57	30Zn Zinc 65.38	31Ga Gallium 69.72	32Ge Germa- nium 72.60	33As Arsenic 74.91	34Se Selenium 78.96	35Br Bromine 79.916				36Kr Krypton 83.7
5	37Rb Rubid- ium 85.48	38Sr Stron- tium 87.63	39Y Yttrium 88.92	40Zr Zirco- nium 91.22	41Nb Niobium 92.91	42Mo Molyb- denum 95.95	43Tc Techne- tium 99	44Ru Ruthe- nium 101.7	45Rh Rhodium 102.91	46Pd Palla- dium 106.71	
	47Ag Silver 107.880	48Cd Cadmium 112.41	49In Indium 114.76	50Sn Tin 118.70	51Sb Antim- ony 121.76	52Te Tellu- rium 127.61	53I Iodine 126.92				54Xe Xenon 131.3
6	55Cs Cesium 132.91	56Ba Barium 137.36	57La* Lantha- num 138.92	72Hf Hafnium 178.6	73Ta Tanta- lum 180.88	74W Tungsten 183.92	75Rh Rhenium 186.31	76Os Osmium 190.2	77Ir Iridium 193.1	78Pl Platinum 195.23	
	79Au Gold 197.2	80Hg Mercury 200.61	81Tl Thallium 204.39	82Pb Lead 207.21	83Bi Bismuth 209.00	84Po Polonium 210	85At Astatine 210				86Rn Radon 222
7	87Fr Fran- cium 223	88Ra Radium 226.05	89Ac** Actinium 227								

6	*58-71 Lantha- nide Series	58Ce Cerium 140.13	59Pr Praseo- dymium 140.92	60Nd Neody- mium 144.27	61Pm Prome- thium 147	62Sm Sama- rium 150.43	63Eu Euro- pium 152.0	64Gd Gadoli- nium 156.9	65Tb Tebium 159.2	66Dy Dyspro- sium 162.46	67Ho Holmium 164.94	68Er Erbium 167.2	69Tu Thulium 169.4	70Yb Ytter- bium 173.04	71Lu Lute- cium 174.99
7	**90-101 Actinide Series	90Th Thori- um 232.12	91Pa Protoac- tinium 231	92U Uranium 238.07	93Np Neptu- nium 237	94Pu Pluto- nium 239	95Am Ameri- cium 243	96Cm Curium 245	97Bk Berke- lium 249	98Cf Califor- nium 249	99E Einstein- ium 255	100Fm Fermi- um 255	101Mv Mendele- vium 256	102No Nobe- lium	103Lw

This fourth group fills up normally in the elements from copper to krypton; in krypton it contains 8 electrons, acquiring a certain degree of completion (like the eight-electron outer group of argon) and thus giving rise to the inertness of krypton. However, this group remains eight-electron only in two elements following krypton: rubidium and strontium. It then builds up first to 18 electrons in the elements from yttrium to palladium, and then up to 32 in the rare-earth elements. With this are associated the anomalies in the chemical and physical properties that are characteristic of elements from yttrium to palladium and of the rare earths. The number of electrons in the fourth group remains constant throughout the remaining part of the Periodic Table. From this it follows that the completed fourth group contains 32 electrons. All heavy elements from the 70th (ytterbium) contain four completed groups (2-, 8-, 18-, and 32-electron) and a certain number of uncompleted groups. Assigning to the four completed groups the numbers 1, 2, 3, and 4, it is easy to see that the maximum number of electrons in each group (2, 8, 18, and 32) is expressed by the formula $2n^2$, where n is the number of the group.

21. Atomic Energy Levels

Spectrum of the H atom and of ions with one electron. The presence of discrete groups of electrons in the electronic structure of atoms points to *discreteness* in the energy states of the atom. This discreteness is expressed most vividly in atomic spectra: optical and X-ray. It has already been pointed out that, unlike X-ray spectra, optical spectra are associated with the outer electrons of the atom. This is evident, in particular, from the fact that the energy changes that correspond to optical spectra usually have magnitudes of several electron-volts, i.e., are comparable to the first ionisation potentials that correspond to the binding strength of precisely the outer electrons of the atom.

A characteristic peculiarity of atomic spectra is their *linear structure*, which permits describing the spectrum of each element by specific values of wavelengths λ or frequencies ν. Separate groups, or *series*, of lines in atomic spectra obey definite, series laws. These laws (or regularities) are particularly prominent in the spectrum of the simplest atom, hydrogen.

As early as 1885, Balmer demonstrated that the wavelengths of nine lines of hydrogen (these lines were measured by Hagenbach), four of which lie in the visible region of the spectrum (λλ 7500-4000 A), are expressed by the following simple formula:

$$\lambda = \lambda_0 \frac{m^2}{m^2 - n^2}$$

where $\lambda_0 = 3645.6$ A, $n=2$ and $m=3, 4, 5, \ldots, 11$.

A spectrogram of this series of the hydrogen spectrum, called the *Balmer series*, is shown in Fig. 30 (at present up to 40 lines of this series are known). From the spectrogram it is seen that the distance between each pair of adjacent lines diminishes regularly, and in the region of short wavelengths the lines converge to a certain limit (*the series limit*). By extrapolation to $m=\infty$, from

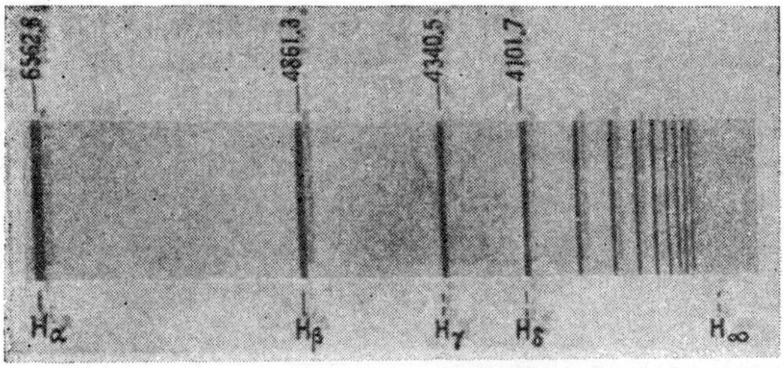

Fig. 30. Emission spectrum of hydrogen atom in visible and near ultraviolet regions (Balmer series)

the preceding formula, called the *Balmer formula*, we obtain the wavelength $\lambda = \lambda_0$ that corresponds to the limit of the Balmer series. Passing now from wavelengths to frequencies or to wave numbers,* the Balmer formula may be rewritten in the form

$$\nu = R\left(\frac{1}{n^2} - \frac{1}{m^2}\right). \tag{21.1}$$

The quantity R, equal to $3.288 \times 10^{15}\ \text{sec}^{-1}$ or $109{,}677.58\ \text{cm}^{-1}$, is called the *Rydberg constant*, after the scientist who found that this constant could be used to represent numerous spectra. As already pointed out, in the Balmer formula $n=2$. However, Balmer himself already regarded his formula as something more general. For instance, he suggested the existence of a series characterised by the value $n=3$. This series was actually discovered later by Paschen (1908). The *Paschen series* is expressed by the formula

$$\nu = R\left(\frac{1}{3^2} - \frac{1}{m^2}\right), \quad m=4, 5, \ldots$$

* The wavelength λ is connected with the frequency ν by the relation $\lambda = c/\nu$, where c is the velocity of light. In spectroscopy, the wave number $1/\lambda$ is also frequently called the frequency. This provisional frequency is expressed in cm^{-1} in distinction to ν, which is expressed in sec^{-1}.

Lyman discovered a series that obeys the formula

$$\nu = R\left(\frac{1}{l^2} - \frac{1}{m^2}\right), \quad m = 2, 3, \ldots$$

Thus, the Balmer formula (21.1) was firmly established experimentally and was taken as the basis for the theory of spectra.

From the Balmer formula it is easy to obtain a general expression for the energy of the hydrogen atom. Indeed, according to the quantum theory (Planck, 1902) light is emitted or absorbed by an atom only in definite portions, or quanta, of magnitude $h\nu$, which permits connecting the frequency ν of each spectral line with energy change of the atom ΔE by the relation (cf. formula (16.2))

$$h\nu = \Delta E. \tag{21.2}$$

From this it is seen that to discrete spectral lines there correspond discrete energy states, or energy levels of the atom. Designating the latter for the hydrogen atom by the subscripts n and m, we obtain $\Delta E = E_m - E_n$. Comparing this expression with (21.1), we find *

$$E_n = -\frac{hR}{n^2}. \tag{21.3}$$

Series similar to the hydrogen series were detected also in the spectra of ionised helium, lithium, beryllium, and other elements. The series that belong to the ions He^+, Li^{++}, Be^{+++}, etc., that is, to ions which, like the H atom, have only one electron (*hydrogen-like* ions), are expressed by the formula

$$\nu = Z^2R\left(\frac{1}{n^2} - \frac{1}{m^2}\right), \quad m = n+1,\ n+2, \ldots \tag{21.4}$$

It will be seen that (21.1) is a particular case of (21.4), which passes into (21.1) when $Z = 1$. Consequently, the following ex-

---

* Formula (21.3) is obtained under a definite normalisation of the energy of an atom, in accordance with which $E_n = 0$ when $n = \infty$. As we shall see below, such normalisation corresponds to a zero energy of the ionised atom, i. e., of the system $H^+ + e$ in the case of infinite recession of the electron from the nucleus ($r = \infty$). Naturally, in this case, $E_n < 0$ corresponds to finite values of r, which is expressed by the minus sign in (21.3).

pression * should be considered as a more general expression for the energy of an atom or ion with one electron:

$$E_n = -\frac{hR}{n^2} Z^2. \qquad (21.5)$$

Due to the fact that, according to (21.2), the frequencies of the spectral lines are expressed as the difference in the energy divided by the Planck constant h, it is expedient, in place of the energy E_n, to introduce the quantity

$$T_n = \frac{|E_n|}{h},$$

called a *term*. From (21.5) we obtain, for the terms of a hydrogen-like atom or ion, the expression

$$T_n = \frac{R}{n^2} Z^2. \qquad (21.5')$$

It may be noted that the (21.5′) is frequently called the Balmer formula.

From the series formula (21.4) it follows that part of the lines in the spectrum of ions ($Z > 1$) should coincide, in frequency, with the hydrogen lines. Thus, for example, representing the frequencies of the lines of He^+ in the series $n = 4$ (called the *Pickering series*) on the basis of formula (21.4),

$$\nu = R\left(\frac{1}{2^2} - \frac{1}{(m/2)^2}\right), \quad m = 5, 6, 7, \ldots,$$

we obtain a formula which differs from the above for the Balmer series in the hydrogen spectrum in that the number in the denominator of the second term, in the case of hydrogen, assumes only integral values (3, 4, 5, ...), whereas in the case of helium we have $m/2 = 5/2, 3, 7/2, 4, \ldots$, i.e., double the number of ν values. Whence it follows that the spectrum of a helium ion should contain twice the number of lines of the hydrogen spectrum, and this was found to be so in experiment.

Another feature in which the spectra of the ions He^+, Li^{++}, etc., differ from the hydrogen spectrum is that the lines of these spectra, which should have had coinciding wavelengths, are actually somewhat displaced one relative to the other. This is

* This expression is obtained from the more general expression

$$E_n = -\frac{hRZ^2}{n^2} + C$$

(C is a constant) with appropriate normalisation of energy.

seen, for example, from Table 7, which gives the wavelengths or lines of the Balmer series of hydrogen ($n=2$) and those of the Pickering series ($n=4$) of helium: the wavelengths of the hydrogen lines exceed by approximately 2 A the wavelengths of the corresponding He^+ lines.

This shift is due to the fact that in the formulas (21.4) and (21.5) the values of the Rydberg constant for different atoms or ions are somewhat *different*. Thus, spectroscopic measurements put the Rydberg constants for the H atom and the He^+ ion at $R_H = 109{,}677.58\ cm^{-1}$ and $R_{He+} = 109{,}722.26\ cm^{-1}$. Computing, in (21.4), the relative shift of lines in the appropriate series in the spectra of hydrogen and helium, we get

$$\frac{\Delta\nu}{\nu_H} = \frac{\Delta\lambda}{\lambda_H} = \frac{R_{He_+} - R_H}{R_H} = 0.00041$$

Substituting into this formula $\lambda = 5000$ A, in accordance with the data in Table 7, we find $\Delta\lambda = 2$A.

Table 7

Lines of the Balmer series (H) and the Pickering series (He^+) in the visible region of the spectrum

Element	Wavelength in A						
H	6562.80	—	4861.33	—	4340.47	—	4101.74
He^+	6560.13	5411.55	4859.34	4541.61	4338.69	4199.85	4100.00

The isotopes of the same element likewise have different values of R. For example, for the isotopes of H, D, and T we have $R_H = 109{,}677.58\ cm^{-1}$, $R_D = 109{,}710.48\ cm^{-1}$, and $R_T = 109{,}715.97\ cm^{-1}$. As in the preceding case (H and He^+), this difference leads to a certain shift of lines in the spectra of various isotopes (*isotope shift*). To take an example, for the lines of the Balmer series in the spectra of H and D it is of the order of 1A. It may be noted that it was this effect that led to the discovery of deuterium (Urey, 1932). As we shall see later on (Sec. 22), this difference in Rydberg constants is due to mass differences of the nuclei. It will also be noted that the isotopic shift of spectral lines is particularly great in the case of the light elements, though in the heavy elements it is quite prominent: isotopic shift was detected even in such an element as uranium. The following values were obtained for the wavelengths of the line λ 4,244 A of the five uranium isotopes: 4,244.373 (U^{238}), 4,244.226(U^{236}), 4,244.122(U^{235}), 4,244.075(U^{234}), and 4,243.977A(U^{233}).

From the foregoing it follows that, on the average, there is $\Delta\lambda = 0.039$ A to each unit of mass.

From (21.5) it follows that the energy of an atom (ion) with one electron takes on the following discrete series of values: $-hRZ^2$, $-1/4hRZ^2$, $-1/9hRZ^2$, ..., 0. The least of these values, $-hRZ^2$, obviously corresponds to the ordinary (*ground*, or *normal*) state of the atom, while the greatest (0), to the ionised state. The difference of these values should be equal to the ejection energy of the electron, that is, to the energy of ionisation eI of the atom. We thus have

$$I = \frac{hRZ^2}{e}. \tag{21.6}$$

Substituting into (21.6) the values of the constants h, R, and e, we find the following values of ionisation potentials (in volts): 13.606 (H), 54.403 (He^+), 122.420 (Li^{++}), 217.657 (Be^{+++}), 340.127 (B^{++++}), 489.84 (C^{+++++}), etc.

The energy values intermediate between minimum and maximum correspond to *excited states* of the atom (ion). According to Bohr, the transitions of an atom from one discrete energy state to another should be attended by the emission or absorption of monochromatic light. The energy levels and the spectrum of the hydrogen atom are given in Fig. 31.

The experiments of Franck and Hertz. The presence of excited levels in the atom was proved directly in experiments by Franck and Hertz (1912). When the atoms of a given gas are bombarded by electrons of definite velocity, measurements are made of the energy losses of the electrons colliding with the gas atoms and, simultaneously, observations are made of the emission spectrum produced by the electron bombardment. The first experiments with mercury vapour demonstrated that electrons accelerated by an electric field with a potential difference < 4.9 V and, consequently, having an energy K less than 4.9eV are reflected from the mercury atoms *elastically*, that is, without noticeable loss of energy. In this case, naturally, there is no emission. But when the electron energy is increased to 4.9 eV (and higher), slow electrons appear; this shows that electrons with energy 4.9eV transfer this energy to the mercury atoms *in toto*. Simultaneously, the mercury vapour begins to luminesce. In the spectrum of this luminescence we observe only a single line with $\lambda =$ $= 2537$ A. Multiplying the frequency of this line by the Planck constant h, we obtain an energy of 4.87eV, which practically coincides with the critical electron energy of 4.9eV. This result should obviously be interpreted as meaning that an electron of energy 4.9eV colliding with a mercury atom excites

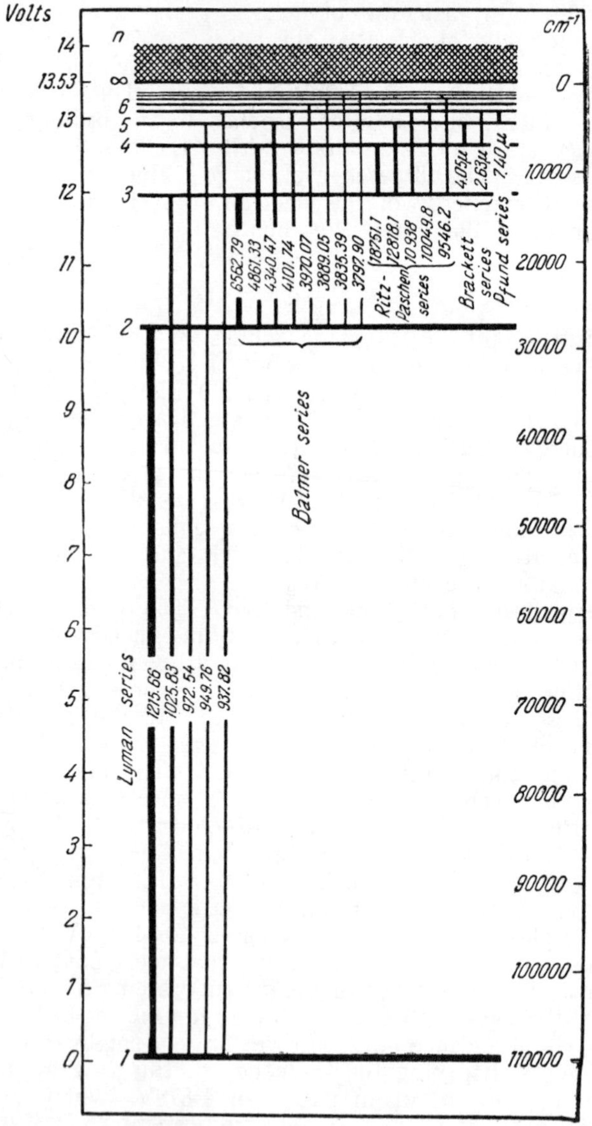

Fig. 31. Energy levels of hydrogen atom

the latter, that is, causes a transition of the atom from the ground level to an appropriate excited level. Emission of the line 2537 A is due to the reverse transition of an excited atom to the ground state. This and similar experiments conducted with various gases point to discrete energy states (levels) of atoms that coincide with the levels found from their spectra.

Spectra of alkali metals. Series regularities, like those of the hydrogen spectrum, were established also in the spectra of other elements. Thus, an analysis of the optical spectra of the alkali metals revealed the following series:

principal series: $\nu = \frac{R}{(1+s)^2} - \frac{R}{(m+p)^2}$, $m = 2, 3, \ldots,$

diffuse series: $\nu = \frac{R}{(2+p)^2} - \frac{R}{(m+d)^2}$, $m = 3, 4, \ldots,$

sharp series: $\nu = \frac{R}{(2+p)^2} - \frac{R}{(m+s)^2}$, $m = 2, 3, \ldots,$

fundamental series: $\nu = \frac{R}{(3+d)^2} - \frac{R}{(m+f)^2}$, $m = 4, 5, \ldots,$

etc. In the foregoing series formulas the quantities s, p, d, f are proper fractions and are certain parameters which have a *constant value* for each series, i.e., for definite groups of levels of the given element. Depending upon which of these parameters is used to characterise a given energy level or term, we distinguish s-, p-, d-, f-, etc., terms. On the basis of designations of terms used in spectroscopy, according to which the s-terms, or terms expressed by the formula $\frac{R}{(m+s)^2}$, are denoted by the symbol ms or mS, p-terms expressed by the formula $\frac{R}{(m+p)^2}$, by the symbol mp or mP, etc., the foregoing series formulas may be represented in the form $\nu = 1S - mP$, $\nu = 2P - mD$, $\nu = 2P - mS$ and $\nu = 3D - mF$.

Designating the parameters s, p, d, f, by the letter a, any term of an alkaline element may be represented by the general formula

$$T = \frac{R}{(m+a)^2} \tag{21.7}$$

which is called the *Rydberg formula*. In view of the correspondence between (21.7) and the Balmer formula (21.5′), which in the case of the H atom takes the form

$$T_n = \frac{R}{n^2},$$

it is advisable to express the sum $m+a$ as

$$n_{eff}=m+a=n+\delta. \tag{21.8}$$

A formula of the form (21.8) with δ independent of the number n was proposed by Rydberg. Later, Ritz derived a more precise formula in which δ is expressed by the series

$$\delta=\delta_1+\delta_2\frac{1}{n^2}+\dots \tag{21.9}$$

From experiment it follows that the quantity δ_1, called the *Rydberg correction*, is negative and exceeds, in absolute magnitude, δ_2 (*the Ritz correction*); here we have $\delta_2>0$. The quantity $\Delta=|\delta|$ is called the *quantum defect*. As may be seen from (21.7), the sequence of values of the number n:n, $n+1$, $n+2$, ... is determined by the sequence of the ordinal number m:m, $m+1$, $m+2$, ... Obviously, when a and δ are small, the numbers m and n coincide.

The values of n_{eff} (known as the *effective quantum number*) for the lower s-, p-, d-, and f-terms of the alkaline metals are given in Table 8. In the first row of this table are also given the values of the number n for the H atom. We see that in a number of cases (the d-term of lithium and the f-term of lithium and sodium) m is an integer that coincides with the corresponding number n for the hydrogen atom.

Table 8

Effective quantum numbers of the lower s-, p-, d-, and f-terms of atoms of the alkali metals

Elements \ Terms	s	p	d	f
1 H	1.000	2.000	3.000	4.000
3 Li	1.588	1.959	2.998	4.000
11 Na	1.627	2.117	2.990	3.999
19 K	1.770	2.234	2.854	3.993
37 Rb	1.805	2.289	2.767	3.988
55 Cs	1.869	2.351	2.552	3.978

From the foregoing it follows that the degree of deviation of the energy levels of the atoms of the alkaline elements from the corresponding levels of the hydrogen atom, which degree is determined by the magnitude of the correction δ, is less the higher the given level, that is, the greater the number n. Designating the hydrogen atom term characterised by the number n as $T_H=R/n^2$, we obtain, on the basis of (21.7) and (21.8),

$$\sqrt{\frac{T_H}{T}}=1-\frac{\delta}{n},$$

in other words, as n increases, T tends to T_H. This result may be interpreted as follows. As the energy of the atom increases, the mean distance of an electron from the nucleus increases and the field acting on the electron approaches ever closer to the Coulomb field of the one-electron atom H. For this reason, the system $H^+ + e$ is but slightly different, in energy, from the system $Me^+ + e$ (here, Me denotes an atom of an alkaline element).

It may be further noted that for the energy levels of ions with one outer electron, i.e., of ions Be^+, B^{++}, C^{+++}, ... or Mg^+, Al^{++}, Si^{+++}, ... we obtain the following expression:

$$E=-\frac{hRZ_a^2}{n_{eff}^2}, \tag{21.10}$$

which is similar to the expression (21.5). Here, Z_a denotes the charge of the atomic core of the ion. Everything that has been said above concerning the correspondence of the terms of atoms of alkaline elements to those of the H atom obviously also refers to the correspondence of the terms of these ions to the terms of ions with one electron (He^+, Li^{++}, etc.). The appropriate expression for the term is of the form

$$T=\frac{RZ_a^2}{n_{eff}^2}. \qquad (21\ 10')$$

On the basis of the foregoing interpretation of the difference in the terms of a multi-electron atom or ion and the terms of the H atom or of a hydrogen-like ion it may be concluded that the energy of an atom (or ion) with one outer electron is determined by the character of the electric field (acting on this electron) of the remaining portion of the atom (the atomic core). To characterise this field we introduce a certain effective charge $eZ^*=e\,(Z-z)$, where Z is the charge of the nucleus and z is a constant which may approximately be interpreted as a quantity defining the degree of screening of the nucleus by the remaining electrons (for this reason, the constant z is called the *screening constant*). Then for the term of a multi-electron atom or ion we may write, in place of expression (21.7), an equivalent expression:

$$T=\frac{R}{n^2}Z^{*2}=R\,\frac{(Z-z)^2}{n^2}. \tag{21.11}$$

According to this formula, the quantity $\sqrt{T/R}$ for various atoms and ions with one outer electron must be a linear function of the nuclear charge Z:

$$\sqrt{T/R} = \frac{1}{n}\left(Z - z\right). \quad (21.12)$$

It will be readily seen that this same linear function of Z is satisfied also by the square root of the frequency of similar lines (for instance, of lines that are the first members in the series, etc.). Indeed, considering the screening constant z for two combining levels to be approximately the same, we obtain, on the basis of (21.11),

$$\sqrt{\frac{\nu_{nm}}{R}} = \frac{\sqrt{m^2 - n^2}}{nm}(Z - z). \quad (21.13)$$

We note that this relationship expresses the so-called *Moseley law*, first established for X-ray spectra (see below).

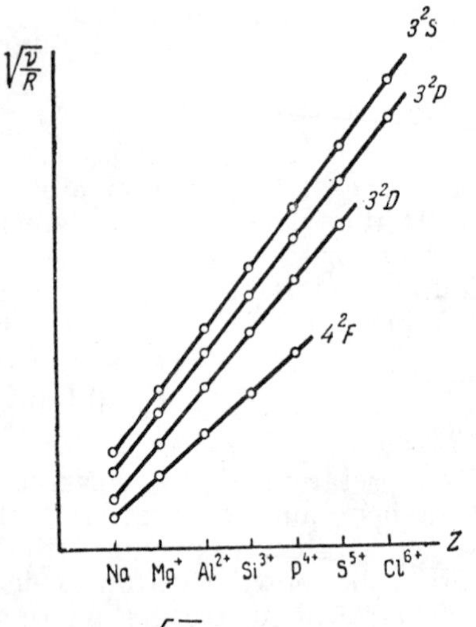

Fig. 32. $\sqrt{\frac{\nu}{R}}$ versus Z for the lower terms of Na, Mg^+, Al^{++}, etc.

Formulas (21.12) and (21.13) have been shown valid by numerous experimental findings. The regularity expressed by (21.12) for the various energy levels (terms) of the sodium atom and the ions of Mg^+, Al^{++}, etc., is shown in Fig. 32.

X-ray spectra. Investigations of X-rays emitted by different elements likewise point to definite discrete energy levels due to the shell structure of the electronic cloud of the atom. The presence of energetically different groups of electrons in the electronic clouds of atoms is prominently revealed in the absorption spectra of X-rays, to take but one instance. The continuous nature of these spectra indicates that as a result of the absorption of a quantum of X-rays an electron is ejected from the atom (photoelectric effect). Indeed, the ionisation of various substances when irradiated with X-rays is a well-known property of these rays.

The absorption coefficient of X-rays μ, which enters into the well-known formula

$$I = I_0 e^{-\mu l} \quad (21.14)$$

(I_0 and I are the intensities of the incident and transmitted rays, l is the thickness of the absorbing layer), exhibits a peculiar variation with the wavelength λ: while increasing monotonically with the wavelength, μ, at certain values characteristic of each substance $\lambda=\lambda_K$, λ_L, λ_M, ... (and $\lambda_K<\lambda_L<\lambda_M<\ldots$), diminishes discontinuously (Fig. 33). Since atoms have discrete energy groups of electrons, this is interpreted very simply as follows.

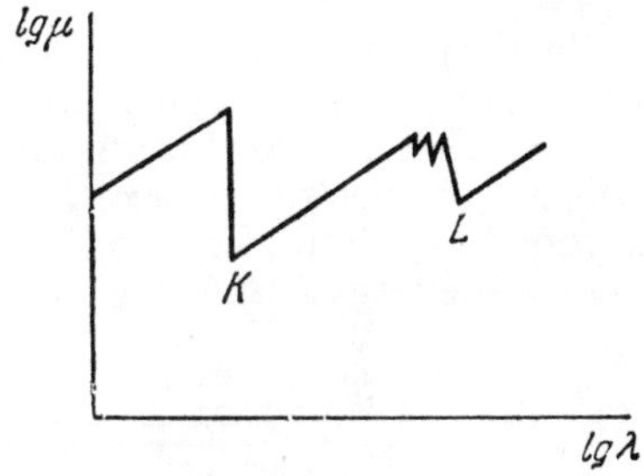

Fig. 33. Absorption coefficient of X-rays for silver as a function of wavelength

A quantum with energy $h\nu>h\nu_K$ is capable of ejecting from the atom any of its electrons, including the most strongly bound ones (K-electrons), the binding energy of which is equal to $h\nu_K$. Quanta with energy $h\nu_L<h\nu<h\nu_K$ eject from the atom any electron with the exception of K-electrons. This is explained by the sharp drop in the absorption coefficient observed near $\lambda_K=c/\nu_K$. A similar jump near $\lambda_L=c/\nu_L$ points to the existence of a group of electrons with binding energy $h\nu_L$ (L-electrons) which cannot be ejected from the atom when the energy of the quantum $h\nu$ becomes less than their binding energy, etc.

The frequencies λ_K, λ_L, λ_M, ... that correspond to the wavelengths ν_K, ν_L, ν_M, ... coincide with the limiting frequencies of the appropriate series in the spectra of the so-called *characteristic* X-rays. Like optical atomic spectra, the latter consist of separate lines that group into series K-, L-, M-, etc. The line distribution in each of these series is the same as in optical series (for instance, in the Balmer series, Fig. 30): with increasing frequency, the distance between lines diminishes regularly and the lines converge to a certain limit (the series limit). In the most shortwave region of the spectrum lies the K-series with a threshold frequency ν_K; this is followed by the L- (threshold frequency ν_L), M- (threshold frequency ν_M), etc., series.

An analysis of the characteristic X-ray spectra shows that the threshold frequencies approximately satisfy the following relationship:

$$\nu_K:\nu_L:\nu_M:\ \ldots\ =\frac{1}{1}:\frac{1}{4}:\frac{1}{9}\ \ldots,$$

which, on the basis of (21.2), may be rewritten in the form

$$-E_K : -E_L : -E_M : \ldots = \frac{1}{1^2} : \frac{1}{2^2} : \frac{1}{3^2} : \ldots,$$

whence it follows that

$$-E_n = \frac{A}{n^2}.$$

We thus obtain a scheme of energy levels that resembles the scheme of levels of the hydrogen atom (see Fig. 31). According to this scheme, excitation and the series structure of characteristic X-ray spectra are explained as follows. When one K-electron is removed from an atom (this requires the expenditure of $h\nu_K = A$ energy, and the atom passes from the K level to the

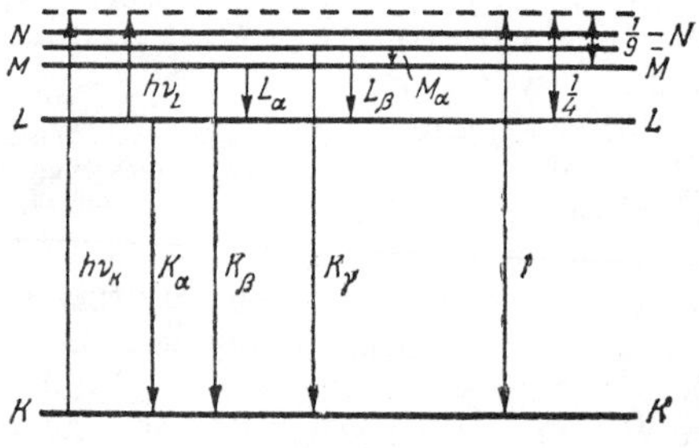

Fig. 34. Excitation mechanism of X-rays

level shown in Fig. 34 by the dashed line) the vacated place in the K-group is taken by an electron from the L-, M-, or any other group. If the transition is by an L-electron, the first and longest-wave line in the K-series is emitted, K_α; if by an M-electron, the line K_β, etc. Accordingly, when one of the L-electrons is removed from the atom, we have the transitions $M \to L$, $N \to L$, ..., which are attended by the emission of lines L_α, L_β, ... (L-series), etc., as shown in Fig. 34.

According to this scheme, the frequency of the K_α line should be expressed by the formula

$$\nu = \frac{A}{h}\left(\frac{1}{1^2} - \frac{1}{2^2}\right) = \frac{3}{4}\frac{A}{h}.$$

The value of A may be obtained from the following data. Moseley (1913) showed that there is a linear relationship between the square root of the frequency of definite lines of the characteristic X-ray spectra of various elements (for instance, the lines K_α or L_α, etc.) and their atomic number Z (cf. (21.13)).

In the particular case of K_α lines, this relation is given by the following approximate expression:

$$\sqrt{\frac{\nu}{R}}=\sqrt{\frac{3}{4}}(Z-1)$$

where R is a quantity that coincides with the Rydberg constant. Comparing these latter two expressions, we find $A=hR(z-1)^2$ and, consequently,

$$E_n=-\frac{hR(Z-1)^2}{n^2} \quad \text{or} \quad T_n=\frac{R(Z-1)^2}{n^2}, \quad n=1, 2. \quad (21.15)$$

Equation (21.15) turns out to be identical with (21.11), if in the latter we put $z=1$. On the basis of the physical meaning of the screening constant z this result may be interpreted as follows. As we saw when considering the ionisation potentials of various elements, the group of most firmly bound electrons, which we should obviously identify with the K-group, contains *two* electrons. For this reason, the L-electron (the transition of which to the K-level is associated with the emission of the K_α line) is acted upon by the nuclear charge Ze screened by only one electron, i.e., the charge $(Z-1)e$; this finds expression in (21.15).

From the foregoing discussion it may be seen that atoms of various elements are built up on the same principle. Its characteristic features are as follows. All atomic electrons are distributed into discrete energy groups. The energy of the electrons of each group is determined by the number n which represents the number of the group. The most firmly bound electrons and, consequently, those closest to the nucleus form the two-electron K-group ($n=1$). This is followed by the L-group ($n=2$), which contains a maximum of eight electrons, the M-group ($n=3$) with a maximum of 18 electrons, etc. The groups K, L, and M are gradually filled up as the nuclear charge increases beginning with the H atom, which in the ground state has one K-electron. However, as has already been pointed out (Sec. 20), there are a number of places in the Periodic Table where the regularity of filling of electron groups breaks down.

22. Mechanical Model of the Atom

Bohr-Sommerfeld theory. The facts which we have reviewed above and the concepts about the structure of the electronic cloud of the atom that follow from them are evidence of the complexity of atoms. The problem of atomic structure has been on the agenda since Mendeleyev, in 1869, discovered the periodic law of the chemical elements. Out of the chaos caused by the indeterminateness of the number of diverse and independent chemical elements there emerged an orderly system of elements that reflected their dialectical unity, the underlying factor of which was the unified structure of the atoms of all elements made up of electrons and nuclei. The progress of nuclear physics that followed the discovery of radioactivity (Becquerel, 1896) yielded irrefutable evidence of the interconvertibility of the elements, thus establishing a genetic interconnection of the elements and their mutual kinship.

The experiments of Rutherford (1911) on the scattering of alpha particles by a variety of elements that led to the discovery of the atomic nucleus (see Secs. 8 and 9) served as the starting point for the construction of a modern theory of the atom. Rutherford arrived at a planetary model of the atom, in which electrons revolve about a heavy nucleus like planets round the sun. The planetary model of the atom served as the basis for Bohr's theory of the hydrogen atom (1913), which was the first quantitative theory of the atom.

The hydrogen atom, which consists of a nucleus (proton) and only one electron, was naturally the first object of theoretical investigation. Yet even here the theory encountered difficulties that could not be surmounted by classical physics alone. One of the stumbling blocks was that an electron revolving about a nucleus and, consequently, experiencing acceleration should, on classical electrodynamics, be continually radiating energy and should ultimately and inevitably fall onto the nucleus.

The only way to surmount this difficulty was to give up classical electrodynamics and consider it inapplicable to processes occurring inside the atom. Reasoning from this fact, Bohr postulated the existence of stable electron orbits in the atom, and suggested that orbital motion was not attended by the radiation of energy.

From the viewpoint of the planetary model, the mechanical problem of the motion of electrons in an atom is identical with that of the motion of celestial bodies in a planetary system. The identity of these two problems is evident from the fact that both in atomic physics and in astronomy one deals with central forces that obey the inverse square law (the laws of Coulomb and Newton). And so the entire mathematical apparatus of classical mechanics that had been worked out in connection with astronomical problems could be applied directly to solving the atomic problem.

The latter reduces to the well-known problem of celestial mechanics concerning the motion of so-called multiply periodical point systems, which have the distinguishing feature that their motion may be decomposed into simple periodical components. Given N degrees of freedom, the state of motion of such systems is described by means of N generalised coordinates q_i and N generalised momenta p_i $(i = 1, 2, 3, \ldots, N)$, the latter being defined as partial derivatives of the kinetic energy of the system K with respect to the corresponding generalised velocities $\dot{q}_i = \frac{dq_i}{dt}$, or

$$p_i = \frac{\partial K}{\partial \dot{q}_i}. \tag{22.1}$$

The total energy of the system E, which, in the general case, is a function of the coordinates and the momenta, $H(q, p) = E$ (Hamiltonian function), satisfies the following 2N differential equations:

$$\dot{q}_i = \frac{\partial H}{\partial p_i} \quad \text{and} \quad \dot{p}_i = -\frac{\partial H}{\partial q_i}. \tag{22.2}$$

The characteristic property of these equations, called *Hamiltonian*, or *canonical*, is their *invariance* to any transformation of coordinates. Integration of equations (22.2) yields the solution to the mechanical problem.

Proceeding from the invariance of the canonical equations, it is frequently possible to find a coordinate system in which the Hamiltonian function (the energy of the system) is independent of the coordinates (or of part of the coordinates). Designating such coordinates (called angular, or cyclical) by w_i and their corresponding momenta by I_i, we will obviously have here, in place of equations (22.2), equations of the form

$$\dot{w}_i = \text{const} = \omega_i \quad \text{and} \quad \dot{I}_i = 0,$$

from which we straightway find the integrals of motion

$$w_i = \omega_i t + \delta_i \quad \text{and} \quad I_i = \text{const}. \tag{22.3}$$

We will not dwell on the methods of obtaining canonical equations in the new coordinate system (of transformation to cyclic coordinates), but will only point out that the condition for such transformation (from coordinates and momenta q, p to w, I) is fulfilment of the equalities

$$I_i = \oint p_i dq_i \tag{22.4}$$

where the integration is extended to the entire region of variation of the coordinate q_i.

Classical mechanics does not impose any special conditions on the integrals I_i (called *phase integrals*), as a result of which the problem of the atom as considered within the framework of classical theory remains indeterminate. For one thing, we are not able to calculate the energy of the atom in its various energy states. Bohr eliminated this indeterminateness by subjecting the phase integrals to definite *quantum conditions* which reflect experimentally known (Sec. 21) quantised energy states of atoms. According to Bohr, these quantum conditions are expressed by the following equalities:

$$I_i = \oint p_i dq_i = n_i h \tag{22.5}$$

where n_i are integral numbers, so-called *quantum numbers*.*

Atom (ion) with one electron. Considering an atom with one electron and a nuclear charge Ze (besides the H atom, these include the ions He^+, Li^{++}, Be^{+++}, etc.), we have, in the simplest case of circular orbits,

$$K = \frac{J\dot{\varphi}^2}{2}$$

where $J = \frac{mM}{m+M} r^2$ is the moment of inertia of the atom (m and M are the mass of the electron and the nucleus, respectively) and $\dot{\varphi}$ is the angular velocity of rotation of the electron and the nucleus (separated by a distance r) about their common centre of gravity. Computing the momentum $p = \frac{\partial K}{\partial \dot{\varphi}} = J\dot{\varphi}$, we find from the condition (22.5) **

$$\int_0^{2\pi} p\,d\varphi = 2\pi J\dot{\varphi} = n_\varphi h = nh$$

or

$$p = J\dot{\varphi} = \hbar n_\varphi = \hbar n. \tag{22.6}$$

From the quantum condition (22.6) and the condition of dynamic equilibrium expressed by the equality of centrifugal force and the force of Coulomb attraction of the nucleus and the electron,

$$\frac{J\dot{\varphi}^2}{r} = \frac{e^2 Z}{r^2}, \tag{22.7}$$

---

* It will be readily seen that the phase integrals I have the same dimensions as the Planck constant h, the dimensions of action: energy multiplied by time.

** It will be noted that the equality $J\dot{\varphi} = \text{const}$ expresses the Kepler law of areas.

we obtain two equations for the two unknowns r and $\dot{\varphi}$. The solution of these equations gives expressions for the radius of steady-state orbits and for the linear velocity of the electron:

$$r = r_n = \frac{h^2}{4\pi^2 e^2} \frac{m+M}{mM} \frac{1}{Z} n^2 \tag{22.8}$$

and

$$v_n = \frac{M}{m+M} r\dot{\varphi} = \frac{4\pi e^2}{h} \frac{M}{m+M} Z \frac{1}{n}. \tag{22.9}$$

Substituting here the numerical values, we get, for the radius (minimum) of a one-quantum (n = 1) Bohr orbit of the H atom (Z = 1), the value

$$r_1 = 0.529 \text{ A},$$

and for the maximum velocity of the electron* in the H atom

$$v_1 = 2.19 \times 10^8 \text{ cm/sec}.$$

Further, since $2K = -V = \frac{e^2 Z}{r}$ (see (22.7)), we obtain $E = \frac{V}{2} = -\frac{e^2 Z}{2r}$ for the total energy of the atom $E = K + V$, whence, on the basis of (22.8), we find

$$E_n = -\frac{2\pi^2 e^4}{h^2} \frac{mM}{m+M} \frac{Z^2}{n^2} = \frac{hRZ^2}{n^2} \tag{22.10}$$

where

$$R = \frac{2\pi^2 e^4}{h^3} \frac{mM}{m+M}. \tag{22.11}$$

The value of R computed from (22.11) coincides, with great accuracy, with the experimentally obtained value of the Rydberg constant. Thus, the theoretical expression for the energy of an atom with one electron (22.10) is in quantitative agreement with experiment (cf. formulas (21.3) and (21.5)). It may also be noted that (22.11) precisely conveys the experimentally observed dependence of the Rydberg constant on the mass of the nucleus (see p. 136).

The motion of electrons in circular orbits is obviously a special case of the motion of a particle in a field of central forces. The general solution of this problem leads to elliptical orbits. As applied to the atom, this problem was solved by Sommerfeld (1916).

Here, the system (atom) has two degrees of freedom and its kinetic energy is a function of $\dot{\varphi} = \frac{d\varphi}{dt}$ and of $\dot{r} = \frac{dr}{dt}$. According-

* The angular velocity of an electron in the ground state of the H atom is $\dot{\varphi}_1/2\pi = \omega_1 = 6.6 \times 10^{15}$ revolutions per second.

ly, we have two quantum conditions (22.5) and *two* quantum numbers: *azimuthal*, n_φ, and *radial*, n_r. The number n, equal to the sum $n_\varphi + n_r$, is called the *principal quantum number*.

The eccentricity of the electron orbit ε is determined by the relationship between n_φ and n:

$$\varepsilon = \sqrt{1 - \left(\frac{n_\varphi}{n}\right)^2}. \quad (22.12)$$

Circular orbits are obtained in the special case $n_\varphi = n$, i. e., $n_r = 0$.

The atomic energy is expressed by the equation

$$E = -\frac{e^2 Z}{2a}$$

where a is the semi-major axis of the ellipse equal to

$$a = \frac{\hbar^2}{me^2} \frac{1}{Z} n^2. \quad (22.13)$$

Substituting a (22.13) into the expression for energy, we obtain the same equation (22.10) as is the case of circular orbits. Con-

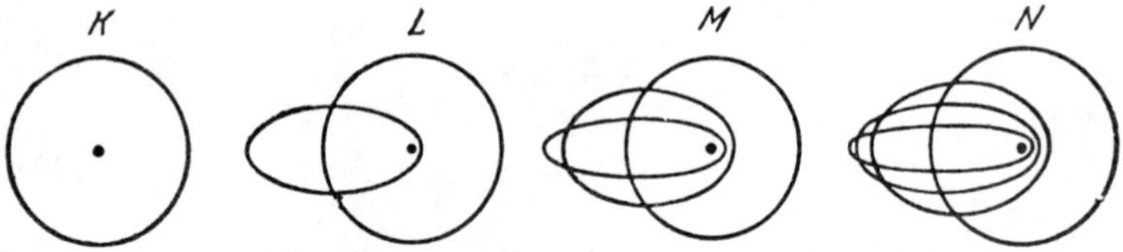

Fig. 35. Bohr-Sommerfeld orbits of hydrogen-like atom

sequently, for a given value of the principal quantum number n the energy of an atom (ion) is independent of the shape of the orbit.

The assemblage of orbits of a hydrogen-like atom for n = 1, 2, 3, and 4 (states K, L, M, and N) is given in Fig. 35.* We see that when n = 1 (K) there is only one (circular) orbit in accordance with the fact that the condition n = 1 is fulfilled only in the case of a single definite value of each of the quantum numbers n_φ and n_r, namely, $n_\varphi = 1$ and $n_r = 0$, since the value $n_\varphi = 0$ should obviously be excluded in all cases. Indeed, when $n_\varphi = 0$ we obtain from (22.12) an eccentricity of the orbit equal to 1, as a result of which the semi-minor axis tends to zero. When n = 2 (L) there are two orbits, circular and ellipti-

* The value of a in this figure is the same for all orbits. Actually, according to (22.13), a increases with n as n^2.

cal, in accordance with two pairs of values of the numbers n_φ and n_r: 2,0 and 1,1, etc. In the general case the given value of n of the principal quantum number is obtained by means of n different combinations of numbers n_φ and n_r: $n_\varphi = 1, 2, 3, \ldots, n$ and $n_r = 0, 1, 2, \ldots, (n-1)$. Thus, for each given value of n we have n different states of the atom with identical energy, i.e., they are indistinguishable with respect to energy. Such states are called *degenerate*. Let it be noted that in quantum statistics an elevated statistical weight * is attributed to degenerate states.

However, investigation of the structure of hydrogen lines by means of instruments with high resolution shows that in reality there is a slight splitting of the "degenerate" levels. Hence, degeneracy of the levels of a hydrogen atom (as also the levels of the ions He^+, Li^{++}, etc.) is only *apparent* and these levels, due to the slight degree of their splitting, may be regarded as practically degenerate.

The feeble level splitting (removal of degeneracy) is also obtained in the case of a more precise solution of the mechanical problem of the atom with one electron if we take into account the dependence of the mass of the electron on its velocity (Sommerfeld, 1916). In this case (relativistic problem), in place of (22.10) for the energy of the atom (ion) we obtain the following approximate expression:

$$E_{n,\, n_\varphi} = -\frac{hRZ^2}{n^2} - \frac{h\alpha^2 RZ^4}{n^4}\left(\frac{n}{n_\varphi} - \frac{3}{4}\right) \tag{22.14}$$

$\left(\alpha = \frac{2\pi e^2}{hc}\right.$, c is the velocity of $\left.\text{light}\right)$, the first term of which coincides with (22.10), and the second gives a slight correction. For the ground level of the H atom ($n = n_\varphi = 1$), this correction amounts to about 0.001% and diminishes rapidly as the principal quantum number increases. Although the correction is small (because the speed of the electron in the atom is less than 1% of the speed of light), the essential thing is that the energy of the atom is now a function not only of the number n, but also of the number n_φ. Therefore, states with the same n but with different n_φ will differ somewhat in energy, which is what signifies splitting of a "degenerate" level (into n components).

We also point out that in the relativistic theory of the atom the electronic orbits are no longer closed, but take the shape of a rosette (Fig. 36). In this case, the motion of an electron may be pictured as motion in a closed flat orbit that precesses

* The statistical weight is an a priori probability of state. The same statistical weight of various states indicates, for one thing, that these states are encountered with the same frequency undeı identical conditions.

with a certain angular velocity. However, since the angular velocity of precession is such that during one circuit of the electron around the nucleus the orbital axis turns through an angle $\Delta\varphi$ (Fig. 36), which does not exceed 0.01, the electron orbits of the hydrogen atom may be considered closed — to the approximation to which one can speak of n-degeneracy of the energy levels of the H atom.

Due to the smallness of the correction term in (22.14), the latter may be rewritten in the form

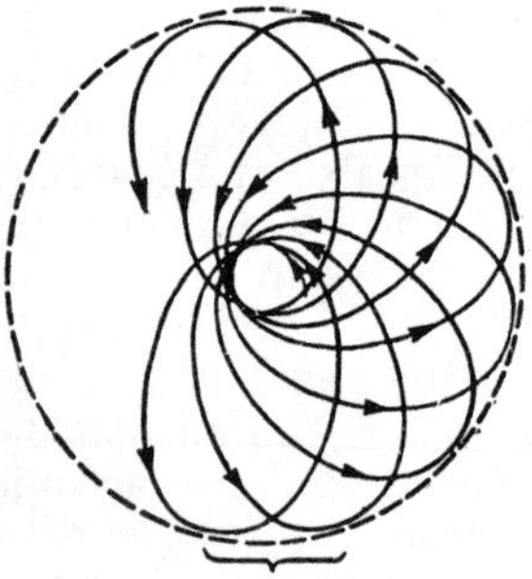

Fig. 36. Orbital precession (Sommerfeld rosette)

$$E_{n,\,n_\varphi} = -\frac{hRZ^2}{[n - f(n,\,n_\varphi)]^2} = -\frac{hRZ^2}{n^{*2}} \qquad (22.15)$$

where

$$f(n,\,n_\varphi) = \frac{\alpha^2 h^2}{2}\left(\frac{1}{n_\varphi} - \frac{3}{4}\right) \text{ and } n^* = n - f(n,\,n_\varphi).$$

In this form, the expression for the energy of an atom (or ion) with one electron is somewhat similar to the Rydberg formula (21.10) for the energy of atoms of the alkaline elements or of corresponding ions with one extra electron.

Positronium. Mesonic atoms. In connection with an atom (ion) with one electron we shall discuss briefly atoms of a peculiar sort discovered in nuclear physics, namely, *positronium* and *mesonic atoms*. Positronium appears when positrons are slowed down in a substance by interaction with electrons; it represents a system consisting of an electron and a positron that revolve about a common centre of gravity, and is very similar to the hydrogen atom. Using the formulas derived above for the H atom, it is possible to calculate the various constants of positronium. For example, in view of the equality of mass of the positron and electron, from equation (22.8) it follows that the orbital radii of positronium should exceed by a factor of two the corresponding orbital radii of the H atom. For instance, in the ground state of positronium ($n=1$) the orbital radius is approximately 1 A. Accordingly, the energy of dissociation of positronium into a positron and an electron comes out to one half the ionisation potential of the H atom.

Further, depending on the mutual orientation of the spins of the positron and the electron positronium can exist in two states (Fig. 45, p. 209): orthopositronium, in which the spins of the particles are parallel and which has a mean lifetime $\tau = 1.4 \times 10^{-7}$ sec, converting into *three* γ-photons,* and parapositronium with antiparallel spins and a lifetime of 1.25×10^{-10} sec, converting to *two* photons. The ground level of orthopositronium (*triplet* state) lies above the ground level of parapositronium (*singlet* state) by only 0.84×10^{-3} eV. Since for a number of molecules with an odd number of electrons (for instance, NO) the distance between levels with different orientation of spin is small (in NO this distance is 13.6×10^{-3} eV), an ortho $\longrightarrow$ para transition (by collision of positronium with such molecules) is already possible at room temperature:

$$\text{orthopositronium} + \text{NO}\,(^2\Pi_{1/2}) = \text{parapositronium} + \text{NO}\,(^2\Pi_{3/2}).$$

Due to a great difference in the lifetime (which is inversely proportional to the probability of annihilation) of the ortho- and parastates of positronium, the ortho $\longrightarrow$ para process leads to an acceleration of annihilation. Observation of this effect was what led to the experimental discovery of positronium (Deutsch, 1951).

Another special type of atom are the mesonic atoms. The hypothesis expressed as early as 1940 (Tomonaga and Araki that negative mesons, prior to their capture by the nucleus or prior to their spontaneous decay, can continue revolving about the nucleus for some time thus forming a mesonic atom, was subsequently corroborated experimentally. It was found that mesons interacting with a substance gave rise to γ-radiation associated with the transition 2P — 1S in the mesonic atom and with energy of the order of several MeV. It was demonstrated that there exist both μ-mesonic atoms (μ^--meson revolving round a nucleus) and π-mesonic atoms (π^--meson) with different lifetimes.

In contrast to positronium, the radii of the meson orbits in mesonic atoms turn out considerably less than the radii of electron orbits. Indeed, due to the fact that the meson mass is 200-300 times (see p. 83) that of the electron, the radii of the meson orbits must be the same number of times less than the radii of the electron orbits, as follows from (22.8). Therefore, electrons in orbits far from the nucleus should not exert a perceptible effect on the mesons in mesonic atoms.

Computing, from (22.8), the radius of the meson orbit closest to the nucleus, i.e., the quantity $r = \frac{m_e}{m_\mu} r_1 \frac{1}{Z}$ (m_e and m_μ are the masses of the electron and meson, respectively), we obtain

* Decay into three photons is due to the law of conservation of momentum since the spin of the photon is equal to $\hbar$.

for various nuclei (at $Z=1$) radii equal to 2.5×10^{-11} cm (μ-mesonic atom) and 2.0×10^{-11} cm (π-mesonic atom) * and (at $Z=30$) 8.3×10^{-13} cm and 6.5×10^{-13} cm, respectively, and (at $Z=100$) 2.5×10^{-13} cm and 2.0×10^{-13} cm, respectively. Comparing these numbers with the nuclear radii computed from (9.5) (p. 43): 2×10^{-13} cm for $Z=1$, 6.2×10^{-13} cm for $Z=30$, and 9.3×10^{-13} cm for $Z=100$, we see that the meson not only revolves at close distances from the nucleus, as is the case of light nuclei, but already in the case of nuclei with $Z=30$ (and more) it should penetrate the nucleus.

Due to the closeness of the meson orbits to the nucleus (to say nothing of penetration into the nucleus) the dimensions of the nucleus and its structure, which can no longer be regarded as a point charge, affect the mesonic atom levels. As a result, there are changes in the order of the levels of the mesonic atom. For instance, unlike the H atom, the 2S-level in μ-mesonic antimony ($Z=51$) lies above the 2P-level, while the 3S-level is above 3P and 3D. It is also necessary to take into account interaction between the meson and the nucleons of the nucleus. From what has been said it is clear that the study of mesonic atoms is very important for an understanding of the structure of nuclei and particle interaction and also for investigations into the mesons themselves.

Atoms of the alkaline elements. As has already been pointed out above (p. 141), the experimentally observed close or complete coincidence of the high terms of atoms of alkaline elements with the corresponding hydrogen terms may be associated with the fact that in the former the electric field of the atomic core differs but slightly from the field of a point charge. In this case, obviously, the orbit of the outer electron is situated entirely outside the atomic core (*non-penetrating orbits*): due to the considerable distance from it of the outer electron, interaction of the latter with the inner electrons may be regarded as a slight perturbation superimposed on the Coulomb attraction of the outer electron by the atomic core.

This perturbation may be accounted for by expanding the potential energy V of the outer electron in the atom of an alkaline element in a power series of the small quantity r_1/r, where r is the distance of the outer electron from the nucleus, while r_1 is the radius of a one-quantum Bohr orbit of the H atom:

$$V(r) = -\frac{e^2Z_a}{r}\left[1 + c_1\left(\frac{r_1}{r}\right) + c_2\left(\frac{r_1}{r}\right)^2 + c_3\left(\frac{r_1}{r}\right)^3 + \dots\right]$$

* These figures are obtained for the following values of meson mass: $m_\mu = 207\, m_e$ (μ-meson) and $m_\pi = 273\, m_e$ (π-meson).

where c_1, c_2, etc., are constants determined by the nature of the distortion (perturbation) of the Coulomb field of the nucleus. Here, for generality, we have introduced the charge of the atomic core Z_a, which is equal to 1 in the case of alkaline elements. Summing V (r) and the kinetic energy of the electron

$$K=\frac{\mu}{2}(\dot{r}^2+r^2\dot{\varphi}^2)$$

$\left(\text{here, } \mu=\frac{mM}{m+M} \text{ is the reduced mass}\right)$, which energy, due to $p_r=\mu\dot{r}$ and $p_\varphi=\mu r^2\dot{\varphi}=p$, may be rewritten in the form

$$K=\frac{1}{2\mu}\left(p_r^2+\frac{p^2}{r^2}\right),$$

we obtain the total energy

$$E=\frac{1}{2\mu}\left(p_r^2+\frac{p^2}{r^2}\right)-\frac{e^2Z_a}{r}-\Delta V$$

where

$$\Delta V=\frac{e^2Z_a}{r}\left[c_1\left(\frac{r_1}{r}\right)+c_2\left(\frac{r_1}{r}\right)^2+\ldots\right].$$

From the expression obtained for the total energy E, we find the radial momentum

$$p_r=\sqrt{2\mu\left(E+\frac{e^2Z_a}{r}+\Delta V\right)-\frac{p^2}{r^2}},$$

and further, according to the Bohr quantum condition $\oint p_r dr=n_r h$,

$$\oint\sqrt{2\mu\left(E+\frac{e^2Z_a}{r}+\Delta V\right)-\frac{p^2}{r^2}}\,dr=n_r h=(n-n_\varphi)\,h.$$

From this integral (omitting all intermediate operations) we obtain the energy of the atom in the form of the following series:

$$E=-\frac{hRZ_a^2}{n_{eff}^2}=-\frac{hRZ_a^2}{n^2}\left(1+\frac{2Z_a c_1}{nn_\varphi}+\frac{2Z_a^2c_2}{nn_\varphi^3}+\frac{Z_a^3\left(3-\frac{n_\varphi^2}{n^2}\right)c^3}{nn_\varphi^5}+\ldots\right).\qquad(22.16)$$

Disregarding terms containing the product of small quantities c_i, from expression (22.16) and in complete agreement with the empirical relationship of Ritz (21.9), we find

$$n_{eff}=n-\frac{Z_a c_1}{n_\varphi}-\frac{Z_a^2 c_2}{n_\varphi^3}+Z_a^3 c_3\left(-\frac{3}{2n_\varphi^5}+\frac{1}{2n^2 n_\varphi^3}\right)+\ldots=$$
$$=n+\delta_1+\frac{\delta_2}{n^2}+\ldots,$$

where the Rydberg correction

$$\delta_1=-\left(\frac{Z_a c_1}{n_\varphi}+\frac{Z_a^2 c_2}{n_\varphi^3}+\frac{3Z_a^3 c_3}{2n_\varphi^5}+\ldots\right) \quad (22.17)$$

and the Ritz correction

$$\delta_2=\frac{Z_a^3 c_3}{2n_\varphi^3}+\ldots \quad (22.18)$$

In these expressions, for the corrections δ_1 and δ_2, as also in the expression for the energy of an atom (22.16), the constants c_i remain indeterminate. In the Born and Heisenberg theory (1924), this indeterminateness is eliminated in the following manner. The motion of the outer electron is regarded as motion of an atomic core in a Coulomb field perturbed by the field of a *dipole* that is due to polarisation of the atomic core (Me^+ ion) in the field of the outer electron.

Introducing the polarisation coefficient α, defined as the dipole moment induced by a field, the intensity of which is equal to unity, and considering the field of the electron $\mathscr{E}=\frac{e}{r^2}$ uniform throughout the extent of the atomic core, we obtain $\mathfrak{r}=\alpha\mathscr{E}=\frac{\alpha e}{r^2}$ for the induced dipole moment $\mathfrak{r}$. This dipole acts on the electron with a force $F=\frac{2\mathfrak{r}e}{r^3}=\frac{2\alpha e^2}{r^5}$, whence for the additional potential energy of the electron we find

$$\Delta V=-\frac{\alpha}{2}\frac{e^2}{r^4}.$$

In the expression for the additional potential energy of the electron ΔV we can therefore disregard all terms, with the exception of the term with the coefficient c_3. Comparing this term, equal to $-\frac{e^2 Z_a}{r}\left(\frac{r_1}{r}\right)^3 c_3$ with the expression obtained for ΔV, we find $c_3=\frac{\alpha}{2Z_a r_1^3}$. Substituting this value of c_3 (together with $c_1=c_2=c_4=\ldots=0$) into equations (22.17) and (22.18), we obtain the following expressions for the corrections δ_1 and δ_2:

$$\delta_1 = -\frac{3}{4}\frac{\alpha Z_a^2}{r_1^3}\frac{1}{n_\varphi^5} \qquad (22.19)$$

and

$$\delta_2 = \frac{\alpha Z_a^2}{4r_1^3}\frac{1}{n_\varphi^3}, \qquad (22.20)$$

from which it follows, for the quantum defect Δ, that

$$\Delta = \frac{3}{4}\frac{\alpha Z_a^2}{r_1^3}\frac{1-\frac{n_\varphi^2}{3n^2}}{n_\varphi^5}. \qquad (22.21)$$

It should be noted that according to (22.19) and (22.20) both corrections have different signs, and in accordance with experiment the Ritz correction $\delta_2 > 0$. Further, since $n_\varphi \leqslant n$ it follows from these equations that $\frac{|\delta_1|}{\delta_2/n_2} \geqslant 3$, i.e., that a greater role is played by the Rydberg correction (again in agreement with experiment).

Calculations of the quantum defect Δ, on the basis of (22.21) and also by means of the more precise formula (24.17) obtained from a solution of the quantum-mechanical problem of an atom with one outer electron (sec. 24), reveal (as was to be expected) satisfactory agreement with experiment only in the case of circular orbits, for which the quantum defect is small (see (22.21)) due to large values of $n_\varphi = n$.

The reason for the quantitative nonagreement of theory and experiment in the case of elliptical orbits lies in the penetration of these orbits into the atomic core (*penetrating orbits*), as a result of which the principal premise of the Born-Heisenberg theory concerning the large distance of the outer electron from the other electrons of the atom no longer holds. By way of illustration let us examine the orbit of a sodium atom characterised by the quantum numbers $n=3$ and $n_\varphi=1$.* Using the formulas of the one-electron problem and evaluating, for this orbit, the minimum distance of the electron from the nucleus $r_{min} = a(1-\varepsilon)$, where a is the semi-major axis of the ellipse and ε is its eccentricity, we find $r_{min} = 0.27$ A due to the fact that $a = 0.53 \times 3^2$ A $= 4.75$ A and $\varepsilon = \sqrt{8/3} = 0.943$. On the other hand, equating the radius of the sodium atomic core to the radius of the ion Na^+, we get

* As we shall see below (p. 183), this orbit corresponds to the lower s-term of the Na atom, i.e., to the ground state of the atom.

$r_a = 0.95$ A. We thus see that a sodium electron moving in the orbit under consideration must penetrate the atomic core to more than 2/3 of its radius.

The atomic problem that takes into account orbital penetration of the outer electron into the atomic core is solved as follows. The orbit is taken to consist of two parts (outer and inner, which is situated inside the atomic core); in the outer portion of the orbit the electron experiences the action of a point charge eZ_a (in the case of a neutral atom $Z_a = 1$), in the inner portion, the action of a certain effective (also point) charge eZ_i, which may be sufficiently large due to a reduction in the screening effect of the inner electrons (Fig. 37).

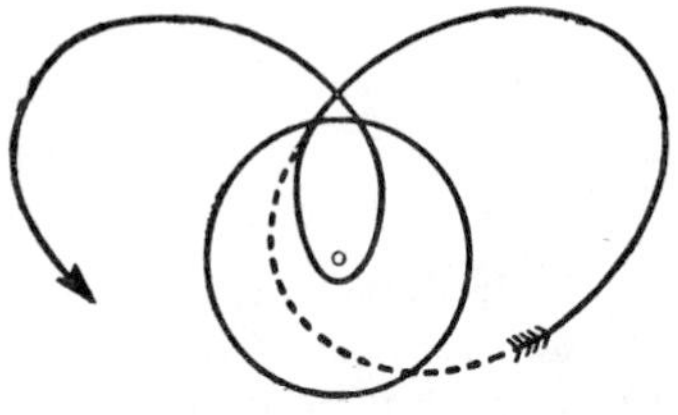

Fig. 37. Penetrating orbit

Underlying quantitative evaluations of atomic terms for the case of penetrating orbits is the following model of the atomic core proposed by Schrödinger (1921) and generalised by Wentzel (1923). According to the latter, the atomic core is a series of concentric charged spheres, each of which possesses a definite surface charge. The charge acting on the electron (Z_i) depends on the depth of penetration of the orbit into the atomic core. The simplest solution of the problem is for the case of the so-called completely penetrating orbits (Fig. 37), which may be regarded as consistin of two ellipses (dashed line in Fig. 37): one entirely inside the atomic core, the other, the outer ellipse. For each ellipse we can introduce its radial quantum numbers n_{ri} and n_{ra} and, accordingly, the principal quantum numbers n_i and n_a, which are equal to $n_i = n_{ri} + n_\varphi$ and $n_a = n_{ra} + n_\varphi$ (since the angular momentum p is conserved, the number n_φ is the same for both ellipses). Further, due to the fact that the inner ellipse is totally inside the atomic core, the energy of the outer electron will be equal to its energy in the outer orbit, i.e., to the quantity

$$E = -\frac{hRZ_a^2}{n_a^2} = -\frac{hRZ_a^2}{n_{eff}^2}. \tag{22.22}$$

Summing the numbers n_i and n_a and noting that the true principal quantum number of the penetrating orbit $n = n_r + n_\varphi = n_{ri} + n_{ra} + n_\varphi$, we obtain $n_{eff} = n_a = n + n_\varphi - n_i$, i.e.,

$$\Delta = n - n_{eff} = n_i - n_\varphi. \tag{22.23}$$

Denoting the semi-major axis of the inner ellipse by a, we have

$$a=\frac{r_1}{Z_i}n_i^2,$$

and, further, due to the fact that the maximum distance of the electron from the nucleus in the inner ellipse should equal the radius of the atomic core r_a, we have

$$a(1+\varepsilon)=r_a.$$

Eliminating from the two latter equalities the quantity a and recalling that

$$\varepsilon=\sqrt{1-\frac{n_\varphi^2}{n_i^2}},$$

we obtain the following approximate equation for the quantum defect $\Delta=|\delta|$

$$\Delta=\frac{\frac{r_a}{r_1}Z_i}{\sqrt{2\frac{r_a}{r_1}Z_i-n_\varphi^2}}-n_\varphi. \tag{22.24}$$

It will readily be seen that expression (22.24), like (22.21), decreases with increasing n_φ. Indeed, having in view the terms that are characterised by the values $n_\varphi=1$ and 2, and noting that the quantity Z_i, like r_a/r_1 is noticeably greater than unity, we can expand in a series the radical in (22.24) and, differentiating with respect to n_φ, we find that $\frac{d\Delta}{dn_\varphi}<0$.

The values Δ for the s-terms as computed from the rather more precise formula (24.19) derived from (22.24), are found to be in good agreement with experiment (see p. 184). From this it follows that we are here dealing with practically completely penetrating orbits. Worse agreement, with experiment, of the computed values of the quantum defect for the p-terms may be regarded as an indication that in this case the electron orbits are no longer completely penetrating.

As was pointed out above (p. 151), feeble splitting of the hydrogen terms is in agreement with the fact that the olectron orbits of the H atom are practically closed. For this reason, it is natural to expect that in the atoms of the alkaline elements, where splitting is great, the electrons will be revolving about the nucleus in orbits of clearcut rosette-like shape. This conclusion is confirmed by calculation of the angular velocity of precession of the orbits. This calculation may be carried out on the basis of the approximate theory of Born and Heisenberg. Let us find the equation of the electron orbit (equation of the trajectory) in an atom of an alkaline element. Computing the azimuthal momentum and radial momentum from formula (22.1),

$$p_\varphi = p = mr^2\varphi \quad \text{and} \quad p_r = mr$$

and, further,

$$\frac{p_r}{p} = \frac{1}{r^2}\frac{dr}{d\varphi} = -\frac{ds}{d\varphi}$$

where $s = \frac{1}{r}$, we rewrite the expression for energy E in the form

$$E = \frac{p^2}{2m}\left[\left(\frac{ds}{d\varphi}\right)^2 + s^2\right] - e^2Z_a s - \frac{\alpha e^2}{2} s^4.$$

Differentiating the latter expression with respect to φ, we find

$$\frac{d^2s}{d\varphi^2} = \frac{me^2Z_a}{p^2} - s\left(1 - \frac{2me^2\alpha}{p^2} s^2\right). \tag{22.25}$$

This equation, which is the sought-for equation of the trajectory of the electron, is not integrated in final form. However, taking into account the approximate nature of the initial expression for E, it is possible to simplify equation (22.25) by replacing the quantity s^2 in the brackets with its mean value, which may be obtained from

$$\overline{s^2} = \overline{\frac{1}{r^2}} = \frac{1}{\tau}\int_0^\tau \frac{1}{r^2}\,dt.$$

On the basis of the Kepler law of areas $\frac{1}{2} r^2 \frac{d\varphi}{dt} = \frac{\pi ab}{\tau}$ and, consequently, $\frac{1}{\tau}\frac{1}{r^2}dt = \frac{d\varphi}{2\pi ab}$ so that

$$\overline{s^2} = \frac{1}{2\pi ab}\int_0^{2\pi} d\varphi = \frac{1}{ab}. \tag{22.26}$$

Substituting $\overline{s^2}$ into equation (22.25) in place of s^2, we get

$$\frac{d^2s}{d\varphi^2} = \frac{me^2Z_a}{p^2} - \left(1 - \frac{2me^2\alpha}{abp^2}\right) s. \tag{22.27}$$

The solution to this simplified equation is the function

$$s = A + B\cos\gamma\varphi \tag{22.28}$$

where

$$\gamma = \sqrt{1 - \frac{2me^2\alpha}{abp^2}} \tag{22.29}$$

and

$$A = \frac{me^2 Z_a}{p^2} \frac{2}{\gamma^2}.$$

Evaluating $r_{min} = \frac{1}{s_{max}} = \frac{1}{A+B}$ and $r_{max} = \frac{1}{s_{min}} = \frac{1}{A-B}$, we find, from the well-known relation

$$\varepsilon = \frac{r_{max} - r_{min}}{r_{min} + r_{max}},$$

that $\varepsilon = B/A$ and, hence,

$$s = \frac{1}{r} = A(1 + \varepsilon \cos \gamma\varphi). \tag{22.30}$$

This equation differs from the equation of an unperturbed ellipse by the factor γ with which orbital precession is associated. Indeed, since $\gamma \neq 1$, an electron at perihelion for $\varphi = 0$ comes to perihelion once more not at $\varphi = 2\pi$ but at $\gamma\varphi = 2\pi$, i.e., when $\varphi = 2\pi/\gamma > 2\pi$. Consequently, during the time of a complete revolution of an electron in its orbit the major axis of the ellipse turns through the angle

$$\Delta\varphi = \frac{2\pi}{\gamma} - 2\pi = \frac{1-\gamma}{\gamma} 2\pi \tag{22.31}$$

(see Fig. 36). Accordingly, the angular velocity of precession will be

$$\Omega = \frac{\Delta\varphi}{\tau}.$$

Dividing Ω by the angular velocity of the electron in the orbit

$$\omega = \frac{2\pi}{\tau},$$

we obtain

$$\frac{\Omega}{\omega} = \frac{\Delta\varphi}{2\pi} = \frac{1-\gamma}{\gamma}. \tag{22.32}$$

Evaluating the ratio Ω/ω, we see that Ω and ω are close as to order of magnitude. Indeed, transforming expression (22.29) to the form

$$\gamma = \sqrt{1 - \frac{2\alpha}{r_1^3 n_\varphi^3 n^3}} = \sqrt{1 - \frac{13.5 \times 10^{24} \alpha}{n_\varphi^3 n^3}}$$

(here we note that $b = a\,(n_\varphi/n)$, $a = r_1 n^2$, $p = \hbar n_\varphi$ and $r_1 = \hbar^2/e^2 m = 0.529$ A) and substituting into it the values of the polarisation coefficients of the ions of alkaline elements (see p. 183) from formula (22.32), we obtain, for the s-terms ($n_\varphi = 1$), $\Delta\varphi = 10°$-$40°$. Comparing this result with the angular velocity of precession of hydrogen orbits, the precession being characterised by the quantity $\Delta\varphi$ that does not exceed 0.01° (see p. 152), we see that as was to be expected the rosette-like character of the orbits in the atoms of the alkaline elements is very pronounced.

It should be pointed out that precession also occurs in the case of penetrating orbits (Fig. 37); due to the strong attraction experienced by the electron inside the atomic core, the angular velocity of precession in this case should be greater than in the case of non-penetrating orbits. It may be demonstrated that the angular velocity of precession Ω varies in the same sense as $|\delta|$. For this reason, one should expect that in the case of penetrating orbits, Ω and ω should be close in value.

Magnetic properties of the atom in the Bohr-Sommerfeld theory. In the Bohr-Sommerfeld theory the magnetic properties of atoms receive the following pictorial interpretation. An electron revolving about a nucleus may be regarded as a certain closed electric current $i = e/\tau$ (τ is the orbital period of the electron*). To this current there corresponds a definite magnetic moment $\mu = iS$, where $S = \pi ab$ is the area of the orbit (a and b are the semi-major and semi-minor axes of the ellipse), whence it follows that $\mu = \pi abe/\tau$ Since $\pi ab/\tau = {}^1/_2 (r^2\dot{\varphi}) = p/2m$ (cf. p. 160), we have

$$\frac{\mu}{p} = \frac{1}{2}\frac{e}{m}. \tag{22.33}$$

Substituting $p = \hbar n_\varphi$ into (22.33), for the magnetic moment of an electron orbit we get

$$\mu = \frac{\hbar}{2}\frac{e}{m} n_\varphi = \mu_B n_\varphi, \tag{22.34}$$

whence it follows that the magnetic moment of the atom, like its angular momentum p, is a quantised quantity representing a multiple of a certain elementary magnetic moment

$$\mu_B = \frac{\hbar}{2}\frac{e}{m}. \tag{22.35}$$

The latter quantity is numerically equal to 9.271×10^{-21} erg·oersted^{-1} and is called the *Bohr magneton*.

Since for the ground state of the hydrogen atom $n_\varphi = n = 1$, we must conclude that the magnetic moment of the H atom is equal to one Bohr magneton. Also equal to this quantity should

* The idea that magnetism is due to certain (hypothetical) molecular currents was expressed by Ampere in 1822.

be the magnetic moments of the atoms of the alkali metals, and the atoms of copper, silver, and gold, the ground state of which is the s-state characterised by the azimuthal quantum number $n_\varphi = 1$.*

The first direct measurements of the magnetic moment, or, more precisely, the projections of the magnetic moment of atoms on the direction of the magnetic field were carried out by Stern and Gerlach in 1921 with atoms of silver. By passing a beam of silver atoms through an inhomogeneous magnetic field, they found that the original beam is split into two beams of the same intensity. Subsequently, this phenomenon became known as the *Stern-Gerlach effect*. Phipps, Taylor, and Wrede likewise observed the splitting of a beam of hydrogen atoms into two beams. A similar effect was noted in the case of the atoms of sodium, potassium, copper, iron; in the case of nickel atoms there are three beams, while diamagnetic zinc, cadmium, mercury, and also helium do not exhibit any splitting at all.

The only way to understand splitting of a beam of identical atoms in a magnetic field is to assume that the atoms are specifically and differently *orientated* with respect to the field direction. Indeed, denoting the field gradient by $\frac{\partial H}{\partial z}$ and assuming the magnetic moment of the atom equal to $\mu = ml$, where m is the "magnetic mass" and l is the length of the elementary magnet, we obtain the following expression for the force acting on the magnetic moment:

$$F = m\left(H + l\cos\alpha\frac{\partial H}{\partial z}\right) - mH = ml\cos\alpha\frac{\partial H}{\partial z} = \mu\cos\alpha\frac{\partial H}{\partial z}.$$

From this expression it is seen that the force acting on the atoms in an inhomogeneous magnetic field is proportional to the projection of the magnetic moment of the atom on the field direction $\mu' = \mu\cos\alpha$. Thus, from the fact of splitting of the beam there inevitably follows different and also discrete (in the sense of specific values of the angle $\alpha = (\boldsymbol{\mu}, \mathbf{H})$, orientation of atoms in the magnetic field.

The beam splitting of hydrogen atoms, like the other atoms of the first group, is such that half the atoms are deflected from the original direction to one side and half, the same distance to the other side. Whence it follows that in the case of these atoms $\cos\alpha$ takes on two values that are equal in absolute magnitude but opposite in sign. It is impossible from the Stern-

* Due to mutual compensation of the moments of separate electrons, the magnetic moment of the atomic cores of the alkaline elements is zero.

Gerlach experiments (and from any experiments for that matter) to determine separately the magnitude of the magnetic moment of an atom and $\cos\alpha$, since all manifestations of interaction of the atom with the magnetic field are determined by the quantity $\mu' = \mu\cos\alpha$; for this reason, the values of μ and $\cos\alpha$ remain indeterminate. And only very arbitrarily, by considering one of the orientations of these atoms parallel ($\cos\alpha = +1$) and the other antiparallel ($\cos\alpha = -1$) to the field, is it possible to identify the absolute value of the projection of the moment μ' with the moment μ itself and thus determine the latter from the magnitude of splitting of the atomic beam. The magnetic moments thus measured of the atoms of the first group turned out exactly equal to *one Bohr magneton* (μ_B).

Also pointing to different orientation of atoms in a magnetic field (*space quantisation*) is the study of the effect of the latter on atomic spectra. Since the energy of an atom in a magnetic field varies by the magnitude

$$\Delta E = \mu H \cos(\boldsymbol{\mu}, \mathbf{H}), \tag{22.36}$$

in the absence of "quantisation" of angles $\alpha = (\boldsymbol{\mu}, \mathbf{H})$ one should expect a certain diffuseness of the spectral lines as compared with the lines emitted or absorbed by the atom in the absence of a field. Yet experiment shows that in a magnetic field we have *splitting* of spectral lines into a definite number of components (*Zeeman effect*, see Sec. 30), which indicates that ΔE and, consequently, the projection of the magnetic moment $\mu' = \mu\cos\alpha$ take on definite discrete values in a magnetic field.

The space quantisation of atomic elementary magnets in a magnetic field, which is so clearcut in the Stern-Gerlach effect and in the Zeeman effect, was established also theoretically in 1916 by Debye and Sommerfeld. Considering the motion of an electron about a nucleus in three-dimensional space, that is, in the coordinates r, ϑ, ψ (ϑ is the angle between the normal to the plane of the electron orbit and the polar axis, ψ is the angle reckoned on the equatorial plane from its line of intersection with the plane of the orbit), it is possible to obtain further generalisation of the mechanical problem of the atom, the solution of which yields (for the energy of the atom) an earlier obtained expression (22.10). The essentially new result of the more general solution of the problem consists in the fact that the projection of the orbital angular momentum p on the direction of the polar axis turns out to be a *quantised* quantity:

$$p' = p\cos\vartheta = m_\varphi \hbar \tag{22.37}$$

where m_φ is an integer. Substituting into (22.37) $p = n_\varphi \hbar$ (22.6) we find

$$\cos\vartheta = \frac{m_\varphi}{n_\varphi}. \tag{22.38}$$

Thus, $\cos\vartheta$ can assume only definite discrete values, i.e., the electron orbit is definitely and discretely oriented in space (space quantisation). From formula (22.38) it follows that the maximum and minimum values of the quantum number m_φ must be equal to n_φ and $-n_\varphi$, respectively. Hence, due to the integrality of m_φ, it may be equal to

$$m_\varphi = \pm n_\varphi, \ \pm(n_\varphi - 1), \ \pm(n_\varphi - 2), \ \ldots, \ \pm 1, \ 0,$$

i.e., it may assume $2n_\varphi + 1$ different values.

From equalities (22.37) and (22.33) it follows that

$$\mu' = \mu\cos\vartheta = \frac{\hbar}{2}\,\frac{e}{m}\,m_\varphi = \mu_B m_\varphi. \tag{22.39}$$

Thus, also the projection of the magnetic moment of the atom is quantised. Given an outer magnetic (or electric) field, the direction of the polar axis becomes fixed in space. Assuming $\vartheta = (\boldsymbol{\mu}, \mathbf{H}) = \alpha$, we obtain the following expression for the projection of the magnetic moment on the direction of the magnetic field:

$$\mu' = \mu\cos\alpha = \mu_B m_\varphi. \tag{22.40}$$

Since the quantum number m_φ determines the magnitude of the projections of the magnetic moment, it may be called the *magnetic quantum (orbital) number*.

Intrinsic contradictions of the Bohr theory. The postulate underlying the Bohr theory concerning the quantisation of momentum, which is expressed by the quantum conditions (22.5), follows from the empirical expression for the energy of the atom (21.5). For this reason, coincidence with experiment of the atom-energy values calculated on the basis of this postulate cannot be regarded as experimental confirmation of the Bohr theory. The experimental verification of the Bohr theory must consist in a correlation of experimentel data of such properties of the atom as were not used in constructing the theory. Among others, they are the magnetic properties of the atom. As we have already seen, the results of theory, both as regards the magnitude of the magnetic moment of atoms and the phenomenon of space quantisation, are in close agreement with experiment. However, a more detailed examination of the magnetic properties of atoms shows that this correspondence is only qualitative and, actually, apparent. Consequently, these results of theory do not coincide with experimental findings, they contradict them.

Indeed, since the principal term of hydrogen (this goes for all the other atoms of the first group also) is the S-term, to this term is assigned the azimuthal quantum number $n_\varphi = 1$, whence, on the basis of formula (22.38), we get the following *three* values of $\cos\alpha$: $+1$, 0, -1. Thus, one should expect that a beam of atoms of any element of the first group in an inhomogeneous magnetic field will be split into *three* beams, whereas in reality we observe a splitting into *two* beams (p. 164). Another fact that refers to the Stern-Gerlach effect and also contradicts the conclusions of theory is splitting into two beams in the case of thallium, the magnetic moment of which (calculated on the assumption of $\cos\alpha = \pm 1$) turns out, however, to be equal to $1/3\ \mu_B$ in place of an integral multiple of μ_B.

This divergence from experiment points to profound internal contradictions in the Bohr theory, which are particularly prominent when investigating the so-called *fine structure* of atomic terms. A detailed study of the structure of the spectra of various elements shows that the greater part of their spectral lines has a *multiplet*, or fine, structure and consists of several components. For example, all the lines of the principal and sharp series of the alkaline elements are *doublets* (recall the well-known D-line of sodium — the first member in the principal series — which is a doublet with components D_1 and D_2), while the lines of the diffuse series and the Bergmann series are *triplets*. The fine structure of spectral lines is an indication of the multiplicity of atomic terms. To account for the latter, Uhlenbeck and Goudsmit (1925) expressed the view, later confirmed by vast experimental material, that the electron possesses *spin*, the interaction of which with the orbital angular momentum is what leads to splitting of the term.

However, within the framework of the Bohr theory, attempts at a consistent quantitative interpretation of the multiplet structure of atomic terms on the basis of this assumption encounter difficulties of a fundamental nature. In particular, from the doublet structure of the P-, D-, etc., terms of an atom with one outer electron it may be concluded that space quantisation of spin in the field of the orbital angular momentum of the electron leads to two different orientations of spin. However, unlike all the other terms, the S-terms are *simple*, which indicates an absence of interaction of spin and orbital angular momentum in this case. And the latter is possible only in the absence of an intra-atomic magnetic field, i.e., when the orbital angular momentum of the atom is equal to zero, which, if we take into account (22.34), leads to $n_\varphi = n = 0$. Thus, calculating the energy of the S-states of an atom with one electron, for instance, the ground state of the H atom, we must put $n=n_\varphi=1$, whereas when calculating the orbital angular momentum in the same state of the atom one has to put $n=n_\varphi=0$ (which leads to $|E|=\infty$).

This intrinsic contradiction of the Bohr theory was only one of the signs that it was untenable. The Bohr theory was likewise incapable of solving the mechanical problem of the helium atom: all attempts at calculating the energy and the magnetic moment of the He atom encountered the same difficulties as in the simple case of the H atom. The contradictory nature of the Bohr theory also became evident in attempts to evaluate the intensities of spectral lines: an approximate (asymptotic) solution of this problem was given by Bohr by means of introducing the so-called *correspondence principle*; but this principle is based on the laws of classical electrodynamics, the inapplicability of which to intra-atomic processes was postulated by Bohr as one of the basic principles of his theory.

An experimental verification of the Bohr theory thus shows that it is capable of giving a satisfactory and semi-quantative explanation only of an extremely limited number of experimental facts. The subsequent development of physics showed that this limitedness of the Bohr theory (the theory proceeds from the concepts of classical physics into which Bohr artificially introduced quantum laws alien to it) is rooted in the limitedness of classical concepts concerning microparticles.

CHAPTER 4

THE QUANTUM-MECHANICAL THEORY OF THE ATOM

23. Wave Equation

Amplitude equation. The problem of the atom, which could not be adequately solved by the intrinsically contradictory and, essentially, semi-empirical theory of Bohr, was completely solved by *quantum* or *wave, mechanics* constructed on a wider basis than the old theory. Quantum mechanics is based on the the concept of the wave-like properties of particles, and first of all on the wave-like properties of the electron (Sec. 7).

The creators of quantum mechanics, Born, Heisenberg and Jordan (1925), and Schrödinger (1926), used different mathematical tools. Whereas Born, Heisenberg and Jordan reduced the mathematical apparatus of the new theory to *matrix calculus*, which operates with an assembly of coordinates of a system of oscillators representing each real atom, the mathematical interpretation of Schrödinger is based on replacing the equations of motion of classical mechanics with a *wave equation*, which describes a certain wave process in accordance with the wave properties of matter in the sense of the de Broglie theory. Schrödinger (1926) demonstrated the identity of both forms of quantum mechanics. Henceforward we shall confine ourselves to the Schrödinger form, in which the wave properties of particles are reflected by a *wave function* (φ) obtained from solution of the wave equation.

In wave optics, the propagation of a certain physical quantity φ with a velocity u is described by the equation

$$\Delta\varphi = \frac{1}{u^2}\frac{\partial^2\varphi}{\partial t^2}.$$

In this equation, called the wave equation, $\Delta\varphi$ is the Laplacian operator of the function φ:

$$\Delta\varphi = \frac{\partial^2\varphi}{\partial x^2} + \frac{\partial^2\varphi}{\partial y^2} + \frac{\partial^2\varphi}{\partial z^2}.$$

In the case of harmonic oscillations with a frequency ν, we may put

$$\varphi = \psi e^{2\pi i \nu t} \tag{23.1}$$

where $\psi(x, y, z)$ is the amplitude of oscillations of the quantity φ. It will be noted that on the basis of the relation $E = h\nu$ which is one of the expressions of wave-particle duality (see p. 32), the frequency ν may be replaced by the energy E, whence it follows that

$$\varphi = \psi e^{2\pi i \frac{E}{h} t} . \tag{23.2}$$

Calculating $\frac{\partial^2 \varphi}{\partial t^2} = -4\pi^2 \nu^2 \varphi$ and substituting this quantity into the initial wave equation, we obtain

$$\Delta\varphi + 4\pi^2 \frac{\nu^2}{u^2} \varphi = 0$$

or, since $\lambda = \frac{u}{\nu}$,

$$\Delta\varphi + \frac{1}{\lambda\!\!\!^{-2}} \varphi = 0$$

where $\lambda\!\!\!^- = \lambda/2\pi$. Omitting the temporal factor $e^{2\pi i \nu t}$, we get the following equation for the function ψ (*amplitude equation*):

$$\Delta\psi + \frac{1}{\lambda\!\!\!^{-2}} \psi = 0. \tag{23.3}$$

In the wave equation of quantum mechanics, which has the form of equation (23.3), the quantity λ is the de Broglie wavelength $\lambda = \frac{h}{g}$ (7.2) or $\lambda\!\!\!^- = \frac{\hbar}{g}$ $\left(\hbar = \frac{h}{2\pi}\right)$. Bearing in mind the problem of the motion of an electron and expressing its momentum g in terms of the kinetic energy K, $g = \sqrt{2mK}$, we get $\frac{1}{\lambda\!\!\!^{-2}} = \frac{2mK}{\hbar^2}$. Substituting this expression for $\frac{1}{\lambda\!\!\!^{-2}}$ into the wave equation (23.3), we reduce it to the form

$$\Delta\psi + \frac{2m}{\hbar^2} K\psi = 0. \tag{23.4}$$

As already pointed out (p. 31), the wave properties of light are most evident when the dimensions of the spatial region in which the light waves are propagated are commensurable with their wavelength. The same should occur also in the case of electrons. Calculating the de Broglie wavelength (7.2) for an atom (ion) with one electron and comparing it to the radius of a Bohr orbit, we readily see the commensurability of both quantities. Indeed, from (22.10) and (22.11) for the kinetic energy $K = -E_n$ we find $K = \frac{e^4Z^2}{2\hbar^2 n^2} \frac{mM}{m+M}$, whence it follows that $g = \sqrt{2\frac{mM}{m+M}K} = \frac{e^2Z}{\hbar n} \frac{mM}{m+M}$. Substituting this quantity into formula $\lambda\!\!\!^{-} = \frac{\hbar}{g}$ (7.2), we get

$$\lambda\!\!\!^{-} = \frac{\hbar^2}{e^2Z} \frac{m+M}{mM} n. \qquad (23.5)$$

For the radius of the Bohr orbit we have (see (22.8))

$$r = \frac{\hbar^2}{e^2Z} \frac{m+M}{mM} n^2.$$

Correlating r with (23.5) we get

$$r = \lambda\!\!\!^{-} n, \qquad (23.6)$$

which is the commensurability of r and λ at least for not too great n. Whence it follows that the laws of classical mechanics cannot be used to describe the motion of an electron in an atom, and the problem must be solved on the basis of the wave equation of quantum mechanics.

Physical meaning of the wave function. Before passing over to a quantum-mechanical solution of the problem of the atom, let us clarify the physical meaning of the wave function ψ. It is easy to establish a mutual correspondence between wave and corpuscular concepts. Indeed, considering, for instance, the intensity of an electron beam, we determine it, from the corpuscular viewpoint, as a quantity proportional to the density of the beam, i.e., to the number of electrons per cubic centimeter. But on the wave concept, since the wave intensity is proportional to the square of its amplitude, the intensity of the electron beam should be set proportional to the quantity ψ^2 or, more precisely (since the wave function in the general case may be a complex quantity), to the square of its modulus $|\psi|^2 = \psi\psi^*$ (ψ and ψ^* are complex conjugate quantities). Thus, $|\psi|^2$ acquires the meaning of density. Proceeding from this interpretation of the function $|\psi|^2$ and multiplying it by the electron charge and the element of volume dV, we obtain a quantity which, obviously, will have the meaning of the charge of this element of volume $e|\psi|^2 dV$; integrating over the whole volume, we get the charge of this volume. The wave function is ordinarily normalised so that the magnitude of this charge is assumed equal to the electron charge, whence it follows that

$$\int |\psi|^2 \, dV = 1. \tag{23.7}$$

This interpretation of $|\psi|^2$ is arrived at also by the following reasoning. Since the wave equation (23.3) is identical with the equation that describes elastic vibrations of a liquid sphere, it may be taken that the vibrational process in the atom described by this equation is analogous to the above-mentioned vibrations of the sphere. It is precisely this analogy that underlies the concept, introduced by Schrödinger, of the electron in the atom as a negatively charged *cloud*. Since the energy of vibrations of a liquid sphere is proportional to the quantity $|\psi|^2$ (and in the case of the atom we deal with the vibrations of an electric charge) it is in this case natural to assume $|\psi|^2$ proportional to the density of the charge. If we normalise the function ψ, subjecting it to the condition

$$e \int |\psi|^2 \, dV = e \quad \text{or} \quad \int |\psi|^2 \, dV = 1$$

(dV is an element of intra-atomic volume), which condition expresses the fact that the total charge of the electron cloud is equal to e, then $e|\psi|^2$ may be considered the charge density.

However, the function ψ allows for a different interpretation, too, which is more consonant with the spirit of quantum mechanics with its statistical, probabilistic interpretation of physical processes. Namely, according to Born, the quantity $|\psi|^2 dV$ is the *probability* of finding an electron in a given element of volume dV. From this point of view the quantity $|\psi|^2$ is frequently called the *probability density*, while the function ψ itself is the *amplitude of probability*. In this case, the normalising condition (23.7) indicates that the probability of finding an electron anywhere inside the atom is unity.

From the probabilistic interpretation of the wave function it follows that the position (trajectory) of a moving electron cannot be determined to any desired degree of accuracy, as is the case in classical mechanics. Calculating the quantity $|\psi|^2$ from the wave equation, we can determine only the probability of finding an electron at a given point of space. This peculiarity of quantum mechanics is expressed, in the most general form, by Heisenberg's *uncertainty principle*. One of the mathematical formulations of this principle states that

$$\Delta x \times \Delta p = \hbar. \tag{23.8}$$

Here Δx is the measure of uncertainty of the geometric position of an electron and Δp is a measure of the uncertainty of its momentum ($p = mv$). Whence it follows that the more precisely we determine the momentum or the energy of the particle (electron), the less precisely we can determine its position. In particular, from the fact that the energy of an electron in the steady state of an atom is strictly fixed, it follows that it is impossible to define its orbit. The uncertainty principle arises from the necessity of taking simultaneous account of two aspects of the elementary particle (electron): corpuscular and wave.

Incorrect interpretations of the corollaries that follow from the uncertainty principle have given rise to a series of idealistic philosophical distortions. Particularly great were the distortions in connection with the causality principle. Thus, Heisenberg, already in 1927, in the paper in which he enunciated the principle, wrote: "... quantum mechanics has definitely established that the law of causality is untenable". Yet negation of the causality principle leads to fideism. Thus, Eddington, in his book *The Nature of the Physical World* states that it may be that the reasoning of modern science permits of the conclusion that religion has become acceptable to a common sense scientific mind beginning with 1927.

These and similar idealistic "conclusions" drawn by certain scientists in connection with the uncertainty principle are based on a certain misunderstanding associated mainly with impermissible attempts to describe the motion of a microparticle by means of the concepts of classical mechanics, while ignoring its wave properties. The fallacy in this approach to the problem was most clearly stated by Langevin, who said the following with regard to the uncertainty principle: "Experience tells us that it is impossible to define exactly, at one and the same instant, the position and velocity of a particle. We immediately draw the conclusion that uncertainty underlies the laws of nature. However, why should we not assume that our corpuscular concept is inadequate, that it is impossible to represent the intra-atomic world by extrapolating to the limit our macroscopic conception of a moving body. From the fact that nature does not give an exact answer to the question concerning particle motion it would be too pretentious on our part to conclude that there is no determinism in nature. It is much simpler to say: the problem has been badly posed — in nature there is no corpuscular microparticle...".

Free-particle motion. Returning to the wave equation (23.4), let us solve it first for a free electron, i.e., for an electron moving outside a field of force. It may readily be shown that in this case, by separating the variables, equation (23.4) reduces to three identical equations corresponding to motion along the axes x, y, and z. In other words, a three-dimensional problem is reduced to a one-dimensional one. Indeed, putting

$$\psi(x, y, z) = X(x)\,Y(y)\,Z(z), \quad K = K_x + K_y + K_z$$

and computing the Laplacian $\Delta\psi$, from (23.4) we get the equation

$$\frac{d^2X}{dx^2} + \frac{2m}{\hbar^2} K_x X = 0 \tag{23.9}$$

and two analogous equations for Y and Z.

The solution of equation (23.9) has the form

$$X = A_x \sin(B_x x + C_x) \tag{23.10}$$

and exists for any energy values of the electron K_x, if the space in which the electron moves is boundless $(-\infty \leqslant x \leqslant \infty)$.

The situation is different when a particle (electron) moves in a confined volume. Thus, if the motion along the x axis is limited to the region $0 \leqslant x \leqslant a_x$ the boundary conditions take on great significance in the solution of the problem. They may be formulated as follows. Since the electron cannot get outside the indicated region, the probability that the electron will find itself on the boundaries of this region, i.e., at $x = 0$ and at $x = a_x$, must be zero. And since this probability is determined by the quantity $|X|^2$ (see p. 171), we get the following boundary conditions: $X = 0$ when $x = 0$ and when $x = a_x$. The first yields $\sin C_x = 0$, i.e., $C_x = 0$, the second, $\sin(B_x a_x + C_x) = 0$, i.e., $B_x = \frac{n_x \pi}{a_x}$, where n_x is an integer. Thus, the solution to equation (23.9) has the form

$$X = A_x \sin \frac{n_x \pi}{a_x} x.$$

Computing $\frac{d^2X}{dx^2}$ and substituting this quantity together with X into equation (23.9), we obtain

$$K_x = \frac{\hbar^2}{2m} \frac{n_x^2}{a_x^2}. \tag{23.11}$$

Analogous expressions are obtained for the components of the kinetic energy of the electron along the y and z axes. For the total kinetic energy we have

$$K = \frac{\hbar^2}{2m} \left(\frac{n_x^2}{a_x^2} + \frac{n_y^2}{a_y^2} + \frac{n_z^2}{a_z^2} \right). \tag{23.12}$$

From this result it follows that the kinetic energy of a free electron moving in a limited volume is a *quantised* quantity. True, it must be said that due to the smallness of $\hbar^2/2m$ (of the order of 10^{-26}CGS) this property of the kinetic energy of the electron is significant only in sufficiently small volumes confining its free motion. For this reason, in most practical cases the energy of a free electron may be considered (to a high degree of accuracy) as a continuous arbitrary quantity. In such cases, the motion of a free electron may be evaluated, without any essential error, on the basis of classical mechanics.

Schrödinger equation. The essential difference in the motion of a bound electron (for example, in the atom) and a free electron consists in the fact that whereas the potential energy of the latter is zero, the bound electron moving in a field of force has potential energy in addition to kinetic energy. Substituting into equation (23.3) the quantity $\frac{1}{\lambda\!\!\!^{-2}}=\frac{g^2}{\hbar^2}=\frac{2}{\hbar^2}\frac{Mm}{m+M}K$ (see p. 169) and replacing the kinetic energy by the difference in the total and potential energies, $K=E-V$, we transform this equation to the form

$$\Delta\psi+\frac{2}{\hbar^2}\frac{mM}{m+M}(E-V)\psi=0. \qquad (23.13)$$

Equation (23.13), which was first derived by Schrödinger (1926) is called the *Schrödinger equation.* It underlies the solution of many problems of atomic physics.

Before going over to a consideration of specific problems, let us note the following peculiarity of the quantum-mechanical approach to the solution of these problems on the basis of Schrödinger's wave equation. From the theory of differential equations it is known that the solution of any equation that satisfies the physical conditions of the given problem is possible only for definite values of the parameters that enter into the equation. These parameter values are called *characteristic numbers*, or *eigenvalues* of the given problem, to which there correspond solutions ψ_n called *eigenfunctions.*

In the Schrödinger equation, the total energy of the system is the constant parameter. For this reason, the assembly of eigenvalues E_n in any concrete case of the solution of this equation. represents the entire totality of energy levels of the given system. Thus, in quantum mechanics the physical problem of quantisation reduces to a mathematical problem of the solution of the wave equation.

24. Atom (Ion) with One Electron

Solution of the Schrödinger equation. The problem of a hydrogen-like atom, i.e., an atom or ion consisting of a nucleus and one electron, is a problem of the motion of an electron in the Coulomb field of the nucleus (the one-electron problem). Assuming the nuclear charge equal to Ze and introducing the expression for the potential energy of the atom $V=-\frac{e^2Z}{r}$ into equation (23.12), we obtain

$$\Delta\psi+\frac{2}{\hbar^2}\frac{mM}{m+M}\left(E+\frac{Ze^2}{r}\right)\psi=0. \qquad (24.1)$$

In spherical coordinates, r, ϑ, φ, associated with Cartesian coordinates x, y, z by the relations

$$x=r\sin\vartheta\sin\varphi, \quad y=r\sin\vartheta\cos\varphi, \quad z=r\cos\vartheta,$$

equation (24.1) assumes the form

$$\frac{1}{r^2}\frac{\partial}{\partial r}\left(r^2\frac{\partial\psi}{\partial r}\right)+\frac{1}{r^2\sin^2\vartheta}\frac{\partial^2\psi}{\partial\varphi^2}+\frac{1}{r^2\sin^2\vartheta}\frac{\partial}{\partial\vartheta}\left(\sin\vartheta\frac{\partial\psi}{\partial\vartheta}\right)+$$
$$+\frac{2}{\hbar^2}\frac{mM}{m+M}\left(E+\frac{Ze^2}{r}\right)=0,$$

which permits separation of the variables. Introducing the functions R, Θ, Φ:

$$\psi(r,\vartheta,\psi)=R(r)\Theta(\vartheta)\Phi(\varphi)=R(r)S(\vartheta,\varphi), \qquad (24.2)$$

we transform this equation to the form

$$\frac{1}{R}\frac{d}{dr}\left(r^2\frac{dR}{dr}\right)+\frac{2}{\hbar^2}\frac{mM}{m+M}\left(E+\frac{Ze^2}{r}\right)r^2+$$
$$+\frac{1}{S\sin^2\vartheta}\frac{\partial^2 S}{\partial\varphi^2}+\frac{1}{S\sin\vartheta}\frac{\partial}{\partial\vartheta}\left(\sin\vartheta\frac{\partial S}{\partial\vartheta}\right)=0.$$

The latter equation is thus separated into the two following equations:

$$\frac{1}{R}\frac{d}{dr}\left(r^2\frac{dR}{dr}\right)+\frac{2}{\hbar^2}\frac{mM}{m+M}\left(E+\frac{Ze^2}{r}\right)r^2=\lambda \qquad (24.3)$$

and

$$\frac{1}{S\sin^2\vartheta}\frac{\partial^2 S}{\partial\varphi^2}+\frac{1}{S\sin\vartheta}\frac{\partial}{\partial\vartheta}\left(\sin\vartheta\frac{\partial S}{\partial\vartheta}\right)=-\lambda \qquad (24.4)$$

where λ is a certain constant. Further, substituting into the latter equation $S(\vartheta,\varphi)=\Theta(\vartheta)\Phi(\varphi)$, it may, in turn be separated into the following two equations, setting $\frac{1}{\Phi}\frac{d^2\Phi}{d\varphi^2}=-m_l^2$:

$$\frac{1}{\sin\vartheta}\frac{d}{d\vartheta}\left(\sin\vartheta\frac{d\Theta}{d\vartheta}\right)+\left(\lambda-\frac{m_l^2}{\sin^2\vartheta}\right)\Theta=0 \tag{24.5}$$

and

$$\frac{d^2\Phi}{d\varphi^2}+m_l^2\Phi=0. \tag{24.6}$$

The solution of the latter equation, to the accuracy of a certain constant factor, has the form

$$\Phi=e^{\pm i|m_l|\varphi} \tag{24.7}$$

or, assuming negative values of the number m_l along with positive values,

$$\Phi=e^{im_l\varphi}. \tag{24.8}$$

The unambiguity of the solution demands that m_l be an *integer*.*

As for the equation for $\Theta(\vartheta)$, by introducing a new variable $x=\cos\vartheta$ and by putting $\Theta(\vartheta)=(1-x^2)^{|m_l|/2}v(x)$, we first transform this equation to

$$(1-x^2)v''-2(|m_l|+1)xv'+(\lambda-|m_l|-m_l^2)v=0$$

where v' and v'' denote the first and second derivatives of the function $v(x)$ with respect to x, respectively. To find the solution to the latter equation we put $y=(x^2-1)^l$ where l is an integral positive number. Taking logarithms and then differentiating y with respect to x, we get

$$(1-x^2)y'+2lxy=0.$$

From this equation, after differentiating it $k+1$ times with respect to x and denoting

$$z=\frac{d^ky}{dx^k}=\frac{d^k(x^2-1)^l}{dx^k},$$

we get the equation

$$(1-x^2)z''-2(k-l+1)xz'+(2l-k)(k+1)z=0,$$

which turns out identical to the equation for the function $v(x)$ on the condition that

$$v=cz,\ |m_l|+1=k-l+1 \text{ and } (2l-k)(k+1)=\lambda-|m_l|-m_l^2,$$

where c is some constant.

---

* In this case, the condition of uniqueness may be written in the form $e^{im_l\varphi}=e^{im_l(\varphi+2\pi)}$, whence there follows the integrality of m_l.

From the latter equalities we find $k=l+|m_l|$ and

$$\lambda=l(l+1). \tag{24.9}$$

And the equality $v=cz$ gives the solution to the equation for the function v in the form

$$v(x)=c\frac{d^{l+|m_l|}}{dx^{l+|m_l|}}(x^2-1)^l,$$

from which we find

$$\Theta(\vartheta)=c(1-x^2)^{|m_l|/2}\frac{d^{l+|m_l|}}{dx^{l+|m_l|}}(x^2-1)^l, \quad x=\cos\vartheta. \tag{24.10}$$

This expression is the solution to the initial equation for the function Θ for any *integral* values of the number m_l contained between $+l$ and $-l$. But as will be seen from (24.10), for the values $|m_l|>l$, Θ converts to zero. Thus for a given l (the physcal meaning of this number will be clarified later) we have $2l+1$ solutions of Θ that correspond to the following $2l+1$ values assumed by the number m_l:

$$m_l=\pm l, \quad \pm(l-1), \quad \pm(l-2), \ \ldots, \ \pm 1, \ 0. \tag{24.11}$$

All these solutions are finite in the entire space of the coordinate ϑ, which is essential in connection with the above established physical meaning of the function ψ.

Now turning to the solution of the equation for the radial function R (24.3), we rewrite it (taking into account (24.9)) in the form

$$\frac{d^2R}{dr^2}+\frac{2}{r}\frac{dR}{dr}+\left[A+2\frac{B}{r}-\frac{l(l+1)}{r^2}\right]R=0$$

where

$$A=\frac{2}{\hbar^2}\frac{mM}{m+M}E \quad \text{and} \quad B=\frac{1}{\hbar^2}\frac{mM}{m+M}e^2Z.$$

Let us first find the asymptotic solution of this equation, which holds for large r. We rewrite the preceding equation for this case in the form

$$\frac{d^2R}{dr^2}+AR=0$$

Its solution has the form

$$R=C_1e^{\sqrt{-A}r}+C_2e^{-\sqrt{-A}r}.$$

We can obviously satisfy the necessary demand for the finiteness of the function R for all values of coordinate r (also for the case when $r=\infty$) by putting $C_1=0$. Thus, the asymptotic solution to equation (24.3) will have the form ($C=C_2$):

$$R(r)=Ce^{-\sqrt{-A}r}.$$

We obtain the general solution to this equation (which solution holds for any r) by considering C a function of r. Introducing the new variable $\varrho=2\sqrt{-A}r$, we transform equation (24.3) to

$$C''+\left(\frac{2}{\varrho}-1\right)C'+\left[\left(\frac{B}{\sqrt{-A}}-1\right)\frac{1}{\varrho}-\frac{l(l+1)}{\varrho^2}\right]C=0.$$

The solution to the latter equation is

$$C=\sum_{\nu=0}^{\nu=k} a_\nu \varrho^{\nu+l}$$

which is confirmed by simple substitution.

Substituting the quantities C, $C'=\sum a_\nu(\nu+l)\varrho^{\nu+l-1}$ and $C''=\sum a_\nu(\nu+l)\times(\nu+l-1)\varrho^{\nu+l-2}$ into the equation for C and equating to zero the sum of the coefficients in the term containing ϱ in any degree, we obtain the following recurrent formula:

$$[(\nu+l+1)(\nu+l)+2(\nu+l+1)-l(l+1)]a_{\nu+1}=$$
$$=\left(\nu+l+1-\frac{B}{\sqrt{-A}}\right)a_\nu,$$

which connects the coefficients of the polynomial C and permits expressing all coefficients in terms of one (for instance, in terms of a_0). Thus, to the accuracy of a constant factor, the function R may be represented in the following general form:

$$R(r)=e^{-\rho/2}\sum_{\nu=0}^{\nu=k} a_\nu\varrho^{\nu+\cdot},\quad \varrho=2\sqrt{-A}r. \tag{24.12}$$

By virtue of the necessarily finiteness of the function ψ, the polynomial C must likewise be finite, which is accounted for by its breaking off at the kth term. In such a case, the coefficients of the polynomial a_{k+1}, a_{k+2}, ..., must obviously be zero, and from the recurrent formula for the coefficients a_ν we obtain (putting $\nu=k$)

$$\frac{B}{\sqrt{-A}}=k+l+1=n.$$

Substituting the foregoing values of A and B, we find (taking into account (22.11)):

$$E=E_n=-\frac{2\pi^2e^4}{h^2}\frac{mM}{m+M}\frac{Z^2}{n^2}=-\frac{hRZ^2}{n^2}. \tag{24.13}$$

This expression coincides exactly with the expression for the energy of a hydrogen-like atom (22.10) in the Bohr theory, which is characterised by the principal quantum number n. Consequently, the number

$$n = k + l + 1 \tag{24.14}$$

turns out identical to the principal quantum number of Bohr's atomic theory. The quantum number n, according to (24.14), is composed of the numbers k and l, which can take on positive integral values beginning with zero. Obviously, the maximal values of these numbers for a given n are equal to $n-1$.

Correlating (24.14) with the formula $n = n_r + n_\varphi$ (p. 150) obtained from the Bohr theory, we see that the numbers k and l must be in a certain correspondence with the numbers n_r and n_φ. To establish this correspondence we do as follows. Calculating the mean radius of the elliptical Bohr orbit of the hydrogen atom, we find*

$$\bar{r} = \frac{1}{\tau}\int_0^\tau r\,dt = r_1 n^2\left[1 + \frac{1}{2}\left(1 - \frac{n_\varphi^2}{n^2}\right)\right].$$

On the other hand, a quantum-mechanical calculation of the mean distance of the electron from the nucleus in the H atom yields:

$$\bar{r} = \int \psi_{nl} r \psi_{nl}^* dv = r_1 n^2\left[1 + \frac{1}{2}\left(1 - \frac{l(l+1)}{n^2}\right)\right].$$

Identifying both values of $\bar{r}$, we obtain

$$n_\varphi^2 = l(l+1). \tag{24.15}$$

Atoms of alkaline elements and the quantum characteristic of spectral terms. An approximate solution to the Schrödinger equation (23.13) may readily be obtained also for atoms or ions with one outer electron on the assumption that this electron is at a sufficiently large distance from the nucleus, as a result of which its interaction with the remaining electrons in the atom may be regarded as a slight perturbation superimposed on the Coulomb attraction of the atomic core. As we have seen above (Sec. 22), such an approximation is taken in the Born-Heisenberg theory for electron orbits that do not penetrate into the atomic core.

Solving the problem to this approximation, we put, in the Schrödinger equation

$$\Delta\psi + \frac{2}{\hbar^2}\frac{mM}{m+M}(E - V)\psi = 0,$$

* In the integration, use is made of the equation of the ellipse and the relation derived from Kepler's law of areas $r\,dt/\tau = r^2 d\varphi / 2\pi ab$.

the potential energy V equal to

$$V = -\frac{e^2 Z_a}{r} + \Delta V$$

where the energy of perturbation ΔV is small compared with the energy of Coulomb interaction between the electron and the atomic core. Taking advantage of the expression given on p. 156 for the quantity ΔV,

$$\Delta V = \Delta E = -\frac{\alpha e^2}{2r^4},$$

and replacing $1/r^4$ by its mean value

$$\overline{\frac{1}{r^4}} = \int \psi_{nl} \frac{1}{r^4} \psi_{nl}^* dv = \frac{3Z_a^2}{2r_1^4} f(n, l)$$

where

$$f(n, l) = \frac{1 - \frac{l(l+1)}{3n^2}}{n^3 (l - {}^1/_2)\, l\, (l + {}^1/_2)(l+1)(l + {}^3/_2)},$$

we obtain

$$\overline{\Delta E} = -\frac{3}{4} \frac{\alpha e^2 Z_a^2}{r_1^4} f(n, l).$$

When $\Delta V = \Delta E = \text{const}$, the Schrödinger equation differs from the equation of the one-electron problem (24.1) in only one respect: in place of the eigenvalue E we have to substitute $E - \Delta E$. For this reason, solution of the Schrödinger equation in this case, instead of (24.13), will have the form

$$E - \overline{\Delta E} = -\frac{hRZ_a^2}{n^2} = E_H,$$

or

$$E = E_H \left(1 + \frac{\overline{\Delta E}}{E_H}\right).$$

Computing the ratio $\overline{\Delta E}/E_H$ on the basis of the expressions for $\overline{\Delta E}$ and E_H found above, we obtain, after a few transformations,

$$\frac{\overline{\Delta E}}{E_H} = \frac{3}{2} \frac{\alpha Z_a^2}{r_1^3} n^2 f(n, l).$$

Substituting this quantity into the expression for the energy of the atom E, we represent this expression in the form of the Rydberg formula, due to the smallness of $\overline{\Delta E}/E_H$:

$$E_{n,\,l}=-\frac{hRZ_a^2}{n_{eff}^2}=-\frac{hRZ_a^2}{(n-\Delta)^2} \tag{24.16}$$

where the quantum defect

$$\Delta=-\delta_1-\frac{1}{n^2}\delta_2=\frac{3}{4}\frac{\alpha Z_a^2}{r_1^3}\frac{1-\frac{l(l+1)}{3n^2}}{(l-{}^1/_2)\,l\,(l+{}^1/_2)(l+1)(l+{}^3/_2)}. \tag{24.17}$$

From this formula it will be seen that for a given n, the quantum defect sharply diminishes with increase in the quantum number l. Comparing (24.17) with the earlier derived (on the basis of the Bohr theory) and less accurate formula (22.21), it is evident that they are in fair agreement if we take $n_\varphi^2=l(l+1)$ (see (24.15).

From (24.16) we obtain, for the terms of alkaline elements or the corresponding ions,

$$T_{n,\,l}=\frac{RZ_a^2}{(n-\Delta)^2}. \tag{24.18}$$

A correlation of the theoretical expressions for the terms of alkaline elements (24.18) with the empirical formula (21.7) permits attributing to the terms of these elements definite values of the quantum numbers n and l; this is of great importance for the systematics of atomic states.

Substituting Δ (24.17) into the expression for $\frac{\overline{\Delta E}}{E_H}$, we find

$$\frac{\overline{\Delta E}}{E_H}=2n^2\Delta.$$

Since by the conditions of the problem $\overline{\Delta E}/E_H<1$, from the obtained relation it follows that $\Delta<1/2n^2$, i.e., $\Delta<1/8$, 1/18, 1/32, ..., respectively for n=2, 3, 4, ... Referring to Table 8 (p. 140), we see that for all the f-terms given and also for the d-terms of lithium and sodium and the p-term of lithium, the effective quantum number n_{eff} differs from the closest integer by not more than 0.04 (in the case of the p-term of lithium), which is in agreement with the foregoing values of the upper limit of Δ. For this reason, we may conclude, with a fair measure of probability, that the n_{eff} numbers (rounded off to integers) for these terms must be equal to the principal quantum numbers to which they correspond. Consequently, to the lower f-terms of all five elements characterised by the n_{eff} numbers 4.000, 3.999, 3.993, 3.988, and 3.978 (see Table 8) we assign the principal quantum number n=4; to the d-terms of lithium and sodium

($n_{eff}=2.998$ and 2.990) $n=3$, and to the p-term of lithium ($n_{eff}=1.959$) $n=2$.

As for the remaining terms given in Table 8, additional data are needed to find the principal quantum numbers that correspond to them. For instance, on the basis of $n_{eff}=2.117$ we exclude $n=2$ for the lower p-term of sodium and we can take $n=3$ as a probable value. The confirmation is as follows. Since, when $n=3$, the quantum number l assumes three values, $l=2$, 1, and 0, one of which corresponds to term 3d, it is natural to assign the two others to the lower p- and s-terms, i.e., to identify them with the terms 3p and 3s. We thus obtain the terms 4f, 3d, 3p, and 3s as the lower terms of sodium.

Having identified the lower p-term of lithium with the term 2p, due to the fact that when $n=2$ the number l takes on two values (1 and 0), it is natural to assign them to the terms p and s. Consequently, as lower terms of lithium we will have 4f, 3d, 2p and 2s.

Similarly, we get the terms 4s, 4p, 3d and 4f, etc., for the lower terms of potassium. A very important result here is that the values of the principal quantum number of the basic terms of alkaline elements, that is, the lower s-terms, coincide with the numbers of periods in the Periodic Table, the first elements of which are the alkaline elements 2 (Li), 3 (Na), 4 (K), 5 (Rb), 6 (Cs). On the other hand, $n=1$ corresponds to the ground state of the hydrogen atom that opens up the first period. From this we conclude that the electrons of the outer electron group must have the same value of the principal quantum number as the first element that opens up the given period. To illustrate, $n=1$ for both electrons of helium also follows from the fact that the solution of the problem of the He^+ ion yields $n=1$ for one electron and that both electrons in He are equally firmly bound to the nucleus (equivalent electrons). Further, to the electrons of the outer electron group of elements of the second period (from Li to Ne) we must assign $n=2$. This conclusion likewise stems from the approximate equivalence of these electrons. The outer electrons of the third period have $n=3$, etc. This result receives theoretical substantiation from the viewpoint of the general principles of quantum theory (see Sec. 26).

The quantum defect Δ is very weakly dependent on the principal quantum number but strongly dependent on the quantum number l. This makes it easy to find the values of the latter for various terms. Table 9 gives the calculated and measured values of Δ for the lower terms of the alkaline elements. Due to the fact that the quantum defect diminishes radically with increasing quantum number l (see p. 181), the underlying computational assumption is made that to the least values of Δ there corresponds the greatest l (possible for a given n). Whence, for all f-terms ($n=4$) we obtain $l=3$, for the d-terms of lithium and sodium $l=2$ (since $n=3$), for the p-terms of lithium $l=1$ (since $n=2$); $l=0$ must correspond to the s-terms. Thus, from an analysis of the experimental values of Δ on the basis of equation (24.17), we obtain the following relation of atomic terms and the quantum numbers l that describe them:

Term	s p d f ...
l	0 1 2 3 ...

The foregoing theory of atoms (or ions) with one outer electron, assuming sufficient distance of the latter from the atomic core, may be considered sufficiently accurate only for small Δ. The limited applicability of the theory is most prominent when examining Δ for the various elements and various terms given in Table 9: it is seen that both in the horizontal rows and in the vertical columns there is a sharp discontinuity of Δ, which is out of all proportion to the variation of Δ in accordance with the formula (24.17). For example, when passing from the sodium term 3p to the 3d-term, Δ should diminish by a factor of roughly 25, whereas in reality it decreases nearly 100 times; in the case of potassium, when passing from the 3d-term to 4f, Δ diminishes 30 times instead of 7; when passing from the potassium term 3d to the sodium term 3d, Δ diminishes 20 times instead of 5.

Table 9

Theoretical and experimental values of the quantum defect $\Delta = n - n_{eff}$ for the lower terms of alkaline elements*

Term / Element	s	p	d	f
Li	0.412 —	0.041 (0.034)	0.002 (0.002)	0.000 (0.000)
Na	1.373 —	0.883 (0.237)	0.010 (0.010)	0.001 (0.001)
K	2.230 —	1.776 (1.150)	0.146 (0.045)	0.007 (0.007)
Rb	3.195 —	2.711 (1.970)	1.233 (0.084)	0.012 (0.012)
Cs	4.131 —	3.649 (3.440)	2.448 (0.153)	0.022 (0.023)

* The brackets indicate Δ_{theor}; in calculating them, the following values of polarisation coefficients of the ions of alkaline metals α are taken (in units of 10^{24} cm^3): 0.03 (Li^+); 0.19 (Na^+); 0.89 (K^+); 1.50 (Rb^+); 2.60 (Cs^+).

From Table 9 it will be seen that the calculated and measured values of Δ practically coincide only for terms separated by the step-wise line from lower terms, which, as a rule, correspond to the elliptical Bohr orbits.

As already stated (p. 157), the inapplicability of equation (24.17) in the case of large Δ is due to the existence of electron orbits that penetrate into the atomic core. Substituting $n_\varphi^2 = l(l+1)$ and $n_\varphi \approx l + \frac{1}{2}$ into (22.24), which was derived on the basis of Bohr's theory and which takes into account the penetration of the outer electron into the atomic core, we get

$$\Delta = \frac{\frac{r_a}{r_1} Z_i}{\sqrt{2\frac{r_a}{r_1} Z_i - l(l+1)}} - \left(l + \frac{1}{2}\right). \qquad (24.19)$$

Evaluations of the terms of sodium and also of the ions Mg^+ and Al^{++} from equation (24.19), under certain assumptions con-

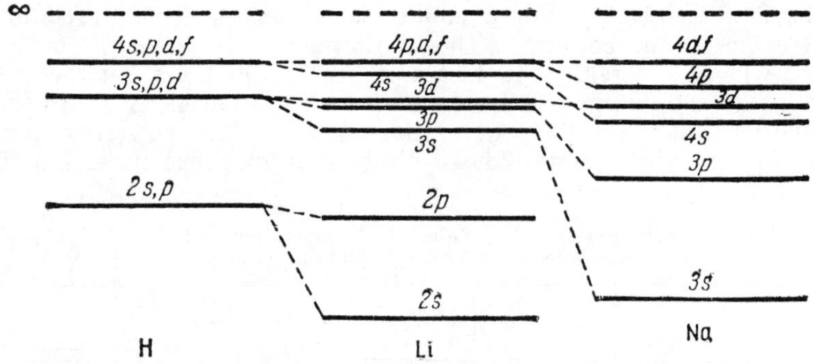

Fig. 38. Optical terms of H, Li, and Na

cerning the structure of the intra-atomic electric field, which determines the magnitude of the effective charge Z_i, yielded satisfactory agreement with experiment, particularly in the case of the s-terms. For the lower s-term of sodium (3s), $\Delta = 1.36$, whereas measurements yield $\Delta = 1.37$.

From (24.17) and (24.19) it follows that due to $n_{eff} < n$ the hydrogen terms must lie *above* the terms of the alkaline elements that are characterised by the same values of the principal quantum number. From these formulas it likewise follows that due to the decrease of Δ with increasing l for a given value of the number n, the s-term must lie *below* the p-term, the p-term *below* the d-term, etc. What is more, the distances between the s-, p-, d-, ... terms must be less the greater n and the smaller α, i.e., the lighter the element. All these regularities are seen in Fig. 38, where the experimentally obtained terms of the light alkaline elements lithium and sodium are correlated with corresponding terms of hydrogen; the ground levels of the ions Li^+, Na^+, and H^+ are made to coincide. We note that the lithium term 1s and the sodium terms 1s, 2s, and 2p, which are not given in Fig. 38, refer to terms exhibited in the X-ray spectra of these elements.

The extremely weak splitting of the terms of the H atom, due to the fact that in this case n_{eff} differs very slightly from the principal quantum number n (cf. p. 152), could not be given in Fig. 38 on the required scale.

Orbital and spin angular momenta. Due to the correspondence between the new azimuthal quantum number l and Bohr's azimuthal quantum number n_φ (24.15), which determines the momentum (and also the magnetic moment) of a Bohr electron orbit

$$p = \hbar n_\varphi,$$

one should expect that the orbital angular momentum of the electron in the atom will be characterised by the number l. Substituting into the previous formula $\sqrt{l(l+1)}$ in place of n_φ, we get

$$p = \hbar \sqrt{l(l+1)}. \tag{24.20}$$

An exact quantum-mechanical calculation also leads to this formula. Without carrying out the computations, we shall show that (24.20) is valid in the following special case of the solution of the Schrödinger equation; this case will be of interest later on (in connection with the rotational energy of diatomic molecules).

Considering a system of two opposite point charges revolving in circular orbits about a common centre of gravity, we must (due to the constancy of r) put $\frac{dR}{dr}$ and $\frac{d^2R}{dr^2}$ equal to zero in the equation for the function R, whence it follows that

$$A + 2\frac{B}{r} - \frac{l(l+1)}{r^2} = 0.$$

Substituting into this equation A and B (p. 177), we rewrite it in the form

$$E = \frac{\hbar^2}{2J} l(l+1) - \frac{e^2 Z}{r}$$

where $J = \frac{mM}{m+M} r^2$ is the moment of inertia of the system. Comparing this expression with the expression $E = K + V$ and noting that $V=-e^2Z/r$, for the kinetic energy we get

$$K=\frac{\hbar^2}{2J}\,l\,(l+1).$$

Substituting K in the form

$$K=\frac{J\varphi^2}{2}=\frac{p^2}{2J}$$

and comparing this expression with the one derived above, we find

$$p=\hbar\sqrt{l\,(l+1)},$$

i.e., an expression that coincides with (24.20).

Formula (24.20) for the orbital angular momentum is substantially different from the Bohr expression (22.6), approaching the latter only for large values of l ($l\gg 1$), when the numbers l and n_φ practically coincide. But in the case of small values of l, the expressions (24.20) and (22.6) yield sharply divergent values of angular momenta p. To illustrate, when $l=0$, and, hence, when $n_\varphi=1$ (s-orbit), we obtain $p=0$ for the quantum-mechanical atom and $p=\hbar$ for the Bohr atom.

The orbital magnetic moments computed for the Bohr and wave atoms differ just as significantly, because due to the proportionality between the magnetic moment and the angular momentum of the orbit, the orbital magnetic moment of the wave atom turns out proportional to the quantity $\sqrt{l\,(l+1)}$ and

$$\mu=\sqrt{l\,(l+1)}\,\mu_B, \qquad (24.21)$$

whereas, according to (22.34) in the Bohr theory $\mu=n_\varphi\mu_B$.

As to the question of space quantisation of electron orbits, it is to be expected, proceeding from the fact that the number of m_l may assume the values (see (24.11))

$$m_l=\pm l,\ \pm(l-1),\ \ldots,\ \pm 1,0$$

like the number m_φ in Bohr's theory that takes on the values (see p. 165)

$$m_\varphi=\pm n_\varphi,\ \pm(n_\varphi-1),\ \ldots,\ \pm 1,\ 0,$$

and from the correspondence between the numbers l and n_φ, that space quantisation of orbital angular momentum in quantum mechanics will be determined by the number m_l. Indeed, the quantum-mechanical calculation of the energy of an atom in a magnetic field leads to the expression

$$\Delta E=\frac{\hbar}{2}\frac{e}{m}Hm_l=\mu_B Hm_l, \qquad (24.22)$$

from which, representing ΔE in the form $\mu H \cos(\boldsymbol{\mu}, \mathbf{H})$, we find, for the projection of the magnetic moment on the field direction,

$$\mu' = \mu \cos(\boldsymbol{\mu}, \mathbf{H}) = \mu_B m_l \qquad (24.23)$$

like a similar expression in the Bohr theory (22.40):

$$\mu' = \mu_B m_\varphi .$$

We further indicate that the number m_l also determines the projection of the angular momentum of the orbit, i.e.,

$$p_l' = \hbar m_l \qquad (24.24)$$

(cf. $p' = \hbar m_\varphi$ in the Bohr theory).

We thus see that the projections of orbital angular momenta p and μ in quantum mechanics are, like in the Bohr theory, integral multiples of $\hbar$ and μ_B, respectively, whereas the dependence of the angular momenta on the quantum number is more complex than in the Bohr theory.

It will readily be seen that the quantum-mechanical theory of the atom is devoid of those inner contradictions that emerged when considering the multiplet structure of atomic terms on the basis of the Bohr theory. Indeed, as follows from (24.21), the intra-atomic magnetic field (due to the motion of the electron) is present in all states of the atom, with the exception of the s-states, in which case the magnetic field is absent due to $l = 0$. For this reason, in all states of the atom, excepting the s-states, we find space quantisation of spin in the intra-atomic magnetic field that leads to multiplet (doublet) splitting of terms (see below, p. 207). In the s-states, space quantisation is naturally absent, and the s-terms are simple (single).

In contrast to the Bohr theory, quantum mechanics also gives a correct quantitative interpretation of the behaviour of atoms in an external magnetic field; this behaviour is seen in the Stern-Gerlach and Zeeman effects, and also in the behaviour of atoms in an electric field (Stark effect), where space quantisation is particularly prominent. We have already pointed out (p. 164) that in an inhomogeneous magnetic field a beam of hydrogen atoms, and also of atoms of the other elements of this group, is split into *two* symmetrical beams of the same intensity (Stern-Gerlach effect). Comparing this picture of splitting with the formula $\mu' = \mu \cos\alpha$ it should be concluded that in the case of elements of the first group, i.e., of elements whose atoms have one outer electron and are in the s-state, μ' takes on *two* values that are equal in absolute magnitude. From the viewpoint of space quantisation of spin, this result is interpreted as follows.

Since the orbital magnetic moment of a normal hydrogen atom is equal to zero, the magnetic moment manifested in the Stern-Gerlach effect must be attributed to the electron. Whence it follows that two possible orientations of the H atom in an external magnetic field are due to space quantisation of spin. Introducing the quantum number s to characterise the angular momentum and magnetic moment of the electron (by analogy with the number l) and the number m_s to characterise the various orientations of the latter in a magnetic field (similar to the number m_l) on the assumption that between the numbers m_s and s we have the same relation as between the numbers m_l and l (see (24.11)), we get

$$m_s = \pm s, \ \pm(s-1), \ \ldots,$$

i.e., $2s+1$ values of the quantum number m_s and, consequently, $2s+1$ orientations of spin in a magnetic field. Since experiment gives only *two* orientations, it is obvious that $2s+1=2$, whence it follows that $s=\frac{1}{2}$ and $m_s=\pm\frac{1}{2}$.

Representing the intrinsic angular momentum of the electron (spin) as p_s and its projection as p'_s by means of formulas analogous to (24.20) and (24.24), we find

$$p_s = \hbar\sqrt{s(s+1)}, \quad s=\frac{1}{2}, \tag{24.25}$$

$$p'_s = \hbar m_s, \quad m_s = \pm\frac{1}{2}. \tag{24.26}$$

Further, as has already been pointed out (p. 164), measuring the magnitudes of magnetic splitting of the beam of hydrogen atoms in the Stern-Gerlach experiment leads to the value of magnetic moment of the H atom, i. e., to a value of the moment of the electron equal to one Bohr magneton. However, since these measurements do not yield the moment itself but its projection on the field direction, i.e., the quantity μ'_s, it is obvious that we must put

$$\mu'_s = \pm\mu_B = \pm\frac{\hbar}{2}\frac{e}{m}. \tag{24.27}$$

Comparing the expressions for μ'_s (24.27) and p'_s (24.26) and replacing the ratio μ'_s/p'_s by the ratio μ_s/p_s (due to both the angular momentum and magnetic moment being parallel), we find

$$\frac{\mu_s}{p_s} = \frac{e}{m}. \tag{24.28}$$

We see that for an electron, unlike the electron cloud (orbit), the ratio of magnetic moment to angular momentum has an *anomalous* value: whereas for the orbit this ratio is

$$\frac{\mu_l}{p_l}=\frac{1}{2}\frac{e}{m},$$

for the electron it is expressed by a quantity *twice* as great.

Thus, the introduction of spin yields a fourth independent quantum number m_s (in addition to the numbers n, l, and m_l), which is necessary for a description of the optical and magnetic properties of atoms. The twofold orientation of spin observed in an external magnetic field and corresponding to two possible values of the quantum number m_s, which may be called the *magnetic spin number*, also occurs in the internal magnetic field of the atom (due to the magnetic moment of the electron cloud). Because of interaction of the latter with the spin, the atom obtains a certain additional energy (see Sec. 26) that differs for different orientations of spin. As a result, each state of the atom characterised by the value $l \neq 0$ is split into two states (doublets). Such is the origin of the doublet structure of atomic terms, in particular the terms of the alkaline elements.

Wave model of the atom. As has already been pointed out (p. 171), quantum mechanics does not enable one to determine the position of an electron in an atom, i.e., to indicate the shape of an electron orbit, the very concept of which in quantum mechanics is merely conventional. However, we can compute to any degree of accuracy, the *probability* of finding an electron at a given point in the atomic space, which permits constructing some sort of a physical *model* of a quantum-mechanical atom.

Let us consider some quantum states of a hydrogen-like atom. The ground state of the atom in this case is the state corresponding to n=1, and, hence, $l=m_l=0$. An electron in this state belongs to the K-group (n=1) and is an s-electron ($l=0$). For n=2 we obtain the following four states: 1) $l=m_l=0$, the corresponding term is the 2s-term (L-group, L_I); 2) $l=1$, in the absence of an outer magnetic (or electric) field, a triply degenerate 2p-term (L-group, L_{II} and L_{III}) in accordance with three possible values of the magnetic quantum number $m_l=0, \pm 1$. We will confine ourselves to these few states and omit computational details of the respective wave functions, giving only the results (Table 10).

In Table 10, $s=(n/2)\varrho=Z\ r/r_1$, where $r_1=\hbar^2/me^2$ is the radius of a one-quantum Bohr orbit of the H atom. The following is to be noted in connection with normalisation of the

Table 10

The function ψ (normalised) for one- and two-quantum states of a hydrogen-like atom

n	l	m_l	term, group	$\theta(\vartheta)$	$R(\rho)$	$\psi_{\text{normal}} \sqrt{\pi}\left(\frac{r_1}{Z}\right)^{3/2}$
1	0	0	1s, K	1	$e^{-\rho/2}$	e^{-s}
2	0	0	2s, L_I	1	$2(\varrho-2)e^{-\rho/2}$	$\frac{1}{4\sqrt{2}}(2-s)e^{-s/2}$
2	1	0	2p, L_{II}	$\cos\vartheta$	$6\varrho e^{-\rho/2}$	$\frac{1}{4\sqrt{2}}se^{-s/2}\cos\vartheta$
2	1	± 1	2p, L_{III}	$\sin\vartheta$	$6\varrho e^{-\rho/2}$	$\frac{1}{8}se^{-s/2}\sin\vartheta e^{\pm i\varphi}$

function ψ. Earlier, when solving the Schrödinger equation for a hydrogen-like atom, we determined the functions R, Θ, Φ with an accuracy only to a certain constant factor. For this reason, the function ψ likewise was computed with an accuracy to this factor, which, however, may be unambiguously determined from the normalisation condition (23.7). It was in this way that the normalising factor $(1/\sqrt{\pi})\,(Z/r_1)^{3/2}$ in Table 10 was obtained.

A consideration of the wave function as dependent on the coordinates of the electron gives some idea of the distribution of the probability of finding an electron at a certain point of intra-atomic space. Thus, given a certain arbitrary direction that corresponds to definite values of the angles ϑ and φ, we can study the distribution of probability along a radius vector drawn from the centre of the atom (nucleus); here, this probability will depend only on the factor $|R|^2$ ($|\Theta|^2=$const and $\Phi^2=$const). The appropriate probability distribution is depicted in Fig. 39, where the dimensions of the corresponding Bohr orbits are also indicated. For the unit of distance we take the radius of a one-quantum Bohr orbit r_1 (in the drawing, $a_1=r_1$). The shaded areas correspond to the quantity $D=4\pi r^2|R|^2$, which determines the probability of finding an electron in the spherical layer $4\pi r^2\,dr$, equal to $D\,dr$. We note that D is maximum at a distance equal to the mean radius of a Bohr orbit if in the expression for $\bar{r}$ (p. 179) n_φ^2 is replaced by $l(l+1)$.

This fact indicates a certain similarity between the Bohr model of the atom with its discrete electron orbits and the wave model. However, the curves in Fig. 39 rather illustrate features of radical difference than features of similarity between the two models. For one thing, these curves show that unlike an electron of the Bohr atom, an electron of the wave theory can be located at *any point* in intra-atomic space with a *finite* probability that becomes zero only at an infinitely large distance from the

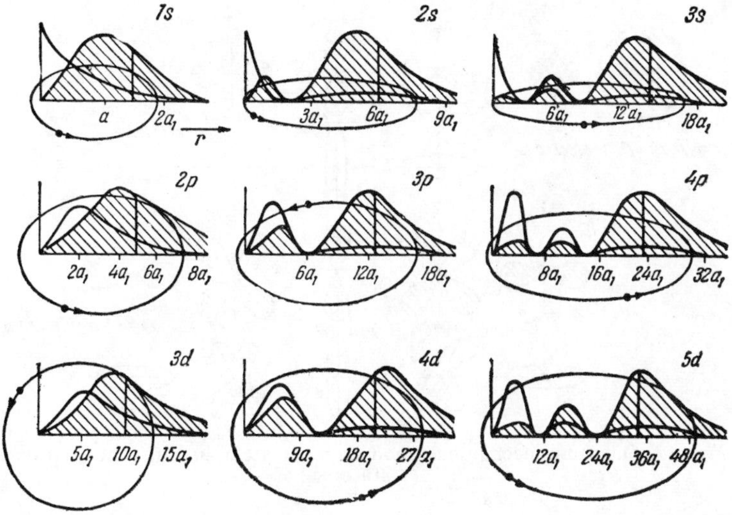

Fig. 39. Probabilities of finding an electron in a quantum-mechanical atom (at a distance r from the nucleus)

nucleus. Averaging, in time, of the position of an electron with respect to the nucleus in a single atom, or averaging the electron positions at a given instant of time in a large number of identical atoms is what leads to the concept of the electron cloud. This concept yields a more correct picture of distribution of the electron charge in an atom than does the Bohr model.

Of special interest is the study of probability distribution over angles ϑ and φ. It is readily seen that the probability is not dependent on the angle φ: indeed, $|\Phi|^2 = \Phi\Phi^* = e^{im_l\varphi}e^{-im_l\varphi} = 1$. Whence it follows that an electron cloud possesses axial *symmetry*.

As for the distribution of probability over angle ϑ, by specifying a definite distance from the nucleus r ($|R|^2 = \text{const}$) we can find this distribution by computing the values $|\Theta|^2$ for different ϑ. The result of such computation is graphically depicted in Fig. 40, where we also have the corresponding orientation of the Bohr orbit under each drawing. These drawings were made according to the rules of constructing ordinary vector diagrams: on the radius vectors drawn from the origin (nucleus) at appropriate angles ϑ are plotted lengths proportional to the values of quantity $|\Theta|^2$, and the ends of these lengths are connected by a continuous curve (circles and figure-8's).

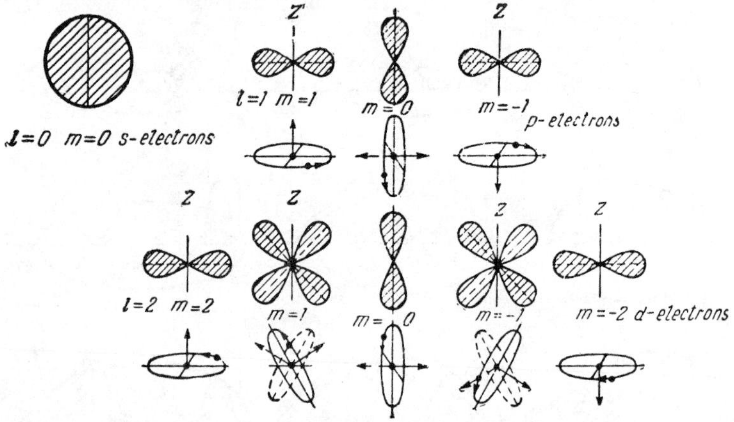

Fig. 40. Quantum-mechanical models of H atom in different quantum states

From Fig. 40 it will be seen that to the s-terms ($l=0$) there corresponds a *spherical symmetry* of the electron cloud. It may be shown by simple calculations that superposition of probability distributions for all possible values of the magnetic number m_l for constant values of the numbers l and n (*equivalent electrons*) leads to a total probability that is independent of the angle ϑ:

$$\sum_{m_l=-l}^{m_l=+l} |\Theta(\vartheta)|^2 = \text{const}, \tag{24.29}$$

i.e., also to spherical symmetry of the corresponding electron cloud (similar to the symmetry of the cloud of an s-electron).

Let us demonstrate this for the particular case $l=1$ (equivalent 2p-electrons), for which we already have the calculated values of the function ψ_{normal} (Table 10). We shall find the following expressions for the quantity $|\psi_{\text{normal}}|^2$ (we omit the factor $(1/\sqrt{\pi})(Z/r_1)^3$):

$$\frac{1}{32} s^2 e^{-s} \cos^2\vartheta \, (m_l=0) \quad \text{and} \quad \frac{1}{64} s^2 e^{-s} \sin^2\vartheta \, (m_l=\pm 1);$$

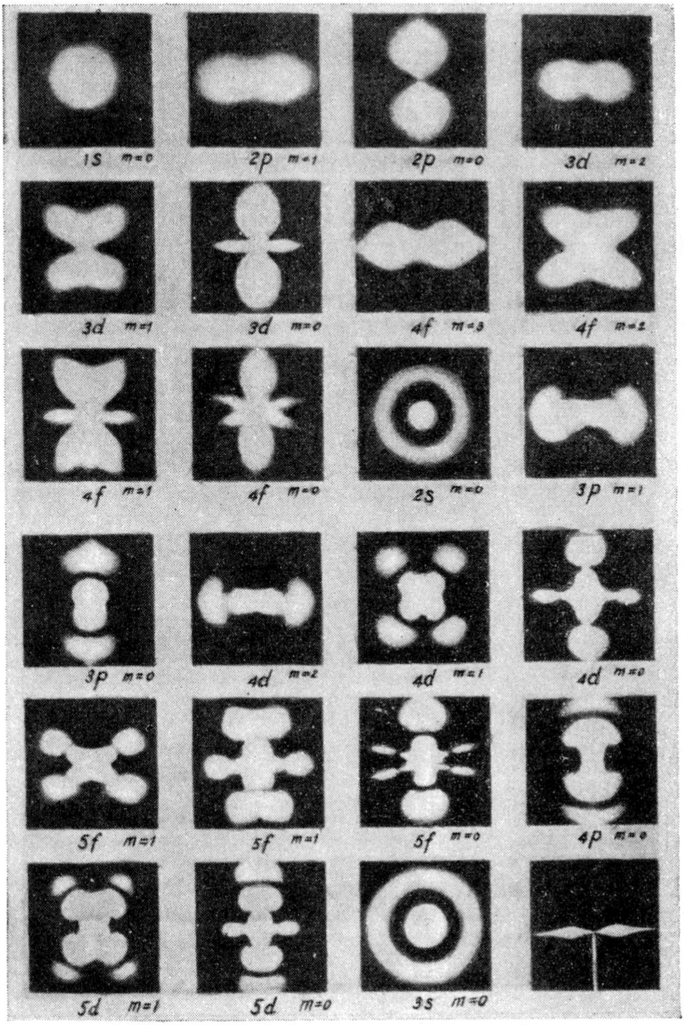

Fig. 41. The electron cloud of an atom (ion) with one electron in different quantum states of the atom (after White)

by summing we obtain the quantity $\frac{1}{32}s^2e^{-s}$ which is independent of the angle ϑ.

Comparing the probability distribution in the case of p- and d-electrons with orientation of the appropriate Bohr orbits

(Fig. 40), we see that the latter correspond only to maximum probability. Thus, in the case of p-electrons with $m_l = \pm 1$, maximum probability is found for the plane $\vartheta = \pi/2$ (perpendicular to the z axis), i.e., for a plane in which the appropriate Bohr orbits are located. However, as is seen from the figure, the electron probability has finite (different from zero) values also in the other planes. This circumstance alone shows how complicated is the motion of an electron (considered as a particle) in an atom and the inadequacy that follows therefrom of the classical concepts of coordinates and momenta for the description of this motion. However, by virtue of a certain correspondence between the quantum-mechanical and the Bohr models of the atom, which emerges from Fig. 39 and Fig. 40, present-day atomic theory makes successful use of these concepts and also of the Bohr theory as a whole, which has the advantage of pictorialness.

The pictures of the electron cloud shown in Fig. 41 in different states of the hydrogen atom are an attempt to give a pictorial model of the wave atom. These pictures were obtained by White by photographing special rotating mechanical models performing motion in space in accordance with the distribution law of $|\psi|^2$.

25. Two-Electron Atom (Ion)

Solution of the problem of an atom (ion) with two electrons by perturbation theory. The wave equation for an atom with many electrons may be written in the form

$$\sum_{k=1}^{k=N}\left[\left(\frac{\partial^2\psi}{\partial x_k^2}+\frac{\partial^2\psi}{\partial y_k^2}+\frac{\partial^2\psi}{\partial z_k^2}\right)+\frac{2m}{\hbar^2}\left(\frac{e^2Z}{r_k}-V_k\right)\psi\right]+\frac{2m}{\hbar^2}E\psi=0. \quad (25.1)$$

Here, N is the number of electrons in the atom, E is the total energy of the atom, r_k is the distance of the *k*th electron from the nucleus and

$$V_k=\sum_{i=1}^{i=N}\frac{e^2}{r_{ki}}$$

where r_{ki} is the distance between the *k*th and *i*th electrons. Like the many-body problem in classical mechanics, equation (25.1) does not admit of an exact solution. Therefore, various kinds of approximate methods have to be used.

One of the most fruitful and widely used approximate methods is the *method* of *perturbation theory*. It is applied both in classical (celestial, for instance) mechanics and in quantum mechanics. The principal difficulty in solving the many-body problem of classical mechanics (for example, the problem of a planetary system) and also the many-electron problem of quantum mechanics consists in the necessity to account for the interaction of the electrons (planets). In perturbation theory, this interaction is accounted for in successive approximations. Disregarding this interaction completely we get a solution to a zero approximation. In solving the problem to a *first* approximation it is assumed that this interaction is slight and introduces only a small distortion (perturbation) into the result obtained for the zero approximation, and it is taken that the energy of perturbed motion, to this approximation, is equal to the sum of the energy of the unperturbed motion (zero approximation) and the mean energy of interaction (averaged over the unperturbed motion, see below).

The simplest case of a many-electron system is the helium atom, the problem of which was a stumbling block for the classical (Bohr) theory of the atom. In quantum mechanics, this problem received an exhaustive solution by the method of perturbation theory (Heisenberg, 1926).

The wave equation for the helium atom or for an ion with two electrons (Li^+, Be^{++}, B^{+++}, C^{4+}, etc.) has the form

$$\frac{\partial^2\psi}{\partial x_1^2}+\frac{\partial^2\psi}{\partial y_1^2}+\frac{\partial^2\psi}{\partial z_1^2}+\frac{\partial^2\psi}{\partial x_2^2}+\frac{\partial^2\psi}{\partial y_2^2}+\frac{\partial^2\psi}{\partial z_2^2}+$$
$$+\frac{2m}{\hbar^2}\left(E+\frac{e^2Z}{r_1}+\frac{e^2Z}{r_2}-\frac{e^2}{r_{12}}\right)\psi=0 \tag{25.2}$$

obtained from (25.1) when $N=2$. Disregarding, in the zero approximation, the energy of mutual repulsion of the electrons e^2/r_{12}, we obtain a solution to equation (25.2) in the form of a product of two functions $\psi_{n_1}(x_1, y_1, z_1)$ and $\psi_{n_2}(x_2, y_2, z_2)$:

$$\psi(x_1, y_1, z_1, x_2, y_2, z_2)=\psi_{n_1}(x_1, y_1, z_1)\,\psi_{n_2}(x_2, y_2, z_2)$$

each of which is a solution of one of the equations of the form

$$\frac{\partial^2\psi_k}{\partial x_k^2}+\frac{\partial^2\psi_k}{\partial y_k^2}+\frac{\partial^2\psi_k}{\partial z_k^2}+\frac{2m}{\hbar^2}\left(E_k+\frac{e^2Z}{r_k}\right)\psi_k=0, \qquad k=1,\ 2,$$

obtained by separation of the initial wave equation. Thus, to a zero approximation, the problem of the two-electron atom reduces to the problem of an atom with one electron, the solution of which leads to eigenfunctions determined by (24.2), (24.8), (24.10), and (24.12), and to the characteristic numbers $E_n=-2\pi^2me^4Z^2/h^2n^2$ that express the energy of an atom in an appropriate quantum state. The total energy of a two-electron atom (ion), to a zero approximation, is obviously equal to the sum

$$E = E_{n_1} + E_{n_2}.$$

Passing to the first approximation, we first solve the problem of the ground state of the helium atom and the corresponding ions. According to perturbation theory, the mean energy of perturbation (the energy of the mutual repulsion of the electrons) is expressed by the integral

$$\Delta E = \frac{\int |\psi|^2 \frac{e^2}{r_{12}} dv}{\int |\psi|^2 dv}, \qquad dv = dv_1 \, dv_2, \tag{25.3}$$

which, upon normalisation of the function ψ, passes into the integral

$$\Delta E = \int |\psi|^2 \frac{e^2}{r_{12}} dv. \tag{25.3a}$$

The integral (25.3a) is taken over all possible positions of the electrons. The function ψ is the product of the wave functions for the ground state of a hydrogen-like atom $\psi_1 = \frac{1}{\sqrt{\pi}} \left(\frac{Z}{a_1}\right)^{3/2} e^{-\rho/2}$ (unperturbed motion), i.e.,

$$\psi = \frac{Z^3}{\pi a_1^3} e^{-\frac{Z}{a_1} r_1} e^{-\frac{Z}{a_1} r_2}.$$

In the variables $\varrho_k = \left(\frac{2Z}{a_1}\right) r_k$, for an element of volume of six-dimensional space in polar coordinates we obtain the expression

$$dv = \left(\frac{a_1}{2Z}\right)^6 \varrho_1^2 d\varrho_1 \sin\vartheta_1 d\vartheta_1 d\varphi_1 \varrho_2^2 d\varrho_2 \sin\vartheta_2 d\vartheta_2 d\varphi_2.$$

Substituting the latter, together with the wave function ψ, into the expression for the energy of perturbation ΔE, we get

$$\Delta E = \frac{Ze^2}{2^5 \pi^2 a_1} \int_0^\infty \int_0^\pi \int_0^{2\pi} \int_0^\infty \int_0^\pi \int_0^{2\pi} \frac{e^{-(\varrho_1+\varrho_2)}}{\varrho_{12}} \varrho_1^2 d\varrho_1 \sin\vartheta_1 d\vartheta_1 d\varphi_1 \varrho_2^2 d\varrho_2 \sin\vartheta_2 d\vartheta_2 d\varphi_2,$$

where $\varrho_{12} = \left(\frac{2Z}{a_1}\right) r_{12}$. Evaluation of the integral in this expression yields $20\pi^2$, whence it follows that $\Delta E = 20\pi^2 (Ze^2/2^5\pi^2 a_1) = 5/4\,(Ze^2/2a_1) = 5/4\,(2\pi^2 me^4 Z/h^2) = -5/4\,(ZE_H)$,

where E_H is the energy of a normal H atom; in absolute magnitude it is equal to the energy of ionisation (13.60 eV). Thus, to a first approximation, for the total energy of a two-electron system we have

$$E=-\frac{2\pi^2me^4Z^2}{h^2}-\frac{2\pi^2me^4Z^2}{h^2}+\frac{5}{4}\frac{2\pi^2me^4Z}{h^2}=\left(2Z^2-\frac{5}{4}Z\right)E_H. \quad (25.4)$$

The energy values of total ionisation of a helium atom and of ions with two electrons calculated from this formula are given in Table 11 (third column). The second column gives the zero-approximation evaluation ($E=2Z^2E_H$) and the fourth column, the measured values of ionisation energy.

Table 11

Calculated (to a zero approximation, $-E_0$, to a first approximation, $-E_1$) and measured ($-E_{meas}$) values of ionisation energy of the helium atom and of ions with two electrons (in eV).

Ionisation energy / Elements	$-E_0$	$-E_1$	$-E_{meas}$	$\frac{E_1-E_{meas}}{E_{meas}}\times 100\%$
He	108.76	74.78	78.98	5.3
Li^+	244.71	193.73	198.04	2.2
Be^{++}	435.04	367.06	371.51	1.2
B^{3+}	679.75	594.78	599.43	0.8
C^{4+}	978.84	876.88	881.83	0.6

From the table it is seen that already in the first approximation the theory gives satisfactory agreement with experiment. By improving the methods of calculation it is possible to increase their accuracy appreciably. Thus, Hylleraas developed a variational method of approximate solution of the Schrödinger equation and obtained practically total agreement of calculated values of the first ionisation potential of helium and of ions with two electrons and the measured values of this quantity, as may be seen from the following:*

* In Hylleraas' calculations, as also in a spectroscopic determination of the measured values of ionisation potentials (I_{meas}), such values of the Rydberg constant are taken that differ from the presently accepted and more precise values. For this reason, I_{calc} and I_{meas}, as given here, differ from the more precise values of ionisation potential: 24.586 (He), 75.62 (Li^+), 153.85 (Be^{++}), 259.30 (B^{3+}), 391.99 V (C^{4+}). We note that on the calculations of Kinosita, the ionisation potential of helium is 24.586 V, which coincides exactly with the measured value 24.5860 ± 0.0001 V.

	He	Li^+	Be^{++}	B^{3+}	C^{4+}
I_{calc}	24.46	75.26	153.13	258.09	390.12
I_{meas}	24.47	75.28	153.10	258.1 ± 0.2	389.9 ± 0.4

It may be added that Hylleraas subsequently also calculated (by his method) the energy of the ions H^- and H_2^+. The values, obtained from his evaluations, of the electron affinity of the H atom (0.71eV) and the heat of dissociation of the molecular ion H_2^+ (2.72 eV) are in good agreement with the findings of other methods.

Exchange degeneracy. Up till now we have considered cases when, to a zero approximation, the problem reduces to the solution of wave equations for a hydrogen-like atom in the ground state, i.e., cases of the ground state of a system with two electrons. Let us now solve the general problem when any states of the hydrogen-like atom are possible, so that the wave function of the unperturbed problem (zero approximation) must be taken in the form given on p. 196. Denoting in abbreviated form all the coordinates of the first electron (x_1, y_1, z_1) by the number 1, and the coordinates of the second electron (x_2, y_2, z_2) by 2, we rewrite the function ψ in the form

$$\psi = \psi_{n_1}(1)\,\psi_{n_2}(2).$$

However, this solution is not the only one that corresponds to the given values of the principal quantum number n_1 and n_2 and, consequently, to the given value of energy of the atom (to the zero approximation under consideration). Indeed, in view of the fact that the electrons are *indistinguishable*, a solution is also possible when the first electron is in state n_2 and the second in state n_1, i. e., a solution of the form

$$\psi = \psi_{n_1}(2)\,\psi_{n_2}(1).$$

We thus have two states of the system $\psi_{n_1}(1)\,\psi_{n_2}(2)$ and $\psi_{n_1}(2)\,\psi_{n_2}(1)$ with the same energy (a *doubly degenerate* state). This degeneracy, which is due to the indistinguishability of the electrons and to their interchangeability that follows therefrom (or the possibility of their exchange) is called *exchange degeneracy*.

Due to exchange degeneracy, a more general solution of the problem is given by linear combinations of both preceding particular solutions: either

$$\psi_S = \psi_{n_1}(1)\,\psi_{n_2}(2) + \psi_{n_1}(2)\,\psi_{n_2}(1) \qquad (25.5)$$

$$\psi_A = \psi_{n_1}(1)\,\psi_{n_2}(2) - \psi_{n_1}(2)\,\psi_{n_2}(1). \qquad (25.6)$$

The first of these solutions, ψ_S, which does not change through an interchange of electrons (interchange of the numbers 1 and 2), is *symmetrical*, while the second, ψ_A, which reverses its sign if the electrons are interchanged, is called *antisymmetrical*.

When we take account of perturbation, i.e., the mutual repulsion of the electrons e^2/r_{12}, exchange degeneracy disappears and to the eigenfunctions there now correspond *different* energy values E_S and E_A into which the initial doubly degenerate level splits.

Combining (25.5) and (25.6) and taking the square of the modulus of the combined function, we have

$$|\psi|^2 = \psi_{n_1}(1)\,\overset{*}{\psi}_{n_1}(1)\,\psi_{n_2}(2)\,\overset{*}{\psi}_{n_2}(2) +$$

$$+\psi_{n_1}(2)\,\overset{*}{\psi}_{n_1}(2)\,\psi_{n_2}(1)\,\overset{*}{\psi}_{n_2}(1) \pm 2\psi_{n_1}(1)\,\overset{*}{\psi}_{n_1}(2)\,\psi_{n_2}(1)\,\overset{*}{\psi}_{n_2}(2). \qquad (25.7)$$

Substituting (25.7) into the expression for the mean energy of perturbation (25.3) and noting that by virtue of the symmetry of the perturbing term e^2/r_{12} relative to both electrons (1 and 2) the first two terms (25.7) yield the same result, we obtain

$$\Delta E = \frac{\iint \left\{ |\psi_{n_1}(1)|^2 |\psi_{n_2}(2)|^2 \pm \psi_{n_1}(1)\,\overset{*}{\psi}_{n_1}(2)\,\psi_{n_2}(1)\,\overset{*}{\psi}_{n_2}(2) \right\} \frac{e^2}{r_{12}}\, dv_1 dv_2}{\iint \left\{ |\psi_{n_1}(1)|^2 |\psi_{n_2}(2)|^2 \pm \psi_{n_1}(1)\,\overset{*}{\psi}_{n_1}(2)\,\psi_{n_2}(1)\,\overset{*}{\psi}_{n_2}(2) \right\} dv_1 dv_2}. \qquad (25.8)$$

Expression (25.8) contains four integrals: two in the numerator and two in the denominator. Let us first consider the integrals in the numerator. The first one, which we shall designate by C, is

$$C = \int |\psi_{n_1}(1)|^2 \frac{e^2}{r_{12}} |\psi_{n_2}(2)|^2\, dv_1\, dv_2 \qquad (25.9)$$

and has the following physical meaning. Since the quantity $e|\psi_{n_1}(1)|^2$ represents the charge density of the first electron (this quantity has the more exact meaning of "probability density"), while the quantity $e|\psi_{n_2}(2)|^2$ is the charge density of the second electron, the integral C obviously expresses the energy of Coulomb interaction of the electrons (on the condition that they are distinguishable). For this reason, the integral C is called the *Coulomb integral* (usually when it is divided by e^2).

As to the second integral in the numerator (25.8), which we designate by A,

$$A = \int \psi_{n_1}(1)\,\overset{*}{\psi}_{n_2}(2)\,\frac{e^2}{r_{12}}\,\psi_{n_1}(2)\,\overset{*}{\psi}_{n_2}(1)\, dv_1 dv_2, \qquad (25.10)$$

it does not have such a simple physical meaning. As follows from the foregoing, it arises from exchange degeneracy caused by the indistinguishability of the electrons, and cannot be interpreted within the framework of classical theory. This integral is called an *exchange integral* (also when it is divided by e^2).

However, it must be stressed that neither is the above "interpretation" of the C integral consistent or, for this reason, exact. Indeed, as has already been pointed out, this integral may be regarded as expressing the energy of Coulomb repulsion of electrons only on the assumption of indistinguishability of the electrons, and this contradicts experiment. Whence it follows that the division into Coulomb (C) and exchange (A) atomic energy is arbitrary and is the result of an inexact interpretation of the physical meaning of the C integral. It may be added that the appearance of two integrals (C and A) in the expression for the mean perturbation energy of (25.3) is due to particularities in the method of perturbation theory applied to solving the two-electron problem. An exact physical meaning is retained only in the sum of integrals $C+A$, which, according to (25.3), is equal to the mean value of Coulomb potential energy of mutual electron repulsion, since the denominator of expression (25.8) is equal to unity on the condition that the functions ψ_{n_1} and ψ_{n_2} are normalised. Indeed, the first term of the denominator in this expression $\int|\psi_{n_1}(1)|^2|\psi_{n_2}(2)|^2 dv_1 dv_2$ in accordance with the normalisation condition of wave functions $\int|\psi_{n_1}(1)|^2 dv_1 = \int|\psi_{n_2}(2)|^2 dv_2 = 1$ equals 1, the second term, $\int\psi_{n_1}(1)\psi^*_{n_1}(2)\psi_{n_2}(1)\psi^*_{n_2}(2)\,dv_1 dv_2$, by virtue of the orthogonality of the wave functions expressed by the equalities $\int\psi_{n_1}(1)\psi_{n_2}(1)\,dv_1 = \int\psi_{n_1}(2)\psi_{n_2}(2)\,dv_2 = 0$, is zero. Thus, for the perturbation energy we get

$$\Delta E = C \pm A. \tag{25.11}$$

Due to indistinguishability of the electrons, the quantity $|\psi|^2$ (25.7), which determines the electron probability (or density of the electron cloud), must be symmetric with respect to transposition of electrons, i. e., it must not change sign in the process: $|\psi(1, 2)|^2 = |\psi(2, 1)|^2$. Whence it follows that the wave function itself may be both symmetric and antisymmetric: $\psi(1, 2) = \pm\psi(2, 1)$; this property is indeed satisfied by the wave functions (25.5) and (25.6).

Spin function. Pauli principle. The function ψ, which is a solution to the Schrödinger equation, is, however, insufficient for a complete characteristic of the appropriate quantum state of the atom, since this requires that the electron spin also be taken into account. Introducing "spin coordinates" of the electrons in addition to the coordinates x, y, z and assuming at least approximate separation of the variables in the total wave equation, which includes spin coordinates as well, we can represent the total wave function in the form

$$\Psi = \psi S \tag{25.12}$$

where S is the function of spin coordinates (*spin function*).

Like the function ψ, the spin function possesses definite properties of symmetry. Introducing the spin function α to describe the state of an electron corresponding to a positive value of spin projection $\left(m_s = +\frac{1}{2}\right)$ and the spin function β to describe a state with negative value of projection $\left(m_s = -\frac{1}{2}\right)$, we can represent the general solution of the spin part of the wave equation in the form of the following four functions:

$$S = \alpha(1)\,\alpha(2),$$
$$S = \beta(1)\,\beta(2),$$
$$S = \alpha(1)\,\beta(2) + \alpha(2)\,\beta(1),$$
$$S = \alpha(1)\,\beta(2) - \alpha(2)\,\beta(1).$$

The first three functions are, obviously, symmetric with respect to a transposition of electrons, the latter is antisymmetric. Let us designate the symmetric and antisymmetric spin functions by the symbols S_S and S_A, respectively. To the first three functions there correspond values of total projection $m_s = m_{s_1} + m_{s_2} = \pm 1$ and 0; to the last, the value 0. Whence it may be concluded that the first three functions refer to a triply degenerate state of an atom characterised by total spin $S = 1$, the latter, to a state with total spin $S = 0$.

In accordance with the symmetry of the functions ψ and S, the total wave function Ψ may be symmetric or antisymmetric. The functions $\Psi_S = \psi_S S_S$ and $\Psi_S = \psi_A S_A$ are obviously symmetric, and the functions $\Psi_A = \psi_s S_A$ and $\Psi_A = \psi_A S_S$ are antisymmetric. However, not all of them correspond to real states of the atom; this is connected with the so-called *Pauli principle* (1925), which is one of the general principles underlying modern quantum statistics. According to the Pauli principle, an atom cannot have two or more electrons characterised by the same values of the four independent quantum numbers, for example, n, l, m_l, and m_s. It will readily be seen that only antisymmetric wave functions satisfy this principle. Indeed, assuming two electrons with quantum numbers identical, transposition of these electrons will yield a state identical with the initial state, and, consequently, $\Psi_{12} = \Psi_{21}$. For the antisymmetric function we have: $\Psi_{12} = -\Psi_{21}$.

Obviously, both these conditions are satisfied only by a function that is identically equal to zero, which signifies the impossibility of this state (in which all quantum numbers of the two electrons are the same). Hence, the condition for satisfying the Pauli principle is the condition of *antisymmetry* of the total wave function. Such is the quantum-mechanical formulation of the Pauli principle.

When this principle is taken into account by total wave functions that correspond to actual states of a two-electron system (for example, a helium atom), there can only be total wave functions $\Psi_A = \psi_S S_A$ and $\Psi_A = \psi_A S_S$. In the case of

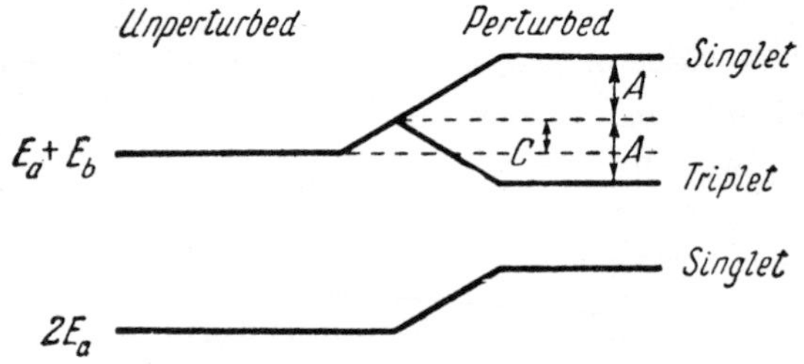

Fig. 42. Lower terms of He atom

equivalent electrons, that is, electrons characterised by the same values of the quantum numbers n and l and with identical m_l as well, the Pauli principle, in addition, excludes the state characterised by the function $\Psi_A = \psi_A S_S$, since in this case $m_{s_1} = m_{s_2}$, which contradicts the principle. An obvious instance of identical n, l, and m_l of both electrons is, for example, the ground state of the helium atom, to which there correspond minimum possible values of quantum numbers, i.e., $n_1 = n_2 = 1$, $l_1 = l_2 = 0$ and $m_{l_1} = m_{l_2} = 0$. Since the orbital angular momenta of both electrons and the total spin angular momentum of the normal helium atom are zero, its total angular momentum is also zero and, hence, the statistical weight is unity. Let us also consider the case of $n_1 = 1$ and $n_2 = 2$. In this case, both antisymmetric states are possible: $\Psi_A = \psi_S S_A$ and $\Psi_A = \psi_A S_S$. The first one is a singlet ($S = 0$) and has statistical weight 1, the second is a triplet ($S = 1$) and has statistical weight 3. Since to a singlet state there corresponds perturbation energy $\Delta E = C + A$, and to a triplet, perturbation energy $\Delta E = C - A$, the triplet level will be situated *below* the singlet. From the foregoing we get a picture of the lower energy levels of the He atom as shown in Fig. 42. From this figure it follows that the ground level of the helium atom must be a singlet and the first excited level a triplet. This conclusion has been experimentally corroborated not only in the case of the helium atom and the ions Li^+, Be^{++}, B^{+++}, etc., but also in the case of many-electron atoms or ions with two outer electrons (for instance, Mg, Zn, Cd, Hg, or Al^+, Tl^+, etc.). For one thing, all the foregoing atoms or ions are diamagnetic in the ground state, thus indicating that these states are singlet.* It may be added that the energy levels of the helium atom, calculated to a first approximation, coincide with the observed values to within 20-30%. For a first approximation, this agreement between calculated and measured energy values of the He atom should be considered quite satisfactory.

Atom (ion) with large number of electrons. The method of perturbation theory, like the variational method of Hylleraas, which is successfully applied in the solution of the problem of an atom with a small number of electrons such as the helium atom and also certain other problems, encounters great difficulties when applied to many-electron systems, where it is very difficult to account for the perturbation energy. For this reason, other methods of calculation must be resorted to when dealing with such systems. Here, statistical methods have proved particularly fruitful.

One of these methods—the Thomas (1926)-Fermi (1928) method—proceeds from a statistical atomic model that presumes a continuous distribution of electron density (in the atom), which is connected with the intra-atomic electric field by the Poisson equation. Substituting, into the latter, the electron density calculated on the basis of quantum statistics and the Pauli principle, we obtain the following differential equation for the field potential (*Thomas-Fermi equation*):

$$\frac{d^2\varphi}{dx^2} = \frac{\varphi^{3/2}}{\sqrt{x}}, \tag{25.13}$$

where

$$\varphi(x) = \frac{1}{Ze} r (\chi - \chi_a), \qquad x = \frac{r}{\mu}$$

(r is the distance from the nucleus, μ is a quantity proportional to the radius of a one-quantum Bohr orbit r_1, χ is the field potential at the distance r and χ_a is the potential in outer space, equal to Ze/r, where Z is the charge of the ion; in the case of a neutral atom $\chi_a = 0$). Integration of this equation under specific boundary conditions that correspond to the given problem is what under-

* Accordingly, the magnetic moment of the He atom in the ground state is zero, unlike the magnetic moment of the triplet state, for which measurements yield $2\mu_B$.

lies the solution of problems of atomic physics by the Thomas-Fermi statistical method.

By way of illustration, it may be noted that on the basis of the statistical model of the atom, Fermi considered the question: beginning with what value of Z do the s-, p-, d-, etc., orbits in the ground state first make their appearance in the Periodic Table? In this case, the problem reduces to finding (by integration of the appropriate differential equation with the use of the function φ, which is obtained by solving the Thomas-Fermi equation) the values of the atomic number Z at which the number of electrons characterised by a given value of the quantum number l becomes equal to 1. In this way, in accordance with experiment, Fermi found that the value $l=1$ (p-electrons) first appears at $Z=5$ (boron), $l=2$ (d-electrons), at $Z=21$ (scandium), and not at $Z=19$, i.e., immediately following argon, as might be expected in regular filling of the quantum states. In the same way, Fermi found that the f-orbits ($l=3$) first appear not in silver ($Z=47$), as should be expected in the case of uniform filling of the orbits, but much later, at $Z=55$ (caesium), whereas the true value is $Z=58$ (cerium).

Of the other applications of the Thomas-Fermi method, we note the calculation of the Rydberg corrections for s-terms carried out by Fermi and Amaldi on the basis of this method, calculation of X-ray M-levels (Rasetti), etc. It should be noted that the Thomas-Fermi statistical model proved exceedingly convenient for describing the internal properties of electron clouds of atoms and quite unsuitable for describing the external properties, such as the diamagnetism of atoms.

Whereas the Thomas-Fermi method does not require solution of the Schrödinger equation, the Hartree (1927)-Fok (1930) method (another statistical method) is based on this equation. In the latter method, the electric field of all electrons, except the field created by the selected electron, is replaced by a certain average time-constant field * which Hartree called a "self-consistent field". To surmount the chief difficulty of the method (this has to do with isolating the field of the chosen electron), Fok ** developed a very effective procedure based on the exchange effect. Introduction of a "self-consistent field" permits solving the approximate Schrödinger equation for this electron. One of the results of the solution of the problem is the possibility of assigning to each selected electron definite quantum numbers n, l, and m_l. In this way it is

* We have already encountered substitution of an electron field by a certain average field in the problem of atoms of alkaline elements by the Born-Heisenberg method (see p. 156).

** Later, Slater succeeded in greatly simplifying Fok's equations.

possible to find the quantum numbers for all electrons of a complex atom, which is of great fundamental importance, for it permits extending the results of systematics of electron states established for a one-electron atom to an atom with any number of electrons.

Using this method, Hartree calculated a large number of atoms and ions: Rb^+, Cl^-, Cu^+, He, O, K, Cs, Be, Ca, F^-, Hg. In Sommerfeld's words: "Thanks to the many years of purposeful, intensive work of Hartree, the problem of integration of Schrödinger's equation is practically solved even for heavy atoms (Hg!)".

The Hartree-Fok method was also used to calculate the diamagnetic susceptibility for Ar and K^+ (the results closely coincided with experiment), for which purpose the Thomas-Fermi method, as we pointed out above, proved unsuitable. The Hartree-Fok method was likewise successfully applied in calculating the probabilities of quantum transitions in atoms (see Sec. 28). It may be added that of late, due to improvements in computational methods, the number of calculated atoms and ions has increased considerably.

CHAPTER 5

THE SPECTROSCOPY OF ATOMS

26. Systematics of Atomic States

Multiplet (fine) structure of atomic terms. Atom (ion) with one outer electron. The principal factor determining the atomic properties which depend on the electronic structure of the atom is the *electron configuration* of the atom in the given state. By electron configuration is understood the distribution of electrons in quantum states characterised by the quantum numbers n and l. Due to the fact that for a given value of the principal quantum number n the number l can assume n values 0, 1, 2, ..., n — 1, we have the following double diversity of electron states (terms):

1s	2s	3s	4s	5s	...
	2p	3p	4p	5p	...
		3d	4d	5d	...
			4f	5f	...
				5g	...

To every state there corresponds a definite electron *subgroup* with a maximum number of electrons equal to $2(2l+1)$. This number is determined by the possible values (for a given l) of the quantum number m_l and by the two values of the number m_s, with account taken of the limitations imposed by the Pauli principle.

A definite contribution to the energy of the atomic state is made by the magnetic interaction of the orbital angular momenta and the intrinsic angular momenta of the electrons (spins). In an atom (or ion) with one electron, one has to take into account the interaction of orbital angular momentum and the spin of this single electron. Above (p. 187) it is interpreted, for the sake of clarity, as space quantisation of spin in an intra-atomic magnetic field. A more correct picture of the interaction of spin and orbital angular momentum is given in Fig. 43; according to this picture, the interaction consists in space quantisation of both angular momenta (vectors $\mathbf{l}$ and s) relative to the direction of the resultant angular momentum (vector j). Calculation of the absolute magnitude of the latter leads to the expression

$$p = \hbar\sqrt{(l \pm s)(l \pm s + 1)}. \qquad (26.1)$$

By introducing the quantum number j (the *total angular-momentum quantum number*) to characterise the resultant angular momentum, we can represent expression (26.1) also in the form (cf. (24.20) and (24.25))

$$p = \hbar\sqrt{j(j+1)}. \qquad (26.2)$$

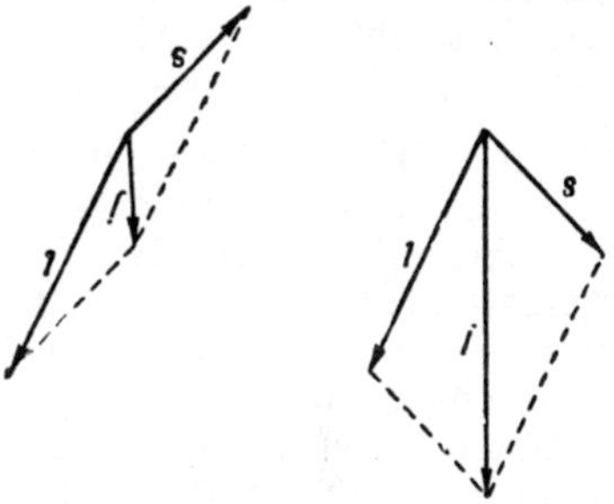

Fig. 43. Interaction of orbital angular momentum $\mathbf{l}$ and spin s

From (26.1) and (26.2), it follows that

$$j = l \pm s = l \pm \frac{1}{2}. \qquad (26.3)$$

Thus, for each state corresponding to a definite value of the quantum number l (with the exception of the state $l = 0$), we obtain two values of the total angular-momentum quantum number, $j = l + 1/2$ and $j = l - 1/2$, which may be used to describe the components of doublet splitting that arises from the interaction of the vectors $\mathbf{l}$ and s.

Table 12

Terms of atoms and ions with one outer electron described by means of total angular-momentum quantum number (j)

Terms	l	j					
s	0	1/2					
p	1	1/2	3/2				
d	2		3/2	5/2			
f	3			5/2	7/2		

Table 12 gives the values, obtained from (26.3), of the total angular-momentum quantum number for various terms (states) of a hydrogen-like atom or ion and also for the terms of an atom or ion with one outer electron and with an atomic core having the structure of a noble gas.* Since, by virtue of $l = 0$, there is no interaction of the vectors $\mathbf{l}$ and s in the case of s-states of the atom (ion), for these states we have $j = s$, i.e., one value of the number j (simple terms). In contrast, to all other terms in Table 12 there correspond two values of the quantum number j.

* In all these cases the concepts of atomic and electron terms are identical.

Representing the orbital and spin angular momenta, and also the resultant angular momentum of the atom in the form of vectors (see Fig. 43), it is possible to conceive the atom in any quantum state as a certain *vector model* built up from the vectors l, s and the vector

$$\mathbf{j}=\boldsymbol{l}+\mathbf{s}. \tag{26.4}$$

In view of (26.3), to the *geometric* addition of vectors (26.4) there corresponds an *algebraic* addition of appropriate quantum numbers. This greatly simplifies the classification of atomic states by reducing it to a simple combinatorial analysis of numbers. Since the problem of this classification is not to determine the absolute values of the terms but to find the number of possible terms and to describe their properties, we can, by replacing the addition of vectors with the addition of corresponding quantum numbers, greatly simplify and render more vivid the vector model itself. Thus, considering conditionally that the vectors $\boldsymbol{l}$ and s are parallel and replacing the precise expressions of angular momenta

$$p_l=\hbar\sqrt{l(l+1)},\quad p_s=\hbar\sqrt{s(s+1)}\quad \text{and}\quad p=\hbar\sqrt{j(j+1)}$$

by their approximate expressions

$$p_l=\hbar l,\quad p_s=\hbar s\quad \text{and}\quad p=\hbar j$$

(i.e., attributing to the vectors the maximum values of their projections), we may write the resultant angular momentum as an algebraic sum of angular momenta p_l and p_s, i. e., $p=\hbar j=$ $=p_l\pm p_s=\hbar(l\pm s)$. The significant point here is that we thus obtain a correct relationship of quantum numbers j, l, and s; this is readily seen if in the preceding equality we cancel $\hbar$.

We may add that, like the projections of the orbital angular momentum (24.24) and the spin (24.26), the projection of the resultant angular momentum of the atom (on a certain direction z) is expressed by the formula

$$p'=\hbar m \tag{26.5}$$

where the *magnetic quantum number* m, having the same meaning as the earlier introduced magnetic orbital quantum number (m_l) and magnetic spin quantum number (m_s), in this case takes on the following values:

$$m=j,\ j-1,\ j-2,\ \ldots,\ -(j-2),\ -(j-1),\ -j, \tag{26.6}$$

i.e., $2j+1$ values.

Fine structure of the terms of an atom (ion) with two outer electrons. In passing to an atom with two outer electrons, we must take into account the interaction of four angular momenta—two orbital, $\boldsymbol{l}_1$ and $\boldsymbol{l}_2$, and two spin, $\mathbf{s}_1$ and $\mathbf{s}_2$. It will be found convenient to consider the following two cases: 1) when the predominant interaction is between vectors $\boldsymbol{l}_1$, and $\boldsymbol{l}_2$ and vectors $\mathbf{s}_1$ and $\mathbf{s}_2$, and 2) when the predominant interaction is between vectors $\boldsymbol{l}_i$ and $\mathbf{s}_i$ ($i=1, 2$). In the first of these cases, called *Russell-Saunders coupling*, the vector of the resultant orbital angular momentum appears as a result of the interaction of vectors $\boldsymbol{l}_1$ and $\boldsymbol{l}_2$:

$$\mathbf{L}=\boldsymbol{l}_1+\boldsymbol{l}_2$$

and the vector of resultant spin as a result of the interaction of spins $\mathbf{s}_1$ and $\mathbf{s}_2$:

$$\mathbf{S}=\mathbf{s}_1+\mathbf{s}_2.$$

From the vector model (see above) we obtain the following values of the appropriate quantum numbers:

$$L=l_1+l_2,\ l_1+l_2-1,\ l_1+l_2-2,\ \ldots,\ |l_1-l_2| \quad (26.7)$$

(maximum value of $L=l_1+l_2$ corresponds to parallel orientation of the vectors $\boldsymbol{l}_1$ and $\boldsymbol{l}_2$ in the vector model; minimum $L=|l_1-l_2|$, to their antiparallel orientation) and

$$S={}^1/_2\pm{}^1/_2,\ \text{i.e.,}\ S=1 \text{ and } 0. \quad (26.8)$$

The mutual orientation of vectors $\boldsymbol{l}_1$ and $\boldsymbol{l}_2$ (for $l_1=2$ and $l_2=3$) and spins in the vector model of an atom with two outer electrons is given in Figs. 44 and 45, respectively.

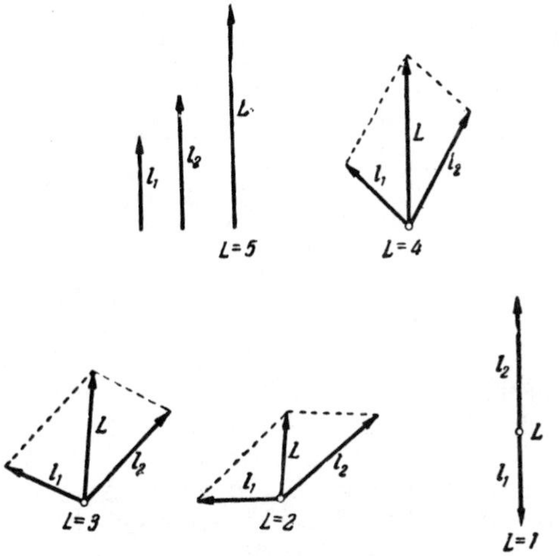

Fig. 44. Mutual orientation of orbital angular momenta in the vector model of an atom with two outer electrons

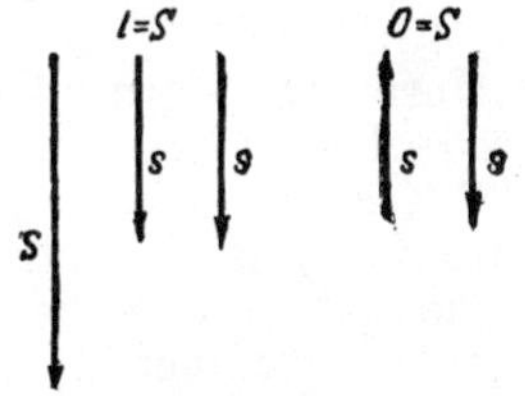

Fig. 45. Mutual orientation spins in the vector model of an atom with two outer electrons

As a result of the interaction of vectors **L** and **S** (this interaction is weaker than that of $\boldsymbol{l}_1$, $\boldsymbol{l}_2$ and $\mathbf{s}_1$, $\mathbf{s}_2$), a vector of total angular momentum of the atom appears:

$$\mathbf{J}=\mathbf{L}+\mathbf{S}; \tag{26.9}$$

this vector is described by the quantum number J. By virtue of various possible mutual orientation of the vectors **L** and **S**, this number takes on the following values:

$$J=L+S,\ L+S-1,\ L+S-2,\ \ldots,\ |L-S|. \tag{26.10}$$

As will be readily seen, the number of different values of J when $L \geqslant S$ is $2S+1$ and when $L \leqslant S$, is $2L+1$.

Taking into consideration the foregoing, we obtain a set of terms of an atom with two electrons as shown in Tables 13 and 14. Since, in the case under consideration, the number S takes on two values, 1 and 0, we get *two* systems of terms here: a system of *singlets* ($S=0$, $J=L$) and a system of *triplets* ($S=1$, $J=L+1$, L, $L-1$). The quantum numbers that correspond to the terms of both systems are given in Tables 13 and 14.

Table 13
Singlet terms of an atom with two electrons

Term	L	J			
^1S	0	0			
^1P	1		1		
^1D	2			2	
^1F	3				3

Table 14
Triplet terms of an atom with two electrons

Term	L	J				
^3S	0		1			
^3P	1	0	1	2		
^3D	2		1	2	3	
^3F	3			2	3	4

Here, the term designations are different from those earlier used. The symbols s, p, d, ... , are used to denote the *terms of individual electrons*; these terms are characterised by definite values of the azimuthal quantum number l. In our case we have to do with the *terms of an atom* that are characterised by the quantum number L. To designate them we introduce the capital letters S, P, D, ... Let it be noted that in the case of atoms or ions with one outer electron, the numbers L and l have the same meaning: the symbols S, P, D, ... and the symbols s, p, d, ... , obviously, also denote one and the same thing—terms of the outer electron, which are at the same time also terms of the atom (ion). Naturally, the introduction of new symbols does not exclude the earlier symbols because when dealing with an atomic term we often have to take into account the states of the individual electrons; these states give an indication of the origin of the term. Thus, the D-term ($L=2$) of an atom with two electrons may be constructed from one s- ($l_1=0$) and one d-electron term ($l_2=2$). However, a D-term (naturally, a different one) may be obtained also from two p-electron terms ($l_1=l_2=1$).

From this example it is clear that a fuller characterisation of a term requires the use of both symbols (upper-case and lower-case). Thus, designating the above-mentioned D-terms by the symbols sdD and ppD, or p^2D, where the lower-case symbols indicate the corresponding electronic terms, we define more precisely the origin of the atomic term. The only thing to add is that usually when designating terms in this way, we also indicate the values of the principal quantum numbers of the electrons, for instance 1s3dD, 3s3dD, 2p3pD or $(3p)^2D$.

To distinguish atomic terms belonging to different multiplet systems, a *left-hand superscript* (see Tables 13 and 14) is used to indicate the *multiplicity* of the system to which the given term belongs. We note that the multiplicity of the system is equal to $2S+1$, where S is the quantum number that determines the total spin of the atom. According to the foregoing, the multiplicity of a term coincides with the multiplicity of the system only when we have terms characterised by the number $L \geqslant S$.

Finally, the *right-hand subscript* is generally meant to indicate the number J corresponding to the given term (or component of the term), for instance, $(4s)^2\ {}^3S_1$. In this specific case, the indication of J is not essential since the term ${}^3S$, like all S-terms, is a simple term due to the fact that $L=0$ and $J=S$. However, in the case of a multiplet term, it is absolutely necessary to indicate the number J, the values of which are used to differentiate the different components of the term. Such are the terms ${}^3P$, ${}^3D$, etc., given in Table 14 and represented by the symbols ${}^3P_0$, ${}^3P_1$, ${}^3P_2$, ${}^3D_1$, ${}^3D_2$, ${}^3D_3$, etc. In exactly the same way, the doublet P-terms of alkaline elements ($L=l=1$, $J=3/2$, $1/2$) are denoted by the symbols $np\,{}^2P_{3/2}$ and $np\,{}^2P_{1/2}$, etc. It is sometimes necessary to indicate also the states of the electrons in the inner groups. For example, indicating the states of all 11 electrons in the Na atom, we designate the principal term of the latter ($n=3$, $L=l=0$, $J=S=1/2$) as follows: $(1s)^2\ (2s)^2\ (2p)^6\ 3s\ {}^2S_{1/2}$.

In the overwhelming majority of cases the character of the atomic term is determined by the configuration (states) of the outer electrons. This occurs in all cases when the inner electrons form closed subgroups and is due to both the orbital and spin angular momenta of the closed subgroups being equal to zero, which is a necessary corollary of the Pauli principle. For one thing, this corollary is manifested in the diamagnetism of all ions whose electron shells consist of closed subgroups. It follows from the foregoing that the systematics of states of an atom (or ion) with one or two outer electrons is also applicable to an atom (ion) with any number of inner electrons, on the condition that the latter form closed subgroups.

This type of interaction of electronic angular momenta (Russell-Saunders coupling) is the most widespread. For this reason, the usual classification of atomic terms is based on the assumption of this type of interaction being predominant. In comparatively rare cases, however, we observe other types of interaction of the angular momenta. To illustrate, in the case of heavy elements, the second type of interaction—(j, j) *coupling*—from among those indicated on p. 206 has been established. Predominant in this case is the interaction of the orbital and spin angular momenta of one and the same electron, as a result of which the vectors $\mathbf{j}_i = \boldsymbol{l}_i + \mathbf{s}_i$ (cf. (26.4)) arise. Interaction of the vectors $\mathbf{j}_1$ and $\mathbf{j}_2$ (which is weaker than interaction of the vectors $\boldsymbol{l}_i$ and $\mathbf{s}_i$) leads, further, to the total angular momentum vector of the atom:

$$\mathbf{J} = \mathbf{j}_1 + \mathbf{j}_2 \tag{26.11}$$

characterised by the quantum number J. In the case of (j, j) coupling, the quantum numbers L and S, obviously, have no meaning; and the same goes for the above-considered classification of atomic terms based on these numbers.

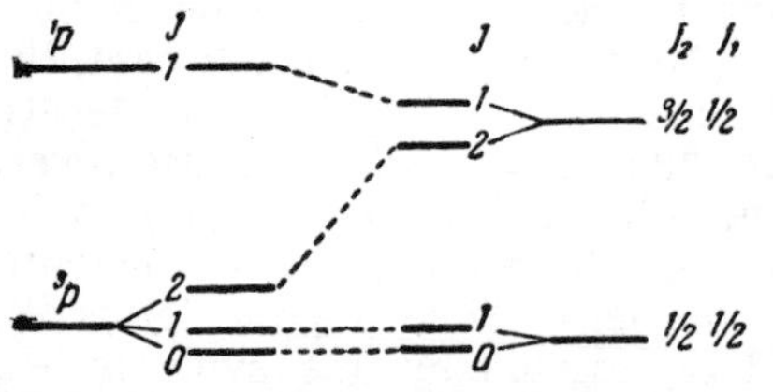

Fig. 46. Relative positions of the terms of an sp configuration in Russell-Saunders coupling (left) and in (jj) coupling (right)

Let us consider the case of atomic terms obtained from the electron configuration sp. Since we have $l_1 = 0$ and $l_2 = 1$, and, hence, L = 1, and also S = 1 and 0, we have the following terms in Russell-Saunders coupling: $^3P_{012}$ and $^1P_1$. For (j, j) coupling we have $j_1 = 1/2$ and $j_2 = 3/2$ and 1/2. Due to the strong coupling between angular momenta $\boldsymbol{l}_2$ and $\mathbf{s}_2$, to the electron states characterised by the numbers $j_2 = 1/2$ and $j_2 = 3/2$ there correspond extremely different energies. The comparatively weak interaction of the vectors $\mathbf{j}_1$ and $\mathbf{j}_2$ leads to splitting of each one of these levels into two components characterised, in the case of $j_2 = 1/2$, by the quantum numbers J = 1 and 0 and, in the case of $j_2 = 3/2$, by the numbers J = 2 and 1. The relative positions of the atomic terms corresponding to this electron configuration is given in Fig. 46, where the terms obtained in Russell-Saunders coupling are shown to the left, and those obtained in (j, j) coupling are shown to the right. Since the latter coupling is comparatively uncommon, we shall henceforward consider only atomic terms corresponding to Russell-Saunders coupling.

Terms of atoms with any number of electrons. The systematics of atomic terms considered above in application to the case of an atom with two electrons may be readily extended to an atom with any number of outer electrons. In this general case, the orbital angular momentum vector of the atom is

$$\mathbf{L} = \sum \boldsymbol{l}_i, \tag{26.12}$$

and the quantum number L that describes it is expressed by the formula

$$L = \sum l_i, \quad \sum l_i - 1, \quad \sum l_i - 2, \ \ldots \tag{26.13}$$

Similarly, for the quantum number that determines the total spin of the atom, we obtain

$$S = \sum s_i, \quad \sum s_i - 1, \quad \sum s_i - 2, \ \ldots \tag{26.14}$$

The total angular momentum vector of the atom **J** and the quantum number that determines it are expressed by the same formulas (26.9) and (26.10) in the general case of any number of electrons as in the case of two electrons.

Atomic terms corresponding to different electron configurations (taking into account the Pauli principle) are given in Table 15 and Table 16. The number of the corresponding terms is given in parentheses. We note a much smaller number of terms (due to the Pauli principle) in equivalent electrons (Table 16) as compared with the number of terms in nonequivalent electrons (Table 15).

From the tables it is seen that, as a rule, to each electron configuration there corresponds several atomic terms. It has already been pointed out that the problem of classification of atomic terms does not include a determination of the absolute values of the terms and their relative positions. This problem is solved by computing the energy of the atom, i.e., by an approximate solution of the appropriate wave equation, which entails great mathematical difficulties. Let us note that on the basis of a solution to this problem it is possible, in specific cases, to establish general semi-empirical rules, by means of which it is sometimes possible to get a definite picture of the relative positions of the atomic terms. For example, from a solution of the wave equation for a helium atom it was found (p. 202) that, given

Table 15

Atomic terms in nonequivalent electrons (different n)

Electron configuration	Terms
s s	^1S, ^3S
s p	^1P, ^3P
s d	^1D, ^3D
p p	^1S, ^1P, ^1D, ^3S, ^3P, ^3D
p d	^1P, ^1D, ^1F, ^3P, ^3D, ^3F
d d	^1S, ^1P, ^1D, ^1F, ^1G, ^3S, ^3P, ^3D, ^3F, ^3G
s s s	^2S (2), ^4S
s s p	^2P (2), ^4P
s s d	^2D (2), ^4D
s p p	^2S (2), ^2P (2), ^2D (2), ^4S, ^4P, ^4D
s p d	^2P (2), ^2D (2), ^2F (2), ^4P, ^4D, ^4F
p p p	^2S (2), ^2P (6), ^2D (4), ^2F (2), ^4S, ^4P (3), ^4D (2), ^4F
p p d	^2S (2), ^2P (4), ^2D (6), ^2F (4), ^2G (2), ^4S, ^4P (2), ^4D (3), ^4F (2), ^4G
p d f	^2S (2), ^2P (4), ^2D (6), ^2F (6), ^2G (6), ^2H (4), ^2I (2), ^4S, ^4P (2), ^4D (3), ^4F (3), ^4G (3), ^4H (2), ^4I

Table 16

Atomic terms in equivalent electrons (n and l are the same)

Electron configuration	Terms
s^2	^1S
p^2	^1S, ^1D, ^3P
p^3	^2P, ^2D, ^4S
p^4	^1S, ^1D, ^3P
p^5	^2P
p^6	^1S
d^2	^1S, ^1D, ^1G, ^3P, ^3F
d^3	^2P, ^2D (2), ^2F, ^2G, ^2H, ^4P, ^4F
d^4	^1S (2), ^1D (2), ^1F, ^1G (2), ^1I, ^3P (2), ^3D, ^3F (2), ^3G, ^3H, ^5D
d^5	^2S, ^2P, ^2D (3), ^2F (2), ^2G (2), ^2H, ^2I, ^4P, ^4D, ^4F, ^4G, ^6S

the same electron configuration, lowest energy corresponds to parallel orientation of spins ($S=1$). Extending this conclusion to other atoms, it may be concluded that of the entire set of terms belonging to a given electron configuration, the lowest terms will be those that have the greatest multiplicity. This conclusion is corroborated by numerous examples. Thus, according to Table 16, the terms ^1S, ^1D and ^3P belong to configuration p^2 which is observed, for instance, in the case of the lower terms of C, Si, Ge,

Sn, and Pb. According to the preceding rule, the triplet term ^3P should be lowest; this term is indeed the principal term of all the enumerated atoms (see Table 18). In exactly the same way, the principal term of atoms N, P, As, Sb, and Bi is the term ^4S (see Table 18), which has the greatest multiplicity of all terms belonging to the configuration p^3 (^2P, ^2D, and ^4S).

Natural multiplets. Up till now, when considering the problem of the number of components of multiplet (fine) splitting of atomic terms, we left open the question of the magnitude of this splitting (called *natural splitting* in contrast to artificial splitting of terms in a magnetic or electric field). Turning to this latter problem, we will consider the simplest case of *doublet splitting* of the terms of an atom (ion) with one outer electron.

As has already been pointed out (p. 207), multiplet splitting of atomic terms results from magnetic interaction of the vectors $\boldsymbol{l}$ and s in the atom. For this reason, solution of the problem of the magnitude of doublet splitting reduces to calculating the energy of interaction of these vectors. Below we give a solution to this problem for an atom with one electron and nuclear charge Z.

According to classical electrodynamics, an electron moving with velocity v in an electric field of intensity $\mathfrak{E}$, is acted upon by a magnetic field of intensity

$$\mathfrak{H}=\frac{1}{c}[\mathfrak{E}\cdot\mathbf{v}],$$

where the brackets denote the vector product of vectors $\mathfrak{E}$ and $\mathbf{v}$. In coordinates fixed in the moving electron, the vector $\mathfrak{E}$ will be

$$\mathfrak{E}=\frac{eZ}{r^3}\mathbf{r}.$$

Noting that the angular momentum of the electron is

$$\boldsymbol{l}=m[\mathbf{r}\cdot\mathbf{v}]$$

(the mass of the nucleus is taken to be infinitely large as compared with the electron mass), we will have, for the vector of the magnetic field,

$$\mathfrak{H}=\frac{eZ}{mcr^3}\boldsymbol{l}.$$

If the vector of the magnetic moment proper of the electron is $\boldsymbol{\mu}_s$, then its energy in the magnetic field $\mathfrak{H}$ may be written in the form:

$$\Delta E=-\frac{1}{2}(\boldsymbol{\mu}_s\cdot\mathfrak{H})=+\frac{eZ}{2mc}\overline{\frac{1}{r^3}}\,(\boldsymbol{\mu}_s\cdot\boldsymbol{l}).$$

Here, the factor 1/2 appears when passing to coordinates fixed in the nucleus. The parentheses denote the scalar product of the vectors. Calculating the quantity $\overline{\frac{1}{r^3}}$, we find

$$\overline{\frac{1}{r^3}} = \int \psi_{n,\,l} \frac{1}{r^3} \psi^*_{n,\,l}\, dv = \frac{Z^3}{r_1^3 n^3 l\,(l + {}^1/_2)\,(l+1)}.$$

Further, replacing the magnetic moment of the electron by its spin, on the basis of formula (24.28) we obtain (μ_s and s have opposite signs due to the fact that the electron charge is negative; here, μ_s is expressed in the CGSM system):

$$\mu_s = -\frac{e}{mc}\,s.$$

Consequently, the product $(\mu_s \cdot l)$ is rewritten in the form

$$(\mu_s \cdot l) = -\frac{e}{mc}(s \cdot l),$$

where

$$(s \cdot l) = |s|\,|l| \cos(s,\ l);$$

$|l|$ and $|s|$ are the absolute values of the vectors l and s, which, according to (24.20) and (24.25), are

$$|l| = \hbar\sqrt{l\,(l+1)} \text{ and } |s| = \hbar\sqrt{s\,(s+1)}.$$

Substituting the expressions obtained for $\overline{\frac{1}{r^3}}$ and $(\mu_s \cdot l)$ into the formula for the interaction energy of the vectors l and s and introducing the Rydberg constant

$$R = \frac{2\pi^2 me^4}{h^3}$$

and the *fine-structure constant*

$$\alpha = \frac{e^2}{\hbar c},$$

we transform this formula to

$$\Delta E = -\frac{\hbar R\alpha^2}{\hbar^2}\,\frac{Z^4}{n^3 l\,(l + {}^1/_2)\,(l+1)}\,|l|\,|s| \cos(l,\ s).$$

The cosine of the angle between vectors l and s may be found by using the classical rule of the parallelogram, from which it follows that

$$|j|^2 = |l|^2 + |s|^2 + 2\,|l|\,|s| \cos(l,\ s),$$

or

$$|l||s|\cos(\boldsymbol{l}, s) = \frac{j(j+1) - l(l+1) - s(s+1)}{2}\hbar^2.$$

Using this expression, we finally obtain

$$\Delta E = -\frac{hR\alpha^2Z^4}{n^3 l(l+{}^1/_2)(l+1)} \frac{j(j+1) - l(l+1) - s(s+1)}{2}. \quad (26.15)$$

Since the total angular-momentum quantum number j has two values, $j = l + {}^1/_2$ and $j = l - {}^1/_2$ (26.3), for term-energy changes due to interaction of $\boldsymbol{l}$ and s in these two cases, we obtain

$$\left.\begin{aligned} \Delta T_{ls}^{+} &= -\frac{R\alpha^2Z^4}{2n^3(l+{}^1/_2)(l+1)} \quad \text{for } j = l + {}^1/_2, \\ \Delta T_{ls}^{-} &= \frac{R\alpha^2Z^4}{2n^3 l(l+{}^1/_2)} \quad \text{for } j = l - {}^1/_2. \end{aligned}\right\} \quad (26.16)$$

Comparing (26.16) and (22.14) we see that in the latter formula the relativistic correction, which we rewrite in the form (cf. p. 184).

$$\Delta T_p = \frac{R\alpha^2Z^4}{n^3}\left(\frac{1}{l+{}^1/_2} - \frac{3}{4n}\right), \quad (26.17)$$

has the same order of magnitude as ΔT_{ls}. Therefore, when determining the splitting of terms one must also take into account the relativistic correction. Combining (26.16) and (26.17), we get

$$\left.\begin{aligned} \Delta T^{+} &= \Delta T_{ls}^{+} + \Delta T_p = \frac{R\alpha^2Z^4}{n^3}\left(\frac{1}{l+1} - \frac{3}{4n}\right) \quad \text{for } j = l + {}^1/_2, \\ \Delta T^{-} &= \Delta T_{ls}^{-} + \Delta T_p = \frac{R\alpha^2Z^4}{n^3}\left(\frac{1}{l} - \frac{3}{4n}\right) \quad \text{for } j = l - {}^1/_2. \end{aligned}\right\} \quad (26.18)$$

Taking into account the relation $j = l \pm {}^1/_2$, formulas (26.18) may be given as a single formula:

$$\Delta T^{\pm} = \Delta T_j = \frac{R\alpha^2Z^4}{n^3}\left(\frac{1}{j+{}^1/_2} - \frac{3}{4n}\right). \quad (26.19)$$

From (26.18) we get, for the doublet splitting of the term of an atom (ion) with one electron,

$$\Delta T = \Delta T^{-} - \Delta T^{+} = \frac{R\alpha^2Z^4}{n^3 l(l+1)}. \quad (26.20)$$

Verification of (26.19) and (26.20) in the case of the hydrogen spectrum and also the spectrum of ionised helium He^+ ($Z^4 = 16$) gives good agreement between theory and experiment.

An approximate theoretical expression may also be obtained for the magnitude of splitting of the terms of atoms of the alkaline elements and of ions with one outer electron. Taking advantage of Bohr concepts concerning penetrating orbits and considering the motion of an outer (*optical*) electron in an atom as motion in two ellipses—inner and outer (see p. 158), for each of these ellipses we can compute the mean value of Z/r^3 that enters into the expression for the interaction energy of the vectors $\boldsymbol{l}$ and s. Substituting the product $l(l+{}^1/_2)(l+1)$ in place of n_φ^3 (cf. the formula for $\overline{\frac{1}{r^3}}$ given on p. 216), we get

$$\left(\overline{\frac{Z}{r^3}}\right)_i = \frac{Z_i^4}{r_1^3 n_i^3 l(l+{}^1/_2)(l+1)}$$

and

$$\left(\overline{\frac{Z}{r^3}}\right)_a = \frac{Z_a^4}{r_1^3 n_a^3 l(l+{}^1/_2)(l+1)}$$

where Z_i is the effective charge acting on an electron inside the atomic core, Z_a is the charge acting on an electron in the outer part of the orbit (which for a neutral atom may be put equal to unity, for a single charged ion, to 2, etc.), n_i and $n_a = n_{eff}$ are the principal quantum numbers corresponding to both orbits (cf. p. 158). Denoting the periods of revolution of the electron in these orbits by τ_i and τ_a, respectively, we find the mean value of Z/r^3 in the form

$$\overline{\frac{Z}{r^3}} = \frac{\left(\overline{\frac{Z}{r^3}}\right)_i \tau_i + \left(\overline{\frac{Z}{r^3}}\right)_a \tau_a}{\tau_i + \tau_a}.$$

Substituting into the formula $\tau = 2\pi mab/p$ (p. 162), $b = a\,(n_\varphi/n)$, $p = \hbar n_\varphi$, and $a = r_1 n^2/Z$, we obtain $\tau = (2\pi m r_1^2/Z^2)\,n^3$ and, consequently,

$$\tau_1 = 2\pi m r_1^2 \frac{n_i^3}{Z_i^2} \quad \text{and} \quad \tau_a = 2\pi m r_1^2 \frac{n_a^3}{Z_a^2},$$

whence we find

$$\overline{\frac{Z}{r^3}} = \frac{Z_i^2 + Z_a^2}{\frac{n_i^3}{Z_i^2} + \frac{n_a^3}{Z_a^2}} \, \frac{1}{r_1^3 l(l+{}^1/_2)(l+1)},$$

or, approximately, since $Z_i^2 \gg Z_a^2$,

$$\overline{\frac{Z}{r^3}} = \frac{Z_i^2 Z_a^2}{r_1^3 n_a^3 l(l+{}^1/_2)(l+1)}.$$

Using this formula and

$$(\mathbf{s}\cdot\boldsymbol{l}) = |\boldsymbol{l}|\,|\mathbf{s}|\cos(\boldsymbol{l},\ \mathbf{s}) = \hbar^2\frac{|\mathbf{j}|^2 - |\boldsymbol{l}|^2 - |\mathbf{s}|^2}{2},$$

for the interaction energy of vectors $\boldsymbol{l}$ and $\mathbf{s}$ (see p. 216)

$$\Delta E_{ls} = -\frac{e^2}{2c^2m^2}\left(\frac{\overline{Z}}{r^3}\right)(\mathbf{s}\cdot\boldsymbol{l})$$

we get

$$\Delta E_{ls} = -\frac{hR\alpha^2 Z_i^2 Z_a^2}{n_{eff}^3\, l\,(l+{}^1/_2)(l+1)}\,\frac{j(j+1) - l(l+1) - s(s+1)}{2}.$$

Substituting $j = l \pm {}^1/_2$ into this formula and passing to ΔT, we find

$$\Delta T_{ls}^{\pm} = \pm\frac{R\alpha^2 Z_i^2 Z_a^2}{n_{eff}^3\, l\,(l+{}^1/_2)(l+1)}\,\frac{(l+{}^1/_2)\pm{}^1/_2}{2}. \qquad (26.21)$$

From this equation, for the magnitude of doublet splitting of terms of an atom or ion with one outer electron $\Delta T = \Delta T^+ - \Delta T^-$, we obtain (omitting the subscript ls)

$$\Delta T = \frac{R\alpha^2 Z_i^2 Z_a^2}{n_{eff}^3\, l\,(l+1)}. \qquad (26.22)$$

This expression is called the *Landé formula*.

Since the effective charge Z_i in the Landé formula is not very amenable to theoretical determination, it is usually considered a certain empirical parameter. For this reason, in addition to (26.22), frequent use is made of an equivalent formula:

$$\Delta T = \frac{R\alpha^2 Z_{eff}^4}{n^3 l\,(l+1)}, \qquad (26.23)$$

which may be obtained directly from (26.20) by replacing the nuclear charge Z by some effective charge $Z_{eff} = Z - z$ (cf. p. 141) and in which the quantity z plays the role of the empirical parameter.

A comparison of equations (26.22) and (26.23) with extensive experimental material on the width of the doublets of alkaline elements and ions isoelectronic to them yields satisfactory agreement of theory and experiment. From these equations it follows that the magnitude of doublet splitting ΔT is determined by the values of Z, n, and l. As for ΔT as a function of Z, since the "screening constant" z varies with Z rather slowly (for example, from a comparison of the splittings of the 2p-term of lithium and the 3p-term of sodium it follows that when passing from Li to Na z increases from 2.0 to 7.5, i. e., by 5.5 units, whereas Z increases by $11-3=8$ units), theory predicts rapid growth of the magnitude of doublet splitting with the atomic number. This emerges from a consideration of the data in Table 17, which gives the experimental values of the magnitude of splitting of lower ^{2}P-terms ($\Delta T = {}^2P_{3/2} - {}^2P_{1/2}$) of the alkaline elements. The table also gives the appropriate values of Z.

Table 17

Doublet splitting of lower ^{2}P-terms of the atoms of alkaline elements

Element	Li	Na	K	Rb	Cs
ΔT, cm^{-1}	0.34	17.196	57.72	237.60	554.0
Z	3	11	19	37	55

Experimental data referring to the multiplet structure of atomic spectra show that the magnitude of natural splitting of terms of all elements is found to be very dependent upon the atomic number. This relationship is similar to that observed in the case of alkaline metals. These findings strongly suggest that the multiplet splitting of the terms of all elements, as regards dependence on the atomic number of the element, satisfies a regularity similar to (26.22) or (26.23).

Returning to the doublet terms of alkaline elements and the ions corresponding to them, we may further show that the dependence, which follows from (26.22) and (26.23), of the magnitude of doublet splitting on the quantum numbers n and l (or n_{eff}) is in satisfactory agreement with experiment. We note a sharp fall in ΔT with increasing principal quantum number, particularly for small n,* and a still greater decrease with increase of the number l, i. e., when passing from p- to d-, f-, ... terms (for constant n).**

Another essential thing to point out is the following. As will be seen directly from (26.21), the terms that correspond to the value of the total angular-momentum quantum number $j=l+{}^1/_2$ should lie *above* the terms with $j=l-{}^1/_2$. This order of terms is actually observed in the case of all double P-terms of alkaline elements for any values of the principal quantum

* To take an example, the doublet splitting of sodium terms 3p, 4p, 5p, 6p, 7p, 8p, ... is 17.20, 5.63, 2.52, 1.25, 0.74, 0.47, ... cm^{-1} or of rubidium terms 5p, 6p, 7p, ... 237.60, 77.50, 35.09, ... cm^{-1}.

** Thus the doublet splitting of rubidium terms 5p and 5d is 237.60 and 2.96 cm^{-1}, of the 6p and 6d terms of caesium, 554.0 and 42.8 cm^{-1}.

number n. However, other terms frequently exhibit the reverse when a component with a smaller value of j is situated above a component with greater j. Such, for instance, are the f-terms of the alkaline elements. Cases are observed when the difference sign $T_{j+1/2} - T_{j-1/2}$ is reversed as n increases. For example, for the d-terms of rubidium 4d, 5d, 6d, ... this difference is expressed by the following numbers: -0.44, 2.96, 2.26, ... cm^{-1}. Similar cases, when the sign of this difference is not consistent with (26.21), have likewise been established for ions with a single outer electron.

A theoretical investigation of this inconsistency shows that it is due to interaction of electrons not accounted for in the theories in which this interaction is replaced by the action of a certain average electric field. We may add that as a result of considering the terms of atoms containing different quantities of outer electrons it was established that in those cases when the number of equivalent electrons in a given subgroup (l) does not exceed one half of the maximum number for this subgroup, i.e., is less than or equal to $2l+1$ (see Sec. 27), in the ground state of the atom the component of the multiplet term with greatest $J=(L+S)$ lies *above* the component with $J=|L-S|$. These terms are called *regular*, in contrast to *irregular*, or *inverted* terms, in which case $J=L+S$ corresponds to the lower-lying component.* For example, considering the p-subgroup, the maximum number of electrons of which is $2(2\times 1+1)=6$, we must conclude that elements with the number of electrons in this subgroup equal to 1, 2, or 3, i. e., elements in the third, fourth, and fifth groups of the Mendeleyev Table, should have regular multiplets in their ground state, whereas elements with the number of p-electrons, 4, 5, or 6 should have irregular multiplets. As an illustration of this rule we give below the terms of the elements of the second and third periods of the Periodic Table that correspond to their ground state:

Li, Na	Be, Mg	B, Al	C, Si	N, P	O, S	F, Cl	Ne, Ar
$^2S_{1/2}$	$^1S_0$	$^2P_{1/2}$	$^3P_0$	$^4S_{3/2}$	$^3P_2$	$^2P_{3/2}$	$^1S_0$

Hyperfine structure of terms. We shall now take up briefly the question of the so-called *hyperfine structure* of spectral terms, which is very important for the general theory of the atom, in particular for nuclear physics. Study of the structure of atomic spectra by means of high-resolution instruments (diffraction gratings, interference spectrographs) shows that most spectral lines,

* Irregular terms are often designated by the subscript i; for example, ^2P_i, ^3P_i, etc.

which according to the systematics of atomic terms (based on account taken of the interaction of vectors $\boldsymbol{l}_i$ and s_i) should be simple, in reality consist of a certain number of closely spaced components. For instance, the line of bismuth λ 4122 A was found to consist of four components with a separation between extreme components 0.44 A (2.60 cm^{-1}), the line of thallium λ 3775 A consists of three components, the separation between components being 0.16 A (1.15 cm^{-1}), etc. Since this hyperfine structure of spectral lines is also observed in elements having one isotope (for instance, bismuth), it cannot be explained by the isotopic effect (see p. 136). What is more, by calculating the magnitude of isotope shift from the formula

$$\Delta\lambda = \lambda \frac{m \Delta M}{M^2} \tag{26.24}$$

(m is the electron mass, M the mean mass, and ΔM the mass difference of the isotopes) obtained from the relation (for heavy elements)

$$\frac{\Delta\lambda}{\lambda} = \frac{R_1 - R_2}{R_1}$$

(R_1 and R_2 are the Rydberg constants for both isotopes) — for instance, for isotope splitting of the above-given line of thallium, which has two isotopes with atomic weights 203 and 205 — we get $\Delta\lambda = 0.0001$ A. This is considerably less than that of the observed hyperfine splitting $\Delta\lambda = 0.16$ A.

Pauli (1924) proposed seeking an explanation of hyperfine structure in a certain asymmetry in the nucleus. If it is taken that the nucleus has a certain angular momentum (and a magnetic moment corresponding thereto), the hyperfine splitting of terms may be attributed to the magnetic interaction of nuclear angular momentum with the electronic magnetic moment of the atom. Like the earlier considered (p. 215 et seq.) spin-orbit coupling of the electron, this interaction may be expressed in terms of the interaction of the vectors **i** and **J**, where **i** is a vector corresponding to the nuclear angular momentum (spin). In this case, the total angular-momentum vector of the atom F is obtained as a geometric sum of the vectors **i** and **J**,

$$\mathbf{F} = \mathbf{i} + \mathbf{J}, \tag{26.25}$$

and, consequently, the quantum number (corresponding to it) as one of the values

$$F = J + i, \quad J + i - 1, \ \ldots, \ |J - i|. \tag{26.26}$$

Whence, for the number of components of hyperfine structure of a term characterised by the total angular-momentum quantum number J, we obtain $2J+1$ for $i \geqslant J$ and $2i+1$ for $i \leqslant J$. By determining, from an analysis of the hyperfine structure, the number of sublevels into which a simple level is split, it is very often possible to establish uniquely the magnitude of the nuclear angular momentum, particularly if the relative intensities of the components of the hyperfine structure of the spectral lines have also been measured.

By way of illustration let us take the D-line of sodium. From the fact that each of the components of this doublet ($3p^2P_{1/2}$ — — $3s^2S_{1/2}$ and $3p^2P_{3/2} - 3s^2S_{1/2}$) is split into two components, it may be concluded that the hyperfine structure of these lines is independent of splitting of the term $^2P_{1/2,\,3/2}$ (due to the weakness of this splitting) and is determined by the splitting of the ^2S-term. Whence, for the number i we have $i \geqslant 1/2$. The unknown value of i is found from a comparison of the measured ratio of intensities of both components of hyperfine structure with the calculated ratio, which is equal to the ratio of statistical weights of the splitting components of the term $^2S\,(2F_+ + 1):(2F_- + 1)$, where $F_+ = i + 1/2$ and $F_- = i - 1/2$. This comparison yields $i = 3/2$.

We note that the numbers i for the stable isotopes of lithium Li^6 and Li^7 are equal to 1 and $3/2$, respectively, for both stable isotopes of potassium, K^{39} and K^{41}, $i = 3/2$, for Rb^{85} $i = 5/2$, and for Cs^{133} $i = 7/2$. We thus see that the nuclear spin of the stable isotopes of the alkaline elements is a quantity of the order of $\hbar$, and for isotopes with even mass numbers (Li^6) i is integral, in contrast to isotopes with odd mass numbers. For the three isotopes of hydrogen H^1, D^2, and T^3, number i has the values $1/2$, 1, and $1/2$, respectively. We note that from this we may draw the conclusion that the spins of the proton and neutron are identical.

If the spin angular momentum of the nucleus is obtained from the number of components of hyperfine splitting of terms, then from the magnitude of the splitting (if the number i is known) we can determine the magnetic moment of the nucleus. In the same way as we calculate the energy of the magnetic interaction of orbital and spin angular momenta, which interaction gives rise to the fine (multiplet) structure of atomic terms (see p. 215 et seq.), we can also calculate the interaction of the magnetic moment of the electron cloud of the atom (characterised by quantum number J) with the magnetic moment of the nucleus (this moment is characterised by the number i).* In this case, in place of the

---

* We note that for a quadrupole electric moment of the nucleus different from zero, the expression for interaction energy of vectors **J** and **i**, besides the term with $\cos(\mathbf{J}, \mathbf{i})$, which is analogous to $\cos(\boldsymbol{l}, \mathbf{s})$ in ΔE_{ls}, will involve a term with $\cos^2(\mathbf{J}, \mathbf{i})$.

Bohr magneton $\mu_B = \frac{\hbar}{2}\frac{e}{m}$ (22.35) the formulas for hyperfine splitting of terms will involve a quantity 1836 times less,

$$\mu_0 = \frac{\hbar}{2}\frac{e}{M_p} \tag{26.27}$$

(M_p is the proton mass), called the *nuclear magneton*. Just as the ratio of the magnetic moment of an electron to its intrinsic angular momentum (spin) is not equal to $^1/_2 \frac{e}{m}$ established for the ratio of orbital angular momenta, but should be replaced by the quantity $g\,^1/_2 \frac{e}{m}$ (see p. 253), and the factor g (called the *gyromagnetic factor*) is in this case equal to 2, the ratio of the magnetic moment of the nucleus to the spin is expressed by the formula

$$\frac{\mu_{nuc}}{p_{nuc}} = g\frac{1}{2}\frac{e}{M_p}.$$

Substituting $p_{nuc} = \hbar\sqrt{i(i+1)}$ into this formula and taking into account (26.27), we get

$$\mu_{nuc} = g\mu_0\sqrt{i(i+1)}. \tag{26.28}$$

Intrinsic angular momenta are usually described not by the absolute values of the angular momenta themselves but by the quantum numbers that correspond to them. In other words, on the basis of the simplified vector model, the magnitude of the angular momentum is replaced by its maximum projection as expressed in units of $\hbar$. Applying this procedure to describe the magnetic moment of the nucleus, we obtain, in place of (26.28),

$$\mu_{nuc} = g\mu_0 i. \tag{26.29}$$

Measurements of the magnetic moments of nuclei yield μ_{nuc} of the order of the nuclear magneton. For example, the stable isotopes of the alkaline elements have the following magnetic moments (expressed in units of μ_0): 0.8213 (Li^6), 3.2532 (Li^7), 2.215 (Na^{23}), 0.391 (K^{39}), 0.217 (K^{41}), 1.340 (Rb^{85}), and 2.572 (Cs^{133}). And since the nuclear magneton μ_0 is 1836 times less than the Bohr magneton μ_B, it follows that the magnitude of hyperfine splitting of atomic terms must be roughly three orders less than that of multiplet splitting. This conclusion is in good agreement with experiment.

We also give the values of the magnetic moments (again in units of μ_0) for the isotopes of hydrogen: H^1 (2.7935), D^2 (0.8574), and T^3 (2.9791). Comparing the magnetic moments of H^1 and D^2 with their spins equal to $^1/_2$ (H^1) and 1 (D^2), we must conclude that the neutron also has a magnetic moment, but that this moment is *negative*. Approximately assuming the spins of the proton and neutron in a deuterium nucleus to be parallel, we find, for the magnetic moment of the neutron: $0.8574 - 2.7935 = -1.9361$. The directly measured magnetic moment of the neutron has a close value: -1.910 ± 0.001. We note that a negative magnetic moment, which is indicative of opposite directions of spin and magnetic moment, i. e., that $g < 0$, is observed in the cases of He^3 (-2.131), Be^9 (-1.1747), Ag^{107} (-0.086), Ag^{109} (-0.159), and certain other isotopes.

In addition to the purely spectroscopic method of studying the hyperfine structure of atomic terms, wide use has been made of the *magneto-resonance method* developed by Rabi and coworkers (1939) and applied in its original or modified form for measuring nuclear spin and the nuclear magnetic moment. The underlying idea of this method, called the *Rabi method*, proceeds from the possibility of varying the orientation of an atomic magnet in a magnetic field (in the sense of space quantisation), i. e., from the possibility of accomplishing the quantum transition $m \rightarrow m'$ by acting upon an atom with long-wave electromagnetic radiation or an oscillating magnetic field; the probability of the process $m \rightarrow m'$ has a maximum value when the frequency of the electromagnetic field coincides with that of the Larmor precession of an atomic magnet (resonance).

From a consideration of the behaviour of an atomic magnet in a homogeneous magnetic field it follows that the action of the field in this case reduces to precession of the magnetic moment about the direction of the magnetic field (Larmor precession) with the frequency

$$\nu = g \frac{e}{4\pi M} \mathfrak{H} \qquad (26.30)$$

(M is the mass of the elementary magnet, $\mathfrak{H}$ is the magnetic-field intensity). Determining the resonance frequency from experiment, we obtain the magnitude of the gyromagnetic factor g*; and from the latter, if we know the spin of the nucleus as well, it is easy to calculate the magnetic moment of the nucleus from (26.29).

27. Genesis of the Periodic System of Elements

The fact that to each electron in an atom we can assign four independent quantum numbers, for example, the numbers n, l, m_l, and m_s** (while taking into consideration the limitations imposed

* For various nuclei, the values of the gyromagnetic factor lie between a magnitude of the order of 0.1 and several units.

** In place of the numbers m_l and m_s we can also take the numbers $j = (l \pm 1/2)$ and $m = (j, j-1, \ldots, -j+1, -j)$.

by the Pauli principle) yields a rigorously logical theoretical substantiation of the existence of closed electron groups in the extra-nuclear structure of the atom. These two principles of the quantum theory of the atom (quantisation of electron states and the Pauli principle) together with a third rule, according to which the ground state of every atom is the state of *least energy*, provide physical proof of the periodic system of elements. The above-mentioned quantum numbers can have the following values: $n=1, 2, 3, \ldots, l=0, 1, 2, \ldots, n-1$, $m_l=\pm l \pm (l-1), \ldots, 0$ and $m_s=\pm 1/2$, whence it follows that the maximum number of electrons that differ by at least one of the four quantum numbers (Pauli principle) for a given value of the principal quantum number is

$$2 \sum_{l=0}^{l=n-1} (2l+1)=2n^2. \tag{27.1}$$

Thus, in complete agreement with experiment (cf. p. 132) we have $2n^2$ for the maximum number of electrons in the n-quantum electron group. These electrons are distributed among n *subgroups* with maximum number of electrons in each subgroup equal to $2(2l+1)$.

In state $n=1$ we get two s-electrons ($l=0$), which form the two-electron K-group of the atom. The K-group cannot accommodate more than two electrons and is a closed electron group that is completed for the first time in the helium atom and does not change from then on anywhere in the Periodic Table. Passing to the group of electrons that are characterised by $n=2$ we note that, here, in addition to s-electrons ($l=0$) there can also be p-electrons ($l=1$). Namely, we have $2(2\times 0+1)=2$ s-electrons and $2(2\times 1+1)=6$ p-electrons. In this way we get an eight-electron L-group consisting of two subgroups: 2s and 2p. Like the K-group, this group, upon completion in neon, remains closed to the end of the Periodic Table. The energy levels that correspond to these groups and subgroups and those that follow them are shown in Fig. 47, where the maximum number of electrons in each group ($2n^2=2$, 8, 18, etc.) and the corresponding values of the principal quantum numbers are shown at the left and the values of the azimuthal quantum numbers are given at the bottom. The maximum number of electrons on a given level is shown at the right.

The L-group is followed by the M-group ($n=3$). Here we have 2 s-electrons, 6 p-electrons, and $2(2\cdot 2+1)=10$ d-electrons falling into three subgroups: 3s, 3p, and 3d. Experiment shows that the maximum number of electrons (18) for the M-group is found only in the heavier elements beginning with copper, $Z=29$.

But in the case of the three light elements Ar, K, and Ca, even the incomplete eight-electron M-group exhibits the properties of a closed group. This is suggested by the chemical and physical properties of the atom Ar and the ions K^+ and Ca^{++}

This and similar facts are explained as follows. When passing from an element with atomic number Z to the following heavier element with number $Z+1$, i. e. when increasing the nuclear charge by unity, the $(Z+1)$th electron occupies a level to which there corresponds the *least* possible energy (we are speaking about the ground states of the atoms). From the filling sequence (observed in experiment) of the electron levels of the first twenty

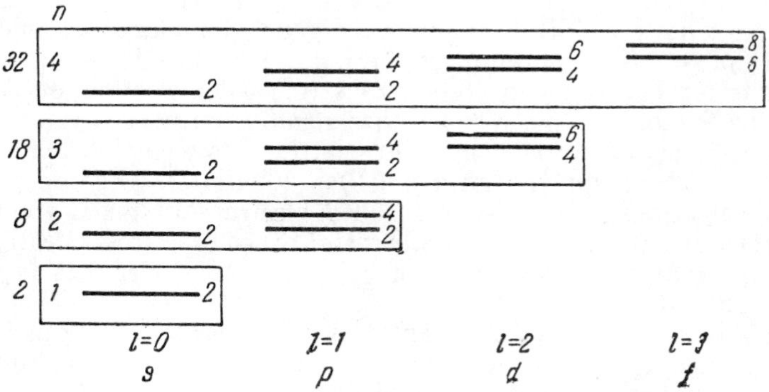

Fig. 47. Electron-shell structure of atoms (schematic)

elements (ending with Ca) it follows that the level above the 3p-level is not the 3d-level as should follow from the scheme in Fig. 47, but the 4s-level since the outer electrons in potassium and calcium that follow Ar are 4s-electrons. Raising the three-quantum level 3d above the four-quantum level 4s is also obtained directly from the statistical model of the atom as calculated by the Thomas-Fermi method (see p. 204).

In the elements following Ca, the levels 4s and 3d overlap. This explains all the anomalies that are observed in the elements beginning with Sc $(Z=21)$ and ending with Cu $(Z=29)$. As follows from spectroscopic data, the outer electrons of Sc and all subsequent elements including Ni $(Z=28)$ are d-electrons. In the element following Ni, copper, the 18-electron M-group is completed for the first time. After copper, everything proceeds normally at first, but only up to Kr $(Z=36)$. Here, and in the next two elements Rb $(Z=37)$ and Sr $(Z=38)$, the growth of the N-group stops at eight electrons because the outer electrons of Rb and Sr occupy the 5s-level and not the 4d-level. Going further, we again have a series of anomalous elements up to Pd ($Z=46$), in which the number of N-electrons reaches 18. Further growth of the N-group, the maximum number of electrons of which is equal to $2\cdot 4^2=32$, temporarily ceases due to a regular growth of the O-group ($n=5$), which in the Ag atom ($Z=47$) has one electron (5s) and in Xe ($Z=54$) eight electrons (two 5s- and six 5p-electrons). This group, like the N-group, is temporarily "frozen", because in Cs ($Z=55$) and Ba ($Z=56$) that follow xenon the outer electrons are on the 6s-level (P-group). Then there are a number of other anomalies that are particularly characteristic of elements of the rare-earths group ($Z=58$ to 71), where the 4f-subgroup of the N-group is gradually filled up. In Hf ($Z=72$) we already have a fully completed N-group (32 electrons) and the start of a further build-up of the next, O-group. In Au ($Z=79$) the latter builds up to 18 electrons (the outer electron of Au is in the P-group). This number then remains unchanged right up to protactinium ($Z=91$), which in addition to completed K-, L-, M-, and N-groups and an $(18+2)=20$-electron O-group, has 9 more electrons in the P-group and 2 electrons in the G-group.

The distribution (as a rule established spectroscopically) of electrons in groups and subgroups for all studied elements is given in Table 18.

The last column of this table gives the principal terms found experimentally. However, there is some ground for finding the type of principal term in the simpler cases theoretically as well. From a consideration of the interaction of vectors $\boldsymbol{l}_i$ and $\mathbf{s}_i$ that belong to equivalent electrons, that is, electrons with the same l_i and the same n_i, Hund (1927) formulated the following rule: of the terms formed by electrons with the same l_i, the lowest, generally speaking, are the terms that correspond to the greatest value of total spin, and among these terms the lowest is the term with the greatest total orbital angular momentum L.

Let us consider an atom containing a certain quantity z of equivalent electrons in addition to all the electrons that have made up the closed groups and subgroups. On the basis of the Pauli principle it may be shown that the maximum value of S cannot exceed $\frac{2l+1}{2}$, i.e., a number obtained when $z=2l+1$ — half the maximum number of equivalent electrons. We must therefore first limit z by the condition $z\leqslant 2l+1$. On this condition,

$$S=S_{max}=\frac{z}{2}, \tag{27.2}$$

which corresponds to all m_s that are the same and equal to 1/2.

Table 18

Electron configurations and types of terms for ground states of the atoms of the elements

Elements	K	L		M			N				Principal term
	1s	2s	2p	3s	3p	3d	4s	4p	4d	4f	
1 H	1										$^2S_{1/2}$
2 He	2										$^1S_0$
3 Li	2	1									$^2S_{1/2}$
4 Be	2	2									$^1S_0$
5 B	2	2	1								$^2P_{1/2}$
6 C	2	2	2								$^3P_0$
7 N	2	2	3								$^4S_{3/2}$
8 O	2	2	4								$^3P_2$
9 F	2	2	5								$^2P_{3/2}$
10 Ne	2	2	6								$^1S_0$
11 Na	2	2	6	1							$^2S_{1/2}$
12 Mg	2	2	6	2							$^1S_0$
13 Al	2	2	6	2	1						$^2P_{1/2}$
14 Si	2	2	6	2	2						$^3P_0$
15 P	2	2	6	2	3						$^4S_{3/2}$
16 S	2	2	6	2	4						$^3P_2$
17 Cl	2	2	6	2	5						$^2P_{3/2}$
18 Ar	2	2	6	2	6						$^1S_0$
19 K	2	2	6	2	6		1				$^2S_{1/2}$
20 Ca	2	2	6	2	6		2				$^1S_0$
21 Sc	2	2	6	2	6	1	2				$^2D_{3/2}$
22 Ti	2	2	6	2	6	2	2				$^3F_2$
23 V	2	2	6	2	6	3	2				$^4F_{3/2}$
24 Cr	2	2	6	2	6	5	1				$^7S_3$
25 Mn	2	2	6	2	6	5	2				$^6S_{5/2}$
26 Fe	2	2	6	2	6	6	2				$^5D_4$
27 Co	2	2	6	2	6	7	2				$^4F_{9/2}$
28 Ni	2	2	6	2	6	8	2				$^3F_4$
29 Cu	2	2	6	2	6	10	1				$^2S_{1/2}$

Elements	K	L	M	N				O					Principal term
	1	2	3	4s	4p	4d	4f	5s	5p	5d	5f	5g	
30 Zn	2	8	18	2									$^1S_0$
31 Ga	2	8	18	2	1								$^2P_{1/2}$
32 Ge	2	8	18	2	2								$^3P_0$
33 As	2	8	18	2	3								$^4S_{3/2}$
34 Se	2	8	18	2	4								$^3P_2$

Elements	K 1	L 2	M 3	N 4s	N 4p	N 4d	N 4f	O 5s	O 5p	O 5d	O 5f	O 5g	Principal term
35 Br	2	8	18	2	5								$^2P_{3/2}$
36 Kr	2	8	18	2	6								$^1S_0$
37 Rb	2	8	18	2	6			1					$^2S_{1/2}$
38 Sr	2	8	18	2	6			2					$^1S_0$
39 Y	2	8	18	2	6	1		2					$^2D_{3/2}$
40 Zr	2	8	18	2	6	2		2					$^3F_2$
41 Nb	2	8	18	2	6	4		1					$^6D_{1/2}$
42 Mo	2	8	18	2	6	5		1					$^7S_3$
43 Ma	2	8	18	2	6	(5)		(2)					$(^6S_{5/2})$
44 Ru	2	8	18	2	6	7		1					$^5F_5$
45 Rh	2	8	18	2	6	8		1					$^4F_{9/2}$
46 Pd	2	8	18	2	6	10							$^1S_0$
47 Ag	2	8	18	2	6	10		1					$^2S_{1/2}$
48 Cd	2	8	18	2	6	10		2					$^1S_0$
49 In	2	8	18	2	6	10		2	1				$^2P_{1/2}$
50 Sn	2	8	18	2	6	10		2	2				$^3P_0$
51 Sb	2	8	18	2	6	10		2	3				$^4S_{3/2}$
52 Te	2	8	18	2	6	10		2	4				$^3P_2$
53 I	2	8	18	2	6	10		2	5				$^2P_{3/2}$
54 Xe	2	8	18	2	6	10		2	6				$^1S_0$

Elements	K 1	L 2	M 3	N 4s	N 4p	N 4d	N 4f	O 5s	O 5p	O 5d	O 5f	O 5g	P 6s	Principal term
55 Cs	2	8	18	2	6	10		2	6				1	$^2S_{1/2}$
56 Ba	2	8	18	2	6	10		2	6				2	$^1S_0$
57 La	2	8	18	2	6	10		2	6	1			2	$^2D_{3/2}$
58 Ce	2	8	18	2	6	10	(2)	2	6				(2)	$(^3H_4)$
59 Pr	2	8	18	2	6	10	(3)	2	6				(2)	(^4I)
60 Nd	2	8	18	2	6	10	(4)	2	6				2	^5I
61 Pm	2	8	18	2	6	10	(5)	2	6				(2)	(^6H)
62 Sm	2	8	18	2	6	10	6	2	6				2	$^7F_0$
63 Eu	2	8	18	2	6	10	7	2	6				2	$^8S_{7/2}$
64 Gd	2	8	18	2	6	10	7	2	6	1			2	^9D
65 Tb	2	8	18	2	6	10	(9)	2	6				(2)	(^6H)
66 Dy	2	8	18	2	6	10	(10)	2	6				2	^5I
67 Ho	2	8	18	2	6	10	(11)	2	6				(2)	(^4I)
68 Er	2	8	18	2	6	10	(12)	2	6				(2)	(^3H)
69 Tu	2	8	18	2	6	10	13	2	6				2	$^2F_{7/2}$

Elements	K	L	M	N				O					P	Principal term
	1	2	3	4s	4p	4d	4f	5s	5p	5d	5f	5g	6s	
70 Yb	2	8	18	2	6	10	14	2	6				2	$^1S_0$
71 Cp	2	8	18	2	6	10	14	2	6	1			2	$^2D_{3/2}$
72 Hf	2	8	18	2	6	10	14	2	6	2			2	$^3F_2$
73 Ta	2	8	18	2	6	10	14	2	6	3			2	$^4F_{3/2}$
74 W	2	8	18	2	6	10	14	2	6	4			2	$^5D_0$
75 Re	2	8	18	2	6	10	14	2	6	5			2	$^6S_{5/2}$
76 Os	2	8	18	2	6	10	14	2	6	6			2	$^5O_4$
77 Ir	2	8	18	2	6	10	14	2	6	7			2	^4F
78 Pt	2	8	18	2	6	10	14	2	6	9			1	$^3D_3$

Elements	K	L	M	N	O				P			Q	Principal term
	1	2	3	4	5s	5p	5d	5f	6s	6p	6d	7s	
79 Au	2	8	18	32	2	6	10		1				$^2S_{1/2}$
80 Hg	2	8	18	32	2	6	10		2				$^1S_0$
81 Tl	2	8	18	32	2	6	10		2	1			$^2P_{1/2}$
82 Pb	2	8	18	32	2	6	10		2	2			$^3P_0$
83 Bi	2	8	18	32	2	6	10		2	3			$^4S_{3/2}$
84 Po	2	8	18	32	2	6	10		2	4			$^3P_2$
85 At	2	8	18	32	2	6	10		2	5			$^2P_{3/2}$
86 Rn	2	8	18	32	2	6	10		2	6			$^1S_0$
87 Fr	2	8	18	32	2	6	10		2	6		1	$^2S_{1/2}$
88 Ra	2	8	18	32	2	6	10		2	6		2	$^1S_0$
89 Ac	2	8	18	32	2	6	10	2	2	6	(1)	(2)	$(^2D_{3/2})$
90 Th	2	8	18	32	2	6	10	2	2	6	2	2	$^3F_2$
91 Pa	2	8	18	32	2	6	10	2	2	6	1	2	^4K
92 U	2	8	18	32	2	6	10	3	2	6	1	2	^5L
93 Np	2	8	18	32	2	6	10	4	2	6	1	2	^6L
94 Pu	2	8	18	32	2	6	10	6	2	6		2	^7F
95 Am	2	8	18	32	2	6	10	7	2	6		2	^8S
96 Cm	2	8	18	32	2	6	10	7	2	6	1	2	^9D
97 Bk	2	8	18	32	2	6	10	8	2	6	1	2	^8H
98 Cf	2	8	18	32	2	6	10	10	2	6		2	^5I
99 Es	2	8	18	32	2	6	10	11	2	6		2	^4I
100 Fm	2	8	18	32	2	6	10	12	2	6		2	^3H
101 Md	2	8	18	32	2	6	10	13	2	6		2	^2F
102 No	2	8	18	32	2	6	10	14	2	6		2	^1S

Since all m_s are the same, the orbital magnetic numbers m_s of all electrons must be different. Here, the maximum value of orbital angular momentum L, will, obviously, be equal to

$$L=L_{max}=l+(l-1)+\ldots+(l-z+1)= \\ =\frac{z}{2}(2l+1-z)=S_{max}(2l+1-z). \qquad (27.3)$$

As for $z>2l+1$, the type of term in this case may be determined by the following reasoning. Since for $z=2(2l+1)$ we have a closed electron subgroup, for which $S=0$ and $L=0$, by eliminating from it a certain number of electrons $2(2l+1)-z$ and assigning to the group of eliminated electrons maximum values of angular momenta S and L, equal, respectively, to

$$S=S_{max}=(2l+1)-\frac{z}{2} \qquad (27.4)$$

and

$$L=L_{max}=l+(l-1)+\ldots+[l-2(2l+1)+z+1]= \\ =\left[(2l+1)-\frac{z}{2}\right][z-(2l+1)]=S_{max}(z-2l-1), \qquad (27.5)$$

for the remaining z electrons we will have the same values S (27.4) and L (27.5).

We take advantage of the formulas obtained to determine the type of principal terms of elements of the second and third periods of the Periodic Table. The outer electron group of these elements contains a maximum of 8 electrons distributed in s- and p-subgroups. We thus have $l=0$ and $l=1$. Let us first consider the terms of elements with one and two s-electrons ($z=1$ and 2). For $z=1$, we find, from formulas (27.2) and (27.3), $S=1/2$ and $L=0$, i.e., the term ^2S. For $z=2$, we obtain, from formula (27.3), $L=-S$, which is meaningful only when $S=L=0$. Whence we get ^1S for the principal term of elements of the second group. Since $l=1$, for elements of the third to eighth groups we get, from formulas (27.2) and (27.3), $S=1/2$ (III), 1 (IV), 3/2 (V), and $L=1$ (III), 1 (IV), 0 (V); and from formulas (27.4) and (27.5): $S=1$ (VI), 1/2 (VII), 0 (VIII), and $L=1$ (VI), 1 (VII), 0 (VIII), i.e., terms ^2P (III), ^3P (IV), ^4S (V), ^3P (VI), ^2P (VII), and ^1S (VIII).

Similarly for the d-subgroup containing 1, 2, ..., 0 electrons, we find, correspondingly, the following groups of terms: ^2D, ^3F, ^4F, ^5D, ^6S, ^5D, ^4F, ^3F, ^2D and ^1S. Comparing these and the earlier results with the data in Table 18, we find exact coincidence of terms observed experimentally with those found on the basis of Hund's rule.

As for the principal terms of the elements, this rule is apparently satisfied for all elements without exception. Hund assumes that his rule must hold for all cases when the interaction ($\boldsymbol{l}_i$, s_i) is small compared with other magnetic interactions. Indeed, given predominant interaction of the vectors $\boldsymbol{l}_i$ and s_i, we are then dealing with a transition from Russell-Saunders coupling (p. 212) to (j, j) coupling, for which the systematics of atomic terms used in formulating the Hund rule does not hold.

As already pointed out, when L and S are meaningless the systematics of atomic terms that uses these numbers obviously becomes impossible too. But since the number J, which characterises the total electronic angular-momentum vector

$$\mathbf{J} = \sum \mathbf{j}_i,$$

is conserved, it is this number that is used to describe individual terms. We note that cases of (j, j) coupling are most frequently encountered among the high excited states of heavy atoms when an optical electron with large principal quantum number is so far away from the other electrons that its interaction with them is secondary as compared with ($\boldsymbol{l}$, s) interaction.

28. Intensity of Spectral Lines

Probabilities of radiative quantum transitions in the atom. The intensity of monochromatic radiation with frequency $\nu_{nn'}$, corresponding to the transition $n' \rightarrow n$, is expressed by the formula

$$I = A_{nn'} N' h\nu_{nn'} \tag{28.1}$$

where $A_{nn'}$ is the number of radiation events per atom per second; this is usually (though erroneously) called the *radiation probability*. N′ is the number of excited atoms (in the source of radiation) at the initial level n′.

The absorption-line intensity expressed by the quantity of absorbed radiant energy ΔI is determined by the absorption probability $B_{nn'}$ and the number of absorbed atoms N, and may be represented by the formula

$$\Delta I = \frac{1}{c} B_{nn'} N h\nu_{nn'} I. \tag{28.2}$$

In (28.2), I denotes the intensity of the incident light.

According to Einstein, the probabilities A and B are connected by the following relation:

$$B_{nn'} = \frac{c^3}{8\pi h\nu^3_{nn'}} \frac{g'}{g} A_{nn'} \tag{28.3}$$

where g′ and g are statistical weights corresponding to the excited and ground states of the atoms. Thus, with the aid of relationship (28.3) and knowing A we can compute B (and vice versa).

These quantities may be determined both experimentally and theoretically. The experimental determination of the probabilities of quantum transitions frequently reduces to measuring the *area of the absorption line*, i.e.,

$$\int_0^\infty \mu(\nu)\, d\nu,$$

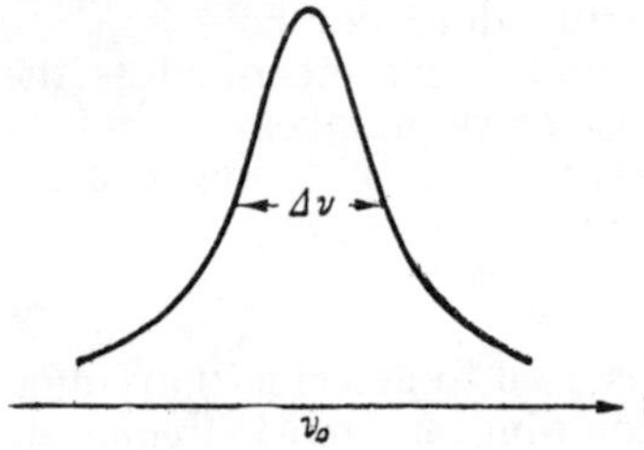

Fig 48. Intensity distribution in spectral line ($\Delta\nu = 2\nu'$ is line width)

which is found from the dependence of the absorption coefficient $\mu(\nu)$ of the appropriate line upon the frequency ν. We note that the intensity distribution within the limits of a given spectral line (this distribution is characterised by the absorption coefficient $\mu(\nu)$ appears as a curve like that shown in Fig. 48. The following relationship obtains between the area of the absorption line and the corresponding probability of absorption $B_{nn'}$:

$$B_{nn'} = \frac{1}{N} \frac{c}{h\nu_{nn'}} \int_0^\infty \mu(\nu)\, d\nu. \tag{28.4}$$

On this basis we can compute $B_{nn'}$ from the measured area of the absorption line.

Another method for experimental determination of the probability of quantum transitions, which was first developed by Rozhdestvensky (1915), is based on the study of anomalous dispersion of gases. In this case, for the dependence of the index of refraction n on the frequency of light oscillations ν, we obtain the following expression from classical electron theory:

$$n_2 - 1 = \frac{e^2}{\pi m} \sum_i \frac{N_i}{\nu_i^2 - \nu^2} \tag{28.5}$$

(e and m are the charge and mass of the electron and N_i is the number of oscillators with a natural frequency ν_i), which, in terms of quantum mechanics, may be rewritten in the form

$$n^2 - 1 = \frac{e^2 N}{\pi m} \sum_{n'} \frac{f_{nn'}}{\nu_{nn'}^2 - \nu^2}. \tag{28.6}$$

Here, $f_{nn'}$ is the so-called *oscillator force* connected with the probability of the corresponding quantum transitions $A_{nn'}$ by the relation

$$f_{nn'}=\frac{g_{n'}}{g_n}\frac{mc^3}{8\pi^2e^2\nu^2_{nn'}}A_{nn'}. \tag{28.7}$$

Determining the quantity $f_{nn'}$ by measuring the index of refraction n as a function of the frequency ν, we find, from (28.7), the corresponding values of the light-emission probabilities $A_{nn'}$. Due to the peculiar relationship between n and ν near the absorption lines $\nu_{nn'}$, the Rozhdestvensky method became known as the *hook method*.

The following reasoning underlies a theoretical (quantum-mechanical) determination of the probabilities of quantum transitions. According to classical electrodynamics, the intensity of electromagnetic radiation of an oscillating dipole is proportional to the square of the second derivative of its electric moment P with respect to time; whence, for radiation intensity of frequency ν, we get the following expression:

$$I=\frac{64}{3}\frac{\pi^4\nu^4}{c^3}P_0^2N' \tag{28.8}$$

where P_0 is the vibration amplitude of the dipole moment. Proceeding from a statistical interpretation of the wave function, the electric dipole moment, which corresponds to an element of intra-atomic volume and to the coordinate q, may be expressed by the formula $e\varphi_n q\varphi_n^* dV$. Whence, integrating over the entire atomic volume, we get the sought-for dipole moment of the atom:

$$P_n=e\int\varphi_n q\varphi_n^* dV=e\int\psi_n q\psi_n^* dV. \tag{28.9}$$

As may be seen from (28.9), the electric dipole moment of an atom in any one of its steady states (n) is a constant. It follows therefrom that an atom of quantum mechanics in a steady state does not emit light.

The result obtained appears to be quite natural, since there are no grounds for believing that the emission of light associated with the transition of an atom from one energy state to another could be due to the electric moment of only one of these states. Dirac gave the correct solution: light emission by an atom is determined by the *transition moment* computed from the formula

$$P_{nn'}=e\int\varphi_n q\varphi_{n'}^* dV. \tag{28.10}$$

Since $n\neq n'$, expression (28.10), unlike (28.9), contains a time-dependent factor $e^{2\pi i\frac{E'-E}{h}t}$ (see (23.2)) which ensures that the derivative of the moment P with respect to time is not equal to zero. The quantity $\frac{E'-E}{h}$ in the exponent of the time factor is the frequency of the light $\nu_{nn'}$ emitted by the atom. The transition moment may, therefore, be expressed by the formula

$$P_{nn'} = eq_{nn'}e^{2\pi i\nu_{nn'}t} \tag{28.11}$$

where the factor $q_{nn'}$ (called the *quasi-moment*) is the vibration amplitude of the transition moment (divided by e), which amplitude is a vector with components

$$q_{nn'}^{(x)} = \int \psi_n x \psi_{n'}^* dV_x, \quad q_{nn'}^{(y)} = \int \psi_n y \psi_{n'}^* dV_y,$$
$$q_{nn'}^{(z)} = \int \psi_n z \psi_{n'}^* dV_z. \tag{28.12}$$

Substituting the square of the modulus of vector $eq_{nn'}$ into formula (28.8) in place of P_0^2, on the basis of (28.1) we obtain the following expression for the radiation probability:

$$A_{nn'} = \frac{64}{3}\frac{\pi^4 e^2}{hc^3}\nu_{nn'}^3 |q_{nn'}|^2. \tag{28.13}$$

According to (28.13), calculation of the radiation probability (and, consequently, also the absorption probability) reduces to calculating the wave functions for the appropriate states of the atom. However, since the latter can be obtained with the required accuracy only in a limited number of cases, a theoretical evaluation of the absolute values of probabilities of quantum transitions (and, thus, the spectral-line intensities) could not become widespread; these probabilities are chiefly determined by experiment.

Selection rules. A much simpler theoretical problem is that of establishing the *possible* quantum transitions, i.e., transitions, the probability of which has a *finite* value. The solution of this problem leads to the establishment of so-called *selection rules* and also *rules of polarisation* of radiation.

If one of the components of $q_{nn'}$ is zero, this means that in the transition $n' \rightarrow n$ the radiation lacks vibrations in the direction of the respective coordinate (we have in mind the direction of vibrations of the electric vector of a light wave). Whence we obtain the rules of polarisation of radiation. However, if $q_{nn'} = 0$ for any direction of vibrations, we get the selection rules. In this case the transition $n' \rightarrow n$ is "*forbidden*". The selection rules and the rules of polarisation are established by calculating the components (28.12) of $q_{nn'}$.

We consider the following case, taking advantage of the solution of the hydrogen-atom problem (Chapter 4). In this case, the components of $q_{nn'}$ in the direction of axis $z\,(q=r\cos\vartheta)$ and in the direction perpendicular to $z\,(q=r\sin\vartheta\sin\varphi$ and $q=r\sin\vartheta\cos\varphi$, or, in complex notation, $q=r\sin\vartheta e^{\pm i\varphi})$, Z and $X\pm iY$, are expressed by the formulas

$$\left.\begin{aligned} Z&=\iiint \psi_{nlm_l}\psi^*_{n'l'm'_l}r^3dr\sin\vartheta\cos\vartheta d\vartheta d\varphi,\\ X\pm iY&=\iiint \psi_{nlm_l}\psi^*_{n'l'm'_l}r^3dr\sin^2\vartheta d\vartheta e^{\pm i\varphi}d\varphi. \end{aligned}\right\} \quad (28.14)$$

Substituting here the expressions for ψ and ψ^* obtained from a solution of the H-atom problem and evaluating the integrals, we find, in particular, that the quantities (28.14) do not become zero solely when $m'_l=m_l$, $m_l\pm1$. Indeed, due to separation of the variables, each of the expressions in (28.14) may be represented in the form of a product of three integrals

$$I_r(r)\,I_\theta(\vartheta)\,I_\varphi(\varphi).$$

The simplest one of them, I_φ, for both components contains the factors

$$\int_0^{2\pi} e^{i(m_l-m'_l)}\,d\varphi \quad\text{and}\quad \int_0^{2\pi} e^{i(m_l\pm1-m'_l)\varphi}\,d\varphi.$$

As will readily be seen, the first of these integrals is different from zero only when $m'_l=m_l$, the second, when $m'_l=m_l\pm1$. This means that the radiation associated with the transition $m'_l\to m_l=m'_l$ will be polarised in a direction normal to the axis z (the electric vector is parallel to the z axis). And the radiation corresponding to the transition $m'_l\to m_l=m'_l\pm1$ will have an electric vector lying in the xy plane. If the direction of the coordinate axes is not specified physically, radiation must obey the general selection rule:

$$\Delta m_l=0,\pm1. \quad (28.15)$$

The total magnetic quantum number M obeys a similar selection rule:

$$\Delta M=0,\pm1. \quad (28.16)$$

Somewhat more involved computations, similar to the foregoing, lead to appropriate limitations for variations of the number l (or L). We thus obtain a selection rule for the azimuthal quantum number:

$$\Delta L=\pm1. \quad (28.17)$$

From this rule, it follows straightway that only the terms S and P,

P and D, etc., can combine, whereas the combinations S—D ($\Delta L = \pm 2$), S—S, P—P ($\Delta L = 0$), etc., are "forbidden" on the basis of rule (28.17).

In addition, we note the following selection rules. The total angular-momentum quantum number J obeys the rule

$$\Delta J = 0, \pm 1. \tag{28.18}$$

Moreover, transitions between such levels as are both characterised by the numbers $J = 0$ are "forbidden". The spin quantum number S obeys the selection rule

$$\Delta S = 0 \tag{28.19}$$

called *prohibition of intercombinations*. According to this rule, combinations of terms are "forbidden" that belong to systems of different multiplicity (intercombinations), for instance, to the singlet ($S = 0$) and triplet ($S = 1$) systems of terms. Finally, we point to the so-called *Laporte rule*, according to which the only possible combination is between even and odd terms (a term is called even or odd depending on whether the sum of the azimuthal quantum numbers of all electrons in the atom is even or odd).

From experiment it follows that quantum "prohibitions" are, for the most part, not absolutely strict, and "forbidden" lines are frequently encountered in atomic spectra, although the intensity is low when compared with ordinary "nonforbidden" lines. One of the main reasons for frequent violations of the selection rules is that in addition to *dipole* radiation it is also possible to have electromagnetic-wave radiation associated with changes in an electric moment of a higher order, primarily in the quadrupole moment of the atom *(quadrupole radiation)* and also *magnetic dipole radiation* due to a change in the dipole magnetic moment of the atom.

The intensity of the quadrupole and magnetic dipole radiations is determined by integrals that differ from the integrals in (28.12), which account for the intensity of dipole radiation. For example, the intensity of quadrupole radiation depends on integrals of the form $\int \psi_n q^2 \psi^*_{n'} \, dV$. For this reason, quadrupole radiation and magnetic dipole radiation obey other selection rules. Thus, both these types of radiation are possible only in even-even or odd-odd combinations (this rule is the opposite of the Laporte rule); further, in the case of quadrupole radiation, we have, in place of rule (28.18), a selection rule $\Delta J = 0, \pm 1, \pm 2$ on the condition that the sum of the total angular-momentum quantum numbers of both combining states is not less than two, and also the selection rule $\Delta L = 0, \pm 1, \pm 2$ (for $L = 0 \not\rightarrow L = 0$); in the case of magnetic dipole radiation, we have the rule $\Delta L = 0, \pm 1$ (in place of rule (28.17) for electric dipole radiation). Experience shows that the ratio of intensities of magnetic dipole and quadrupole radiations to the intensity of dipole radiation is usually 10^{-5}: 1 and 10^{-8}: 1, respectively.

We may also note a weakening of the rigidity of prohibition of intercombinations with increasing atomic number. This weakening is associated with the fact that, here, interaction of the orbital and spin angular momenta of the atom becomes stronger (it is manifested in an increase in multiplet splitting of the terms); theoretically, we may expect strict fulfilment of the selection rule $\Delta S = 0$ only when there is no coupling between L and S.

There are also cases of the selection rules being violated when the radiating (or absorbing) atoms are in the outer electric or magnetic fields or are subject to the action of fields surrounding molecules or ions. Thus, for the case of an electric field, the usual lines are those associated with the transitions S — S, P — P ($\Delta L = 0$), S — D, P — F ($\Delta L = 2$), S — F, P — G ($\Delta L = 3$), which under ordinary conditions are forbidden by the rule $\Delta L = \pm 1$. These and similar violations of the selection rules in an electric field are interpreted theoretically by the fact that the dipole electric moments induced in the atoms by an electric field have, generally speaking, different values depending on the quantum state of the atom. Therefore, transitions of atoms from one state into another should definitely be accompanied by a change in the induced dipole moment. This is the cause of the finite probability of transition, i.e., of the appearance of radiation (*forced* dipole radiation), which is forbidden under ordinary conditions precisely because of no changes in the dipole moment of the atom.

Average lifetime of excited atoms. The different radiation probability observed in different cases permits us to pose the question of the *average lifetime* of excited atoms and of the connection of this quantity with the probability of quantum transitions. A decrease in the number of excited atoms N′ per unit time as a result of radiation is obviously equal to $\frac{dN'}{dt} = -AN'$ (A is the radiation probability), whence it follows that

$$N' = N'_0 e^{-At} \tag{28.20}$$

where N'_0 is the initial number of excited atoms. By introducing the concept of average lifetime of an excited atom τ, determined by the time interval during which the number of excited atoms diminishes e = 2.718... times, we get

$$\tau = \frac{1}{A}. \qquad (28.21)$$

Thus, the average lifetime of an excited atom turns out equal to the inverse magnitude of the probability of the corresponding quantum transition (quantity A, which is usually called the radiation probability, is in fact the *mathematical expectation*, or the frequency, of this process; physically, A denotes the number of transitions accomplished by an excited atom in 1 second). Whence it follows that the less the radiation probability, the greater is τ. In particular, there should be an especially long average lifetime in the case of those excited atoms whose transition to the ground (or a lower-lying) state is forbidden by some selection rule. Such atoms are called *metastable*.

The average lifetime is usually computed from measured values of A. However, there also exist direct experimental methods for determining τ. One of these methods (the *Wien method*) is based on observing attenuation of light in a beam of fast atoms. Measuring the distribution of light along the beam, which is expressed by the formula

$$I = I_0 e^{-\frac{1}{\tau}\frac{x}{v}} \qquad (28.22)$$

(I is the light intensity at a certain point of the beam x and I_0 is the intensity at a distance $x = 0$), and knowing the velocity of the atoms v (measured from the Doppler shift of the spectral lines), we find τ. The values of this quantity measured by various methods are given in Table 19. In the second column are the states of the atoms to which the given values of τ belong.

Table 19

Average lifetime of a number of atoms

Atom	Term	τ, sec
Li	3^2P	6.5×10^{-8}
Na	3^2P	1.5×10^{-8}
Zn	4^3P_1	1.0×10^{-5}
Cd	5^3P_1	2.0×10^{-6}
Hg	6^3P_1	1.5×10^{-7}
Hg	6^3P_0	5×10^{-3}

The following may be pointed out in connection with the data in Table 19. Correlating the values of τ for the terms $^3P_1$, Zn, Cd, and Hg, which terms correspond to the metastable states of these atoms (prohibition of intercombinations) we note a decrease in τ with increasing atomic number. This fact illustrates what was said on p. 239 concerning the laxity of the prohibition of intercombinations.

A particularly long lifetime is found for a mercury atom in the $^3P_0$ state, which is metastable not only by virtue of the prohibition of intercombinations but also due to the rule $J = 0 \nrightarrow J = 0$. Finally, we note that the lifetimes of the states (given in Table 19) of Li and Na, which are ordinary excited states, are of the order of $10^{-8} - 10^{-7}$ sec. This same order of magnitude is obtained for the damping constant of a classical oscillator, which constant (according to electrodynamics) is expressed by the following formula.

$$\tau = \frac{3}{8\pi^2} \frac{cm}{e^2} \lambda^2 \qquad (28.23)$$

where e and m are the charge and mass of the electron, c is the speed of light, and λ is the wavelength of the radiated light. For visible light ($\lambda = 5000$ A), from this formula we get τ of the order of 10^{-8} sec.

It may be added that there is a definite relationship between the average lifetime of an excited atom τ and the width of the spectral lines emitted by this atom (the so-called *natural width* observed in rarefied gases at low temperatures), namely, that the smaller τ, the wider the line. This relationship may be obtained from the uncertainty relation (23.8). Indeed, multiplying and dividing the left side of equality (23.8) by Δt, we can rewrite it (because $\Delta x/\Delta t = v$ and $p = mv$) in the following form: $\Delta E \Delta t = \hbar$, where ΔE denotes indeterminacy in energy and Δt, indeterminacy in time. Identifying the first with indeterminacy in the difference of the energies of the initial and terminal states of the atom, upon which the width of the spectral line depends, and Δt with the average lifetime τ, we obtain the required relationship between the line width and the quantity τ.

We conclude this section by noting that (28.21) is valid only in those cases when only *one* transition is possible to lower-lying states (to one of these states). In the case of several possible transitions, (28.21) must be replaced by the following more general formula:

$$\tau = \frac{1}{\Sigma A_i} \qquad (28.24)$$

where A_i is the probability of an *i*th transition. The quantity ΣA_i is the total probability of all possible transitions from a given excited level to all lower-lying levels of the atom.

29. Atomic Spectra

Atomic spectra of alkaline elements. The structure of atomic spectra is interpreted on the basis of the systematics of atomic states and the selection rules established for the various quantum transitions. In this section we will consider certain atomic spectra and will touch on some extranuclear structural peculiarities and a number of the properties of atoms conditioned by them.

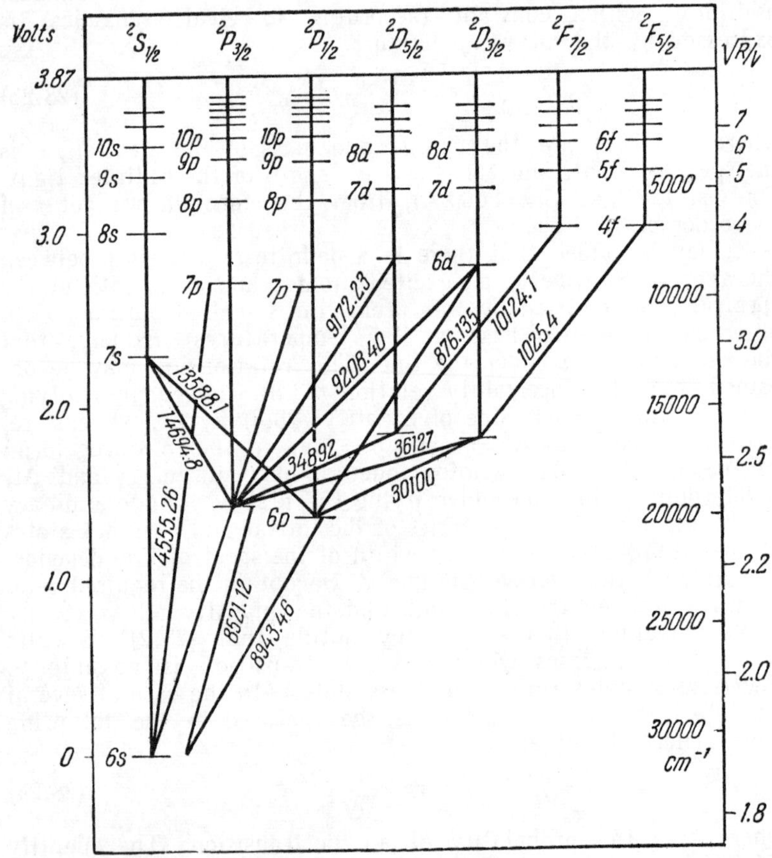

Fig. 49. Radiation terms and the atomic spectrum of caesium

Fig. 49 is a diagram of the energy levels of caesium constructed from an analysis of its optical spectrum. Here, the short horizontal lines depict energy levels (terms); the numbers in the symbolic designations of the terms (to the left of each horizontal line) represent the values of the appropriate principal quantum number.

Unlike the simple ^{2}S-terms, all the remaining terms of the caesium atom (this goes for all atoms or ions with one outer electron) have a doublet structure. However, it must be noted that doublet splitting of the terms ^{2}D and ^{2}F is so small in the case of potassium, sodium, and lithium (which are lighter) that it is practically absent from the spectra of these elements. That is why the level diagram of caesium (heaviest of the alkaline elements) was taken to illustrate the energy levels of an atom with one outer electron. It may be noted that doublet splitting of D-terms was detected in the spectrum of Rb and also in the spectra of the ions Ca^+, Sr^+, and certain other heavier ions having one outer electron.

In Sec. 26 we gave a theoretical formula for doublet splitting of terms of a hydrogen-like atom (26.20) and also the very similar semi-empirical Landé formula (26.22), which he established for doublet splitting of the terms of atoms and ions with one outer electron. The doublet splittings of the lower P-terms of alkaline elements (they illustrate the dependence of the magnitude of splitting on the atomic number of the element, Z) were given in Table 17 (p. 220).

In similar manner, the doublet splitting of other terms of alkaline elements increases with Z. That is why the doublet splitting of D- and F-terms is resolved only in heavy elements.

Transitions between different levels in Fig. 49 are indicated by oblique lines. The number at each line denotes the wavelength of the corresponding spectral line (in Å). This figure contains: two members of the principal series of caesium (^{2}P — ^{2}S) — the doublet 8943.46/8521.12 (the first member) and the doublet 4593.16/4555.26 (the second member of the series); the first member of the sharp series (^{2}S—^{2}P) — the doublet 14694.8/13588.1; the two first members of the diffuse series (^{2}D — ^{2}P) — the triplet 36127/34892/30100 (the first member) and the triplet 9208.40/9172.23/8761.35 (the second member of the series); the first member of the fundamental series (^{2}F — ^{2}D) — the line 10124.1/10025.4, which is an apparent doublet. The apparent doublet nature of the lines of the fundamental series is due to the smallness of doublet splitting of the ^{2}F-terms. In reality, however, the lines of this series (like the lines of the diffuse series) are triplet, which follows from the selection rule $\Delta J = 0, \pm 1$, since this rule (in each case) permits three combinations, namely: $^2D_{3/2} - {}^2P_{1/2}$, $^2D_{3/2} - {}^2P_{3/2}$, and $^2D_{5/2} - {}^2P_{3/2}$ in the case of the diffuse series (the $^2D_{5/2} - {}^2P_{1/2}$ combination is forbidden) and combinations $^2F_{5/2} - {}^2D_{3/2}$, $^2F_{5/2} - {}^2D_{5/2}$, $^2F_{7/2} - {}^2D_{5/2}$ in the case of the fundamental series (the $^2F_{7/2} - {}^2D_{3/2}$ combination is forbidden).

Components of multiplet lines have different intensities determined by the *statistical weights* of the combining terms. The statistical weight of an atomic term is expressed by the formula

$$g=2J+1, \tag{29.1}$$

which is equal to the number of values taken on by the magnetic quantum number M (see p. 208). In respect of this quantum number, each state is $(2J+1)$-fold degenerate, since in the absence of an external magnetic field all $2J+1$ components of a term characterised by the quantum number J have the same energy (the energy difference between these components arises only in a magnetic field and is manifested in the magnetic splitting of the term, see Ch. 6). M-degeneracy of terms results in the fact that among the N atoms in the state ^2P, for example, we have $\frac{2}{2+4}$ N atoms in the $^2P_{1/2}$ state and $\frac{4}{2+4}$ N atoms in the $^2P_{3/2}$ state. In cases when doublet terms combine with simple terms (principal and sharp series), the ratio of the intensities of the components of the doublet line should equal the ratio of statistical weights of the components of the doublet term (i. e., in the case of the term ^2P the quantity $(2\times 3/2+1):(2\times 1/2+1)=2:1$. In the principal and sharp series in the spectra of alkaline elements, the intensities of components of doublet lines are indeed in the ratio 2:1. Calculation of the ratio of intensities of the components of triplet lines in the diffuse series and the fundamental series also leads to agreement with experiment (components of triplets in the diffuse series in the order that they are given on p. 242 have intensities in the ratio 5:1:9; component intensities of triplets in the fundamental series in the order shown on p. 242 are related as 14:1:20).

The lines of the principal series of alkaline elements (like all lines that arise through participation of the ground term of any atom) are called *resonance lines*. When these lines are absorbed, the normal atom passes into one of the excited states, thus becoming capable, upon the reverse transition to the ground state, of emitting light of the same wavelengths (resonating). The reverse emission of light is known as *fluorescence*.

Helium spectrum. Fig. 50 is a diagram of the energy levels of the helium atom. Due to the strictness of prohibition of intercombinations for light elements (see p. 238) we have here two systems of terms that do not combine: a system of singlets (the terms of *parahelium*) and a system of triplets (the terms of *orthohelium*). The triplet terms of helium are exceedingly narrow. The difference between the terms $1s2p\,^3P_2 - 1s2p\,^3P_1$ is only $0.077\ cm^{-1}$, the difference between $1s2p\,^3P_1 - 1s2p\,^3P_0$ is $0.991\ cm^{-1}$. The components of the term $1s3d\,^3D$ have as yet not been separated.

The normal term of the helium atom is $(1s)^2\,^1S_0$. Since the next, in height, term is the triplet term $1s2s\,^3S_1$, which does not combine with the normal term, the helium atom, in the state $1s2s\,^3S_1$, is in a *metastable* state. The impossibility of radiative transition $^3S \rightarrow {}^1S$ makes radiationless transitions of a metastable helium atom to the ground state the only possible ones. This transition may be accomplished in two ways. Namely, by collision with another particle (an electron, for instance) of sufficient

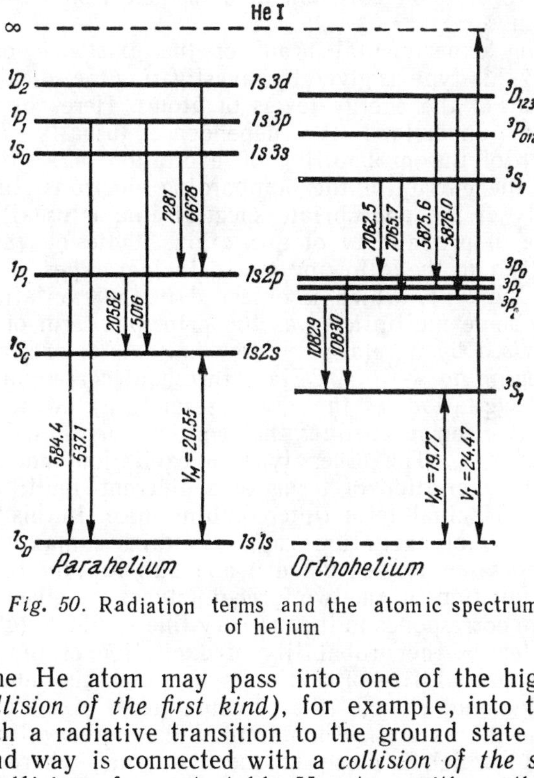

Fig. 50. Radiation terms and the atomic spectrum of helium

energy, the He atom may pass into one of the higher singlet states *(collision of the first kind)*, for example, into the ^1P state, from which a radiative transition to the ground state is allowed. The second way is connected with a *collision of the second kind*, i.e., a collision of a metastable He atom with another particle, as a result of which the excitation energy is imparted to the latter directly.

The possibility, postulated above, of a radiationless intercombination transition $^3S \rightarrow {}^1P$ due to an electron impact follows from the existence of *electron exchange*, which consists in a free (bombarding) electron changing places with one of the electrons of the He atom. This exchange is shown diagrammatically (electrons are designated by arrows) as follows:

$$\underset{\underset{1}{\uparrow}}{e} + He\,({}^3S)_{\underset{2\,3}{\downarrow\downarrow}} \rightarrow He\,({}^1P)_{\underset{1\,2}{\uparrow\downarrow}} + \underset{\underset{3}{\downarrow}}{e}.$$

As a result, the prohibition of intercombinations is removed and the electron can go to the level ^1P. Electron exchange also makes possible a simple interpretation of the possibility of exciting a metastable level upon collision of a fast electron with a normal helium atom. *

Convincing experimental proof of the existence of electron exchange of this type is given by investigating the so-called *excitation functions* of the energy levels of atoms. Here, by excitation function we understand the dependence (usually represented graphically) of the probability of excitation of a given atomic level upon the energy of the bombarding electrons. In this case, the intensity of the appropriate spectral line is usually taken as the measure of probability of excitation. Studies of various spectral lines lead to the following two principal types of excitation functions. One type, which is observed in the excitation of terms having the same multiplicity as the principal term of the atom, is characterised by a relatively slow build-up of excitation probability (beginning with a certain threshold corresponding to the energy of excitation of the given term K_{min}), which attains a maximum at electron energies that considerably (usually several-fold) exceed K_{min}. The other type of excitation functions is observed in the excitation of terms of a different multiplicity than that of the principal term (intercombinations). In this latter case, the probability of excitation rapidly attains a maximum (when $K - K_{min}$ does not exceed 2-3 eV) and also rapidly falls off. The excitation functions of the two foregoing types are given in Fig. 51. One of them corresponds to the mercury line λ 2655 A ($4^1D_2 - 2^3P_1$) and characterises the probability of excitation of the term 4^1D_2, that is, the probability of a process in which the multiplicity of the atom does not change (the principal term of mercury is $^1S_0$). The other — the excitation function of the mercury line λ 2653 A ($4^3D_1 - 2^3P_1$) which is close to the first line — characterises the

* Measurements show that the process of electron exchange in this case is accomplished with high probability. For example, the process $He'\,(1s2s\,{}^1S) + e \rightarrow He''\,(1s2s\,{}^3S) + e + 0.78$ eV for thermal electrons has a cross-section of 3×10^{-14} cm^2, which is two orders of magnitude in excess of the gas-kinetic cross-section equal to $\pi r^2 = 3 \times 10^{-16}$ cm^2, where r is the radius of the helium stom.

probability of excitation of the term 4^3D_1, i.e., the probability of an intercombination transition.

The different types of excitation functions shown in Fig. 51 are to be explained as follows. The excitation probability of a term is determined by its statistical weight, the magnitude of the electric moment corresponding to a given transition, and the electron velocity. Upon the latter are dependent the magnitude and duration of the perturbation that stimulate electron transition in the atom. In the case of intercombination transitions we have

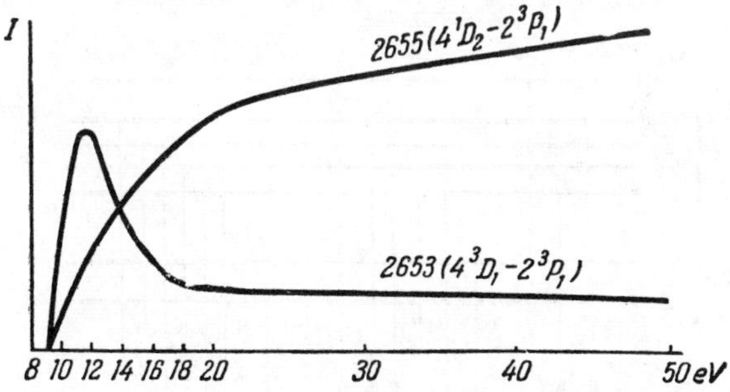

Fig. 51. Two types of excitation function of mercury atom by electron impact

electron exchange of the type described on p. 245. The rapid decrease in excitation probability with increasing velocity (energy) of the exciting electron, which is observed in the case of intercombination transitions, is accounted for by a decrease in the time of interaction between electron and atom, as a result of which the exchange of electrons becomes more and more difficult.

As shown in Fig. 50, the excitation energy of the metastable level of the atom He ($^3S_1$) is equal to 19.77 eV. From this figure, it follows further that the next, in height, level of excitation of helium, level $1s2s^1S_0$ with excitation energy 20.55 eV, is also metastable inasmuch as transition from this level to both lower-lying levels ($1s2s^3S_1$ and $1s1s^1S_0$) is forbidden: transition to the first of these levels is an intercombination, while transition to the second level (the ground level of He) is forbidden by selection rules $\Delta L = \pm 1$ and $J = 0 \not\rightarrow J = 0$.

Mercury spectrum. Fig. 52 is a diagram of the terms of the mercury atom. In contrast to helium, we have here a group of intercombinations. One of the intense lines of the mercury spectrum — the resonance line λ 2537 A — is the intercombination line $^3P_1 - {}^1S_0$. With the exception of prohibition of intercombinations, all the other selection rules are fulfilled here, as in the case of the He atom (Fig. 50). Let us examine one of the selection rules, namely, the rule that excludes combinations of terms with $J=0$. Absence of the lines $^1S_0 - {}^3S_0$ and $^3P_0 - {}^1S_0$ in the mercury spectrum (these lines are actually observed but their intensity is very low) indicates that this rule is strict; whence it follows that the state $6s6p\,^3P_0$ of the mercury atom is metastable.

The energy-level diagrams of He and Hg in Figs. 50 and 52 indicate only those terms that are obtained in the excitation of

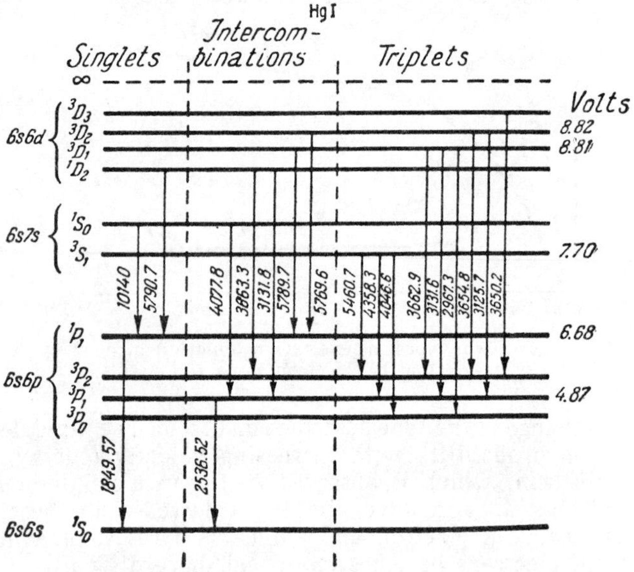

Fig. 52. Radiation terms and the atomic spectrum of mercury

one of the electrons. The state of the second electron is held constant (1s in the helium atom and 6s in the mercury atom). Atomic terms arising in the excitation of only one electron are called *normal* in contrast to *shifted* terms that arise in the excitation of two and more electrons. This difference is manifested not only in the positions of the terms, but in the fact that combinations of displaced terms obey different selection rules. For example, in transitions when there is a simultaneous change in the state of two electrons, the change in the corresponding azimuthal quantum numbers l_1 and l_2 turns out to be different from the change in the total azimuthal quantum number L, and the selection rule for the azimuthal number no longer refers to number L but to the numbers l_1 and l_2. According to Heisenberg, this selection rule is

$$\Delta l_1 = \pm 1, \quad \Delta l_2 = 0, \ \pm 2.$$

Experimentally, displaced terms were detected in helium and also in atoms and ions with two or more outer electrons. The number of shifted terms is particularly great in atoms with complex electronic structure.

Applications of atomic spectroscopy. We conclude this chapter with a brief description of the exceedingly rich and diverse applications of the spectroscopy of atoms. Studies of atomic spectra played an exceptionally important role in learning about the structure of atoms and their properties. The regularities observed in atomic spectra made it possible to learn about the finest details in the electronic structure of atoms, to find a place for every electron in the atom, a place for every element in the Periodic Table. Studies of the fine structure of atomic spectra and their behaviour in external fields of force permitted establishing laws of such general phenomena as that of space quantisation. The establishment of these laws led to a quantitative interpretation of the magnetic properties of atoms and ions. To a large extent, the modern development of atomic physics is due to the successes of spectroscopy.

Intimately bound up with atomic spectroscopy is the development of one of the most important chapters of theoretical astronomy, astrophysics. Spectroscopy tells us about the composition of celestial bodies, the velocities of stars and of whole stellar systems.

No less broad and diverse are the purely practical applications of atomic spectroscopy. They are mainly concentrated around *spectral analysis*, which is widely employed almost in every branch of science and technology.

The spectroscopic method is a powerful method of analysis of ores and minerals and is finding more and more applications. Spectral instruments have become a necessary tool in geological prospecting, making it possible, under field conditions, to determine almost at once the content of a useful element in a given rock. Natural gases and mineral waters are subjected to spectral analysis. Spectroscopic methods are finding ever wider applications in soil analysis and in resolving problems of agricultural chemistry.

Spectral analysis (including X-ray studies) is playing an exceptional part in metallurgy. The need for precise and rapid analyses of specimens in the very process of manufacturing high-quality alloys makes the spectroscopic method one of the basic analytical methods of the factory laboratory. To take an example, spectroscopy has made possible the so-called "express" analysis, which frequently permits practical metallurgical problems to be solved within minutes where ordinary chemical methods of analysis would require hours. This explains why the spectroscopic method of analysis is more and more supplanting conventional chemical testing at modern metallurgical and machine-building plants. The spectroscopic method ensures rapid and simple sorting of alloys and articles, and control of goods.

Particularly outstanding are the advantages of the spectral method when determining *minute quantities* of impurities because this is often beyond the scope of chemistry. Even hundredths of a per cent of an impurity can often appreciably alter the properties of an alloy. The sensitivity of the spectral method may be gauged from the fact that in "pure" platinum with impurities less than 0.001% this method permits detecting Ca, Sr, Pb, and Cu. Spectra show 10^{-11} gm of Sr, 10^{-10} gm of Cd, Mn, and Tl, and 10^{-8} gm of Li and Te. Precision of analysis is usually better than several per cent of the concentration under study, which is quite sufficient for most problems.

Very great also is the role of spectral analysis in biochemistry and medicine where one often has to do with minute quantities of substances not amenable to ordinary chemical analysis. The great importance of these substances in the activities of a given organ, the necessity of localisation and finding the mechanism of action of various substances introduced into the body make the spectral method an effective method of investigation that plays a big role in therapy and diagnostics and in forensic medicine. Only in recent years has the spectral method begun to give way to a still more sensitive and convenient method based on the use of substances labelled with radioactive isotopes.

Spectral analysis is a convincing illustration of the close, organic, connection between theory and practice. Without the solution of intricate problems of atomic spectroscopy, such as that of the probabilities of quantum transitions in atoms that determine the intensities of the spectral lines, quantitative spectral analysis, to which technology is making more and more stringent demands, would be impossible.

The spectral method proceeds from a theory of profound significance, yet at the same time is a strictly practical method.

CHAPTER 6

THE ATOM IN A FORCE FIELD

30. Zeeman Effect

Normal Zeeman effect. As has already been pointed out above, in a magnetic field each level characterised by the quantum number J is split into $2J+1$ sublevels. The number of these sublevels is equal to the number of possible values taken on by the magnetic quantum number M, which determines the magnitude of the projection of total angular momentum of the atom on the direction of the magnetic field. The observed splitting of the spectral lines in a magnetic field, known as the *Zeeman effect* (1896), is the result of this splitting of terms. The nature of magnetic splitting of the various lines is exceedingly diverse, but the number of components and the magnitude of splitting of each line satisfy simple regularities. Lines associated with a combination of the same terms (for instance, lines belonging to a single series) have the same type of splitting (the same number of components). Part of the splitting components, when observed at right angles to the direction of the magnetic field is always polarised parallel to the field * (π-component), while the other components are polarised perpendicular to the field (σ-component).

In the simplest case, the Zeeman effect reduces to a symmetrical splitting of the spectral line ν_0 into *three* components with frequencies ν_{+1}, ν_0, and ν_{-1}, and the magnitude of splitting $\Delta\nu_0 = \nu_{+1} - \nu_0 = \nu_0 - \nu_{-1}$ is equal to

$$\Delta\nu_0 = \frac{\mu_B H}{h} \tag{30.1}$$

where μ_B is the Bohr magneton and H is the magnetic field intensity. This type of splitting is called the *normal* Zeeman effect.** It is observed, for instance, in the system of singlets of He and the group of alkaline earth elements and also in the spectra of

---

* The electric vector in a light ray oscillates parallel to the field.

** The theory of the normal Zeeman effect was developed by Debye and Sommerfeld in 1916.

Zn, Cd, and Hg. Fig. 53 is a photograph of a normal triplet for one of the single lines of cadmium, 6438.47 A ($^1P_1 - {}^1D_2$ transition). Let us find out its origin.

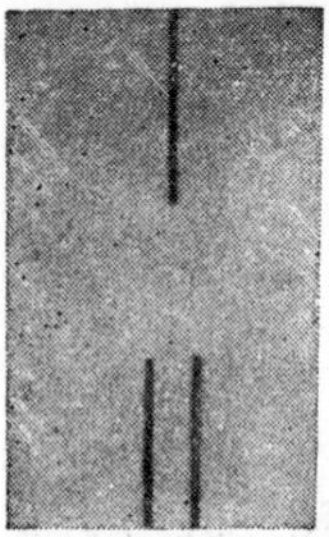

Fig. 53. Normal Zeeman triplet of single line of cadmium 6438.47 A ($^1P - {}^1D$ transition). Top, π-component; bottom, two σ-components

In a magnetic field, the energy of an atom varies by the magnitude

$$\Delta E = M\mu_B H. \qquad (30.2)$$

Consequently, the total energy of the atom in the upper ($^1P_1$) and lower ($^1D_2$) states in a magnetic field is equal to $E' = E_0' + M'\mu_B H$ and $E = E_0 + M\mu_B H$, respectively, whence it follows that

$$\nu_0 = \frac{E' - E}{h} = \frac{E_0' - E_0}{h} + (M' - M)\frac{\mu_B H}{h} =$$

$$= \nu_0 + \Delta M \frac{\mu_B H}{h}.$$

Since according to the selection rule for the magnetic quantum number (p. 237) $\Delta M = \pm 1$ or 0, we get the following values from the foregoing equation for the frequencies of a normal triplet:

$$\nu_{+1} = \nu_0 + \Delta\nu_0,\ \nu_0,\ \nu_{-1} = \nu_0 - \Delta\nu_0.$$

The components ν_{+1} and ν_{-1} of a normal triplet are polarised perpendicular to the field (σ), the components ν_0, parallel to the field (π). It is easy to figure out this type of polarisation on the basis of the rules of polarisation established in Sec. 28: evaluating the components Z and $X \pm iY$ of the quasi-moment $q_{nn'}$ we saw that component Z, which corresponds to oscillations of the electric vector parallel to the field (π-component of radiation), disappears for all $\Delta M > 0$, while the complex component $X \pm iY$, perpendicular to the field (the σ-component of radiation), is different from zero only when $\Delta M = \pm 1$.

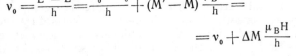

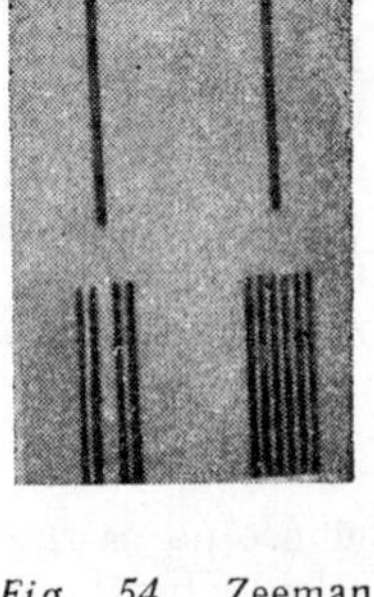

Fig. 54. Zeeman splitting of D-lines of sodium $\lambda\lambda$ 5895.93/5889.96 A ($^2P - {}^2S$ doublet). Top, without field; bottom, with magnetic field

Anomalous Zeeman effect. However, magnetic splitting of the majority of spectral lines, for instance the lines of the triplet system of cadmium and the lines of the alkaline elements, is much more complicated. We can judge of the nature of line splitting in the spectrum of alkaline elements from Fig. 54, which shows the D-lines of sodium, $\lambda\lambda$ 5895.93/5889.96 A ($^2P - {}^2S$ transition). Above are the D-lines in the absence of a magnetic field, below, the same lines in a magnetic field. It will be seen that one of the components of the D-doublet (the $^2P_{1/2} - {}^2S_{1/2}$ line) in a magnetic field is split into 4 components, the second (the $^2P_{3/2} - {}^2S_{1/2}$ line), into 6. In Fig. 55, the splitting of the doublet $^2P - {}^2S$ and the triplet $^2D - {}^2P$ is compared with a normal Zeeman triplet. The dashes above the line refer to π-components, under the line, to σ-components. The numbers to the right indicate the observed distance of

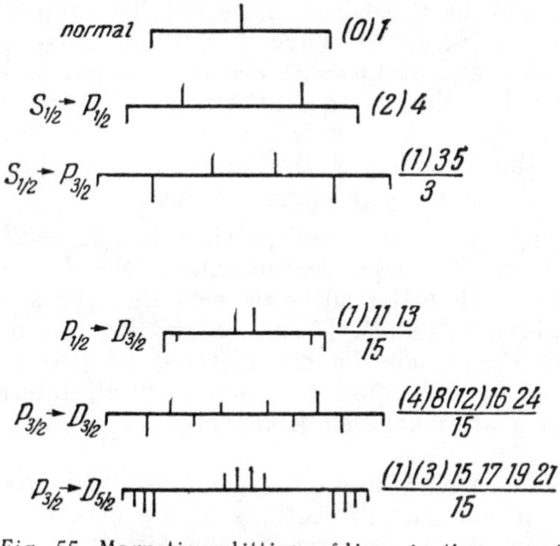

Fig. 55. Magnetic splitting of lines in the normal (upper) and anomalous Zeeman effect

each component of splitting from the initial line (ν_0) in units of normal splitting $\Delta\nu_0 = \mu_B H/h$ (the numbers in brackets refer to π-components, the others, to σ-components).

The Zeeman effect that exhibits a complex splitting of spectral lines is called *anomalous*. The observed complexity of the splitting is due to the fact that the change in energy of the atom in a magnetic field in this case is expressed not by equation (30.2), but by the more involved formula

$$\Delta E = gM\mu_B H \tag{30.3}$$

where g is the *Landé splitting factor* equal to

$$g = 1 + \frac{J(J+1) + S(S+1) - L(L+1)}{2J(J+1)}. \tag{30.4}$$

It will readily be seen that in the case of single terms the Landé factor takes on the value 1 and (30.3 passes into (30.2). Indeed, for a single term S=0, as a result of which the numbers J and L coincide and g (30.4) is unity. Thus, (30.2) may be regarded as a special case of the more general equation (30.3).

The fact that the Landé factor is not equal to unity in the case of multiplet terms (which is what produces the complex pattern of splitting of these terms in a magnetic field), is, in the final analysis, due to the "anomalous" value of the relation of the magnetic moment of the electron to its angular momentum (see p. 189). Let us illustrate this using the simplest case of the doublet S-term. Here, we have $L=0$ and $S=1/2$ and, hence, $J=S$, $M=M_S$, and also $\mu=\mu_S$ and $p=p_S$. We write the general expression for the energy of an atom in a magnetic field $E=E_0+\mu' H$ (μ' is the projection of the magnetic moment of the atom on the direction of the field), and on the basis of the relations $\mu'_s/p'_s=e/m$ and $p'_s=\hbar M_s$ we get $\mu'_s=\hbar(e/m)M_s=2M_s\mu_B$, or, in other words, $\Delta E=E-E_0=2M\mu_B H$. In the case of the term (^2S) under consideration, the Landé factor thus has the value 2. It will readily be seen that the same value of g is obtained also from (30.4). To summarise, then, we have calculated two values of the Landé factor referring to two extreme cases, $S=0$ and $L=0$, and equal to 1 and 2. In all intermediate cases the values of g are computed from equation (30.4) and lie within the limits $1<g<2$.

The Landé formula (30.4) may be obtained from the vector model of the atom. The projections of the magnetic moment and angular momentum of the atom on the direction of the magnetic field may be represented in the form

$$\mu'=\mu_L \cos(\mathbf{L}, \mathbf{H})+\mu_S \cos(\mathbf{S}, \mathbf{H}) \tag{30.5}$$

and

$$p'=p_L \cos(\mathbf{L}, \mathbf{H})+p_S \cos(\mathbf{S}, \mathbf{H}) \tag{30.6}$$

where μ_L, μ_S, p_L and p_S are the orbital angular momentum and spin angular momentum and orbital and spin magnetic moments. Substituting into (30.6)

$$p'=\hbar M,\quad p_L=\frac{2m}{e}\mu_L \text{ and}$$

$$p_S=\frac{m}{e}\mu_S,$$

we get

$$\hbar M=\frac{2m}{e}\left[\mu_L \cos(\mathbf{L}, \mathbf{H})+\frac{1}{2}\mu_S \cos(\mathbf{S}, \mathbf{H})\right],$$

which, together with (30.5), yields

$$\mu'=M\mu_B+\frac{1}{2}\mu_S \cos(\mathbf{S}, \mathbf{H})\left(\mu_B=\frac{\hbar}{2}\frac{e}{m}\right). \tag{30.7}$$

Due to the rapid *precession* of the vector **S** (like **L**) around vector **J**, which in turn precesses about the direction of the magnetic field, the mean values of the components of these vectors on the direction normal to the axis of precession become zero, from which it follows that

$$\mu_S \cos(\mathbf{S}, \mathbf{H}) = \mu_S \cos(\mathbf{S}, \mathbf{J}) \cos(\mathbf{J}, \mathbf{H})$$

or, inasmuch as $\cos(\mathbf{J}, \mathbf{H}) = \hbar \frac{M}{p}$ and $\mu_S = \frac{e}{m} p_S$,

$$\frac{1}{2} \mu_S \cos(\mathbf{S}, \mathbf{H}) = M\mu_B \frac{p_S}{p} \cos(\mathbf{S}, \mathbf{J}).$$

Further, from a triangle constructed on the vectors **S**, **L**, and **J**, we find

$$p_L^2 = p^2 + p_S^2 - 2pp_S \cos(\mathbf{S}, \mathbf{J}),$$

whence

$$\cos(\mathbf{S}, \mathbf{J}) = \frac{p^2 + p_S^2 - p_L^2}{2pp_S}$$

and

$$\frac{1}{2} \mu_S \cos(\mathbf{S}, \mathbf{H}) = M\mu_B \frac{p^2 + p_S^2 - p_L^2}{2p^2}.$$

Substituting the last expression into (30.7) and utilising the quantum-mechanical expressions of moments

$$p = \hbar \sqrt{J(J+1)}, \quad p_L = \hbar \sqrt{L(L+1)} \text{ and}$$
$$p_S = \hbar \sqrt{S(S+1)},$$

and also the equation

$$\mu' = gM\mu_B$$

that follows from (30.3), we get the Landé formula (30.4).

The Landé formula makes it possible to determine g and, hence, the change in energy in a magnetic field in the case of most terms of many atoms. The computed values of the splitting factor for various terms of the alkaline metals are given in Table 20.

Table 20

Landé splitting factor values for doublet terms

Term	L	J = 1/2	3/2	5/2	7/2
^2S	0	2			
^2P	1	2/3	4/3		
^2D	2		4/5	6/5	
^2F	3			6/7	8/7

On the basis of the numbers of this table, we obtain, for the separations between various components of magnetic splitting of terms and the initial term expressed in units of normal splitting $\Delta\nu_0 = \mu_B H/h$, i.e., for the quantity

$$\frac{\Delta E}{h} \Big/ \frac{\mu_B H}{h} = gM,$$

the values given in Table 21. These data permit us to compute the splitting of different lines in a magnetic field.

Table 21

Magnitudes of magnetic splitting of doublet terms

Term	M	g	Mg
$^2S_{1/2}$	1/2, − 1/2	2	1, − 1
$^2P_{1/2}$	1/2, − 1/2	2/3	1/3, − 1/3
$^2P_{3/2}$	3/2, 1/2, − 1/2, − 3/2	4/3	6/3, 2/3, − 2/3, − 6/3
$^2D_{3/2}$	3/2, 1/2, − 1/2, − 3/2	4/5	6/5, 2/5, − 2/5, − 6/5
$^2D_{5/2}$	5/2, 3/2, 1/2 − 1/2, − 3/2, − 5/2	6/5	15/5, 9/5, 3/5, − 3/5, − 9/5, − 15/5

From this table, on the basis of equation

$$\nu = \nu_0 + (M'g' - Mg)\,\Delta\nu_0$$

derived from (30.3), we find, for the components of splitting of the line

$\nu_0^{(1)} = {}^2P_{1/2} - {}^2S_{1/2}$, the values $\nu = \nu_0^{(1)} \pm {}^2/_3\Delta\nu_0$, $\nu_0^{(1)} \pm {}^4/_3\Delta\nu_0$

and for the line $\nu_0^{(2)} = {}^2P_{3/2} - {}^2S_{1/2}$, the values $\nu = \nu_0^{(2)} \pm {}^1/_3\Delta\nu_0$, $\nu_0^{(2)} \pm \Delta\nu_0$, $\nu_0^{(2)} \pm {}^5/_3\Delta\nu_0$. Comparing these data with the experimentally obtained pattern of magnetic splitting of the D-lines (Fig. 54), we readily see the complete agreement of theoretical and experimental data as regards both the number of splitting components and the magnitude of splitting. The polarisation of splitting components as indicated by the selection rules is also in complete agreement with experiment. The splitting of the D-doublet and of appropriate terms in a magnetic field is given in Fig. 56, which also indicates the polarisation of the separate components (π- and σ-components).

Paschen-Back effect. The anomalous Zeeman effect has the following peculiarity. With increasing magnetic field intensity, line splitting increases in proportion to the field until the separate splitting components of two adjacent lines of a given spectral multiplet begin to overlap. At this point, which corresponds to transition from a *weak* field to a *strong* field, the picture changes.

Some components merge, the intensity of others decreases with further increase in field intensity; as a result, given a sufficiently strong field, in place of the multiplet with its complex splitting there remain three lines with *normal* splitting $\Delta\nu_0 = \nu_{+1} - \nu_0 = \nu_0 - \nu_{-1} = \mu_B H/h$, i.e., the normal Zeeman triplet. This phenomenon is known as the *Paschen-Back effect* (1912). The conversion of a complex multiplet (corresponding to this effect) for the case

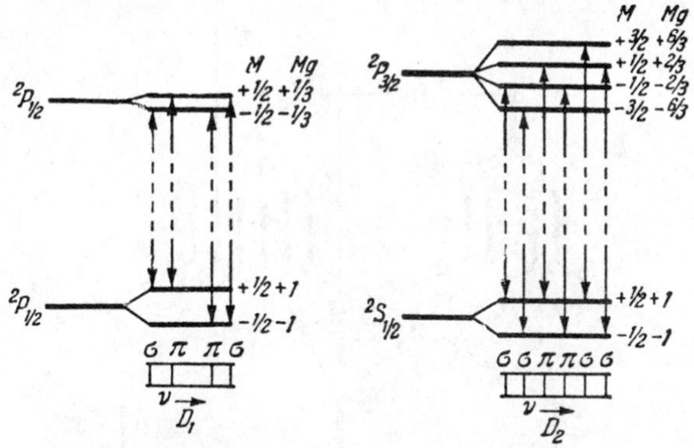

Fig. 56. Splitting of terms $^2P_{3/2}$, $^2P_{1/2}$ and $^2S_{1/2}$ and of components of sodium D-doublet in a magnetic field

of the D-lines of sodium ($^2P - {}^2S$) is shown diagrammatically in Fig. 57.

In accord with what has been said, a weak field is that which causes splitting of terms that is less than natural splitting, i. e., less than the separation between components of the given multiplet. Conversely, magnetic splitting in a strong field is greater than natural splitting. Whence it follows that the concepts of weak and strong fields are relative and are determined by the magnitude of natural splitting of the terms.

If for the measure of splitting of a term in an external magnetic field we take the magnitude of splitting in the normal Zeeman effect and substitute, into (30.2), the value of the Bohr magneton ($\mu_B = 9.23 \times 10^{-21}$ CGSM) and the Planck constant ($h = 6.62 \times 10^{-27}$ erg sec), we obtain $\Delta\nu_0 = 0.47 \times 10^{-4} H$ cm^{-1}, whence it is seen that a field of intensity 10,000 oersteds splits a term into $2\Delta\nu_0 \approx 1$ cm^{-1}. Comparing this value with the natural splitting of the first member of the principal series of sodium and lithium (doublet P-term), 17.18 and 0.34 cm^{-1}, we see that a 10,000-oersted field is strong with respect to the lithium term under consideration, whereas with respect to the corresponding sodium term it is still weak. In accordance with this conclusion, experiment shows that the doublet of lithium λ 6707.85 A, Δλ 0.13 A, unlike the D-lines of sodium, exhibits a complete picture of the Paschen-Back effect in a field of the order of 10^4 oersteds.

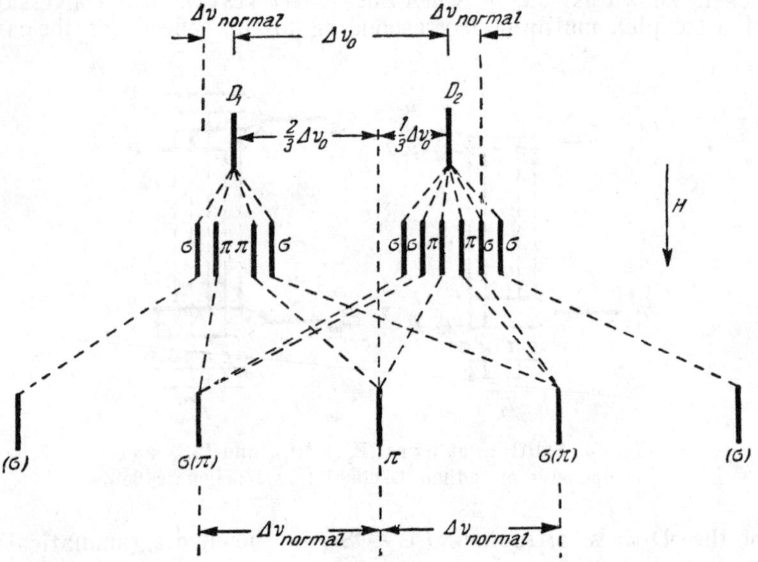

Fig. 57. Splitting of sodium D-doublet in a weak and a strong magnetic field

More precise definitions of a weak field and a strong field provide the key to an understanding of this phenomenon. Indeed, from the fact that a change in the pattern of splitting that leads to a normal triplet sets in when magnetic splitting becomes comparable to natural splitting, it follows that the effect of a strong field is greater than the effect of the intra-atomic field that gives rise to mutual quantisation of the vectors **L** and **S** and the associated natural splitting of the term (see Sec. 26).

From this we must conclude that the behaviour of an atom in a strong magnetic field must be determined by the behaviour of each of the vectors **L** and **S** *separately*; the interaction of the vectors as such should be regarded as a slight perturbation which may be ignored in sufficiently strong external fields. In this case, due to independent quantisation (in the external magnetic field) of the vectors **L** and **S**, we must assign to them independent magnetic quantum numbers M_L and M_S. This is illustrated in Fig. 58, which gives the positions of the vectors **L** and **S**, corresponding to the term ^2P, in a weak (left) and strong (right) magnetic field (simplified vector model).

Using the quantum numbers M_L and M_S, the change in energy of an atom in a strong magnetic field may be represented by the equation

$$\Delta E = (M_L + 2M_S)\mu_B H, \tag{30.8}$$

whence, on the basis of selection rules established for the case of strong magnetic fields,

$$\Delta M_L = 0, \pm 1 \text{ and } \Delta M_S = 0, \tag{30.9}$$

we get a normal Zeeman triplet with components

$$\nu_{+1} = \nu_0 + \Delta\nu_0, \quad \nu_0, \quad \nu_{-1} = \nu_0 - \Delta\nu_0.$$

The centre of this triplet ν_0 lies between the components of the initial (natural) doublet ν_1, ν_2 at distances of $\nu_2 - \nu_0 = {}^2/_3(\nu_2 - \nu_1)$ and $\nu_0 - \nu_1 = {}^1/_3(\nu_2 - \nu_1)$, respectively.

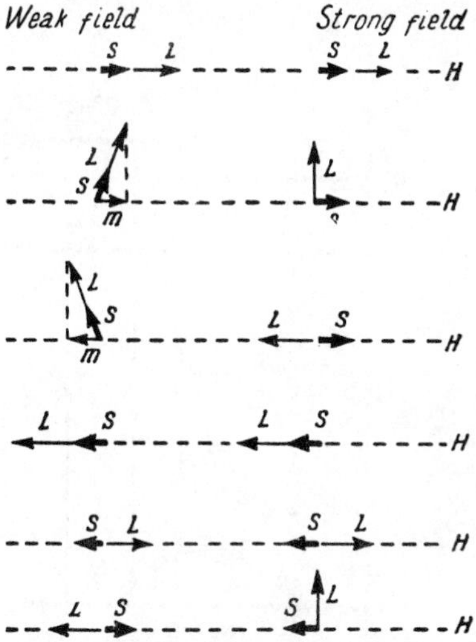

Fig. 58. Space quantisation of the vectors **L** and **S** in a weak and a strong magnetic field

Fig. 59 gives a full picture of change in the nature of splitting of doublet terms ^2S and ^2P when passing from a weak to a strong field. On the left of this figure are two levels: ^2S and ^2P; the energy of interaction of the vectors **L** and **S** is disregarded (the ^2P level is simple). The difference of these levels is equal to a certain quantity W_0. In reality, however, the ^2P level is split (due to interaction of the vectors **L** and **S**) into two sublevels $^2P_{1/2}$ and $^2P_{3/2}$ with energy $W_0 + \Delta E_+$ and $W_0 + \Delta E_-$; note that $\frac{|\Delta E_+|}{|\Delta E_-|} = 1:2$. The arrows ν_1 and ν_2 in Fig. 59 denote the transitions $^2P_{1/2} - {}^2S_{1/2}$ and $^2P_{3/2} - {}^2S_{1/2}$ (natural doublet). In a weak magnetic field, the $^2P_{1/2,\,3/2}$ levels are split into six levels and the $^2S_{1/2}$ level into two. The allowed combinations between these levels yield 10 components of the anomalous Zeeman effect as shown by the 10 arrows in Fig. 59. The six ^2P levels in a strong magnetic field pass into six new levels, two of which coincide. It is precisely the energy

$W_0 = h\nu_0$ that corresponds to the coinciding levels. The remaining four levels are situated above or below the W_0 level by the amount $\mu_B H$ and $2\mu_B H$ respectively. Two components of the ^2S level possess energy $\mu_B H$ and $-\mu_B H$. The allowed combinations $\Delta M_L = 0, \pm 1$ and $\Delta M_S = 0$ of the five upper with the two lower levels yield six

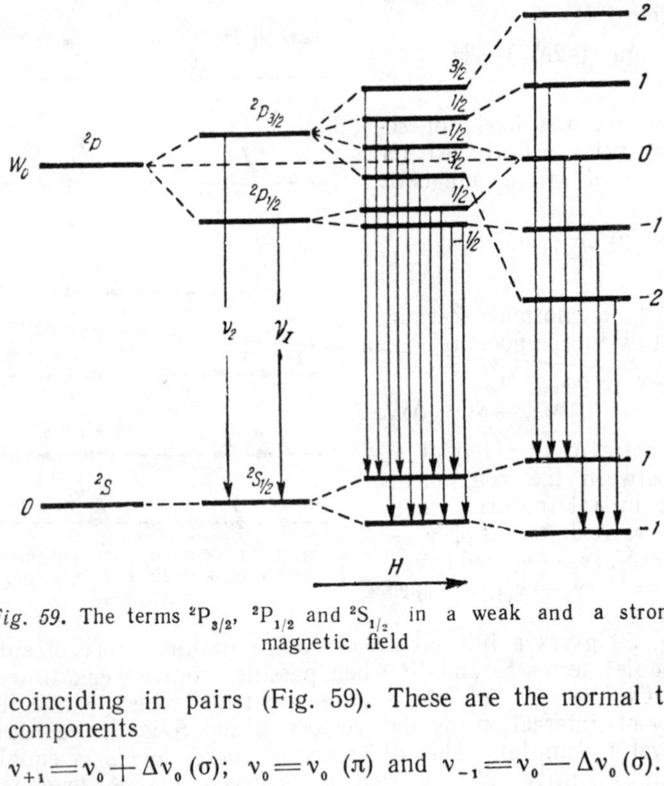

Fig. 59. The terms $^2P_{3/2}$, $^2P_{1/2}$ and $^2S_{1/2}$ in a weak and a strong magnetic field

lines coinciding in pairs (Fig. 59). These are the normal triplet with components

$$\nu_{+1} = \nu_0 + \Delta\nu_0\ (\sigma); \quad \nu_0 = \nu_0\ (\pi) \text{ and } \nu_{-1} = \nu_0 - \Delta\nu_0\ (\sigma).$$

The centre of this triplet ν_0 lies between the components of the natural doublet (ν_1, ν_2) at distances of

$$\nu_2 - \nu_0 = \frac{2}{3}(\nu_2 - \nu_1) \text{ and } \nu_0 - \nu_1 = \frac{1}{3}(\nu_2 - \nu_1)$$

(also see Fig. 56).

The foregoing interpretation of the Paschen-Back effect also explains why prohibition of intercombinations is not strict. As has already been pointed out (p. 240), there is a definite relationship between the intensity of intercombination lines and the magnitude of multiplet splitting of corresponding terms. As further confirmation of this thesis we give Table 22, in which the probabilities of transitions $^3P_1 - {}^1S_0$ ($A = 1/\tau$) are correlated with the magnitudes of natural splitting of lower ^{3}P-terms of the element analogue Zn, Cd, and Hg. The above-mentioned parallelism between A and multiplet splitting is evident from this table. It is readily accounted for on the basis of the data given in this section. As we know, the magnitude of multiplet splitting is determined by the energy of interaction of the vectors **L** and **S**. The stronger this interaction, the greater the splitting of the term. Further, it may be asserted that the stronger the interaction (**L**, **S**), the weaker, relatively, should be the interaction of individual s_i ($\mathbf{S} = \sum s_i$). Here we have a close analogy with the Paschen-Back effect, where strong interaction of the vectors **L** and **S** with an external magnetic field disrupts the mutual coupling of these vectors. For this reason, we should expect that with enhanced (**L**, **S**) interaction, the individual vectors $\mathbf{s}_i$ will become more mobile and, hence, the vector **S**, more readily "changeable". Since a strong (**L**, **S**) interaction corresponds to a greater magnitude of multiplet splitting of the term and since, further, the intercombination transition is associated precisely with a change in the **S** vector, it may be concluded that the probability of intercombination transitions should increase with the magnitude of splitting of terms, an illustration of which is Table 22.

Table 22

Multiplet splitting and transition probabilities in Zn, Cd, and Hg

Element	Zn	Cd	Hg
$^3P_2 - {}^3P_1$, cm^{-1}	389	1172	4261
$^3P_1 - {}^3P_0$, cm^{-1}	190	542	1767
A, sec^{-1}	1×10^5	5×10^5	1.5×10^7

31. Stark Effect

Stark effect in hydrogen. Another important force field, in addition to the magnetic field, is the electric field. The action of an electric field on an atom consists in *polarisation* of the atom. In addition, in an electric field of axial symmetry the magnetic moment of the atom is space-quantised. As a result, the initial energy levels of the atom change, and this is manifested in changes in its spectrum. The action of an electric field on the spectrum of hydrogen was discovered by Stark (1913) who observed the splitting of Balmer lines. This phenomenon is exhibited by the spectra of all elements and became known as the *Stark effect*.

Detailed investigations of electric splitting of the Balmer lines demonstrated that each line in an electric field is split into a certain number of components, that this number increases with the serial number of the line n (principal quantum number of a variable term); observation perpendicular to the direction of the electric field shows that the components are polarised in part parallel to the field (π-components) and in part, perpendicular to the field (σ-components). The components of Stark-splitting group symmetrically about the initial line (this symmetry is absent in the case of other elements) at distances that are multiples of a certain minimum distance ($\Delta\nu_0$). The magnitude of splitting increases in proportion to the field intensity (only hydrogen lines obey this law).

A rigorous solution of the problem of an atom in an electric field is possible only in the case of a hydrogen atom (or ion with one electron). Here, the action of the electric field is accounted for by the introduction, into the Schrödinger equation (23.13), of an "external" energy ez $\mathfrak{E}$, where $\mathfrak{E}$ is the electric-field intensity with a direction parallel to the z axis, and ez is the dipole moment induced in the atom. This is in addition to the "internal" potential energy of the atom $\frac{e^2Z}{r}$. In this case, the Schrödinger equation will have the form

$$\Delta\psi + \frac{2m}{\hbar^2}\left(E + \frac{e^2Z}{r} - ez\mathfrak{E}\right)\psi = 0. \tag{31.1}$$

Introduction of parabolic coordinates ξ, η, φ, connected with the coordinates x, y, z by the relations

$$x = \xi\eta\sin\varphi, \quad y = \xi\eta\cos\varphi, \quad z = \frac{1}{2}(\xi^2 - \eta^2),$$

leads to separation of the variables in equation (31.1) and, hence, to the possibility of solving it by a method similar to that of solving an unperturbed problem. As a result, for the atomic energy in this case we get a rapidly converging power series of the form

$$E = E^0 + E_1^0\mathfrak{E} + E_2^0\mathfrak{E}^2 + \ldots \tag{31.2}$$

A similar result was obtained by Schwarzschild and Epstein as early as 1916 on the basis of the Bohr theory. An evaluation of the coefficients of this series E^0, E_1^0, E_2^0, ... shows that all its terms, beginning with the third, may be discarded without affecting the accuracy of the solution. Then the expression for the energy of a hydrogen atom (or an ion with one electron) in an electric field takes on the following form:

$$E = E^0 + E_1^0 \mathfrak{E} = -\frac{hRZ^2}{n^2} + \frac{3h^2}{8\pi^2 meZ}(n_1 - n_2)\, n\mathfrak{E}. \qquad (31.3)$$

As will be seen from this equation the solution of the problem, to a zero approximation ($\mathfrak{E}=0$), is identical with the solution of the unperturbed problem. The first sufficiently precise approximation yields the Stark effect of the first order relative to the electric-field intensity (*linear* Stark effect). The coefficient

$$E_1^0 = \frac{3h^2}{8\pi^2 meZ}(n_1 - n_2)\, n,$$

which characterises the action of the electric field, is determined by three quantum numbers: the principal quantum number n and the numbers n_1 and n_2 with which it is connected by the relation

$$n = 1 + n_1 + n_2 + \lambda$$

where only λ may be identified with one of the earlier introduced quantum numbers, namely, with the absolute value of the orbital magnetic number m_l: $\lambda = |m_l|$*; n_1 and n_2, like λ, are integral positive numbers and have the values 0, 1, 2, ..., $(n-1)$.

The linear dependence of the magnitude of electric splitting of hydrogen terms, $E - E^0$, upon the numbers n_1 and n_2, and also the fact that both these numbers can assume the same values account for the symmetrical nature of the splitting. Indeed, noting that $n_1, n_2 \geqslant 0$ and $\lambda \leqslant n-1$, from expression (31.3) we get the following pattern of splitting of the first four terms of the H atom $\left(\text{Table 23, where } C = \frac{3h}{8\pi^2 me} = \frac{E_1^0}{h(n_1 - n_2)\, n}\right)$.

From Table 23 it is seen that the number of splitting components rapidly increases with the principal quantum number: term $n=1$ does not split at all, term $n=2$ splits into 3 components, $n=3$, into 6, $n=4$, into 10. In the latter two terms, certain components coincide, so that for the term $n=3$ we obtain five components with different energy and for the term $n=4$, seven. It is easy to see that in general the number of splitting components of a term characterised by the principal quantum number n, is equal to $2n-1$.

By combining these $2n-1$ components of a given term with $2n'-1$ components of some other term we get $(2n-1)(2n'-1)$ lines. Thus, the Balmer line H_α (λ6562.79 A, $n=2$, $n'=3$) will

* Since the angle φ, in the polar and parabolic coordinate frames, denotes the equatorial angle.

Table 23

Splitting of the terms of the hydrogen atom in an electric field

n	n_1	n_2	λ	$C(n_1-n_2)n$	n	n_1	n_2	λ	$C(n_1-n_2)n$
1	0	0	0	0	4	3	0	0	12C
2	1	0	0	2C	4	2	0	1	8C
2	0	0	1	0	4	1	0	2	4C
2	0	1	0	—2C	4	2	1	0	4C
3	2	0	0	6C	4	1	1	1	0
3	1	0	1	3C	4	0	0	3	0
3	0	0	2	0	4	0	1	2	—4C
3	1	1	0	0	4	1	2	0	—4C
3	0	1	1	—3C	4	0	2	1	—8C
3	0	2	0	—6C	4	0	3	0	—12C

split into 15 components, the line H_β (λ4861.33 A, $n=2$, $n'=4$) into 21 components, etc. The lines that correspond to $\Delta\lambda=0$, in accordance with the rule of polarisation for m_l (see p. 236) when observing in a direction perpendicular to the field, should be polarised parallel to the field (π-components), while the lines that correspond to $\Delta\lambda=1$, perpendicular to the field (σ-components).

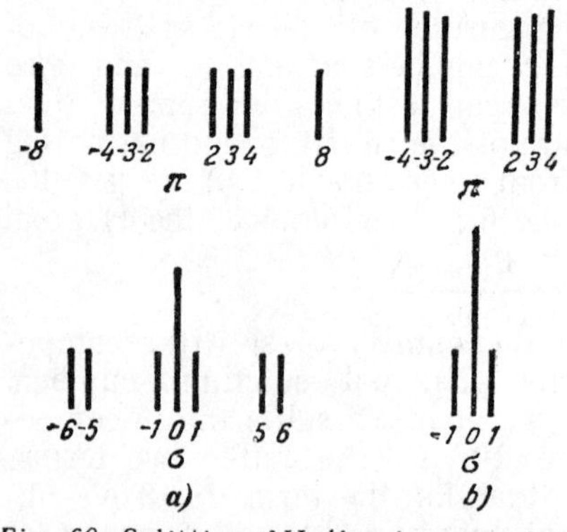

Fig. 60. Splitting of H_α line in an electric field: a) calculated, b) observed

Fig. 60a gives an example of all the 15 components of Stark splitting of the H_α line computed from the following formula (which follows from (31.3))

$$\nu=\nu_0+C[3(n_1'-n_2')-2(n_1-n_2)];$$

above are the π-components, below, the σ-components. The numbers under each line in Fig. 60 represent the factor in square brackets in the preceding formula. Fig. 60b gives the experimentally observed splitting components of the H_α line. A comparison of these two figures shows that the computed lines coincide with the experimentally found lines both as regards the magnitude of splitting and the polarisation of the components. It may be added that good coincidence is also obtained for the intensities of the components (we have in view relative intensities).* The absence, in Fig. 60b of certain lines found in theory is, apparently, due to their low intensity. The situation is similar in the case of other Balmer lines of hydrogen and He^+ lines that have been studied.

Stark effect in complex atoms. Unlike the hydrogen lines, line splitting of other elements in an electric field is unsymmetrical relative to their original position in the spectrum. An idea of the nature of Stark splitting of terms and spectral lines in this case may be had from Fig. 61, which shows the Stark effect of the D-doublet of sodium $\lambda\lambda 5895.93/5889.96$ A ($^2P_{1/2,\,3/2} - {}^2S_{1/2}$). In this figure, the dashed lines designate the original terms, the transitions ($^2P_{1/2} - {}^2S_{1/2}$ and $^2P_{3/2} - {}^2S_{1/2}$) that correspond to them, and the original doublet (below). The solid lines denote the terms, transitions, and lines in an electric field. In accordance with the fact that the energy of the induced dipole (see below) is negative, the energy of the atom in all three states ($^2P_{3/2}$, $^2P_{1/2}$, and $^2S_{1/2}$) in an electric field *diminishes*, and this decrease in energy is more appreciable for the upper terms, as a result of which the spectrum is shifted towards longer wavelengths. Fig. 62 gives the amount of shift ($\Delta\lambda$) of the lines of the potassium doublet $^2P_{1/2,\,3/2} - {}^2S_{1/2}\lambda\lambda\, 4047.20/4044.14$ A as a function of the electric field intensity. It is seen that $\Delta\lambda$, for all three components, varies in proportion to the square of the field intensity (*quadratic* Stark effect).

The quantum-mechanical theory of the quadratic Stark effect of complex atoms was given in 1927 by Unsold. For the magnitude of term splitting, Unsold obtained the following equations **

$$\Delta T = \frac{9e^2\mathfrak{E}^2}{16h^4c^2R^2}\,n^2\left\{\frac{\dfrac{(n^2-L^2)(L^2-M^2)}{4L^2-1}}{T_{L-1}-T_L} - \frac{\dfrac{[n^2-(L+1)^2]\,[(L+1)^2-M]}{4(L+1)^2-1}}{T_L - T_{L+1}}\right\} \tag{31.4}$$

where T_L is the term under consideration (characterised by quantum numbers n and L), T_{L-1} and T_{L+1} are adjacent terms characterised by the same value of n.

The diverse nature of Stark splitting of the spectral lines of hydrogen and of the lines of many-electron atoms is vividly interpreted by the Bohr-Sommerfeld model of the atom, according to

---

* The theoretical distribution of intensity among components of line splitting has been disregarded in Fig. 60a.

** This equation was derived for a weak electric field, with multiplet splitting of the term ignored. Earlier (1922), a similar equation was derived by Becker on the basis of the Bohr theory. At large n, the equations coincide.

which the motion of an electron in a many-electron atom may be regarded as motion in a rapidly precessing orbit (see Sec. 22). The electric centre of gravity of such an orbit coincides with the nucleus, as a result of which the mean shift of the electron with respect to the nucleus (z) becomes zero. For this reason, the Stark effect of the first order should, in the case of such atoms, be absent (at least in relatively weak fields, see below). Designating the polarisation coefficient of an atom by α, we obtain, for the induced dipole moment that arises due to polarisation of the atom in an electric field, the quantity $\alpha\mathfrak{E}$ and for the energy of polarisation, the quantity

$$E = -\alpha\int_0^{\mathfrak{E}} \mathfrak{E}\, d\mathfrak{E} = -\frac{\alpha\mathfrak{E}^2}{2}, \tag{31.5}$$

i.e., the quadratic effect, which is actually observed in the spectra of many-electron atoms.

The nature of the change of atomic terms in an electric field may be established on the basis of a vector model of the atom. In the case of a *weak* field, the action of the latter may be regarded as a slight perturbation that does not disrupt the coupling between the vectors **L** and **S** (that form the vector **J**). The direction of the electric field fixes in space the direction of the z-axis, on which the vector **J** is projected; projections of the latter (in units of $\hbar$) assume the values $M = \pm J, \pm(J-1), \ldots$

Since the polarising action of an electric field on an atom depends on the orientation of the latter with respect to the field direction (the orientation is determined by M), one should expect splitting of the term. However, unlike magnetic splitting, the number of components of electric splitting of a term is not equal to $2J+1$ (the number of different values of M) but to a magnitude roughly half that, since the energy of an atom in an external electric field is determined by the *square* of the number M and, consequently, is the same in two states that differ only by the opposite direction of the projections of vector **J** ($+M$ and $-M$).

Indeed, since the polarisability of an atom and, consequently, its energy in an electric field (31.4) does not depend on the direction of rotation of the electrons and is determined only by the general distribution of electricity in the atom with respect to the field direction, this energy in states $+M$ and $-M$ should be one and the same. Denoting the absolute values of projections of the vector **J** by $\Omega = |M|$ and the coefficients of polarisation that correspond to different orientations of an atom in an electric field by α_Ω, we will obtain as many different coefficients and, hence, the same number of splitting components of the term

$$T = T_0 + \frac{\alpha_\Omega \mathfrak{E}^2}{2h},$$

as the number Ω assumes values (for a given J), namely, $J+1$ in the case of integral J and $J+{}^1/_2$ in the case of half integral J. In this case, all components that correspond to $\Omega \neq 0$ are *doubly* degenerate. Therefore, when a magnetic field is superposed on an electric field, each such component splits into two (corresponding to $+M$ and $-M$) and we get the number of components that correspond to the case of a magnetic field, i.e., $2J+1$.

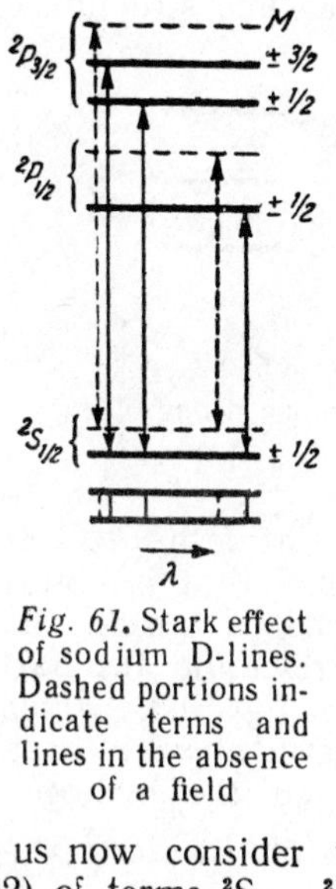

Fig. 61. Stark effect of sodium D-lines. Dashed portions indicate terms and lines in the absence of a field

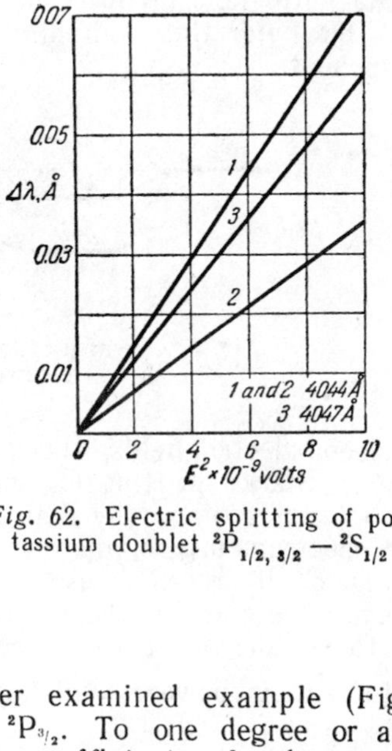

Fig. 62. Electric splitting of potassium doublet $^2P_{1/2,\,3/2} - {}^2S_{1/2}$

Let us now consider the earlier examined example (Figs. 61 and 62) of terms $^2S_{1/2}$, $^2P_{1/2}$ and $^2P_{3/2}$. To one degree or another (depending upon the appropriate coefficients of polarisation α), all three terms are shifted towards lower energies. In addition, the latter one is split into two components $(J+{}^1/_2=2)$ in an electric field. We thus obtain two components $^2P_{3/2}\,(\Omega={}^3/_2,\ {}^1/_2)$ and one compotent each of $2P_{1/2}$ and $^2S_{1/2}\,(\Omega={}^1/_2)$. Combining three components ^2P with the ^2S-term, we get three lines:

$$^2P_{3/2} - {}^2S_{1/2}\,(\Omega'={}^3/_2 \rightarrow \Omega={}^1/_2),\ {}^2P_{3/2} - {}^2S_{1/2}\,(\Omega'={}^1/_2 \rightarrow \Omega={}^1/_2)$$
$$\text{and } {}^2P_{1/2} - {}^2S_{1/2}\,(\Omega'={}^1/_2 \rightarrow \Omega={}^1/_2).$$

Passing to *strong* fields, when the magnitude of electric splitting becomes greater than the natural splitting of the given multiplet term, the interaction of vectors **L** and **S** may be regarded as a slight perturbation superposed on the action of the external field. In this case, the vector **L** is quantised as an independent vector (cf. the Paschen-Back effect), and each term is split into $2L+1$ components, of which only $L+1$ have different energy. To describe these components, use is made of the number $\Lambda=|M_L|$ and the symbols $\Sigma\ (\Lambda=0)$, $\Pi\ (\Lambda=1)$, $\Delta\ (\Lambda=2)$, ... Space quantisation of the vector **L** in an electric field causes it to *precess* about the lines of force of the field, as a result of which the mean value of the **L**-vector component perpendicular to the field becomes zero. The spin **S** is quantised in a magnetic field produced by the **L** (**Λ**)-vector component parallel to the field; this is manifested in the fine structure of each **Λ**-component.

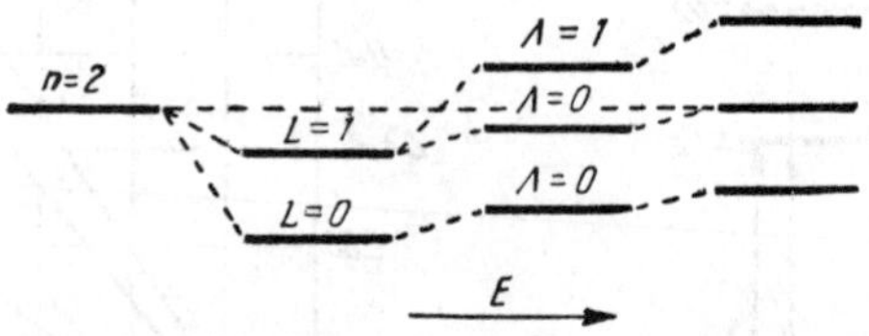

Fig. 63. Term $n=2$ in a weak and a strong electric field

In strong electric fields, the quadratic relationship of the magnitude of Stark splitting (or shift) of lines that is observed for weak fields is replaced by a linear one, and as a result the form of the spectrum begins, more or less, to resemble the pattern of splitting of hydrogen lines. Let us take Fig. 63, which gives a schematic picture of the behaviour of term $n=2$ in an electric field. Here, the level $n=2$ corresponds to the hydrogen term $\frac{R}{n^2}$. In reality, however, this term is split into two terms $\frac{R}{n_1^{*2}}$ and $\frac{R}{n_2^{*2}}$ that correspond to two possible values of the azimuthal quantum number, $L=0$ and 1. In a weak electric field, these terms are split into three terms corresponding to the values of the number $J=L=1$ (two terms) and 0 (one term). Here we take $J=L$, because interaction of spin with the orbital angular momentum is disregarded. In a strong field, these three terms also pass into $2n-1=3$ terms with symmetrical splitting (Stark effect in hydrogen). Transition to the linear effect is due to disturbance of precessional motion of the electrons in the atom, as a result of which the linear effect in a weak field cancels.

Comparing Figs. 63 and 59 we see that the change in the pattern of electrical splitting of terms when passing from weak to strong fields is, to some extent, analogous to the Paschen-Back effect. However, this analogy is stopped by the fact that the effects of higher orders ($\Delta T = a\mathfrak{E} + b\mathfrak{E}^2 + \ldots$) that disturb the symmetry of splitting increase with stronger electric fields. These effects are also found in the hydrogen spectrum (in fields of intensity exceeding 10^5 V/cm). For this reason, Fig. 63 must be regarded as an idealised scheme that is not accomplished in reality.

The Stark effect in a molecular field. A series of facts indicates that the action of a molecular field can, in many cases, be reduced to the action of an electric field. The action of a molecular field frequently manifests itself in broadening of spectral lines, which is due to the interaction of atoms and molecules in their collisions *(collision broadening)*. Without going into a consideration of other causes of broadening of spectral lines (the Doppler effect, for instance), we merely note that when the main part is played by collision broadening there is observed a parallelism between the measured line width and the magnitude of their electrical splitting calculated from the linear Stark effect. Whence it may be concluded that in these cases the cause of line broadening is the action of the electrical molecular field on the atomic terms. The fact that discrete splitting components are not observed is due to inhomogeneity of the molecular field. It may be added that according to Holtsmark the intensity of a medium molecular electric field may be computed from the following formulas: $\mathfrak{E} = 3.25\ eN^{2/3}$ V/cm when the field is created by ions, $\mathfrak{E} = 4.54\ PN$ V/cm when the field is produced by dipoles, and $\mathfrak{E} = 5.5QN^{4/3}$ V/cm when the field is produced by quadrupoles. Here, N denotes the number of ions or molecules in one cubic centimetre, e is the ion charge, P the dipole, and Q the quadrupole moments of the molecule.

Under certain conditions, in addition to broadening one can observe also a splitting of lines under the action of the molecular field, similar to the splitting in an external field. Thus, a study of the ultraviolet absorption spectrum of mercury in various liquid solvents (water, alcohol, hexane) shows (Reichardt and Bonhoeffer, 1931) that in place of the resonance line 2537 A ($^3P_1 - {}^1S_0$) there are *two* lines, which, to a certain degree (dependent on the nature of the solvent and the temperature of the solution), are shifted relative to the resonance line. We may assume that these lines are components of Stark splitting of the line λ 2537 A. This is supported both by the number of components and the order of magnitude of the mean electric field calculated from line splitting. Indeed, since for an excited term $^3P_1$, $L=1$ and for the principal term $^1S_0$, $L=0$, the first one of them should split into $L+1=2$ components, while the second does not split ($L+1=1$). It is as a result of the combination of two splitting components of the term $^3P_1$ with the term $^1S_0$ that there appear two lines in the absorption spectrum of a mercury solution: $\Pi\,(^3P_1,\ \Lambda=1) - \Sigma\,(^1S_0,\ \Lambda=0)$ and $\Sigma\,(^3P_1,\ \Lambda=0) - \Sigma\,(^1S_0,\ \Lambda=0)$.

A comparison of the magnitude of the observed splitting with the splitting of line λ 2537 A in an external electric field of intensity 10^5 V/cm yields, for the molecular field (on the assumption of the quadratic effect), an intensity of about 30×10^6 V/cm, which is in good agreement with the values obtained from other data.

It may be added that extension of the Stark effect theory to atoms in crystals led to the development of a theory of the crystalline field, which represents an important division of theoretical (quantum) chemistry.

CHAPTER 7

THE NATURE OF CHEMICAL FORCES. THE MOLECULE

32. Electrovalent Bond

Electronic concepts in chemistry. Studies of atomic spectra, to which chapters 5 and 6 were devoted, show that all the basic spectral regularities are a clear reflection of peculiarities in the electronic structure and of the nature of the electronic states of the atom. Quite different is the situation as regards the chemical properties of atoms. True, the electronic structure and the electronic states are also essential in manifestations of the chemical properties of atoms. Hewever, there is no sense in considering the chemical properties of an isolated atom because these properties are manifested only in the presence of other atoms with which the given atom interacts chemically. In other words, the effects of chemical properties of an atom, and, hence, these properties themselves belong not to a single atom but to an *ensemble of atoms* (in the simplest case, two atoms), the interaction of which leads to the formation of a molecule. For this reason, in contrast to the spectral properties of atoms, the investigation of their chemical properties, like the study of the chemical forces as such, is naturally based on a study of the structure of molecules and their physical and chemical properties.

The various combinations of atoms of one or several elements in a molecule give rise to the diversity (over a million) of chemical substances found in nature or created artificially. The modern concept of the molecule (like that of the atom) came from chemistry. One of the first to introduce into science the concept of molecules was the founder of physical chemistry, Lomonosov, whose ideas in various branches of knowledge were many decades ahead of scientific thought in the leading countries of the West. Calling atoms elements, molecules corpuscles, and chemical substances fundamentals, Lomonosov wrote in 1741: "Corpuscles differ when their elements differ and are combined in different ways or in different numbers; it is upon this that the infinite diversity of bodies depends. A fundamental is a body consisting of identical corpuscles. A mixed body is one that consists of two or several fundamentals so combined that each separate corpuscle contains fundamentals in the same ratio ... as the entire mixed body." From these words we see that already for Lomonosov constancy in the composition of chemical compounds was not an unsettled question, as many scientists in later years still considered it.

An essential contribution to the development of an understanding of the structure of molecules was made by Butlerov who created the theory of chemical structure (1861), the underlying principle of which is: "Starting with the concept that each *chemical* atom that makes up a body participates in the formation of this body and operates via a specific quantity of force inherent in it (affinity), I call *chemical structure* a distribution of action of this force, as a result of which the chemical atoms (acting upon one another directly or indirectly) combine into a chemical particle." And further: "The chemical nature of a complex particle is determined by the nature of the elementary component parts, their number, and chemical structure."

Butlerov's views on the mutual influence of atoms in a molecule were further developed in the works of his pupil Markovnikov. The Butlerov-Markovnikov doctrine on the mutual effect of atoms became one of the chief components of the theory of structure. However, the chemically established structural peculiarities of different classes of compounds and also numerous empirical regularities and rules were purely descriptive and required an interpretation from the point of view of the internal structure of molecules, i.e., theoretically. This could be done only through physics, which had always played a particularly important role in structural studies of matter and which became still more important with the advent of the electron theory of the atom. Attempts to explain chemical facts on the basis of the latter led to definite concepts concerning the structure and chemical properties of molecules known as *electronic concepts in chemistry*.

The main problem with which chemistry confronted the electron theory of the atom was that of the nature of chemical forces. This is a problem of the physical substantiation of the very existence of molecules. Attempts to resolve this problem within the framework of the Bohr theory of the atom were unsuccessful, and a proper solution began to emerge only with the advent of quantum mechanics. However, due to the fundamental fact that chemical forces are of an *electrical nature*, certain phenomena or groups of phenomena could be interpreted qualitatively and could be given a model-type interpretation even within the framework of the Bohr electron theory of the atom. This includes the problem of *electrovalent chemical bonding*.

Kossel theory. The classical theory of valence deals with such concepts as valence numbers, the type of chemical bond (single, double, and triple bonds), saturated and unsaturated compounds, etc. These concepts require a physical interpretation. The first successful attempt at such an interpretation of the phenomenon of chemical reactivity and valence numbers was made in 1916 by Kossel, who proceeded on the basis of the Bohr theory of the atom and Mendeleyev's Periodic Table. The approach yielded the *closed* nature of the outer eight-electron shells in the atoms of the inert gases, which for this reason were extremely *stable* physically and *saturated* chemically. In the opinion of Kossel, underlying the chemical activity of every atom is its tendency to a closed outer electron shell imitating the electronic structure of an inert-gas atom.

We distinguish valence with respect to hydrogen, or *positive valence*, and with respect to fluorine, or *negative valence*. Positive valence is determined quantitatively by the number of atoms of hydrogen that a given atom is capable of substituting in a chemical compound. Negative valence is determined by the number of atoms of fluorine (or a double number of atoms of oxygen) that are subject to substitution. Considering the maximum positive valence of various elements (we, of course, disregard "anomalous" elements), i.e., the valence that these elements have in their saturated compounds, it will readily be seen that it corresponds exactly to the *number* of the vertical column of the Periodic Table in which the given element lies. To illustrate, sodium, in the first column, is univalent (NaF, Na_2O), magnesium is bivalent (MgF_2, MgO), aluminium is trivalent (AlF_3), silicon is tetravalent (SiF_4, SiO_2), phosphorus is pentavalent (PF_5, P_2O_5), sulphur is hexavalent (SF_6, SO_3), chlorine is septivalent (Cl_2O_7). The valence of inert Ar, in the zero column, is zero. On the other hand, the number of *outer* electrons of an atom is also equal to the number of the corresponding column. Consequently, *the maximum positive valence of an element is equal to the number of its outer electrons*. For this reason, the outer electrons of an atom are frequently called *valence electrons*.

It will readily be seen that the maximum negative valence of an element is equal to the *difference* between the number 8 and the number of outer electrons. Thus, silicon is tetravalent (SiH_4), phosphorus is trivalent (PH_3), sulphur is bivalent (H_2S), chlorine is univalent (HCl). Consequently, as was noticed by Abegg and Bodlander as far back as 1904, the sum of maximum valences (positive and negative) is eight, which is the number of electrons in the L- or M-group (incomplete). This indicates a connection between the valence of an atom and its outer electrons.

It is these regularities related to the stability of the inactive eight-electron shell of the atoms of the inert gases that lead to the concept of atomic valence developed by Kossel. According to this theory, each atom with an incomplete and, therefore, chemically active outer electron group strives towards a complete eight-electron outer shell. This can obviously be done either by the atom *giving up* its extra (outer) electrons or by *acquiring* the needed electrons from other atoms. In the first case the atom is ionised positively exposing a complete inner group of electrons, in the second case, it is ionised negatively and completes its outer electron group at the expense of extraneous electrons. The probability of a given process is determined by how advantageous it is energetically Thus, the atoms Na and Mg, which readily give up their outer electrons due to comparatively low ionisation potentials, are ionised positively. The Na atom with eight M-electrons, i. e., Na + 7 extra electrons would, energetically, be an extremely unstable system, because due to its comparatively low charge ($Z = 11$) the Na nucleus would not be able to hold 18 electrons. Conversely, the Cl atom with 7 outer electrons readily acquires the missing electron, because an enormous energy is required to tear 7 electrons out of the Cl^{+7} ion. We recall that the negative chlorine ion Cl^{-}, even in the free state, has less energy than the system Cl + electron (positive electron affinity).

Due to the low ionisation potentials of atoms of the alkaline elements (Me) and to the great electron affinity of the halogen atoms (X), MeX compounds are readily formed when these two combine. This is a process that proceeds, according to Kossel, by the scheme

$$Me + X \rightarrow Me^{+}\,\overset{\frown}{eX} \rightarrow Me^{+}X^{-}$$

Oppositely charged ions that form this compound mutually attract in accordance with the Coulomb law; the force of this attraction is what gives the compound its strength.

On Kossel's theory, a similar scheme is followed in the formation of all heteropolar chemical compounds. Thus, on this theory the saturation of positive chemical affinity, i.e., the manifestation of positive valence, consists in the atom giving up its valence (outer) electrons, which are captured by the other atoms (combining with this atom) that saturate their negative affinity in this way.

A somewhat generalised Kossel theory of valence can also accommodate definite classes of *complex* compounds, which, according to

Werner, are characterised by what is known as *coordination* bonding. These compounds go beyond the conventional concepts of valence and make up a special group. The characteristic peculiarity of this group is that the maximum valence of a given atom is independent of the number of the group in the Periodic Table in which this atom occurs. Assuming a purely formal existence of special *supplementary* valences alongside the *principal* ordinary valence, one may introduce a *coordination number* which is equal to the sum of the principal and supplementary valences of the given atom and determines the number of univalent atoms or radicals that can combine directly with this atom By way of illustration, let us consider the complex compounds $Ni(CO)_4$, $Fe(CO)_5$, and $Mo(CO)_6$. Since the valence of the CO group is 2, the ccordination numbers of Ni, Fe, and Mo must be 8, 10, and 12, respectively. It is readily seen that these numbers are equal to the number of missing electrons required to bring the electron shell of the given atom up to the closed shell of the inert-gas atom in the immediate vicinity. Indeed, the electrons in the outer shells of these atoms are distributed as follows:

Atom	3s	3p	3d	4s	4p	4d	4f	5s	5p
Fe	2	6	6	2					
Ni	2	6	8	2					
Kr	2	6	10	2	6				
Mo	2	6	10	2	6	5	1		
Xe	2	6	10	2	6	10		2	6

We see that Kr has 10 electrons more than Fe and 8 more than Ni, and Xe has 12 more electrons than Mo. This leads to the conclusion that the complex compounds under consideration are completed systems, the central atom of which has a completed symmetrical shell of the corresponding inert gas. The electrons of atoms or atomic groups (CO) that are in the immediate vicinity of the central atom participate, together with the valence electrons of this atom, in the formation of this shell.

Kossel's theory, which reduces chemical interaction to purely electrostatic forces, is quantitatively applicable only to a very limited range of compounds called *ionic* or *heteropolar*. These compounds have a series of characteristic physical and chemical properties of which the outstanding are ionic structure of their crystal lattices, electrolytic dissociation of their solutions and melts, high melting points, specific spectral properties, etc. The ionic structure of the molecules of these compounds permit considering the chemical intramolecular forces that condition the stability of ionic molecules as forces of electrostatic (Coulomb) attraction between oppositely charged ions. It must, however, be borne in mind that this representation, like any model, is arbitrary.

The theory of ionic molecules. A quantitative theory of ionic molecules was given by Born and Heisenberg in 1925. This theory proceeds from Born's theory of crystal lattices, which is based on the following concepts. In the simplest case of cubic ionic lattices, the potential energy of unit volume of the lattice may, approximately, be represented in the form

$$u = -\frac{ae^2}{r} + \frac{be^2}{r^n} \qquad (32.1)$$

where the term $-\frac{ae^2}{r}$ is the attraction-force potential that expresses the mutual potential energy of oppositely charged ions considered as point charges, while the term $+\frac{be^2}{r^n}$ is the repulsive-force potential. Equilibrium of ions in a crystal is determined by the condition

$$\left(\frac{du}{dr}\right)_{r=r_0} = 0$$

where r_0 is the equilibrium distance between ions (*lattice constant*). From this condition we have

$$b = \frac{a}{n} r_0^{n-1},$$

whence for the energy of the lattice we get

$$u = -\frac{ae^2}{r}\left[1 - \frac{1}{n}\left(\frac{r_0}{r}\right)^{n-1}\right]. \qquad (32.2)$$

The equilibrium energy, accordingly, turns out equal to

$$u_0 = -\frac{n-1}{n}\frac{ae^2}{r_0}. \qquad (32.3)$$

The lattice constant r_0 is determined from X-ray analysis of the crystal. The quantities a and n are found from measurements of the heat of formation of the crystal from the atoms (Q), of the ionisation potential (I) of an electropositive atom, and of the electron affinity (E) of an electronegative atom, and also from the compressibility of the crystal. Indeed, the molecular energy of the crystal lattice $U_0 = Vu_0$ (V is the molar volume). on the basis of the following circular process,

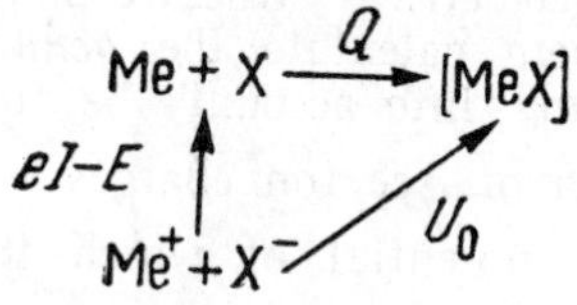

is connected with the quantities Q, I, and E by the relation

$$U_0 = Q + eI - E. \tag{32.4}$$

Thus, the energy of the lattice U_0 may be determined by measuring Q, I, and E. As for the compressibility of the crystal, by proceeding from the definition of the coefficient of bulk compressibility, $\varkappa$,

$$\frac{1}{\varkappa} = -V\frac{dp}{dV},$$

it is possible, due to the fact that

$$p = -\frac{dU}{dV} \text{ and } \frac{dp}{dV} = -\frac{d^2U}{dV^2},$$

to express the quantity $\frac{1}{\varkappa}$ as

$$\frac{1}{\varkappa} = V\left[\frac{d^2U}{dr^2}\left(\frac{dr}{dV}\right)^2 + \frac{dU}{dr}\frac{d^2r}{dV^2}\right].$$

Noting that the volume of the crtystal $V = Nr^3$, where N is the number of molecules in the volume V (and $Nr_0^3 = 1$), we find, from this expression and from (32.2),

$$\frac{1}{\varkappa_0} = \frac{n}{9}u_0.$$

Knowing r_0, $\varkappa_0$, and u_0, it is possible to determine a and n from the latter relation and (32.3). Thus, for ions with the electronic structure of neon (Na^+ and F^-, for instance), we can obtain a value of n close to 7, for ions with the electronic structure of Ar (for example, K^+ and Cl^-), the value $n \approx 9$, for ions with the electronic structure of Kr and Xe, values of $n \approx 10$ and 12, respectively. As may be seen from (32.3), the magnitude of lattice energy is but relatively slightly affected by a change in n. For this reason, a single value of n is often used when considering crystals of one type. For instance, $n = 9$ is often taken for crystals like NaCl. In the case of crystals of this type, a magnitude of the order of unity is obtained for the constant a, called the *Madelung constant*. In the general case, this constant may be calculated from the geometrical structure of the crystal.

Born and Heisenberg calculate the *bond energy* of NaCl-type ionic molecules taking into account the following interactions: 1) Coulomb attraction of free ion charges $\left(-\frac{e^2}{r}\right)$; 2) mutual repulsion of ions, the potential of which they assume equal to $+\frac{be^2}{r^9}$ (see above); 3) attraction of free ion charges by dipoles p_1 and p_2 that appear due to polarisation of the ions $\left(-\frac{ep_1}{r^2}, -\frac{ep_2}{r^2}\right)$ and, finally, 4) interaction of the dipoles $\left(-\frac{2p_1p_2}{r^3}\right)$. Thus, taking into account also the quasi-elastic energy of dipoles $\left(\frac{p_1^2}{2\alpha_1}\right)+\left(\frac{p_2^2}{2\alpha_2}\right)$ (α_1 and α_2 are coefficients of polarisation of the ions), we have, for the potential energy of an ionic molecule (considering the energy of the molecule dissociated into ions equal to zero),

$$U=-\frac{e^2}{r}+\frac{be^2}{r^9}-\frac{ep_1}{r^2}-\frac{ep_2}{r^2}-\frac{2p_1p_2}{r^3}+\frac{p_1^2}{2\alpha_1}+\frac{p_2^2}{2\alpha_2}.$$

From the conditions of polarised equilibrium, $\frac{\partial U}{\partial p_1}=0$ and $\frac{\partial U}{\partial p_2}=0$, we have:

$$p_1=\frac{\alpha_1 e}{r^2}+\frac{2\alpha_1}{r^3}p_2 \text{ and } p_2=\frac{\alpha_2 e}{r^2}+\frac{2\alpha_2}{r^3}p_1,$$

whence, expanding into a power series in terms of $1/r$, we find

$$p_1=\frac{\alpha_1 e}{r^2}+\frac{2\alpha_1\alpha_2 e}{r^5}+\frac{4\alpha_1^2\alpha_2 e}{r^8}+\ldots \text{ and}$$

$$p_2=\frac{\alpha_2 e}{r^2}+\frac{2\alpha_1\alpha_2 e}{r^5}+\frac{4\alpha_1\alpha_2^2 e}{r^8}+\ldots$$

Substituting p_1 and p_2 into the expression for U and disregarding powers of r above the ninth, we get

$$U=-\frac{e^2}{r}-\frac{(\alpha_1+\alpha_2)e^2}{2r^4}-\frac{2\alpha_1\alpha_2 e^2}{r^7}+\frac{be^2}{r^9}.$$

The potential energy of a molecu'e consists of two parts: $U=U_1+U_2$. The first,

$$U_1=-\frac{e^2}{r}-\frac{(\alpha_1+\alpha_2)e^2}{2r^4}-\frac{2\alpha_1\alpha_2 e^2}{r^7}<0,$$

corresponds to the force of attraction, the second,

$$U_2 = \frac{be^2}{r^9} > 0,$$

to the force of repulsion. In Fig. 64, both parts of the potential energy are represented by the curves $U_1(r)$ and $U_2(r)$. Since the second and third terms in the expression for U_1 become perceptible only for small r, at sufficiently large distances the quantity U_1 is determined almost solely by the term e^2/r, and the appropriate portion of the curve $U_1(r)$ is a first-order hyperbola. At these distances, the energy U is totally determined by U_1, because U_2 is here also practically zero. But at short distances, the curve U_1 passes into a higher-order hyperbola, deviating from the original first-order hyperbola (dashed line). Here, U_2 already becomes noticeable and increases rapidly with decreasing distance

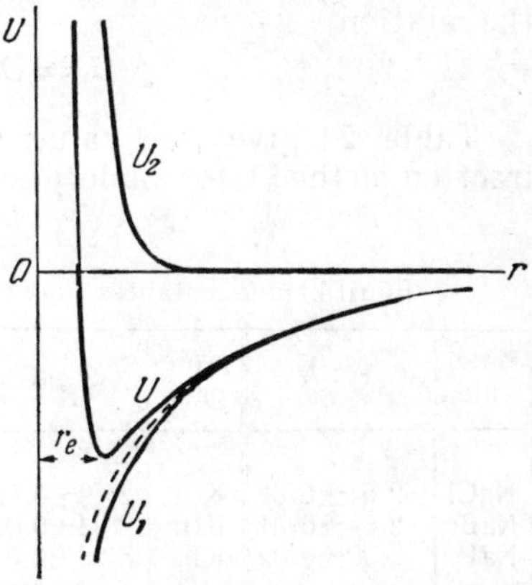

Fig. 64. Interaction energy of ions in ionic molecule

(in accordance with a ninth-order hyperbola). Addition of the curves U_1 and U_2 yields the curve U, which corresponds to total potential energy of an ionic molecule This curve has a *minimum* at a certain definite distance r_e which corresponds to the equilibrium position *(equilibrium distance)*. When $r < r_e$ the quantity U increases rapidly, passing through zero into the region of positive values, which corresponds to a preponderance of repulsion forces.

The quantity r_e is determined by the third condition of equilibrium, $\frac{dU}{dr} = 0$, which expresses equilibrium of all forces inside a molecule. This condition leads to the equality

$$1 + \frac{2(\alpha_1 + \alpha_2)}{r_e^3} + \frac{14\alpha_1\alpha_2}{r_e^6} = \frac{9b}{r_e^8}.$$

Substituting b into the expression for U, we obtain, for the energy of the molecule in an equilibrium state, the expression

$$U_0 = -\frac{e^2}{r_e}\left[\frac{8}{9} + \frac{5(\alpha_1 + \alpha_2)}{18r_e^3} + \frac{4\alpha_1\alpha_2}{9r_e^6}\right]. \qquad (32.5)$$

U_0 is connected with the energy of dissociation of the molecule into two ions D_i by the relation

$$D_i = -U_0. \tag{32.6}$$

Thus, D_i may be computed from (32.5) if the appropriate values of r_e and α are known. We note that D_i is connected with the energy of dissociation of the molecule into neutral atoms D by the relation

$$D_i = D + eI - E. \tag{32.7}$$

Table 24 gives the values of r_e obtained by the electron diffraction method * for molecules of the NaCl type.

Table 24

Equilibrium distances between ions in NaCl-type molecules

Molecule	r_e, A	Molecule	r_e, A	Molecule	r_e, A	Molecule	r_e, A
NaCl	2.51±0.03	KCl	2.79±0.02	RbCl	2.89±0.01	CsCl	3.06±0.03
NaBr	2.64±0.01	KBr	2.94±0.03	RbBr	3.06±0.02	CsBr	3.14±0.03
NaI	2.90±0.02	KI	3.23±0.01	RbI	3.26±0.02	CsI	3.41±0.03

Table 25 gives the values of polarisation coefficients for a number of cations and anions.

Table 25

Polarisation coefficients of ions (in cm³)

Ion	Li^+	Na^+	K^+	Rb^+	Cs^+	F^-	Cl^-	Br^-	I^-
$\alpha \times 10^{24}$	0.075	0.21	0.87	1.81	2.79	0.99	3.05	4.17	6.28

The values of the heats of dissociation (in eV) of molecules of alkali-halogen salts as calculated by means of (32.5) from the data in Table 24 are given in Table 26 ($D_{i,\, calc}$) together

* During recent years, the following highly accurate values of r_e (±0.0001 to ±0.0003 A) have been obtained from microwave spectra: 2.3453 (CsF), 2.3606 (NaCl), 2.6666 (KCl), 2.7867 (RbCl), 2.9062 (CsCl), 2.1704 (LiBr), 2.5020 (NaBr), 2.8207 (KBr), 2.9448 (RbBr), 3.0720 (CsBr), 2.3919 (LiI), 2.7115 (NaI), 3.0478 (KI), 3.1769 (RbI), 3.3150 (CsI). These data are noticeably different from those in Table 24; however, the cause for this difference has not yet been definitely established.

with the values of these quantities measured thermochemically ($D_{i,\ meas}$).

Table 26

Dissociation heats of molecules of NaCl-type salts (in eV)

Molecule	$D_{i,\ calc}$	$D_{i,\ meas}$	Molecule	$D_{i,\ calc}$	$D_{i,\ meas}$
NaCl	5.40	5.27	RbCl	4.69	4.75
NaBr	5.18	5.01	RbBr	4.45	4.36
NaI	4.75	4.62	RbI	4.20	3.87
KCl	4.83	4.96	CsCl	4.44	4.53
KBr	4.61	4.53	CsBr	4.36	4.13
KI	4.21	4.04	CsI	4.02	3.65

It will be seen from this table that the discrepancy between calculated and measured values of D_i does not, in most cases, exceed several per cent.*

Reverting to Fig. 64, it will be seen that the equilibrium distance r_e is the *less* the deeper the minimum of the curve of potential energy U, i.e., the *greater* the energy of dissociation of the molecule. The magnitude of r_e may be roughly evaluated by considering that the energy of the molecule in the equilibrium position is equal to $-\frac{e^2}{r_e}$. Whence, for the magnitude of r_e we find

$$r_e = \frac{e^2}{D_i}\,. \tag{32.8}$$

Decrease of r_e with increasing bonding strength of the molecule (D_i) is observed not only in the case of ionic molecules, as will be seen later on.

The foregoing electrostatic theory permits calculating both the dissociation energy and certain other constants of an ionic molecule, its dipole moment and frequency of natural oscillations.

---

* Apparently, the most precise values are to be considered those of $D_{i,\ meas}$ given in the accompanying table, in which they are correlated with values of $D_{i,\ calc}$ obtained by means of values of r_e calculated from microwave spectra:

Molecule	$D_{i,\ calc}$	$D_{i,\ meas}$	Molecule	$D_{i,\ calc}$	$D_{i,\ meas}$
NaCl	5.85	5.58	KCl	5.13	4.94
NaBr	5.57	5.39	KBr	4.87	4.74
NaI	5.21	5.04	KI	4.65	4.45

It will readily be seen that here, too, the discrepancy between calculated and measured values of D_i does not exceed several per cent.

The *dipole moment* of this type of molecule may be put equal to

$$P = er_e - p_1 - p_2. \tag{32.9}$$

Substituting, into this formula, the expressions given on p. 278 for the moments p_1 and p_2 and utilising the numerical values of the constants r_e and α from Tables 24 and 25, it is possible to calculate the dipole moment of molecules of this type. The values, thus calculated, of the dipole moments are given in Table 27 (P_{calc}). From a comparison of the calculated values with the measured values (P_{meas}) it follows that the accuracy of calculation is about 10%.

Table 27

Dipole moments of the molecules of halogen salts Li, Na, K, and Cs (in debyes *)

Molecule	LiBr	LiI	NaCl	KCl	KBr	KI	CsF	CsCl	CsI
P_{calc}	5.9	6.0	8.3	10.6	10.9	11.8	7.0	9.7	11.0
P_{meas}	6.2	6.6	8.5	10.5	10.4	11.05	7.9	10.4	12.1

The frequency of natural oscillations ω may be determined from an equation for small oscillations:

$$M\frac{d^2r}{dt^2} = -k(r - r_e) \tag{32.10}$$

where $M = \frac{m_1 m_2}{m_1 + m_2}$ is the reduced mass of the molecule (m_1 and m_2 are the atomic masses) and k is the *quasi-elastic force constant*. The latter may be found by expanding the potential energy of the molecule into a Taylor series:

$$U = U_0 + \left(\frac{\partial U}{\partial r}\right)_0 (r - r_e) + \frac{1}{2}\left(\frac{\partial^2 U}{\partial r^2}\right)_0 (r - r_e)^2 + \ldots$$

Here, the subscript 0 is used to denote the values U, $\frac{\partial U}{\partial r}$, etc., for $r = r_e$. By confining the series to the first three terms of the expansion, we obtain, since $\left(\frac{\partial U}{\partial r}\right)_0 = 0$ (the equilibrium-force condition),

$$= U_0 + \frac{1}{2}\left(\frac{\partial^2 U}{\partial r^2}\right)_0 (r - r_e)^2, \tag{32.11}$$

* 1 debye $= 10^{-24}$ CGSE.

whence for the quasi-elastic force we find

$$f=-k(r-r_e)=-\left(\frac{\partial^2 U}{\partial r^2}\right)_0 (r-r_e),$$

and, consequently, $k=\left(\frac{\partial^2 U}{\partial r^2}\right)_0$. The numerical value of the constant k can be obtained by using the foregoing values of r_e and α.

Solution of equation (32.10) for the frequency of natural oscillations yields the following expression:

$$\omega=\frac{1}{2\pi}\sqrt{\frac{k}{M}}. \tag{32.12}$$

The values of ω (ω_{calc}) calculated from this formula are given in Table 28 along with the measured values (ω_{meas}).

Table 28

Oscillation frequencies of NaCl-type molecules

Molecule	NaCl	NaBr	NaI	KCl	KBr	KI	RbCl	RbBr	RbI	CsF	CsCl	CsBr	CsI
ω_{calc}, cm^{-1}	414	353	296	308	243	199	256	184	152	455	221	163	126
ω_{meas}, cm^{-1}	366	302	258	281	213	173	228	166	128	385	209	139	101

Coincidence of calculated and measured values of bond energy and other constants of this type of molecule to the degree of accuracy that the approximate nature of the theory * admits, shows that at least in the case of ionic compounds the treatment of forces of chemical interaction as electrostatic forces has some experimental justification. However, despite these successes of the electrostatic theory in its application to a special case of ionic compounds, it in no way solves the general problem of the nature of chemical bonding. For a long time this problem remained unsolved. All the failures to resolve it during the period that

* Quantitative agreement between theory and experiment is obtained if for the potential energy of the molecule we take (in place of the expression on p. 278) the expression

$$U=-\frac{e^2}{r}-\frac{(\alpha_1+\alpha_2)e^2}{2r^4}-\frac{2\alpha_1\alpha_2 e^2}{r^7}+Ae^{-r/\rho}-\frac{c}{r^6}$$

proposed by Zimm and Mayer. The constants A, ρ, and c in this expression are determined from the condition $\left(\frac{\partial U}{\partial r}\right)_{r_e}=0$ and from the coefficient of bulk compressibility and the potential of van der Waals forces.

preceded the advent of quantum mechanics were due to inadequate information about the electron. Naturally, the problem of chemical bonding could be solved only on the basis of quantum mechanics, the application of which to problems of chemical structure was a new stage in the development of theoretical chemistry. The quantum-mechanical interpretation of chemical regularities and facts emerged as a new trend in the development of the theory that became known as *quantum chemistry*.

33. Covalent Bond

Theory of the hydrogen molecule. One of the greatest attainments of quantum chemistry was a clarification of the nature of the chemical bond. The first step in the application of quantum mechanics to the problem of chemical bonding was the approximate quantum-mechanical analysis of the hydrogen molecule carried out by Heitler and London (1927).

Quantum chemistry proceeds from the wave equation, the form of which depends on the degree of complexity of the molecule. In the case of the hydrogen molecule, the wave equation is

$$\sum_{i=1}^{i=2}\left(\frac{\partial^2\psi}{\partial x_i^2}+\frac{\partial^2\psi}{\partial y_i^2}+\frac{\partial^2\psi}{\partial z_i^2}\right)+\frac{2m}{\hbar^2}(E-V)\psi=0 \qquad (33.1)$$

where

$$V=\frac{e^2}{r_{12}}+\frac{e^2}{r}-e^2\sum_{i=1}^{i=2}\left(\frac{1}{r_{ai}}+\frac{1}{r_{bi}}\right)$$

denotes the potential energy of the molecule. In the expression for the latter, r_{ai} and r_{bi} denote the distances of the *i*th electron from one (a) and the other (b) nucleus, respectively; r_{12} is the distance between the electrons; r is the distance between the nuclei, which distance, upon solution of the equation, may be regarded as a constant parameter *(fixed nuclei)*; E is the total energy of the molecule.

Like a similar equation for a two-electron atom (see Sec. 25), equation (33.1) does not permit of an exact solution. We, therefore, have to resort again to approximate methods of calculation. The problem of the hydrogen molecule was solved by Heitler and London by means of perturbation theory, which had earlier been applied by Heisenberg to a solution of the helium-atom problem (see Sec. 25).

In this method, to calculate the energy of perturbation, which determines the energy of interaction of the atoms, one has to know the "zero solution", i.e., the solution which corresponds to the unperturbed problem (absence of interaction between atoms). In this case ($r=\infty$), equation (33.1) breaks down into two equations that are identical with equation (24.1) for the H atom. The general zero solution that satisfies the set of these equations (i.e., the original wave equation for $r=\infty$) is the function $\psi_a(1)\ \psi_b(2)$, which corresponds to the binding of the first electron to nucleus a and of the second to nucleus b. This solution leads to atomic interaction due to the so-called dispersion forces (see p. 445 et seq.). In the case of H atoms, these forces are insignificant and cannot account for the observed binding strength of the atoms (suffice it to say that the stability of the H_2 molecule is not less than — even somewhat exceeds — the stability of the ionic molecule NaCl).

Due to *indistinguishability* of the electrons, the function which corresponds to binding of the second electron to nucleus a and the first to nucleus b is also a solution of equation (33.1) when $r \to \infty$. For this reason, a more general solution of the problem is the linear combination of the two previous solutions, i.e., the function

$$\psi=\psi_a(1)\ \psi_b(2) \pm \psi_a(2)\ \psi_b(1). \tag{33.2}$$

In the Heitler-London method, the assumption is made that this function, which is an exact solution of equation (33.1) for large distances between atoms, may be regarded as an approximate solution for small interatomic distances. The square of function (33.2),

$$|\psi|^2=|\psi_a(1)|^2\,|\psi_b(2)|^2+|\psi_a(2)|^2\,|\psi_b(1)|^2 \pm$$
$$\pm 2\psi_a(1)\ \psi_b(2)\ \psi_a(2)\ \psi_b(1),$$

multiplied by the normalising factor $\frac{1}{\sqrt{2(1\pm S)}}$ (the integral S is given below) yields the distribution of electrons in the molecule; here, the first two terms in the expression for $|\psi|^2_{\text{norm}}$, which correspond to electrons fixed in the respective atoms, are very frequently incorrectly (inasmuch as we assume the electrons to be distinguishable, though in reality this is not so) interpreted as terms that determine the electrostatic (Coulomb) part of the interaction energy of the atoms; the third term involves the so-called *exchange energy*. In actuality, however, as was shown earlier (p. 200), it is unjustifiable to divide the energy into Coulomb and exchange energy. For this reason, the terms "Coulomb energy" and "Coulomb integral", like the terms "exchange energy" and "exchange integral", are conventional and do not correspond to any concrete physical quantity.

Computation of the perturbation energy (interaction of atoms) by means of function (33.2) yields the energy of interaction U, which may be represented in the form

$$U = E - 2E_0 = \frac{C \pm A}{1 \pm S}. \qquad (33.3)$$

Here, C, A, and S are integrals:

$$C = e^2 \int \left[-\frac{1}{r_{b1}} - \frac{1}{r_{a2}} + \frac{1}{r_{12}} + \frac{1}{r} \right] | \psi_a(1) |^2 | \psi_b(2) |^2 dV_1 dV_2,$$

$$A = e^2 \int \left[-\frac{1}{r_{b1}} - \frac{1}{r_{a2}} + \frac{1}{r_{12}} + \frac{1}{r} \right] \psi_a(1) \psi_b(1) \psi_a(2) \psi_b(2) dV_1 dV_2,$$

$$S = \int \psi_a(1) \psi_b(1) \psi_a(2) \psi_b(2) dV_1 dV_2.$$

The first (C) is conditionally called Coulomb, the second (A), exchange; E_0 is the energy of the ground state of the H atom ($2E_0$ is the energy of the H_2 molecule computed to a zero approximation and equal to the sum of the energies of two isolated atoms of H).

Evaluation of the integrals C and A shows both of them to be *negative*; for all values of r, the integral A is *greater*, in absolute magnitude, than C. The integral S is less than 1. We thus obtain *two* values of energy of the H_2 molecule,

$$U_+ = \frac{C + A}{1 + S} < 0$$

and

$$U_- = \frac{C - A}{1 - S} > 0.$$

The first corresponds to a *stable* state of the molecule, the second to an *unstable* state.

Calculating the probability density $|\psi|^2$ for the electron cloud, it may be shown that in the stable state of the molecule, the distribution of density corresponds to a concentration of electrons (electron cloud) *between nuclei*, whereas in the unstable state the electrons tend to move away from the centre of the molecule. The distribution of density for both states of the H_2 molecule is given in Fig. 65 a and b (in the form of isolines of density). The first (a) corresponds to the stable state of the molecule, the second (b) to the unstable state.

Guided by the Pauli principle, we may demonstrate that in the stable state of the H_2 molecule, the total spin S must equal zero, while in the unstable state S=1. Indeed, since according to the Pauli principle, the total wave function (including the spin function) in any state of the molecule must be antisymmetric (cf. p. 202) and since to the stable state of the molecule (U_+) there corresponds a symmetric orbital function $\psi_a(1)\psi_b(2)+\psi_a(2)\psi_b(1)$, and to the unstable state, the antisymmetric function $\psi_a(1)\psi_b(2)-\psi_a(2)\psi_b(1)$, to the first we must assign an antisymmetric function, and to the second a symmetric spin function. And since the spin function S_A corresponds to $S=0$ and S_S to $S=1$, we get the singlet state as the stable (ground) state of the H_2 molecule and the triplet state as the unstable state. Thus, a pair of valence electrons with antiparallel spins ($S=0$) denotes *attraction*, while a pair with parallel spins ($S=1$) denotes *repulsion*.

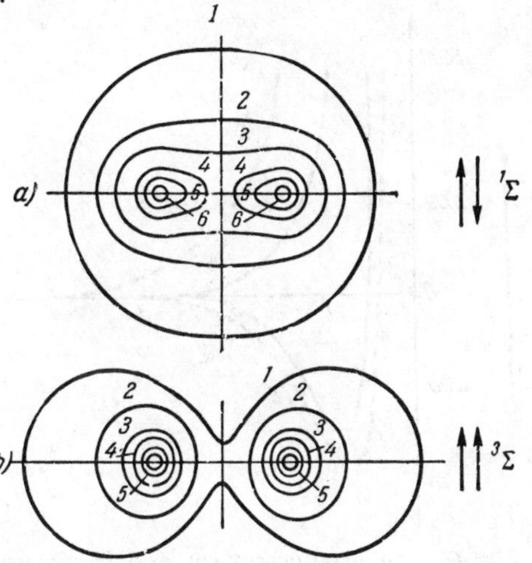

Fig. 65. Distribution of charge density of electron cloud in stable (a) and unstable (b) state of a hydrogen molecule

The Heitler-London theory, despite its approximate nature, made it possible to account for a fundamental fact of chemistry—attraction between neutral atoms and the formation of covalent chemical bonding. However, calculation to a first approximation could not, naturally, yield good quantitative agreement with experiment. Fig. 66 gives curves, obtained by Sugiura using the Heitler-London method, for the energy of a H_2 molecule as a function of the interatomic distances (potential-energy curves) for stable ($^1\Sigma$) and unstable ($^3\Sigma$) states (solid lines). The figure also gives the actual curves (dashed lines) obtained from experiment and by means of a more precise calculation (see below). Discrepancy between the results of the approximate Heitler-London-Sugiura calculation and the actual curves of potential energy is evident from the fact that for the heat of dissociation and the equilibrium distance of the H_2 molecule (according to Sugiura) we get 72 kcal/mol and 0.86 A in place of the experimental values of 103.2 kcal/mol and 0.74 A. Later, James and Coolidge performed the calculations to higher approximations; in the 17th approximation, the value of the dissociation heat of H_2 (103.19 ± ± 0.30 kcal/mol) practically coincides with the experimental value (103.24 ± 0.02 kcal/mol), and the equilibrium distance does not differ from the measured value.*

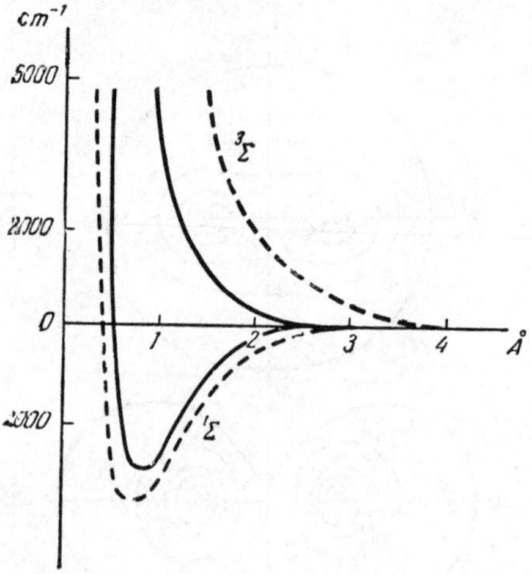

Fig. 66. Potential-energy curves of H_2 molecule after Heitler-London-Sugiura (dashed lines are actual curves)

A series of similar calculations were carried out also for other simple molecules (HeH, LiH, BeH^+, Li_2, LiF, CH, N_2, O_2, F_2, etc.). Due to the large number of electrons in a molecule, these calculations are, naturally, far more complicated than in the case of a hydrogen molecule.

The method of electron pairs. Up till now we have considered such properties of chemical bonding as are equally characteristic of simple and complex molecules; the calculations do not contain

* In the same way, the calculated value of the heat of dissociation of a molecular ion of hydrogen H_2^+ (61.056 ± 0.014 kcal/mol) practically coincides with the experimental value of this quantity (61.065 ± 0.043 kcal/mol).

any assumptions that fundamentally limit the applicability of calculations solely to simple molecules. Therefore, these calculations and the interpretation (based on them) of many earlier chemical views can, obviously, be extended also to complex (polyatomic) molecules. True, due to their complexity, the calculations in this case are nearly always purely qualitative or semiquantitative.

The above-discussed Heitler-London method, which was originally applied to the analysis of the H_2 molecule and extended to other molecules, became known as the *method of electron pairs* (Slater, Pauling). Its characteristic feature, which becomes evident already in the case of the simplest molecules, such as H_2 and H_2^+, is the fact that it takes into account two or more structures that do not correspond to any actual states of the molecule and that play a purely auxiliary role in the analysis. For the molecules H_2 and H_2^+, such auxiliary structures are $H_a(1)+H_b(2)$ and $H_a(2)+H_b(1)$ (see p. 285) and, respectively, $H_a+H_b^+$ and $H_a^++H_b$ In the case of more complex molecules, one must take into account, in addition to structures associated with indistinguishability of electrons or nuclei (as in the case of H_2 and H_2^+), structures that correspond to different distribution of chemical bonds between atoms in a molecule. To find these structures, it is common to use valence schemes in which each pair of atoms with antiparallel electron spins is connected by a line, as is common practice in chemistry for denoting single chemical bonds.* As Rumer has shown by means of quantum mechanics, given N electrons capable of participating in more than one chemical bond (such bonds are called *nonlocalised bonds*), the number of different independent, or canonical, valence schemes is

$$\frac{N!}{\left(\frac{N}{2}\right)!\left(\frac{N}{2}+1\right)!}.$$

For example, six electrons participate in the nonlocalised bonds of the benzene molecule C_6H_6 and, consequently, according to the above formula we have five independent valence schemes. Taking into account only electrons participating in nonlocalised bonds, these five schemes may be represented as follows:

* In the so-called *resonance theory,* these schemes are called *resonance structures* (see p. 291).

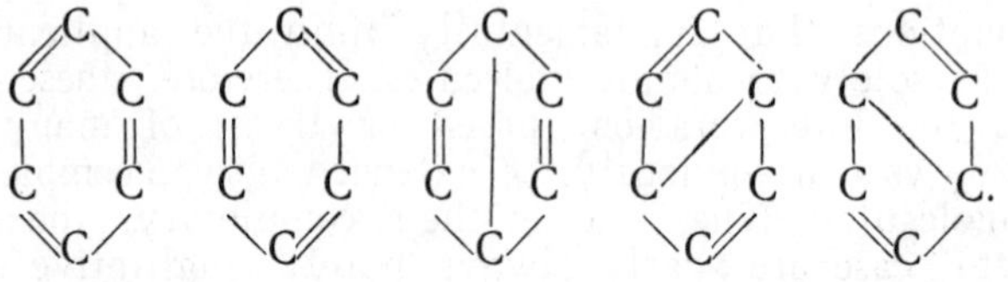

To a zero approximation, in the method of electron pairs, each valence scheme is described by a certain wave function ψ_i,* while the total wave function, which corresponds to a given state of the molecule, is, according to quantum mechanics, a linear combination of functions ψ_i,

$$\Psi = \Sigma a_i \psi_i, \tag{33.4}$$

where the coefficients a_i describe the portion of appropriate distribution of valence bonds in a given state of the molecule described, to a zero approximation, by the wave function Ψ.** In the general case, the coefficients a_i are found from the condition of minimum energy of the molecule. In certain cases the relative values of these coefficients may be evaluated even without calculating the energy. Inasmuch as the interaction energy diminishes very rapidly as the distance between the interacting atoms*** increases, we may take it that in the case of benzene the quantities a_i, which are, obviously, the same for the first two valence schemes (which correspond to the structure of the benzene molecule as proposed by Kekulé), will significantly exceed a_i for the three latter schemes (Dewar structures), i.e., $a_1 = a_2 \gg a_3, a_4, a_5$. And so, in this same zero approximation, we may write

$$\Psi = a(\psi_1 + \psi_2),$$

in other words, the structure of a benzene molecule may, approximately, be regarded as the result of superimposing two Kekulé structures. Due to the symmetry of the benzene molecule (this symmetry is retained even when one takes into account all five valence schemes), the bond between each pair of adjacent atoms of carbon comes out intermediate between the simple C—C and double C=C bonds (*aromatic bond*), and all six carbon-carbon bonds in the C_6H_6 molecule are equivalent. We note that the symmetry of the C_6H_6 molecule follows from various chemical and physical data. Thus, spectroscopic data indicate that benzene

* The ψ_i functions include auxiliary structures that correspond to indistinguishability of electrons or nuclei.

** In the resonance theory, the coefficients a_i express the weights of appropriate structures.

*** Roughly as $e^{r_0/r}$, where r_0 is a constant that may be called *the radius of action of exchange forces.*

possesses an axis of symmetry of the sixth order. The measured distance between adjacent atoms of carbon has only one value and is 1.40 A, which is intermediate between the length of the isolated C—C (1.54 A) and C=C (1.32 A) bonds. It may also be added that benzene, like other aromatic compounds, has a decidedly anisotropic diamagnetic susceptibility, which is satisfactorily accounted for only when one assumes that all the electrons participating in nonlocalised bonds (so-called *pi-electrons*) are generalised and the molecule has, in a certain sense, the properties of a superconductor. *

A large number of different classes of compounds was considered by means of zero-approximation valence schemes of the electron-pair method. This method explained the existence of numerous compounds that cannot be depicted by ordinary structural formulas. These include, primarily, compounds with conjugated bonds, in particular, organic compounds with alternating double and simple carbon-carbon bonds, ions of the type H_3O^+, CO_3^{--}, etc. Calculations showed a direct relationship between the diverse properties of these molecules and their structures.

It should, however, be kept in mind that the zero approximation of the electron-pair method is very crude and that the valence schemes in this method are only a computational procedure and are not accomplished in real molecules. Still less sense is there to speak of resonance of valence schemes or of the resonance of structures as a special quantum-mechanical phenomenon. This is the chief methodological error of the resonance theory, which interprets one of the peculiarities of the approximate method of electron pairs as an expression of objective reality. Suffice it to say here that in other approximate methods or in other approximations of the electron-pair method, there are no valence schemes ("resonating structures") at all. However, if we disregard the interpretation of the electron-pair method in the resonance theory, it must be admitted that the calculations performed on the basis of this method are correct, within the limits of their accuracy, of course. The great advantage of the zero approximation of the electron-pair method is that it is pictorial, which is absent from all the other more precise methods or more exact approximations of this method and which occasionally allows for a correct interpretation of experimental facts without performing extremely involved computations.

We shall now deal with certain results of approximate methods in which it is taken that the interaction energy of two adjacent

* The diamagnetic anisotropy of benzene and other aromatic compounds was studied by Pauling, London, and others.

atoms in a molecule is independent of the surrounding atoms (Heitler, Rumer). This assumption is somewhat justified by the frequently observed approximate constancy of the bond energy of a given pair of atoms (see Sec. 49). Without going into the details of calculations that reduce to evaluating integrals like those of C, A, and S of the H_2 problem, we confine ourselves to the following result. For the energy of a molecule consisting of a central polyvalent atom A (with valence V) and the atoms B_i around it (with valences V_i, while $\Sigma V_i = V$), we get the expression

$$E = -C - (AB_1) - (AB_2) - \ldots + \\ + (B_1B_2) + (B_1B_3) + (B_2B_3) + \ldots \quad (33.5)$$

Here (on the condition that the interaction energy is divided into a Coulomb part and an exchange part), C is the absolute magnitude of energy of Coulomb interaction of all parts of the molecule, the terms (AB_i) represent the absolute magnitude of energy of exchange interaction between atoms A and B_i, (B_iB_k) is the absolute magnitude of energy of exchange interaction between atoms B_i and B_k. From (33.5) it follows that the exchange interaction of atom A with atoms B_i (like the Coulomb interaction) corresponds to attraction (minus sign), while the exchange interaction of atoms B_i and B_k corresponds to repulsion (plus sign).

Let us also consider the case of interaction of three univalent atoms A, B, and C (London). Calculation of the energy of such a system shows that the interaction energy is significantly *different* for states that correspond to *different multiplicity* of the system. We have already encountered a relationship between multiplicity (determined by $2S+1$) and stability of a system in the case of the H_2 molecule, where the singlet state ($^1\Sigma$, $S=0$) was stable and the triplet ($^3\Sigma$, $S=1$) was unstable. Since a univalent atom has one valence electron and, consequently, has $S_1 = {}^1/_2$, the multiplicity of the system under consideration of three univalent atoms A, B, C may be found by calculating the total spin S, which is composed of three spins S_1 with values of ${}^1/_2$. According to the rule of addition of vectors we find that $S = {}^3/_2$ and ${}^1/_2$, hence, $2S+1=4$ and 2. For the first case (maximum multiplicity), computation of the interaction energy of the system yields

$$E = -C + (AB) + (AC) + (BC), \quad (33.6)$$

i.e., the mutual exchange repulsion of all three atoms.

But in the case of $2S+1=2$, for the interaction energy of the system we get the expression

$$E = -C \pm \\ \pm \sqrt{(AB)^2 + (AC)^2 + (BC)^2 - (AB)(AC) - (AB)(BC) - (AC)(BC)}. \quad (33.7)$$

Here, of the two solutions that correspond to the two signs of the square root, the first (plus sign) refers to a definitely unstable state of the system ($E > 0$). Now to decide the question of the stability of the second state (minus sign), it must be demonstrated that the energy E has a *minimum* for a certain geometric configuration of the system. Due to the mathematical complexity of this problem in its general form, we confine ourselves to a consideration of a particular case that corresponds to such a state of the system when one of the atoms (for instance, the C atom) is removed to an appreciable distance from the others. In this case, we can obviously consider the terms $(AC)^2$, $(BC)^2$, and $(AC)(BC)$ in expression (33.7) small compared with the others. Then we have

$$E \approx -C - \sqrt{(AB)^2 - (AB)(BC) - (AB)(AC)} \approx$$
$$\approx -C - (AB)\left[1 - \frac{(AC)+(BC)}{2(AB)}\right]. \qquad (33.8)$$

From this equality it follows that atoms A and B are *attracted* (stable state of molecule AB), and the removed atom C is *repelled* by them. It will be noted that this *repulsion* of the atom by a stable molecule gives rise to the necessity of *activation* in reactions like

$$AB + C = AC + B,$$

which is in complete agreement with experiment. The experimentally observed *activation energy* is, obviously, the energy necessary to overcome the mutual repulsion of the reacting particles.

Equation (33.8) may likewise be regarded as proof of the fundamental fact long since established in chemistry of the *saturation of chemical forces*, which is manifested in a constancy of composition of chemical compounds and in the stoichiometry of reactions. The saturation of chemical forces first received substantiation in quantum mechanics.

Summarising the result of a quantum-mechanical analysis of a system of three hydrogen atoms, we may conclude that saturation is due to mutual exchange repulsion of electrons with parallel spins. To illustrate the correctness of this conclusion let us examine the following examples. From the fact that molecules HeH are not observed, it follows that the H atom and the He atom, in ground states, mutually repel. Indeed, in the ground state of the He ($^1S_0$) atom its two electrons have antiparallel spins. When the atoms He and H approach, the hydrogen electron can, generally speaking, exchange with each of the He electrons. However, as a result of exchange with an electron with spin antiparallel to the spin of the hydrogen electron, there should arise a state of the helium atom that is forbidden by the Pauli principle because in this state both electrons have the same quantum numbers. Consequently, only the exchange of electrons with parallel spins is possible; but this leads to exchange repulsion of He and H atoms. Similar reasoning suggests the mutual repulsion of an H atom and an H_2 molecule, which again is evident from (33.8). Further, inasmuch as the electronic structures of the inert-gas atoms are built up of pairs of electrons with antiparallel spins, these atoms (like the helium atom) repel the hydrogen atom (like any other atom), thus accounting for the experimentally observed inertness of Ne, Ar, Kr, and the other inert gases. Of the same nature is the mutual repulsion of ions (at small distances) that have the same electronic structures as those of the inert gases, for instance, the Na^+ and Cl^- ions; by virtue of opposite charges, these ions attract at large distances and repel at small distances when the exchange forces of repulsion (with a small radius of action) become predominant (see Sec. 32). Of the very same nature is the mutual repulsion of saturated molecules that finds expression in the extreme difficulty with which they interact chemically.

Atomic and ionic molecules. Thus far when considering molecules to a zero approximation in the electron-pair theory, we have not taken into account such valence schemes as correspond to an *ionic structure* of the molecule. Yet when the Coulomb attraction between the ions is sufficiently great, these schemes may make a substantial contribution to the energy of the molecule. Bearing this in view, even when calculating the energy of an H_2 molecule, one must take into account (in addition to the covalent scheme H — H) the schemes $H^+ — H^-$ and $H^- — H^+$, i.e., instead of the wave function (33.2) we must take the function which may be represented by the sum

$$\Psi = a\psi_{at} + b\psi_{ion} \tag{33.9}$$

where, in the zero approximation of the electron-pair method, ψ_{at} is the function (33.2) while ψ_{ion} is a wave function corresponding to ionic schemes. True, in the case of H_2, a very great energy corresponds to the ionic schemes due to the large ionisation potential and the low electron affinity of the H atom. For this reason, the coefficient b comes out much smaller than the coefficient a. From an approximate analysis of the H_2 molecule, it follows that if the exchange interaction of the H atoms yields 80% of the bond energy of H_2, then the energy due to the ionic structure of the molecule amounts to only 5% (the remaining 15% is accounted for by the Coulomb interaction of the H atoms in the H_2 molecule).

However, in the case of other molecules, the contribution of the ionic valence scheme to the energy of the chemical bond may become very great. Such, for instance, is the case of halogen hydrides, particularly hydrogen fluoride, where, due to the large bond energy of the HF molecule and the considerable electron affinity of the F atom, the energy corresponding to the ionic valence scheme (at distances close to equilibrium) turns out higher than that corresponding to the covalent scheme. This is seen from Fig. 67, which gives the potential curves (calculated by Pauling) that correspond to the ionic and covalent structures of HX molecules (dashed lines) together with the actual potential curves (solid lines) of these molecules. The figure shows that the calculated "ionic" curve HF intersects the "covalent" curve. However, if we take into account both the "covalent" and "ionic" components of the wave function, it turns out that in reality these potential curves do not intersect: one curve passes smoothly into the other; the covalent curve passes into the ionic curve. These new curves are the actual curves of potential energy of the HF molecule (see Fig. 67). Whence it follows that for an HF molecule the coefficients a and b in (33.9) must have close values.

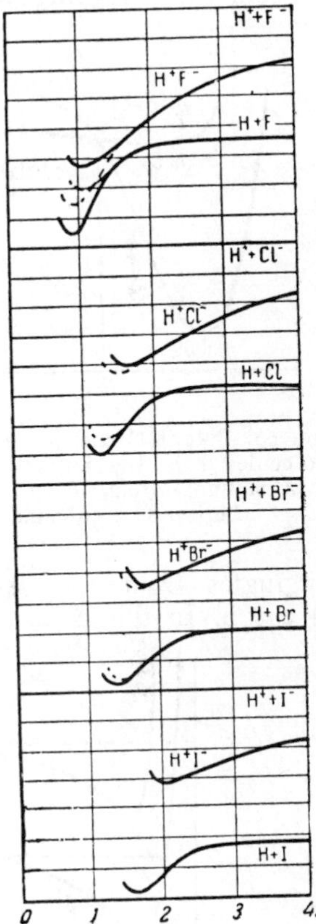

Fig. 67. Calculated (dashed lines) and actual curves of potential energy of HX molecules (X = F, Cl, Br, I), after Pauling

Predominance of ionic structure is particularly great in the case of molecules of the halogen salts of alkali metals, where, due to the small difference between the ionisation potential of an alkali metal atom and the electron affinity of the halogen atom, the "ionic" curve in the region of small interatomic distances lies considerably lower than the "covalent" curve. From an analysis of these molecules it follows that the energy corresponding to the covalent scheme does not exceed several per cent of the total energy, i.e., the bond energy practically fits the ionic valent scheme. This conclusion is in complete agreement with the theory of ionic molecules of Born and Heisenberg (p. 276 et seq.). Fig. 68 shows the potential-energy curves of the NaCl molecule. It is seen that the NaCl molecule, the ground state of which is composed of states of the ions Na^+ and Cl^-, dissociates into neutral atoms.

We must therefore ascertain the absence of any direct relationship between the origin of terms of ionic molecules and the nature of the products of their dissociation.

From the foregoing it follows that the concepts of an atomic molecule as a molecule the ground state of which is composed of the states of neutral atoms, and the concept of an ionic molecule the ground state of which is composed of the ionic states of the atoms, are relative and applicable only in limiting cases. The ground states of the molecules are described by functions (33.9). Here, the following three cases are possible: 1) $a \gg b$. In this case, the ground level of the molecule is determined almost exclusively by the function ψ_{at}, i.e., the ground state of the molecule originates from the states of neutral atoms (atomic molecule). 2) $a \ll b$. In this case the molecule is ionic. 3) Finally, it may

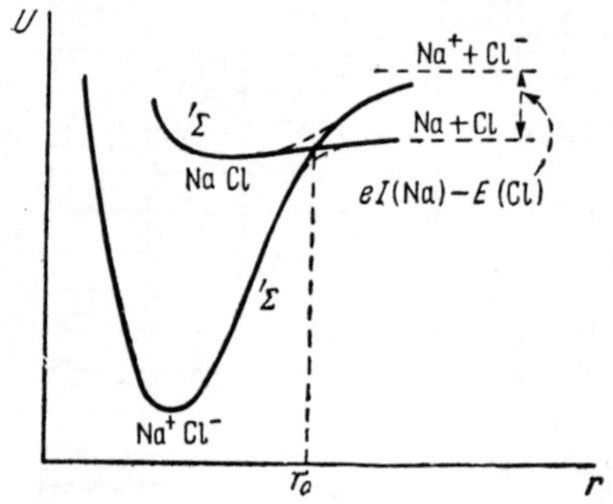

Fig. 68. Potential-energy curves of NaCl molecule. I is the ionisation potential of a sodium atom, E is the electron affinity of a chlorine atom

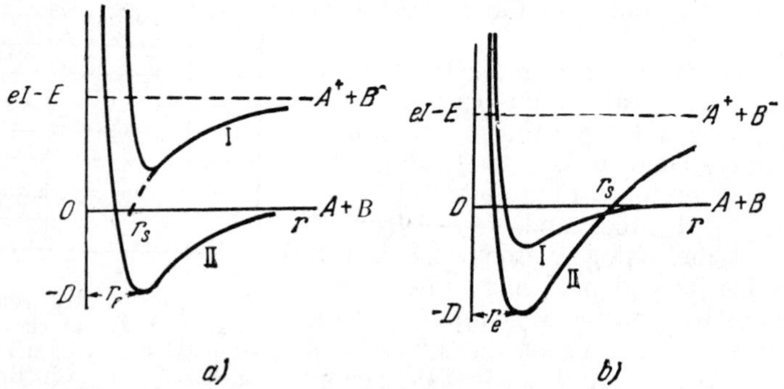

Fig. 69. Potential-energy curves of an atomic (a) and an ionic (b) molecule. D is the energy of dissociation of the ground state of the molecule

be conceived that a and b are of the same order of magnitude. In this case, obviously, the concepts of atomic and ionic molecules are purely relative; in other words, when a predominates one may provisionally speak of an atomic molecule, and when b predominates, of an ionic molecule. It may be noted that the theoretical relationship between the coefficients a and b is ordinarily found from the *minimum* energy.

The atomic or ionic character of a molecule may sometimes be established on the basis of various empirical criteria. For instance, from the foregoing we get the *London criterion*. Let us consider Fig. 69, a and b. Fig. 69 a shows an ionic curve (I) and an atomic curve (II) of potential energy of molecule AB for the case when the ionic level lies considerably higher than the atomic (atomic molecule). Fig. 69 b gives the same curves for an ionic molecule. The horizontal asymptotes of the ionic and atomic curves are separated by a distance $eI - E$. It is seen that while in the case of the atomic molecule a continuation of the hyperbolic branch (dashed line) of the ionic curve (I) intersects the abscissa axis (zero level) at a distance r_s which is *comparable* with the equilibrium distance of the molecule r_e; in the case of an ionic molecule, this branch intersects the zero level at a distance r_s that *appreciably exceeds* r_e. Since the hyperbolic branch of the ionic curve is expressed by the equation

$$U(r) = -\frac{e^2}{r} + (eI - E),$$

for r_s, which corresponds to $U = 0$, we have

$$r_s = \frac{e^2}{eI - E}. \qquad (33.10)$$

Table 29 contains data on determining the structure of certain molecules on the basis of the London criterion.

In the case of two-atomic molecules, and also nonsymmetric polyatomic molecules, the ratio between ψ_{at} and ψ_{ion} (33.9) and the corresponding distribution of the density of the electron cloud of the molecule are frequently manifested in *polarity* of chemical bonds. This polarity is particularly great in ionic molecules in which the chemical interaction of the atoms (ions) can be described by means of electrostatic (Coulomb) forces. Conversely, in the H_2 molecule, as in general in symmetric molecules consisting of the same atoms (for instance, N_2, O_2, F_2), Coulomb interaction, as well as the role of ionic structures (ψ_{ion}) becomes subordinate and the chemical bond is mainly determined by exchange forces: the chemical bonds in such molecules are nonpolar. But in molecules that are intermediate between these two extreme types (in the general case, in an AB molecule consisting of different atoms) ψ_{at} and ψ_{ion} must obviously enter into Ψ in comparable portions, and the degree of polarity of the molecule must vary in line with the relationship of these quantities.

Table 29

The structural nature of molecules determined by the London criterion

Molecule	eI, eV	E, eV	r_s, A	r_e, A	Structure
H_2	13.53	0.74	1.12	0.74	Atomic
HF	13.53	3.62	1.45	0.92	?
HCl	13.53	3.79	1.48	1.28	Atomic
HBr	13.53	3.56	1.44	1.41	"
HI	13.53	3.19	1.39	1.60	"
KF	4.32	3.62	21	(2.31)	Ionic
KCl	4.32	3.79	27	2.79	"
KBr	4.32	3.56	19	2.94	"
KI	4.32	3.19	13	3.23	"

The more different the electrical properties of the atoms comprising a molecule, the more asymmetric its electronic structure and the more substantial the contribution, to the bond, of Coulomb interaction of atoms (ions) and, accordingly, the greater the dipole moment of the molecule, inasmuch as absence of symmetry of the electronic structure may be interpreted as the presence of certain effective charges in both atoms of the molecule.

The degree of asymmetry of the electronic structure of the molecule and the direction of shift of its electron cloud are determined by the relationship of *electronegativities* of the atoms that make up the molecule. According to Mulliken, the sum of the ionisation potential of an atom and its electron affinity is a measure of the electronegativity of the atom. This may be substantiated as follows. We consider the conversion of two neutral atoms A and B into pairs of ions $A^+ + B^-$ and $A^- + B^+$. In the first case, the total change in energy is equal to $eI_A - E_B$, in the second case, $eI_B - E_A$ (I_A and I_B are ionisation potentials, E_A and E_B are electron affinities of atoms A and B). For identical electronegativities of both atoms these energy changes will, obviously, be equal; whence it follows that $eI_A + E_A = eI_B + E_B$; that is, the sums $eI + E$ are equal. The following is a table of the values of electronegativities for several elements in kcal/gm-atom (after Mulliken) *:

Element	F	Cl	Br	I	H	Li
$eI + E$	586	452	418	382	328	135

It is seen that the electronegativities of the halogens and hydrogen fall off in the order $F > Cl > Br > I > H$. From this it fol-

* These values were obtained by means of the ionisation potential which corresponds to removal of the sole unpaired electron.

lows that the electron clouds in molecules of halogen hydrides (HX) must be displaced towards the halogen, and the more considerably the lighter the halogen. Consequently, the dipole moments of HX molecules should be related as HF > HCl > HBr > HI. Indeed, experiment gives the following values of dipole moments of these compounds: 1.74 (HF), 1.03 (HCl), 0.79 (HBr), and 0.38 (HI) debyes. In contrast to halogens, the electronegativity of alkaline elements is less than that of hydrogen. From this we conclude that the electron cloud in the hydride molecules of the alkaline elements must be shifted towards the H atom. *

The difference in electronegativities is particularly great in the case of halogens (X) and alkaline elements (Me). For this reason, in MeX molecules the electron cloud of the pair of valence electrons is so much shifted towards the X atom that it practically localises on this atom, so that grounds appear for speaking of the ionic structure of the molecule Me^+X^-. An experimental confirmation of this conclusion is the close agreement of measured values of the bond energy and of other molecular constants of alkaline-halogen salts with these values computed on the assumption that MeX molecules are built up from ions, the electrostatic interaction of which is responsible for the chemical bond in the molecule (see Sec. 32).

From the foregoing we can conclude that ionic, or electrovalent, bonding is a limiting case of chemical bonding, when the electron cloud of a pair of electrons that are responsible for the chemical bond is shifted to such an extent towards the electronegative atom that these electrons will actually belong to the latter. But in the overwhelming majority of cases the cloud of valence electrons is only more or less shifted towards one of the atoms from the symmetrical position that it would occupy if the electrical properties of atoms comprising the molecule were the same. Bearing in mind both limiting cases (the symmetric electron cloud and the ionic structure), one may, in a relative way, speak of the real structure of a molecule as a certain intermediate structure between these limiting structures.

Due to the difference in physical and chemical properties of molecules with covalent and electrovalent bonds, and also insofar as the limiting cases of purely ionic or purely covalent bonds are comparatively rare, it is meaningful to speak of the *degree of electrovalence* or the *degree of polarity* of chemical bonds. The natural measure of this latter quantity is the *electric dipole moment* (see Sec. 46) inherent in the bond.

* This is corroborated by X-ray studies of crystal lattices of the hydrides of alkaline elements in which the H atom is negative. Related to this is also the large dipole moment of hydride molecules: thus, the computed moment of LiH comes out equal to 6.04 debyes.

34. Theory of Valency

Valence theory (within the framework of the electron-pair theory). The most important generalisation of the results of a quantum-mechanical analysis of simple molecules is the theory of *electron pairs* (frequently called the theory of *spin valence*), which underlies present-day views of covalent bonds. The formal precursor of the spin theory is the theory of Lewis and Langmuir, in which a *pair* of electrons is correlated with each valence line in classical chemistry (simple bond). This view is supported by the experimental fact that, with few exceptions, all unsaturated and, for this reason, chemically unstable compounds have an *odd* number of electrons. The molecules of such compounds have a series of specific properties, for instance, a marked ability for dimerisation; they usually have intense coloration, a paramagnetic moment and other properties characteristic of a chemically unstable molecule. Such, for example, are, for the most part, free radicals (and also free atoms). In contrast, saturated compounds have an *even* number of electrons, yet are diamagnetic, etc.

A common feature of the Lewis-Langmuir theory and the earlier considered Kossel theory (p. 273) is the concept of a tendency of the atoms towards an eight-electron outer shell *(octet)*. However, unlike the Kossel theory, the Lewis-Langmuir theory allows for the participation of a single electron simultaneously in *two* octets. Thus, using Lewis' symbolism, where each outer electron is represented by a dot, the chlorine molecule may be represented schematically as follows:

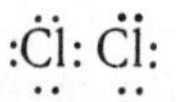

Here, the pair of valence electrons that takes the place of the valence line of classical chemistry (Cl — Cl) belongs simultaneously to both atoms, the electron shells of which thus acquire the needed completion. In exactly the same way, the CCl_4 molecule is represented in the form

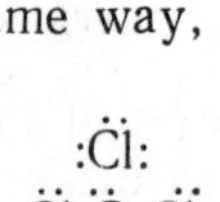

where in the carbon octet there participate four chlorine electrons that are simultaneously part of the octets of the respective chlorine atoms.

In the Lewis-Langmuir theory, double and triple bonds are designated by two and three pairs of dots, respectively; for example,

$$\begin{array}{c} H\quad H \\ \ddot{C}::\ddot{C} \\ \ddot{H}\quad \ddot{H} \end{array} \text{ and } H:C:::C:H.$$

We now have four and six electrons each participating in two carbon octets. The remaining four and, accordingly, two electrons of each carbon octet are, at the same time, involved in a two-electron shell of two hydrogen atoms and, respectively, one hydrogen atom.

A two-electron shell that corresponds to a stable two-electron shell of the He atom is accomplished in the H_2 (H:H) molecule.

Using Lewis symbolism, the ionic molecule NaCl may be represented as

$$Na^+ :\underset{\cdot\cdot}{\ddot{Cl}}:^-.$$

Here, in contrast, for instance, with the homopolar molecule Cl_2, each electron participates only in *one* octet (the inner electrons of the Na^+ ion are not shown).

The nature of homopolar bonding, which remained unsettled in the Lewis-Langmuir theory, was solved as follows in the quantum-mechanical theory. From an analysis of the hydrogen molecule and certain other of the simplest molecules, we may draw the general conclusion that the underlying factor in the chemical interaction of atoms is *electrical* interaction of the component electrons and nuclei and that a simple chemical bond (for example, H—H or Cl—Cl) is represented by a *pair* of electrons with *antiparallel* spins.

The possibility of correlating the valence line of classical chemistry with the electron pair (at least in the case of the simplest molecules) gives theoretical substantiation to the Lewis-Langmuir theory, which is corroborated in general outline by experiment. Since in the case of homopolar bonding each pair of connecting electrons includes, as a rule, electrons belonging to *different* atoms, the valence of the atom should be determined by the number of its *unpaired* electrons (V). Since this number also determines the total spin of an atom in a given quantum state, equal, obviously, to $S = 1/2\,V$, we must have the following relation between the valence of the atom and its spin or the multiplicity of the corresponding term $M = 2S + 1$:

$$V = M - 1, \tag{34.1}$$

which means that the valence of the atom in the given state must be less than the multiplicity of the corresponding term by unity. The semi-empirical view of valence electrons as unpaired outer electrons of an atom turns out to be extremely fruitful in clarifying various peculiarities of chemical bonds. And those cases when a formal use of this concept leads to contradictions with the facts help to extend our knowledge of the nature of chemical linkage.

According to spectroscopic findings, the following terms correspond to the ground states of elements of the second and third series of the Periodic Table (see Table 18):

Li, Na	Be, Mg	B, Al	C, Si	N, P	O, S	F, Cl	Ne, Ar
^2S	^1S	^2P	^3P	^4S	^3P	^2P	^1S

Whence, on the basis of (34.1), we find that Li, Na, B, Al, F, and Cl must be univalent, C, Si, O, and S, bivalent, N and P, trivalent, while the valence of Be, Mg, Ne, and Ar must be equal to zero. As regards the valences of Li, Na, O, F, Ne, and Ar, the theoretical values coincide with the experimentally found values. But in other cases, the theoretical valences are *less* than the experimental.

Thus, from (34.1) we find $V=0$ for the valence of Be and Mg, while in reality these elements are bivalent. This discrepancy between theory and experiment is accounted for by the fact that in the formation of a chemical compound both spins of a closed pair (s^2) of outer electrons of Be and Mg become parallel, which must involve the excitation of one of the electrons (for example, we may assume that a 2s-electron of Be becomes a 2p-electron, and a 3s-electron of Mg, a 3p-electron). Thus, in reality we have *excitation of valence* in the process of chemical interaction (Mecke).

The supposition of excitation of valence of the "nonvalent" atoms Be and Mg during the formation of molecules from these and other atoms is, obviously, tantamount to the assumption that the ground states of the corresponding molecules should arise out of the *excited states* of "nonvalent" atoms. The following facts support this view. The ground state of the BeO molecule (the same goes for the MgO molecule) is a singlet ($S=0$). If this state were composed of ground states of the atoms Be (Mg) and O, which are the states $^1S\,(L=0)$ and $^3P\,(S=1)$, it would have to be a triplet. But when the O (^3P) atom interacts with an excited Be (or Mg) atom, for instance, with an atom in the state $^3P\,(S=1)$, we get states of the BeO (MgO) molecule with spin 2, 1, or 0, that is, quintet, triplet, and singlet states, one of which (the singlet) is the ground state of the molecules BeO and MgO.

The assumption that the ground state of the BeO molecule (and this goes for the molecules MgO, CaO, SrO, BaO, ZnO, CdO, HgO too) is associated with an excited state of the Be atom (Mg, Ca, Sr, Ba, Zn, Cd, Hg, respectively) is likewise confirmed by the following data. For example, considering the formation of molecules BeCl and $BeCl_2$ as a reaction of atoms Be and Cl and, respectively, the reaction of a Cl atom with a BeCl molecule, we should expect that due to the expenditure of energy associated with excitation of the valence of Be, the thermal effect of the $Be + Cl = BeCl\ (D_1)$ reaction should be substantially less than that of the reaction $BeCl + Cl = BeCl_2\ (D_2)$. Since there are no experimental data for BeCl and $BeCl_2$, we take the appropriate data for the halogen salts Zn, Cd, and Hg as given in Table 30. From this table it follows that D_1 are indeed much less (by a factor of 2 to 4) than D_2, which is naturally accounted for on the basis of excitation of valence.

Table 30

The separation energy of halogen atoms in the molecules MeX and MeX_2 (in kcal/mol)

Me	Zn	Cd	Cd	Hg	Hg	Hg
X	Cl	Cl	I	Cl	Br	I
D_1	50.5	46	32	30	23	14
D_2	105	104	50	75	67	57

The participation of excited states in a chemical bond is a very common occurrence. For instance, according to Mecke, valence 4 of carbon, which is a component part of organic compounds, is due to the excited state ^5S (the excitation energy of which is 95.9 kcal/gm-atom). As we saw earlier, a carbon atom in the ground state (^3P) must be bivalent. The valence excitation of the C atom, when it passes from the bivalent state to the tetravalent state, follows directly from a comparison of the thermal effects of the reactions $C + O = CO + 256$ kcal/mol (D_1) and $CO + O = CO_2 + 126$ kcal/mol (D_2). We note here that unlike the earlier considered cases of formation of halogen compounds Zn, Cd, and Hg from atoms, D_1 turns out not less but more than D_2. This is connected with valence excitation in the second stage of the reaction instead of the first stage.

Further, halogen valences above 1 should also be considered as associated with excited states of the atom, like the valences of elements of the sixth group that exceed 2. Comparing the excitation energy of the lowest state $^4P\ (V=3)$ of atoms F, Cl, and Br, equal to 292.7, 205.6, and 180.3 kcal/gm-atom, we see that the excitation energy of the F atom is roughly $1^1/_2$ times the excitation energy of Cl and Br There is just about the same difference in the case of excitation energies of the lowest state $^5S\ (V=4)$ of atoms O, S, Se, and Te, which are 210.8, 150.4, 137.7, and 126.5 kcal/gm-atom, respectively. As was first shown by London, it is with this difference that we should connect the fact that whereas F and O have only valences 1 and 2, respectively, all the other elements of the seventh and sixth groups have different (including higher) valences.

Another illustration of valence excitation is the activation energy in certain reactions where atoms combine directly. Thus, an investigation of the thermal decomposition of nitrous oxide N_2O shows that this reaction, which proceeds as $N_2O \rightarrow N_2 + O$, involves an activation energy of about 60 kcal/mol. Whence, since the separation energy of an O atom from the N_2O molecule is 38.7 kcal/mol, we find, for the activation energy of the reverse reaction, i.e., $N_2 + O = N_2O$, $60 - 39 = 21$ kcal/mol. In this case, the necessity of activation is evident from Fig. 70,* which

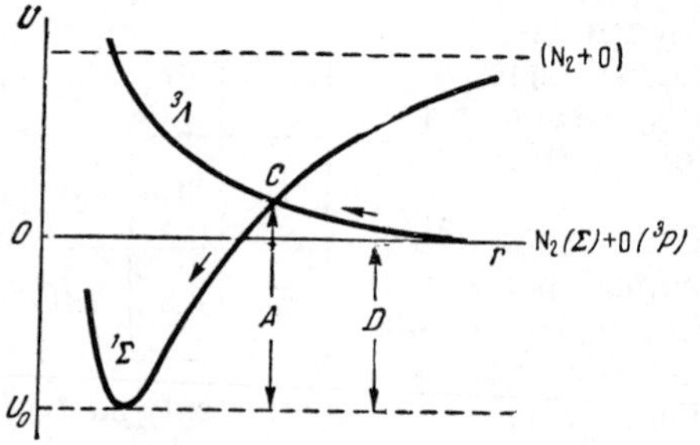

Fig. 70. Interaction between N_2 molecule and O atom in the formation of an N_2O molecule

shows schematically the curves of potential energy of the system $N_2 + O$: the repulsion curve corresponding to an absence of chemical interaction between the nonvalent molecule $N_2\,(^1\Sigma)$ and the atom O and a curve corresponding to the stable molecule N_2O formed from the bivalent excited molecule $N_2\,(^3\Sigma)$ and the atom O. According to Fig. 70, N_2 and O, which are in the ground state, mutually repel; however, the system overcomes this repulsion (at the expense of activation energy) and passes into a stable ground state of the molecule N_2O. It is further seen that the necessary activation energy represents but a comparatively *small portion* of the excitation energy of the nitrogen molecule. Similar ratios occur also in other cases, which explains the comparative ease of valence excitation.

The participation of excited states in chemical linkage (this gives rise to the higher valences of a number of elements) shows

---

* Strictly speaking, the potential energy of the triatomic molecule N_2O as a function of the distances between atoms is denoted by *potential surfaces* and not curves. Therefore Fig. 70 is schematic. In its construction it was taken that the distance between the nitrogen atoms remains constant, which enables us, approximately, to regard this molecule as a diatomic molecule and represent its energy by potential curves.

that formula (34.1) is of limited value and is applicable only in cases when the generation of energy during formation of new chemical bonds does not cover energy expenditure connected with valence excitation, i.e., when valence excitation is energetically impossible and for this reason actually does not take place, otherwise there is or can be valence excitation, as a result of which the valence of the atom will be *greater* than the number of unpaired electrons in its ground state.

Hybridisation. However, only in certain cases, in particular, in the case of weak fields, is it permissible to identify a given valent state of an atom in a molecule with some electron state of an isolated atom. In the general case these states must be distinguished. Essentially, this difference lies in the fact that to both indicated states there correspond *different electron configurations* because for an isolated atom the latter (for instance, configurations sp, sd, sp^2, sp^3, etc.) do not, generally speaking, correspond to the valent states of an atom. Let us illustrate this using elements of the second group. As we have already seen, from the viewpoint of the theory of spin valence, valence 2 of these elements is associated with an excited triplet state to which an electron configuration sp corresponds. If this configuration corresponded to a bivalent state of the atom, one would have to conclude that one of the valence electrons is an s-electron, while the second is a p-electron. Hence, chemical bonds accomplished with these electrons (both the Hg—Cl bonds in the $HgCl_2$ molecule, for example) would have to be nonequivalent, but this contradicts experimental findings. Thus, from the experimental fact of the equivalence of these bonds there follows the identity of the states of both valence electrons in the valent state of the atom. In the quantum-mechanical theory of chemical bonding this fact is interpreted as follows. In the valent state of the atom, which corresponds to the excited electron state sp, each of the two valence electrons is in a *mixed*, so-called *hybridised*, state and not in the s- or p-state. The hybridised state is obtained from these two states and is described by a wave function that is a linear combination of functions corresponding to the s- and p-states. Analysis shows that hybrid functions ensure maximum overlapping of electron clouds and, hence, the strongest linkage.

In the same way, the electron configuration of the tetravalent state of carbon is not identical with the sp^3 configuration of the excited atom C (^5S) that corresponds to it, and it is not true to state that three of the four valence electrons of the C atom are p-electrons, while the fourth is an s-electron. Actually, all four electrons of tetravalent carbon are the *same* because due to hybridisation there are four identical hybridised states in place of three p- and one s-state; in particular, this is apparent from the identity of all four C—H bonds in the CH_4 molecule, the C—Cl bonds in the CCl_4 molecule, etc.

Sigma- and pi-bonds. All the foregoing examples have to do with the case of a simple chemical bond, also called *sigma-bond* in this instance. The electron cloud of the electrons that effect this bond is distributed symmetrically about the line connecting the nuclei. Experimental proof of such symmetry of an electron cloud in the sigma-bond is the possibility, found in the thermo-

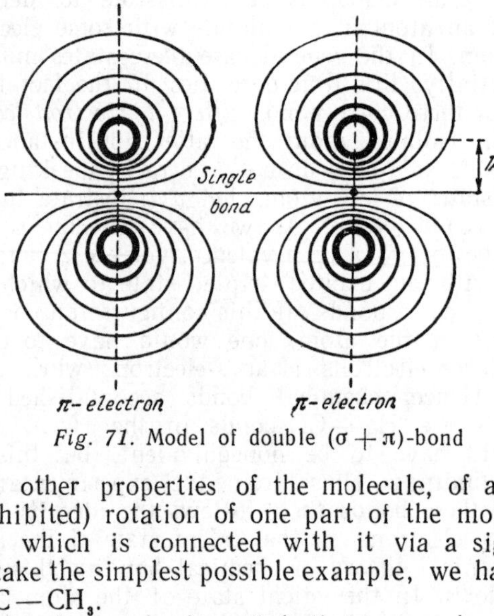

Fig. 71. Model of double (σ + π)-bond

dynamic and other properties of the molecule, of a free (usually somewhat inhibited) rotation of one part of the molecule relative to the other, which is connected with it via a sigma-bond (see p. 349). To take the simplest possible example, we have the ethane molecule $H_3C—CH_3$.

The sigma-bond may be formed both by s- and p-electrons. The chemical bonds in all saturated compounds are always sigma-bonds.

In contrast to saturated compounds, unsaturated and aromatic compounds possess, together with sigma-bonds that bind the skeleton of the molecule, a special type of bond called *pi-bonds*. The peculiarity of these bonds, which are formed by a pair of p-electrons, is due to the absence of axial symmetry of the electron cloud that they form. As a result of mutual overlapping of electron clouds of the two p-(π-)electrons, there are formed (on both sides of the line connecting the nuclei) two "bridges" that impart a specific *rigidity** to the pi-bond. Every *double* bond, for instance, a bond between carbon atoms in the ethylene molecule $H_2C{=}CH_2$,

* The electron cloud of the pi-bond has two planes of symmetry that pass through the line connecting the nuclei.

consists of a sigma- and a pi-bond (Fig. 71). Because of this rigidity of the pi-bond, the relative rotation of parts of the molecule connected by a double bond becomes impossible and is actually not observed.

This is found, in particular, in *cis-trans-isomerism* that is, in the existence of substances of identical composition, but of different geometry expressed in a different relative arrangement of the parts of the molecule and leading to differences in the physicochemical properties of the isomers. Classical examples of cis-trans-isomerism are fumaric acid:

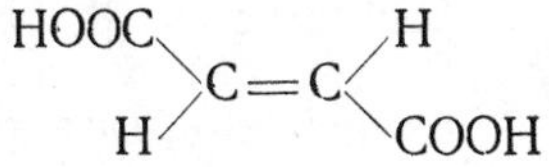

$$\underset{H}{\overset{HOOC}{>}}C=C\underset{COOH}{\overset{H}{<}} \quad \text{(trans)}$$

and maleic acid:

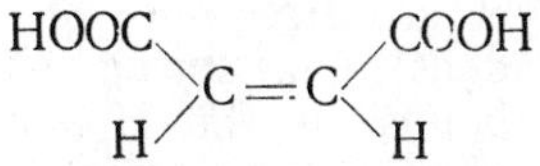

$$\underset{H}{\overset{HOOC}{>}}C=C\underset{H}{\overset{COOH}{<}} \quad \text{(cis)}.$$

The rigidity of the C=C-bond in this and similar cases is so great that the transition of one isomeric form into another is not observed under ordinary conditions. It can occur only when the molecule is acted upon by a sufficiently strong agent that weakens the double bond, for instance, absorption of light by the molecule (*photochemical isomerisation*). It may be presumed that at least as regards photochemical reactions *tautomeric conversion* is accomplished as a result of the transformation of the double bond into a simple bond (when the molecule is excited), which transformation leads to the possibility of free rotation. In this case, the reaction scheme may be represented as follows:

$$\underset{H}{\overset{R}{>}}C=C\underset{R}{\overset{H}{<}} \rightarrow \underset{H}{\overset{R}{>}}\overset{|}{C}-\overset{|}{C}\underset{R}{\overset{H}{<}} \rightarrow \underset{H}{\overset{R}{>}}C=C\underset{H}{\overset{R}{<}}.$$

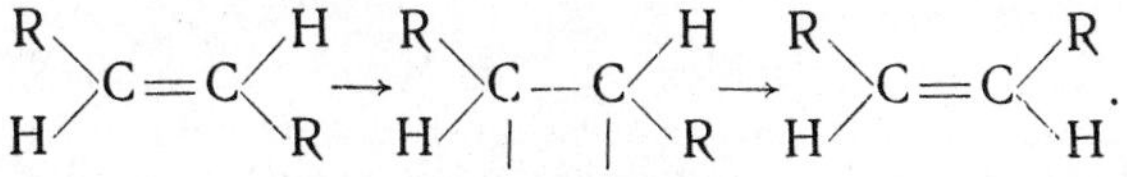

Directed valency. The peculiarities of symmetry of the cloud of p-electrons also explains the experimentally observed phenomenon of *directed* valence bonds (directed valences) which is the underlying principle of *stereochemistry*, or the theory of the geometric, spatial structure of chemical compounds. The first experimental proof of the spatial structure of compounds was obtained by van't Hoff and LeBel, who correlated the phenomenon of optical isomerism with the spatial structure of isomeric molecules, thus laying the foundations of stereochemistry, which has become an integral part of the theory of chemical structure. At present, as a result of numerous experimental investigations into the geometric structure of molecules, it has been established that in addition to molecules of linear and planar form we find triangular and pyramidal molecules, tetrahedral molecules, zigzag, catenary, ring-like molecules, etc. This diversity of molecular shapes was explained on the basis of wave mechanics (Pauling), which proved exceedingly fruitful in this question.

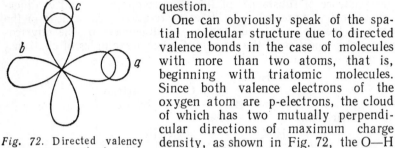

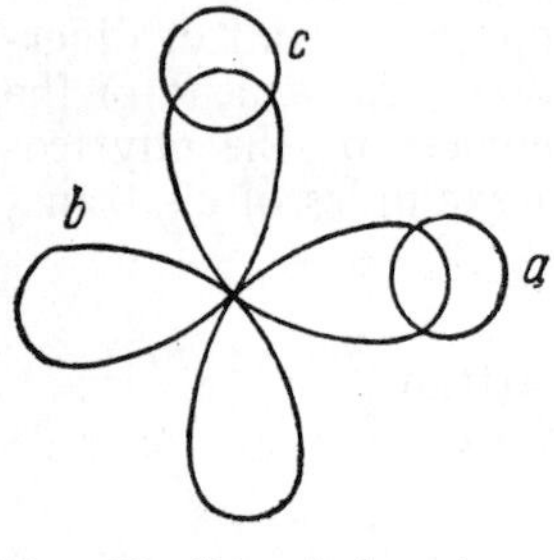

Fig. 72. Directed valency (oxygen atom)

One can obviously speak of the spatial molecular structure due to directed valence bonds in the case of molecules with more than two atoms, that is, beginning with triatomic molecules. Since both valence electrons of the oxygen atom are p-electrons, the cloud of which has two mutually perpendicular directions of maximum charge density, as shown in Fig. 72, the O—H bonds in the H_2O molecule should be at an angle close to 90°, in other words, a water molecule should have a triangular shape. This follows from the principle of quantum mechanics that a maximum overlapping of electron clouds corresponds to the formation of a chemical bond, as a result of which the H atoms should be added to the O atom in the directions of the axes of the p-electrons of the O atom, as is shown in Fig. 72. This conclusion is fully corroborated by experiment, in accordance with which the H_2O molecule has the shape of an equilateral triangle with an angle H—O—H of 105°. Similar in structure are the molecules H_2S (angle H—S—H equal to 92°), H_2Se (angle H—Se—H, 91°), F_2O (angle F—O—F, 104°), Cl_2O (angle Cl—O—Cl, 111°), Cl_2S (angle Cl—S—Cl, 100°), etc.

The fact that in molecules of this type the angles between the same bonds are, in most cases, greater than 90° is explained by the mutual repulsion of electrons with parallel spins belonging to different atoms in the molecule.

Unlike the molecules under consideration, molecules of type MeX_2 (the Me atom is that of an element of the second group, X=F, Cl, Br, I) and also of type MeXR (R is a radical), in which the valence state of the central atom corresponds to sp-hybridisation (see p. 305), have a symmetric linear structure.*

Further, the occurrence of directed valences of the atoms of nitrogen, phosphorus, arsenic, and antimony with their three valence p-electrons is manifested in the *pyramidal* shape of the

* We note that also the $[FHF]^-$ ion with bivalent hydrogen H^-, the valence electrons of which are s-electrons, has a linear structure.

molecules NH_3, PH_3, NF_3, PF_3, PCl_3, PBr_3, AsF_3, $AsCl_3$, $AsBr_3$, $SbCl_3$, etc. However, the molecules of analogous compounds of elements of the third group (BCl_3, BBr_3, $AlCl_3$, etc.) have a plane symmetric shape due to the fact that in the trivalent state of the central atom, as a result of hybridisation of one electron s-state and two p-states, there appear three identical states to which there correspond three electron clouds with axes in a single plane spaced 120° apart. The molecules ClF_3 and BrF_3 are also plane, but unlike the molecules of elements of the third group they are not symmetrical.

The four directed carbon valences are tetrahedral (which has been known since the time of van't Hoff and LeBel) and are manifested in the tetrahedral structure of molecules of such compounds as CH_4, CCl_4 (and analogous compounds of silicon, titanium, germanium, and tin). This is also due to structural peculiarities of the electron cloud of the valence electrons of the C atom: as we have already pointed out, as a result of the hybridisation of one s-state and three p-states there appear four identical electron states, to which four identical bonds of a *tetrahedral* C atom correspond. These bonds are directed along the diagonals of a regular tetrahedron and form angles of 109°28′ between each other.

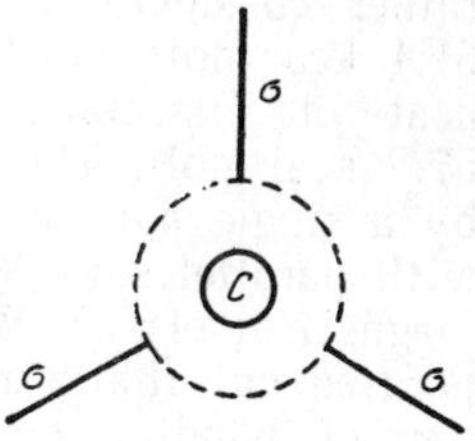

Fig. 73. Trigonal atom of carbon. Cloud of p- (π-) electron shown by dashed line (schematic). Axis of electron is perpendicular to plane of drawing

In complete agreement with experimental findings, it follows from quantum-mechanical analysis that in different compounds the carbon atom may be in *different* valence states with a characteristic (for each of them) structure of the electron cloud. Thus, in saturated compounds the C atom always has a tetrahedral electron-cloud configuration corresponding to four sigma-bonds: whence the tetrahedral structure of molecules like methane and the other structural peculiarities of saturated compounds. In unsaturated compounds with double bond, the C atom forms three symmetric sigma-bonds that lie in one plane at angles of 120° and one pi-bond; the cloud of each of the p-electrons effecting this bond has an axis of symmetry normal to the plane of the sigma-bond, as shown in Fig. 73. In compounds of this type and also in aromatic compounds, the C atom is called *trigonal* (in contrast to tetrahedral). *

* The valence state of the C atom in diamond corresponds to tetrahedral, and in graphite, to trigonal carbon.

The triple carbon bond C≡C consists of two pi-bonds and one sigma-bond. The simplest molecules with triple bonds are linear in form. Such, for example, are the acetylene molecules HC≡CH,* the molecules of prussic acid HC≡N, dicyanogen N≡C—C≡N, etc.

The foregoing facts are a brilliant illustration of the valuable contribution that quantum mechanics has made to the theory of the spatial structure of molecules by giving a physical substantiation to many important principles of stereochemistry.

Valence theory (within the framework of the method of molecular orbits). The theory of spin valence and its equivalent method of electron pairs, which is one of several possible approaches to the problem of chemical bonding, do not provide a complete solution to this problem. Above all, this method is limited by the existence of bonds which are not provided for by pairs of electrons with antiparallel spins. Such, for instance, is the bond in the molecular hydrogen ion H_2^+ that is effected by a *single* electron and has rather considerable strength (the heat of dissociation of H_2^+ is 61.1 kcal/mol, which is more than that of halogen molecules; the heat of dissociation of the strongest of these—chlorine—is 57.2 kcal/mol). The O=O bond in the oxygen molecule is effected by a single pair of electrons with antiparallel spins and one pair with parallel spins (which, for example, is manifested in the paramagnetism of O_2). With regard to the O_2 molecule, it should be pointed out that the demand for antiparallelness of spins in each pair of bonding electrons (which demand also follows from the necessity of satisfying the Pauli principle) is obligatory only in those cases when the s-electrons are valent. But when, for example, the p-electrons are valent, as in the case of the O_2 molecule, the Pauli principle can, generally speaking, be satisfied even without the mutual compensation of spins of the pair. However, such cases are rather rare.

Further, we know of cases of chemical bonds effected by three electrons (for instance, the bond between C atoms in the benzene molecule). There are other kinds of bonds that do not fit into the theory of electron pairs (in the zero approximation of this theory). The inadequacy of the latter theory** is also evident from the following facts: the failure to find molecules of second-group elements and hydrogen containing two H (MeH_2) atoms with

---

* However, in the excited state, the C_2H_2 molecule is bent with an angle C—C—H equal to 120°.

** We should bear in mind here that to a higher approximation the method of electron pairs may be used to describe *all* types of chemical linkage.

considerable (physical) stability of unsaturated molecules (MeH radicals), the chemical stability of molecules with an odd number of electrons, such as NO and ClO_2, the stability of free radicals, for instance, the radical of triphenylmethyl $(C_6H_5)_3C$, etc. All these and similar facts can be interpreted on the standpoint that a very significant role in the formation of chemical bonds is played by *energy* relationships, which are not always taken into account in the qualitative conclusions of the primitive theory of spin valence. In the final analysis, the decisive factor determining the stability of a given chemical compound or the possibility of its existence is the change in energy associated with the formation of the compound.

From this point of view, the most general approach is that developed by Mulliken, Hund, Herzberg, and Lennard-Jones, which states that all the electrons in a molecule are divided into *bonding* electrons, the energy of which diminishes during the formation of a molecule, and *antibonding* electrons, the energy of which increases during the process. Mulliken introduced yet another, intermediate, group of *nonbonding* electrons, the energy of which practically does not change during the formation of a molecule. In the first place, these are the electrons of the inner, most strongly bound, groups. In accordance with the Pauli principle, both the bonding and the antibonding electrons ordinarily occur in the molecule in the form of *pairs* with antiparallel spins; it is necessary, however, to stress the fact that in contrast to the theory of spin valence, the valence line here does not necessarily correspond to a pair of electrons with antiparallel spins (cf. the O_2 molecule, p. 310) and the unpaired electron is not necessarily a valence electron. On this view, the chemical stability of an "unsaturated" (according to the theory of spin valence) NO molecule or the chemical activity of the "saturated" molecules $P \equiv P$* or BH_3 is readily accounted for. For example, the activity of BH_3, which is manifested in the fact that the chemically saturated molecules are the molecules B_2H_6 and not BH_3, should, obviously, be attributed to the presence, in the BH_3 cloud, of electrons capable of becoming bonding electrons in the formation of B_2H_6 out of two BH_3 molecules. With respect to electronic structure, the BH_3 molecule may be likened to an oxygen atom with the same number of electrons (8).

---

* The chemical instability of P_2 as compared with N_2 is evident from the fact that in phosphorus vapour at moderately high temperatures we find P_4 molecules and not P_2 molecules. Accordingly, the heat of formation of P_4 out of two P_2 is positive and equal to 54.5 kcal/mol, whereas, due to the absence of N_4 molecules, we must consider the heat of their formation out of two N_2 molecules as close to zero.

From this viewpoint, to a saturated boron hydride one can assign the structure $H_3B=BH_3$, which is similar to the structure of an oxygen molecule $O=O$.* The radicals CH_2 and NH, to which everything said of BH_3 is applicable, are analogues of BH_3. Similarly, we can also interpret the radicals CN, NO, CO, CCl_3, etc., by attributing the chemical activity to the radical not to the electronic structure of the atoms C or N but to the radical as a whole.

The presence of bonding and antibonding electrons in molecules follows directly from a correlation of the heats of dissociation of neutral and ionised molecules. For example, from the fact that the heat of dissociation of a molecular ion of hydrogen (2.65 eV) is less than that of the molecule H_2 (4.48 eV), we can conclude that both electrons in the stable state of the H_2 ($^1\Sigma$) molecule that form the bond H—H are bonding electrons. In contrast to the $^1\Sigma$ state, in the unstable state $^3\Sigma$ of the H_2 molecule, one electron is a bonding electron and one is an antibonding electron (inasmuch as the Pauli principle requires that one of the electrons should pass to a two-quantum level; this involves a considerable rise in the energy of the molecule), as a result of which there is no bond. For the same reason there is no bond in the He_2 molecule where we have two bonding and two antibonding electrons. Insofar as chemical bonding is ordinarily effected by a pair of electrons, it may be concluded that the *kind* of chemical bond (the number of valence lines) is determined by the *difference* between the number of pairs of bonding electrons and the number of pairs of antibonding electrons. Equality in the number of both sets of electrons signifies that there is no bond. This rule is, of course, purely qualitative because the same bonding effect (in the sense of bond energy) or the same antibonding effect is attributed to each pair of electrons.

Disregarding the inner K-electrons and finding the distribution of electrons in the molecules of N_2 and CO (taking into account the Pauli principle), we may show that there should be four pairs of bonding and one pair of antibonding electrons in the electronic structure of these molecules in the ground state, whence we have a triple bond, as in the molecule N_2 and in CO. The predominance of bonding electrons among the most weakly bound electrons in these molecules is evident from a comparison of the heats of dissociation of the latter with the heats of dissociation of ionised molecules, which can be calculated on the basis of the circular process

---

* We should, however, point out that the B_2H_6 molecule is diamagnetic whereas oxygen is paramagnetic.

$$\begin{array}{ccc} AB & \xleftarrow{eI_M} & AB^+ + e \\ D\uparrow & eI & \uparrow D_+ \\ A+B & \longleftarrow & A+B^+ + e \end{array}$$

from known ionisation potentials of atoms (I) and molecules (I_m) from the equation

$$D_+ = D + eI - eI_m. \qquad (34.2)$$

The values of ionisation potentials of a number of molecules and atoms are given in Table 31, from which, using (34.2), we find $D_+ < D$ for the molecules N_2 and CO. The decrease in heat of dissociation when passing from a molecule to an ion is an indication that a bonding electron has been removed.

Table 31

Ionisation potentials of some molecules and atoms

Molecule	H_2	N_2	CO	O_2	NO	Cl_2	Br_2	I_2	HCl	HBr	HI
I_m, V	15.43	15.65	14.01	12.08	9.23	11.48	10.55	9.28	12.74	11.62	10.38

Atom	H	N	C	O	Cl	Br
I, V	13.53	14.46	11.22	13.55	12.96	11.80

In contrast to molecules H_2, N_2, and CO, in all other cases $D_+ > D$, whence we must conclude that the antibonding electrons are removed in ionisation of the molecule.

The concept of bonding and antibonding electrons is mathematically formulated in the *method of molecular orbits*, the physical essence of which consists in the following. To bare nuclei, which are visualised as fixed at a specific and constant distance from one another (when considering a diatomic molecule), we add electrons, one after the other, and determine the configuration of the resultant electronic system; here we are guided by the Pauli principle and the facts about electron configurations obtained from atomic spectra. The state of each electron is described by a certain wave function that characterises an appropriate *molecular orbit*, the properties of which determine the role of the given electron in the chemical bond. The mathematical solution of the molecular problem via the method of molecular orbits reduces to finding the wave function of the molecule (which is expressed in terms of molecular orbits of the electrons) and to calculating its energy.

The state of a given electron in an isolated atom A is characterised by the wave function ψ_A (*atomic orbit*). When another atom B approaches atom A the state of the electron changes. For a sufficiently large distance between atoms A and B, this altered state may be approximately described by the wave function (molecular orbit), which is a linear combination of the functions ψ_A and ψ_B corresponding to the occurrence of the electron in atoms A and B respectively (atomic orbits), i.e., by the function $\psi_+ = \psi_A + \psi_B$ or the function $\psi_- = \psi_A - \psi_B$.* The first of these functions (ψ_+) corresponds to the state of a *bonding* electron because in this case we have $\psi^2 = \psi_A^2 + \psi_B^2 + 2\psi_A\psi_B$, i. e., an increase in the density of the electron cloud in the space between the nuclei of atoms A and B, which enhances their mutual attraction. Function ψ_- corresponds to the state of an *antibonding* electron; the probability of its occurrence between nuclei A and B is reduced (the minus sign in the expression ψ^2), which signifies a tendency of the electron to pass into an atomic orbit with consequent decrease in stability of the molecule.

As has already been pointed out, the molecular orbits of electrons are calculated in terms of the atomic orbits of the respective atoms. However, there is another approximate way of finding the molecular orbits. We imagine the nuclei to be merged, thus obtaining an atom that corresponds to the initial molecule, which may be called a *united atom*. Here, the molecular orbits and the respective molecular terms pass into orbits and terms of the corresponding united atom. We thus obtain an approximate picture of the molecular orbits in terms of the atomic orbits of a united atom. Calculation of molecular orbits by this method is the more precise the smaller the distance between nuclei. Since, on the contrary, the molecular orbits calculated by means of the first method, i.e., in terms of the atomic orbits of the atoms comprising the molecule, give the most precise description of the actual state of the molecule only for large distances between nuclei, it may be assumed that the molecular orbits for internuclear distances close to equilibrium may be obtained by interpolating between the molecular orbits obtained by these two methods. The interpolation method plays a particularly large part in determining the character and order of the terms of diatomic molecules.

---

* Strictly speaking, these formulas hold only for the case when atoms A and B are the same. In the general case of different A and B, each of the functions ψ_A and ψ_B is multiplied by the factors c_A and c_B, respectively.

To determine the interrelations of the method of molecular orbits and the method of electronic pairs, we correlate these two methods by applying them to the hydrogen molecule. As we saw earlier (p. 289), the wave function corresponding to a stable state of the H_2 molecule may be written, to a first approximation, in the electron-pair method as

$$\psi = \psi_A(1)\,\psi_B(2) + \psi_B(1)\,\psi_A(2).$$

Expressing the molecular orbits of both electrons in terms of atomic orbits and assuming the motion of one electron as independent of that of the other, i.e., disregarding interaction of electrons, we have, in the method of molecular orbits (to the same first approximation),

$$\psi = [\psi_A(1) + \psi_B(1)]\,[\psi_A(2) + \psi_B(2)] = \psi_A(1)\,\psi_B(2) + \psi_B(1)\,\psi_A(2) + \psi_A(1)\,\psi_A(2) + \psi_B(1)\,\psi_B(2).$$

Comparing these two expressions, we see that the wave function calculated by the method of molecular orbits contains two terms other than those corresponding to the location of one electron near nucleus A and the other near nucleus B. These terms correspond to finding both electrons near one or the other of the nuclei, i.e., to two possible ionic structures of the molecule: H^-H^+ and H^+H^-, which were not taken into consideration in the method of electron pairs (however, see p. 289).

In the expression of the wave function calculated by the method of molecular orbits, the terms corresponding to ionic structures appear with the same coefficient (1) as the first two terms. Taking into consideration the fact that mutual repulsion of electrons (which we disregard in this method) must diminish the probability of both electrons being near one nucleus, i.e., the probability of accomplishing ionic structures, their role in the method of molecular orbits must be considered exaggerated. One of the consequences of this fact is that the method of molecular orbits is inadequate to account for the saturation capacity of chemical forces. We thus arrive at the conclusion that both methods (that of electron pairs as employed by Heitler and London, and that of molecular orbits) are one-sided and, for that reason, inadequate. Their restricted nature lies in the fact that the first method, which precludes the possibility of two electrons being located simultaneously at one nucleus, underestimates the role of ionic structures of molecules, whereas the second method, which ignores the mutual repulsion of the electrons and, for this reason, allows for an equal probability of finding both electrons near each one of the nuclei, overestimates the ionic structures.

Obviously, a more precise solution of the problem of choosing the wave function that would be in better agreement with reality should lie in between. To a zero approximation, such a solution in the general form appears to be expression (33.9):

$$\Psi = a\psi_{at} + b\psi_{ion}$$

where the first term denotes the atomic component of the wave function, i.e., those particular solutions of the wave equation (with appropriate coefficients) which correspond to finding the electrons near different nuclei, the second term denotes the ionic component, which corresponds to a simultaneous location of a pair of electrons near a single nucleus. As was pointed out above (p. 296), the relation between coefficients a and b is found from the minimum of potential energy of the molecule.

CHAPTER 8

MOLECULAR SPECTRA

35. Electronic Terms of Molecules

Origin of molecular terms. Experiment shows that molecules have electronic levels or terms similar to the terms of atoms. Above (p. 269) we saw, in the case of the absorption spectrum of mercury solutions, that a molecular field causes the same splitting of atomic terms as is found in an electric field (Stark effect). From this we drew the conclusion that a molecular field is electrical in nature. Here we shall examine another case that confirms this conclusion and is closely related to the problem of the origin of molecular terms. Studies of fluorescence spectra of Hg, Tl, Na, K, Rb, and Cs in the presence of inert gases (at a sufficiently large partial pressure of the latter) show that under these conditions in addition to the ordinary lines of metals, there appear weak *satellites*. For example, according to the data of Kuhn and Oldenberg, in the fluorescence spectrum of mercury vapours excited in the presence of argon or krypton, *two* weak diffuse satellites adjoin the resonance line Hg λ 2537 A ($^3P_1$—$^1S_0$) on the short wavelength side. Here, the number of satellites turns out equal to the number of components of Stark splitting of line 2537 A (see p. 269). Since in other cases, too, the number of satellites of each line equals the number of components of Stark splitting of the respective line, it may be concluded that whereas ordinary lines are emitted by isolated atoms, the satellites are emitted by the same atoms during collisions with atoms of the inert gases. It is the action of the electric field of the latter that gives rise to Stark splitting and the shifting of lines. *

Obviously, at the instant of collision we can consider each atomic pair as a *quasi-molecule*. The energy levels (terms) of such

* This effect is observed only in the case of inert gases due to the fact that other gases have a strong quenching action (*quenching of fluorescence*). For this reason, when excited atoms collide with the molecules of these gases, the energy of excitation converts into other forms of energy, in particular into thermal energy.

a quasi-molecule are precisely those that arise from the levels of the colliding atoms as a result of electrical splitting of these levels. Whence it follows that the greater the magnitude of this splitting, i.e., the stronger the interaction of the colliding atoms, the more considerably the levels of the quasi-molecule must differ from the levels of these atoms. Under the conditions at hand (fluorescence), the interaction energy has an order of magnitude kT, which is several hunderds of calories per gram-molecule. For this reason, the levels of the quasi-molecule are very close to the atomic levels, and corresponding lines are detected in the form of satellites of ordinary lines of the given element. However, in interactions, the energies of which are expressed in thousands and tens of thousands of calories (tenths of an eV and eV's), which is the case when a given pair of atoms forms a stable compound, the difference in the energy levels of the molecule and of the corresponding isolated atoms may become so large that the spectra of both will lie in different regions.

Table 32 gives the lower levels of certain molecules (E_m), for which the characteristic feature is a comparatively weak interaction of the constituent atoms, * together with the levels of the respective atoms (E_a). ** The energy levels of these molecules are not so close to the levels of their constituent atoms as in the case of the quasi-molecules KAr, HgAr, etc.; however, the genetic relation between atomic and molecular levels is obvious here.

In contrast to the comparatively unstable molecules of this kind, in the molecules O_2, N_2, NO, CO, etc., the heats of dissociation of which exceed 100,000 cal/mol ($D > 5$ eV), the genetic relation of molecular levels with the levels of the corresponding atoms is masked by an intense distortion of the atomic levels. Nevertheless, even here this relation can in many cases be established unambiguously (see below).

We thus arrive at the following basic conclusion: *the electronic levels of molecules originate from the levels of the atoms that constitute the molecule as a result of Stark splitting in the electric field of the molecule.*

Systematics of terms of diatomic molecules. Molecular terms may be calculated theoretically. In the simplest case of a molecule with one electron (molecular ion H_2^+) the wave function depends upon the coordinates of the electron x, y, z, the distances between

---

* Here, as usual, the measure of atomic interaction is the heat of dissociation (D) given in the second column in Table 32.

** Quantities E_m and E_a are the energy differences between the given and the ground levels of the respective molecule or atom. The symbols of the corresponding levels (terms) are given in parentheses.

the nuclei r and the angles ϑ and φ, which determine the direction of the axis of the molecule.

Table 32

Lower molecular levels of relatively unstable molecules and levels of atoms (in eV); (D is the heat of dissociation)

Molecule	D, eV	E_m	E_a
Li_2	1.14	1.74 ($^1\Sigma$) 2.54 ($^1\Pi$)	1.85 (2^2P-2^2S)
Na_2	0.76	1.81 ($^1\Sigma$) 2.51 ($^1\Pi$)	2.09 (3^2P-3^2S)
K_2	0.51	1.44 ($^1\Sigma$) 1.90 ($^1\Pi$)	1.60 (4^2P-4^2S)
CdH	0.68	2.82 ($^2\Pi$) 3.50 ($^2\Sigma$) 5.25 ($^2\Sigma$)	3.94 (5^3P-5^1S) 5.40 (5^1P-5^1S)
HgH	0.37	3.32 ($^2\Pi$) 4.20 ($^2\Sigma$)	4.87 (6^3P-6^1S)

Assuming an approximate separation of variables, we may put

$$\psi=\psi(x,\ y,\ z,\ r,\ \vartheta,\ \varphi)=\psi_{el}(x,\ y,\ z)\,\psi_{vib}(r)\,\psi_{rot}(\vartheta,\ \varphi).$$

In this case, the energy of the molecule can also be approximately represented as the sum of the electronic, vibrational, and rotational energies: $E=E_{el}+E_{vib}+E_{rot}$. Hence we get three differential wave equations, the solution of which will give the electronic, vibrational, and rotational energies. E_{el} is obtained by solving the wave equation for the function ψ_{el} *(electronic wave function).*

The molecule as a quantum-mechanical system differs from an atom in the sense that in the molecule the electrons occur in the field of two or several nuclei and not one. For this reason, even in the case of a single electron in a molecule (H_2^+) the field acting on it will not have central symmetry. Considering the distance between nuclei (protons) r as a certain constant parameter, we will have the following Schrödinger equation:

$$\Delta\psi_{el}+\frac{2m}{\hbar^2}(E_{el}-V)\,\psi_{el}=0. \qquad (35.1)$$

In this equation, V is the potential energy of the electron in the field of both nuclei,

$$V=\frac{e^2}{r}-\frac{e^2}{r_1}-\frac{e^2}{r_2}$$

where r_1 and r_2 are the distances of the electron from the first and second nuclei, respectively.

From an analysis of equation (35.1) it follows that, like the wave equation for an atom with one electron, it has solutions for any positive value of energy and only for certain discrete values of negative energy. The first solutions (positive E) correspond to the unstable state of the ion H_2^+ divided into the H atom and the H^+ ion, which are separated by the distance r and have an energy in excess of that of their interaction for $r=\infty$, the second solutions (negative E) correspond to discrete (quantised) states of the H_2^+ ion. The set of these negative eigenvalues of energy E is what corresponds to the energy levels of the H_2^+ ion (for a given distance r between nuclei). The wave functions (eigenfunctions) corresponding to these values of E may be called *orbital* or *molecular* (see p. 314).

The eigenfunctions of equation (35.1) depend not only on the coordinates but also on three quantum numbers, of which only one has precise physical meaning for all values of the parameter r. This number, denoted by the letter λ, determines the projection of the orbital angular momentum of the electron on the axis of the molecule (ion) equal to $\pm\hbar\lambda$. The number λ can take on values $0, 1, 2, \ldots$; depending upon these values the electron is called a σ-, π-, δ-, ... electron. The two other quantum numbers can be expressed in terms of the principal (n) and orbital (l) quantum numbers that characterise the given system in one of two limiting cases: in the case of $r=0$ (merged nuclei) and in the case of $r=\infty$ (separated nuclei). In the first case, the terms of the system are obviously the terms of the He^+ ion, in the second, the terms of the H atom. When the numbers n and l are used for a system of merged nuclei, the states of the electron in H_2^+ are designated by the symbols $1s\sigma$, $2s\sigma$, $2p\sigma$, $2p\pi$, etc., and when the quantum numbers are used for a separated system, by $\sigma 1s$, $\sigma 2s$, $\sigma 2p$, $\pi 2p$, etc.

In the case of a diatomic molecule with the number of electrons greater than one, an exact solution of the wave equation (35.1) is not possible. However, we may examine, approximately, the motion of each individual electron in the averaged field of the remaining electrons, which field is superposed on the field of the nuclei. In such a treatment (cf. the Hartree-Fok method, p. 204), each electron in the molecule may be roughly characterised by quantum numbers n, l, and λ (and also by a fourth—spin quantum number $\sigma=m_s=\pm 1/2$); as in the case of an atom, electrons with the same values of the quantum numbers n and l are called equivalent. By virtue of the Pauli principle, the number of equivalent electrons cannot exceed two for $\lambda=0$ and four for $\lambda\neq0$. Indeed, in the first case (σ-electrons) we have $n_1=n_2$, $l_1=l_2$, $\lambda_1=\lambda_2=0$ and $\sigma_1=-\sigma_2=1/2$, in the second case (π-, δ-, etc., electrons) $n_1=n_2=n_3=n_4$, $l_1=l_2=l_3=l_4$, $\lambda_1=\lambda_2=\lambda$, $\lambda_3=\lambda_4=-\lambda$ and $\sigma_1=\sigma_3=-\sigma_2=-\sigma_4=1/2$. Here, two equivalent σ- or four π- (or four δ-, etc.) electrons form a *closed electron subgroup* characterised by the values $\Lambda=\sum\lambda_i=0$ and $S=0$. Thus, the electronic structure of the molecule, like that of the atom, is built up of discrete groups and subgroups containing definite numbers of electrons. The electron configuration of the molecule and, hence, its energy states or electronic terms are determined by the entire assemblage of molecular orbits, i.e., by the set of quantum numbers of all the electrons of the molecule.

In the overwhelming majority of cases (see below), the following quantum number can be made fundamental to the systematics of electronic terms of diatomic and also linear polyatomic molecules:

$$\Lambda=\sum\lambda_i \tag{35.2}$$

(summation is performed over all electrons of the molecule); this number determines the absolute value of the projection of the total orbital angular momentum on the axis of the molecule. Depending upon the value of $\Lambda=0$, 1, 2, etc., the terms of the molecule are designated by the symbols Σ, Π, Δ, etc.

Let us consider certain states of a molecule that result from given states of the electrons. In the case of a single σ-electron (the remaining electrons in the molecule form closed subgroups) we have the term $^2\Sigma$ ($\Lambda=\lambda=0$, $S=s=1/2$). One π-electron yields a $^2\Pi$-term ($\Lambda=\lambda=1$, $S=1/2$), one δ-electron, a $^2\Delta$-term, etc. Two equivalent σ-electrons (designated by the symbol σ^2) yield the term $^1\Sigma$ ($\sigma_1=1/2$, $\sigma_2=-1/2$), two nonequivalent σ-electrons ($\sigma\sigma$), the terms $^1\Sigma$ ($S=0$) and $^3\Sigma$ ($S=1$). One σ- and one π-electron ($\sigma\pi$) yield $^1\Pi$- and $^3\Pi$-terms. Two equivalent π-electrons (π^2) yield the terms $^1\Sigma$, $^3\Sigma$ ($\Lambda=\lambda_1+\lambda_2=1-1=0$, $S=0,1$) and the term $^1\Delta$ ($\Lambda=\lambda_1+\lambda_2=1+1=2$, $S=0$). The term $^3\Delta$, as one that contradicts the Pauli principle ($\lambda_1=\lambda_2$ $\sigma_1=\sigma_2$), is excluded. But in the case of two nonequivalent π-electrons ($\pi\pi$) we have also the $^3\Delta$-term in addition to the terms indicated for the case of π^2. Thus we see that here, as in the case of an atom, the Pauli principle introduces an appreciable correction into the number of possible terms (see also below).

Of practical interest is the problem of finding all molecular terms that are formed from the various atomic terms. This problem is solved by means of known rules of space quantisation.

As was pointed out in Chapter 6, in a strong electric field the vectors **L** (orbital angular momentum) and **S** (spin) are quantised independently, and the projection of **L** on the direction of the electric field takes on $2L+1$ values in accordance with the number of possible separate values: $\pm L$, $\pm(L-1)$, ..., 0. However, due to the fact that the terms corresponding to the values L and $-L$, $(L-1)$ and $-(L-1)$, etc., have the same energy in an electric field, we obtain only $L+1$ different terms. In the same way the number of projections of the **S** vector on the field direction is equal to $2S+1$ in accordance with the values $\pm S$, $\pm(S-1)$, ... It must be pointed out that the **S** vector does not experience any direct effect from the electric field. However, as in the case of the **L** vector, here too one can speak of **S** projections on the field direction, since, due to precession of the vector **L** about the direction of the electric field, the mean value of the magnetic-field component **L**, normal to the electric field, is zero, and **S** is actually oriented with respect to the component **L** along the field, i.e, with respect to the direction of the electric field.

Let us now examine the levels that appear when two atoms approach each other. If the atoms are separated by a sufficiently small distance (comparable with the distance between the atoms in the molecule), splitting of atomic terms, which is a measure of the interaction of the atoms, may be interpreted as splitting in a strong electric field.* We must then take into account the orientation of each of the vectors $\mathbf{L}_1$ and $\mathbf{L}_2$ of both atoms with respect to the line connecting the centres of the atoms (axis of the molecule) and determining the direction (axis of symmetry) of the intramolecular electric field. Designating the absolute values of projections of all vectors ** on the axis of the molecule in terms of (cf. p. 268) $\Lambda_1 = L_1, L_1-1, \ldots, 0$ and $\Lambda_2 = L_2, L_2-1, \ldots, 0$, respectively, for the total projection we get $(L_1 > L_2)$:

$$\left.\begin{array}{r} \Lambda = \Lambda_1 + \Lambda_2 = \\ = L_1+L_2,\ L_1+L_2-1,\ L_1+L_2-2,\ \ldots,\ L_1-L_2,\ \ldots,\ 1,\ 0 \\ L_1+L_2-1,\ L_1+L_2-2,\ \ldots,\ L_1-L_2,\ \ldots,\ 1,\ 0 \\ L_1+L_2-2,\ \ldots,\ L_1-L_2,\ \ldots,\ 1,\ 0 \\ \ldots\ldots\ldots\ldots,\ 1,\ 0 \\ L_1-L_2,\ \ldots,\ 1,\ 0 \end{array}\right\} \quad (35.3)$$

* It must be said that this does not always occur. Very often the molecular terms correspond to splitting of atomic terms in a weak electric field (see below).

** Here, as before, in a number of analogous cases we express the projections of the vectors in units of $\hbar$.

The quantity Λ may be obtained in a somewhat different manner. Assuming interaction of the atomic vectors $\mathbf{L}_1$ and $\mathbf{L}_2$, which leads to the resultant vector

$$\mathbf{L}=\mathbf{L}_1+\mathbf{L}_2,$$

we get, for the absolute magnitude of the projections of the latter on the axis of the molecule, values expressed by (35.3). We can therefore define Λ as the absolute value of the projection of the total orbital angular momentum of the molecule on its axis. This quantity is obviously also identical with that in (35.2).

Further, denoting the absolute value of the projection of the total spin of the molecule*

$$\mathbf{S}=\mathbf{S}_1+\mathbf{S}_2$$

on its axis in terms of Σ and considering Σ positive when the projections of **L** and **S** have the same sign, and negative when the signs of the projections of these vectors are opposite, we can build up a sum out of Λ and Σ:

$$\Omega=\Lambda\pm\Sigma. \qquad (35.5)$$

Comparing this expression with expression

$$\mathbf{J}=\mathbf{L}+\mathbf{S}$$

(p. 210), which appears in the systematics of atomic terms, we see that the numbers Ω, Λ, and Σ are definitely related to the numbers J, L, and S: namely, the latter express the total, orbital, and spin angular momenta, respectively, while the numbers Ω, Λ and $\pm\Sigma$, the projections of these angular momenta on the axis of the molecule. This makes it possible to build a classification of molecular terms by starting with the quantum numbers Ω, Λ, and Σ.

Generally speaking, the molecular terms characterised by the quantum number $\Lambda>0$ are split into a series of components *(natural splitting)* in accordance with the different orientation of the total spin **S** relative to the axis of the molecule; and, as in the case of atomic multiplets, the multiplicity of the molecular term is determined by the number $2S+1$. We see that the fine structure of molecular terms is of the same origin as the fine structure of atomic terms: it is caused by the magnetic interaction of spin and orbital angular momentum.

To characterise each separate component of a molecular multiplet, it appears natural to take advantage of quantum number Ω

* We note that

$$S=S_1+S_2,\ S_1+S_2-1,\ \ldots,\ |S_1-S_2|. \qquad (35.4)$$

(it corresponds to number J, which plays the same part in the systematics of atomic terms). Thus, as a symbol for a molecular term, like the atomic symbol

$$^{2S+1}\{L\}_J,$$

we get the symbol *

$$^{2S+1}\{\Lambda\}_\Omega,$$

which, in separate cases, is deciphered as $^1\Sigma$, $^2\Sigma$, $^3\Sigma$, $^1\Pi$, $^2\Pi_{1/2}$, $^2\Pi_{3/2}$, $^3\Pi_0$, $^3\Pi_1$, $^3\Pi_2$, etc. In the case of Σ-terms, i.e., $\Lambda=0$, the spin orientation relative to the axis of the molecule is absent, as a result of which the quantum numbers Σ and Ω are devoid of physical meaning.

By way of illustration let us consider the terms of the OH molecule that are obtained from the normal terms of the atoms O(^{3}P) and H(^{2}S). In this case we will have: $L_O=1$, $L_H=0$, $S_O=1$, and $S_H=1/2$, whence, on the basis of equations (35.3) and (35.4), we find: $\Lambda=1$, 0 and $S=3/2$, $1/2$, in other words, the terms $^4\Pi$, $^2\Pi$, $^4\Sigma$, $^2\Sigma$. In the following manner we find the values of number Ω that are necessary in order to distinguish the components of the multiplet terms $^4\Pi$ and $^2\Pi$. In the case of $S=3/2$ (the quadruplet term $^4\Pi$), for the projection Σ we get $\Sigma=3/2$, $1/2$ and in the case of $S=1/2$ (doublet term $^2\Pi$), $\Sigma=1/2$. Consequently, on the basis of (35.5) we have for term $^4\Pi:\Omega=5/2$, $3/2$, $1/2$, $-1/2$ and for the term $^2\Pi:\Omega=3/2$, $1/2$. Thus, we finally get the following set of terms: $^4\Sigma$, $^2\Sigma$, $^4\Pi_{5/2}$, $^4\Pi_{3/2}$, $^4\Pi_{1/2}$, $^4\Pi_{-1/2}$, $^2\Pi_{3/2}$, and $^2\Pi_{1/2}$. We note that according to experimental data the term $^2\Pi$ is the ground term of the OH molecule.

Properties of symmetry of molecular terms. As is evident from equation (35.3) the number of all Σ-, all Π-, etc., terms obtained from a given pair of atomic terms is determined by how many ways (for given L_1 and L_2) one can obtain the appropriate number Λ. The terms of each group differ in the kind of *symmetry* of the wave functions that correspond to them, namely, from a solution of the wave equation for a molecule it follows that whereas in the case of certain terms called *positive* terms the wave function does not change with reversal of the sign of all coordinates of the nuclei and electrons, in the case of other terms *(negative)* the function ψ does change its sign in this process. This separation of terms into positive and negative is particularly important in the case of Σ-terms. Here, if the number of all terms obtained

* Here, $\{L\}$ and $\{\Lambda\}$ designate S, P, D and Σ, Π, Δ, ... in accordance with the values of the numbers L and Λ equal to 0, 1, 2...

from a given pair of atomic terms is even, half of them is positive (Σ^+) and half, negative (Σ^-). For an odd number of terms, the number of Σ^+ terms is greater than that of Σ^- terms when the sum $L_1 + L_2 + \Sigma l_{i1} + \Sigma l_{i2}$ is even, and less than the number of negative terms when this sum is odd. Each of the sums Σl_{i1} and Σl_{i2} is the sum of the orbital quantum numbers of all electrons, respectively, of both atomic terms (out of which the Σ-terms under consideration arise). Let it be noted that the atomic terms with even Σl_i are called *even* and are designated by the symbol $\{L\}_g$, while the terms with odd Σl_i are *odd*, $\{L\}_u$.

As for the terms that correspond to values $\Lambda > 0$, they also split, each into two terms + and —; however, this splitting (called Λ-type *doubling*) is found only when a molecule is in rotation (see Sec. 36). Thus, the terms Π, Δ, etc., turn out to be doubly degenerate because in the absence of rotation, two states $\{\Lambda\}^+$ and $\{\Lambda\}^-$ with identical energy correspond to each of the terms. This degeneracy is connected with the fact that in the absence of rotation the states with projections of L on the axis of the molecule (identical in absolute magnitude but different in sign) have the same energy (see p. 322).

Molecular terms obtained from appropriate atomic terms are given in Table 33 (after Wigner and Witmer, after Mulliken, and after Herzberg).

Table 33

Molecular terms obtained from appropriate atomic terms (after Wigner and Witmer, after Mulliken, after Herzberg)

Atomic terms	Molecular terms
$S_g + S_g$ or $S_u + S_u$	Σ^+
$S_g + S_u$	Σ^-
$S_g + P_g$ or $S_u + P_u$	Σ^-, Π
$S_g + P_u$ or $S_u + P_g$	Σ^+, Π
$S_g + D_g$ or $S_u + D_u$	Σ^+, Π, Δ
$S_g + D_u$ or $S_u + D_g$	Σ^-, Π, Δ
$S_g + F_g$ or $S_u + F_u$	Σ^-, Π, Δ, Φ
$S_g + F_u$ or $S_u + F_g$	Σ^+, Π, Δ, Φ
$P_g + P_g$ or $P_u + P_u$	Σ^+ (2), Σ^-, Π (2), Δ
$P_g + P_u$	Σ^+, Σ^- (2), Π (2), Δ
$P_g + D_g$ or $P_u + D_u$	Σ^+, Σ^-(2), Π (3), Δ (2), Φ
$P_g + D_u$ or $P_u + D_g$	Σ^+(2), Σ^-, Π (3), Δ (2), Φ

The foregoing reasoning is totally applicable to molecules composed of different atoms. But in the case of molecules with the same nuclei (these include $Cl^{35}Cl^{35}$, $Cl^{37}Cl^{37}$, $O^{16}O^{16}$, $O^{18}O^{18}$,

$N^{14}N^{14}$, $N^{15}N^{15}$, etc., and their ions; however, molecules consisting of different isotopes, for instance, $Cl^{35}Cl^{37}$, $O^{16}O^{18}$ or $N^{14}N^{15}$, belong to the earlier considered category) the number of terms turns out, in general, to be *twice as great* as for molecules built up from different atoms (or different isotopes of a single element). This doubling of the number of terms, however, only occurs when the initial atomic states are *different*. It is associated with degeneracy of the initial state (isolated atoms). Indeed, when considering, for example, the formation of a molecular ion of hydrogen from an H atom in the ground state and from a proton H^+, we can proceed from a system in which an electron is connected with one of the H^+ nuclei, say the first, i. e., of a system $(H)_1+(H^+)_2$ or of a system $(H^+)_1+(H)_2$. Obviously, in both cases the energy of the initial state will be the same. The presence of two states of a system corresponding to one and the same energy is an indication of its degeneracy. The degeneracy in the case at hand is called *resonance*, or exchange degeneracy (see p. 198). Solution of the wave equation shows that when nuclei approach, both states obtain different energy, which is what leads to the above-mentioned doubling of the number of terms.

The wave functions corresponding to each pair of terms differ in the kind of symmetry: some change their sign upon transposition of the nuclei, others do not. Terms of the first group are called *odd* and are designated by the symbol $\{\Lambda\}_u$, of the second group, *even*, $\{\Lambda\}_g$. Thus, to determine the number and character of the molecular terms obtained from different (unlike) atomic terms, we may take advantage of the data of Table 33, by replacing in it each term by two terms: $\Sigma^+\rightarrow\Sigma_g^+$, Σ_u^+, $\Sigma^-\rightarrow\Sigma_g^-$, Σ_u^-, $\Pi\rightarrow\Pi_g$, Π_u, etc.

As has already been pointed out, in the case of molecular terms that arise from the *same* terms of identical atoms, doubling of terms does not occur, though here too the division of terms into even and odd remains. From the set of terms resulting from the scheme

$$\left.\begin{array}{rl}\Lambda=\Lambda_1+\Lambda_2=2L, & 2L-1,\ 2L-2\ \ldots,\ 1,\ 0,\\ & 2L-1,\ 2L-2,\ \ldots,\ 1,\ 0,\\ & 2L-2,\ \ldots,\ 1,\ 0,\\ & \ldots,\ 1,\ 0,\\ & 1,\ 0,\\ & 0,\end{array}\right\} \qquad (35.6)$$

we have an even number of terms that correspond to an odd value of Λ (1, 3, 5, ...). Half of these terms is even, half is odd. The remaining terms (with the exception of Σ-terms) available in the odd quantity (2N + 1) are distributed as follows: N terms turn out to be even and N odd; the surplus term is even in the case of even S (singlets, quintets, . . .) and odd in the case of odd S (triplets, septets, . . .). As for Σ-terms, of all the 2L + 1 Σ-terms, L + 1 are Σ^+ terms, the remaining L, Σ^--terms; and in the singlet and quintet systems the Σ^+ terms are even, Σ_g^+, and the Σ^- terms are odd, Σ_u^-, while in the triplet and septet systems the situation is reversed.

By way of illustration let us consider terms that result from the same atomic terms ^3P, for example, from terms of the ground state of two oxygen atoms. In this case we have $L_0 = 1$ and, hence (see(35.6)), $\Lambda = 2, 1, 1, 0, 0, 0$, i.e., we have Δ-, Π- and Σ-terms. Further, from the multiplicity of the initial terms ^3P we find S = 2, 1, 0, i.e., quintets (S = 2), triplets (S = 1), and singlets (S = 0). On the basis of the foregoing rules, for terms available in an even quantity, i.e., for Π-terms, we have $^5\Pi_g$, $^5\Pi_u$, $^3\Pi_g$, $^3\Pi_u$, $^1\Pi_g$, and $^1\Pi_u$. The Δ-terms are terms $^5\Delta_g$, $^1\Delta_g$ (S is even) and $^3\Delta_u$ (S is odd) and Σ-terms are terms $^5\Sigma_g^+$, $^5\Sigma_u^-$, $^5\Sigma_g^+$, $^1\Sigma_g^+$, $^1\Sigma_u^-$, $^1\Sigma_g^+$ (quintet and singlet systems) and $^3\Sigma_u^+$, $^3\Sigma_g^-$ and $^3\Sigma_u^+$ (triplet system).

Hund's cases of molecular terms. The systematics of molecular terms, the basis of which was given above, does not however embrace the entire ensemble of quantum states even of a single molecule. Primarily, the underlying principle of this systematics is the assumption that the molecular electric field which gives rise to splitting of appropriate atomic terms is sufficiently strong to disrupt the coupling between the vectors $\mathbf{L}_i$ and $\mathbf{S}_i$ in the separate atoms. This, obviously, should not always be the case. Moreover, in constructing this systematics we did not take into account the *rotation* of the molecule with which the appearance of a *magnetic* field normal to the axis of the molecule is associated. Later on we shall see that this field exerts an appreciable effect on the interaction of vectors in the molecule.

For this reason, with the aim of extending and generalising the systematics we shall examine the main types of interaction of the different vectors that are characteristic of the *vector model* of a diatomic molecule. Here, we shall also take into account the momentum associated with the rotation of the molecule (vibration of nuclei do not enter into this consideration, inasmuch as vibrational motion has no momentum). In the main, these types were considered by Hund and are known as *Hund's cases* of molecular terms a, b, c, and d.

Case a. The electric field of a molecule is so strong that we may disregard the interaction of individual $\mathbf{L}_i$ with individual $\mathbf{S}_i$, which interaction we designate as ($\mathbf{L}_i$, $\mathbf{S}_i$), as compared with the interaction of different $\mathbf{S}_i$ and as compared with the interaction of $\mathbf{L}_i$ with the electric field of the molecule. As a result of the latter and also due to space quantisation of the **S** vector in the magnetic field of the component of electronic orbital angular momentum along the axis of the molecule, we have Λ and Σ that together yield the quantity Ω. We thus see that the above-constructed systematics of molecular terms corresponds completely to Hund's case a.

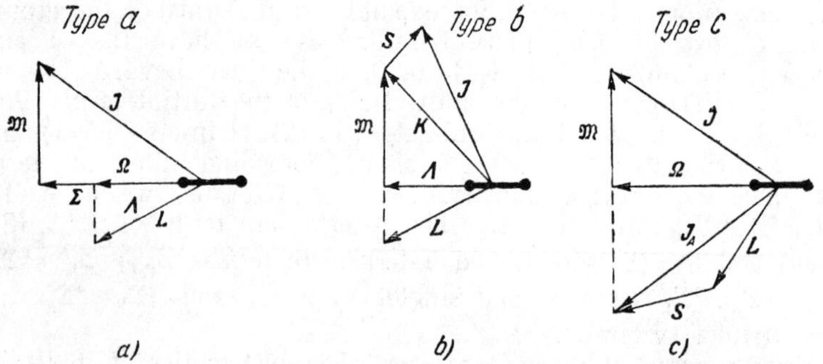

Fig. 74. Vector model of diatomic molecule. Hund's cases a, b, and c

The vector $\mathbf{\Omega}$ directed along the axis of the molecule interacts, further, with the nuclear momentum vector $\mathfrak{M}$ (rotation of the molecule), as a result of which we get a resultant vector **J** that characterises the total angular momentum of the molecule (but without account of nuclear spins). Interaction of vectors $\mathbf{\Omega}$ and $\mathfrak{M}$ leads to their precession about **J**. The mutual positions of the vectors $\mathbf{\Omega}$, $\mathfrak{M}$ and **J** are shown in Fig. 74 a. We note that the quantum number J, which corresponds to the vector **J**, takes on integral values when Σ and Ω are integers; this occurs when there is an even number of electrons.

Denoting the electric field of the molecule by **Z** we can symbolically represent vector interaction corresponding to case a as follows:

$$\{[(\mathbf{L},\ \mathbf{Z}),\ \mathbf{S}],\ \mathfrak{M}\}.$$

Case b. This case may be symbolically represented as

$$\{[(\mathbf{L},\ \mathbf{Z}),\ \mathfrak{M}],\ \mathbf{S}\}$$

(see Fig. 74 b). In this case, according to Fig. 74 b, Λ and $\mathfrak{W}$ yield the resultant vector **K**, which with **S** forms the vector **J**. We see that here the quantum number Σ, and with it also Ω, become meaningless. However, given sufficiently large K (and in the case of Σ-terms, for any K) we can introduce a new quantum number $\mathfrak{S}$, which corresponds to a projection of spin on the axis of rotation of the molecule. Like Σ, $\mathfrak{S}$ assumes the values $\pm S$, $\pm(S-1), \ldots$ We note that when nuclear rotation is increased (increase in K) a transition is possible from case a to case b. Experiment shows that a considerable portion of the electronic terms of a diatomic molecule belongs to this transitional type.

Case c. This type of interaction of vectors is accomplished in a weak electric field that is not capable of disrupting the interaction of vectors $\mathbf{L}_i$ and $\mathbf{S}_i$. As we see, it corresponds to the Stark effect in a weak electric field. In this case, the vector $\mathbf{J}_a$ ("atomic" angular momentum), which is composed of vectors $\mathbf{J}_i$, is as a whole oriented relative to axis z (Fig. 74 c). To summarise, Λ and Σ as independent numbers are here devoid of any meaning. But number Ω, which determines the projection of vector $\mathbf{J}_a$ on the axis of the molecule, is retained. Interaction of vectors $\boldsymbol{\Omega}$ and $\mathfrak{W}$ lead to a resultant vector $\mathbf{J}$. This type of interaction is symbolically depicted as

$$\{[(\mathbf{J}_1, \mathbf{J}_2), \mathbf{Z}], \mathfrak{W}\}.$$

Obviously, transition from the earlier cases to case c should be important in separation of nuclei.

Case d. As for the fourth coupling case, which occurs only in the case of a comparatively small number of molecules and, for this reason, is least significant, we only indicate that it corresponds to a predominance of interaction of the vectors $\mathbf{L}_i$ with rotation of nuclei over interaction of the remaining vectors.

Obviously, the earlier introduced symbol for designating molecular terms,

$$_{2S+1}\{\Lambda\}_{\Omega},$$

is suitable only for case a. If we have case b, the numbers Σ and Ω are devoid of any meaning. Therefore, we have here, as the symbol designating the term,

$$_{2S+1}\{\Lambda\}.$$

As has already been pointed out, the separate components of the multiplet differ in the values of the quantum number $\mathfrak{S}$, which corresponds to the number Σ. Frequently, $\mathfrak{S}$ taken in brackets is placed next to the symbol of the term:

$$_{2S+1}\{\Lambda\}(\mathfrak{S}).$$

Finally, in case c, where the numbers Λ and Σ disappear, the terms are distinguished by the number Ω, which retains physical meaning. The terms belonging to this case are designated, according to Mulliken, by the symbol

$$\{\Omega\}.$$

The foregoing rules, which determine the number and character of molecular terms are, obviously, applicable (to the same extent) to Hund's cases a and b. Analogous rules are operative in regard to case c. The total number of terms that arise out of two atomic terms characterised by the numbers J_1 and J_2 is determined here by the scheme $(J_1 > J_2)$:

$$\left.\begin{array}{r}\Omega = J_1+J_2,\ J_1+J_2-1,\ \ldots,\ J_1-J_2,\ \ldots,\ {}^1/_2 \text{ or } 0,\\ J_1+J_2-1,\ \ldots,\ J_1-J_2,\ \ldots,\ {}^1/_2 \text{ or } 0,\\ \ldots,\ J_1-J_2,\ \ldots,\ {}^1/_2 \text{ or } 0,\\ J_1-J_2,\ \ldots,\ {}^1/_2 \text{ or } 0.\end{array}\right\} \quad (35.7)$$

In the case of $\Omega=0$, we also have *positive* and *negative* terms 0^+ and 0^-, the number of which is the same for an even number of 0-terms. The surplus term for an odd number of terms is the term 0^+ or 0^-, depending on whether the sum $J_1+J_2+\Sigma l_1+\Sigma l_2$ is an even or odd number.

In case of the *same* atoms in *different* states, the number of terms, as before, is *double*; one half of them is *even*, $\{\Omega\}_g$, and the other half, *odd*, $\{\Omega\}_u$.

The number and character of terms in the case of *identical* states of the *same* atoms are obtained directly from the following schemes:

$$\left.\begin{array}{r}\{\Omega\} = \{2J\}_g,\ \{2J-1\}_g,\ \ldots,\ 0_g^+,\\ \{2J-1\}_u,\ \ldots,\ 0_u^-,\\ \cdots\cdots\\ 0_g^+\end{array}\right\} \quad (35.8)$$

and

$$\left.\begin{array}{r}\{\Omega\} = \{2J\}_u,\ \{2J-1\}_u,\ \ldots,\ 0_u^-,\\ \{2J-1\}_g,\ \ldots,\ 0_g^+,\\ \cdots\cdots\\ 0_g^+\end{array}\right\} \quad (35.9)$$

The first, (35.8), has to do with the case of integral J, the second, (35.9), of half-integral J.

Thus, guided by the above rules it is possible to find the entire set of terms of any diatomic molecule. Using these rules, it is possible, in a number of cases, to solve also the reverse problem (which, practically, is no less important) of determining the quantum states of atoms that arise in the dissociation of the molecule.

It may be noted that molecular electrons, like molecular terms, display specific properties of symmetry (in the sense of symmetry of appropriate wave functions). For instance, we distinguish *even* (σ_g-, π_g-, etc.) and *odd* (σ_u-, π_u-, etc.) electrons, the former being electrons to which there correspond even l (for example, $s\sigma$, $d\sigma \longrightarrow \sigma_g$, $d\pi \longrightarrow \pi_g$) and the remaining, odd ($p\sigma$, $f\sigma \longrightarrow \sigma_u$, $p\pi$, $f\pi \longrightarrow \pi_u$). Even electrons with even, or odd with odd, form an even molecular term (Σl is even), and even with odd, an odd term (Σl is odd).

So far we have hardly touched on the question of the relative arrangement of molecular terms. Yet this question is of prime importance for molecular spectroscopy. As already pointed out, it is solved theoretically by quantum-mechanical methods. However, the finding of numerical values of terms and their sequence in a given molecule, even in the case of comparatively simple molecules containing a small number of electrons, presents great mathematical difficulties. For this reason, one frequently has to confine oneself to the construction of a more or less reliable qualitative picture of the terms. Use is made of one of the following semi-empirical methods.

The first, the *method of interpolation* (Hund, Herzberg, Mulliken) consists in the following. If in the Schrödinger equation we assume the distance between nuclei r equal to ∞, we obtain two equations that correspond to two isolated atoms (cf. p. 285). The set of terms corresponding to this limiting state of the molecule (dissociated molecule) will obviously be represented as a simple sum of appropriate atomic terms (the terms of a *separated system*), which may be found either by solving atomic wave equations or may be taken directly from experiment. When the atoms approach, we have Stark splitting of the terms in the electric field of the partner. The set of splitting components of atomic terms is precisely the set of molecular terms that corresponds to the given (large) values of r. Here, the relative arrangement of terms is roughly in accord with the arrangement of components of Stark splitting in an external electric field and can be determined from experiment.

On the other hand, in a wave equation of a molecule we can put $r=0$. We then get an equation for an atom that is isoelectronic to the molecule under consideration, the terms of which are also known. Separating the nuclei mentally, we obtain a field with axial symmetry (an intramolecular electric field), in which the terms of the isoelectronic atom (a *system of merged nuclei*) experience Stark splitting. The set of components of this splitting obviously also corresponds to the terms of the given molecule (for small r). As in the case of an almost separated system (large r), the relative positions of the terms can here be taken from experiment. Knowing molecular terms for large and small r, we can, obviously, by means of *interpolation* determine the more or less probable relative positions of the terms of the given molecule. The scheme of molecular terms thus obtained is verified by comparing it with experiment.

By way of illustration, let us consider the molecule CH. In this case, the terms that correspond to two limiting cases are obtained

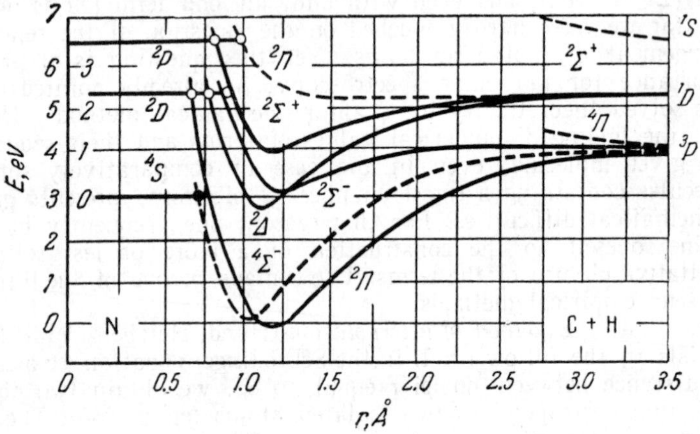

Fig. 75. Origin of energy levels of CH molecule

as a set of terms of the atoms C+H (separated system) and the terms of the N atom (merged nuclei). The lowest terms of the C+H system are ^{3}P (ground state of the C atom) plus ^{2}S (ground state of H) and ^{1}D+^{2}S; the lowest terms of atom N are ^{4}S (ground state of atom N), ^{2}D and ^{2}P. From these terms of the system C+H there arise the following terms of molecule CH: from $^3P+{}^2S \rightarrow {}^2\Sigma, {}^4\Sigma, {}^2\Pi, {}^4\Pi$, and from $^1D+{}^2S \rightarrow {}^2\Sigma, {}^2\Pi, {}^2\Delta$; from the terms of atom N, the terms: $^4\Sigma$ from ^{4}S, $^2\Sigma$, $^2\Pi$, $^2\Delta$ from ^{2}D and $^2\Sigma$, $^2\Pi$ from ^{2}P.

The problem then reduces to correlating terms of the system of almost separated nuclei with terms of the system of almost merged nuclei and to finding the relative positions of the terms. However, since this problem has no entirely unambiguous solution, to find the terms of the molecule we have to be guided by various kinds of additional data, such as: data on the relative positions of the atomic terms (for instance, quadruplet terms as a rule lie lower than doublet, etc.), on the electron configuration of the molecular terms (terms corresponding to one electron configuration of an almost separated system pass into terms of the same configuration of a system of almost merged nuclei), on noncrossing of terms (terms corresponding to a configuration of electrons with the same quantum numbers l and λ do not cross), etc. Finally, experimental data dealing with the optical properties of the molecule under consideration in its various states help to establish a genetic relationship between molecular terms and the terms of the corresponding atoms in the separated system.

Fig. 75 shows the levels of the CH molecule (in the form of curves of potential energy) for various r with an indication of their origin from levels C+H and N (after Mulliken). Of the terms shown here, four are experimentally known, namely, $^2\Pi$, $^2\Delta$, $^2\Sigma^-$, and $^2\Sigma^+$, and the lowest one is the term $^2\Pi$. In this given case, the ambiguity of the picture of molecular levels found by means of the interpolation method is evident from the fact that on the basis solely of these data it is impossible to assign (with complete justification) the term $^2\Pi$ to the ground state of the CH molecule. Here, the chief difficulty is connected with the lack of a combination between the doublet and quadruplet systems (which is due to the lightness of the CH molecule); this does not permit localising the quadruplet levels CH relative to the doublet levels (see footnote on p. 457).

Another semi-empirical method of finding the pattern of molecular terms was developed by Mulliken and is similar to the method employed by Bohr in the study of atomic terms. The essence of this method as applied to a molecule is as follows. To bare nuclei, which are conceived of as being fixed at a definite and constant distance from each other, we successively add electrons and determine the configuration of the systems that emerge; we are guided by the Pauli principle and by data on electron configurations that are known from atomic terms. In this way, the nature of the molecular terms is obtained as a consequence of the configuration of electrons. Mathematically, this method is a method of molecular orbits (see p. 310 et seq.).

The distribution of electrons (due to the Pauli principle) into definite subgroups (like atomic electrons) gives rise to a certain similarity in the properties of the atoms and molecules. This similarity also plays a significant role in an experimental determination of the relative arrangement of molecular terms. It is particularly striking when we compare a molecule with an atom having the same total number of electrons (*isoelectronic* systems) or the same number of outer electrons (*isosteric* systems), for example, the atoms C, N, O, F, and Ne and hydrides isoelectronic to them, that display a remarkable similarity of chemical and other properties. In particular, this similarity finds expression in the *law of displacement of hydrides* established by Grimm. Here, the hydride of a given element that has lost one atom of hydrogen acquires the properties of the hydride of the element that precedes it in the Periodic Table and contains the same number of atoms of hydrogen as the first hydride had originally. Table 34 is an illustration of this law.

Table 34 gives the chemical properties (valence) of the particles under consideration.

Table 34

Law of displacement of hydrides

Number of H atoms \ Group	IV	V	VI	VII	0	I
0	C	N	O	F	Ne	Na^+
1	—	CH	NH	OH	FH	NeH^+
2	—	—	CH_2	NH_2	OH_2	FH_2^+
3	—	—	—	CH_3	NH_3	OH_3^+
4	—	—	—	—	CH_4	NH_4^+
—	4	3	2	1	0	—1
	Valence with respect to hydrogen					

The fact that the valences of the hydrides and the corresponding element in a single vertical column (group) are the same leads to a situation where each group is, to a certain extent, a group of chemical analogues. This may be seen from a comparison of such compounds as $N\equiv N$ and $HC\equiv CH$, NCl_3 and $HCCl_3$, $O=O$ and $H_2C=CH_2$, H_2O and H_2NH, F_2 and $(OH)_2$, H_2N-NH_2 and H_3C-CH_3, etc. In the same way the saturation of molecules HF, H_2O, NH_3, and CH_4 imparts to them the properties of Ne analogues.

The law of displacement also holds with respect to the greater part of the other properties of hydrides. For instance, the optical properties of the molecules and atoms in each vertical column of Table 34 are also close as regards the character and arrangement of terms. For example, comparing the distribution of electrons in the ground states of the HF molecule and the Ne atom

$$\begin{array}{llllll} \mathrm{HF} & 1s\sigma^2 & 2s\sigma^2 & 2p\sigma^2 & 2p\pi^4 & {}^1\Sigma \\ \mathrm{Ne} & 1s^2 & 2s^2 & & 2p^6 & {}^1S, \end{array}$$

we see that in both cases the electronic structures consist of *closed* subgroups, and this leads to the terms ${}^1\Sigma$ and, respectively, ${}^1S$. Another illustration is the OH molecule and the F atom: similar distribution of the electrons in the electron shells (in particular, the presence of an open subgroup with one electron lacking) here, too, leads to identical terms of the ground state,

OH	$1s\sigma^2$	$2s\sigma^2$	$2p\sigma^2$	$2p\pi^2$	$^2\Pi_i$
F	$1s^2$	$2s^2$		$2p^5$	^2P_i.

We may add that both terms form irregular doublets $^2\Pi_i$ and ^2P_i (see p. 221).

The similarity in structures of the electronic shells of atoms and corresponding molecules is frequently manifested not only in the identity of their normal terms but also in the same relative arrangement of a number of other terms. To illustrate this property of electron shells, we compare the terms of the CO molecule and the Mg atom and their ions in Fig. 76. The similarity in the arrangement pattern of CO and Mg terms is perfectly obvious. The reason for this lies in the same number of outer electrons (2) in the CO molecule and the Mg atom. The result is a certain similarity also in their chemical properties (cf. MgO and CO_2, $MgCl_2$ and $COCl_2$, etc.). One should also note the difference in the arrangement of terms of an isosteric atom and molecule, primarily due to the fact that the molecule always has a greater number of terms as compared with the atom isosteric to it; this is because the molecular terms appear as a result of Stark splitting of atomic terms (see p. 318). Thus, in Fig. 76 we ought to add terms $^3\Sigma$ and $^3\Pi$ that are situated between the $a^3\Pi$ and $A^1\Pi$ CO terms (these terms are not shown so as not to make the scheme of terms overcomplicated).

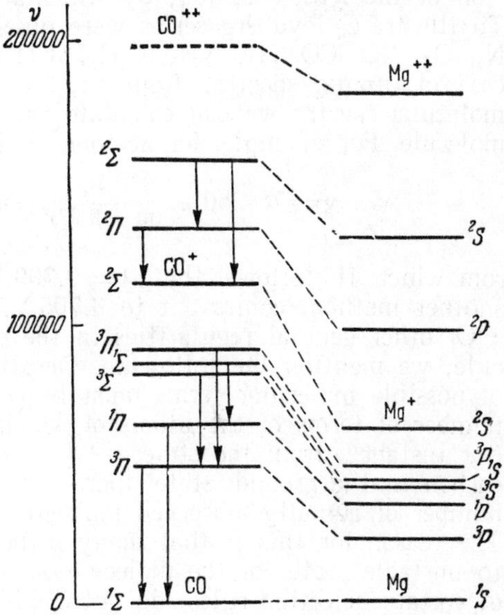

Fig. 76. Diagram of CO and Mg terms (after Sponer)

One could make a large number of correlations similar to that of CO and Mg, and also of isosteric or isoelectronic molecules. Here, we will merely state that the molecules and ions N_2^+, CN, BO, and BeF that have 13 electrons each, like the ion CO^+, have the same first three terms (which are identically arranged): $^2\Sigma$, $^2\Pi$, and $^2\Sigma$ (see Fig. 76). These correlations are valuable in that they can serve as a basis for predicting the optical, chemical, and other properties of molecules which have not yet been studied experimentally in these aspects.

This identity in the structural principle of electronic shells of atoms and molecules explains the fact that molecular terms can frequently be described by a formula similar to the Rydberg equation or the Ritz equation, by which atomic terms are represented. To illustrate, Rydberg series were observed in the spectra of H_2, N_2, O_2, NO, CO, HI, NH_3, C_2H_4, $(CH_3)_2CO$, and C_6H_6. As in the case of atomic spectra, from the limit of the Rydberg series of molecular spectra we can calculate the ionisation potential of the molecule. For example, for acetone Watanabe obtained the formula

$$\nu = 78{,}280 - \frac{R}{(m + 0.97)^2}, \quad m = 2, 3, 4, \ldots,$$

rom which it follows that $I = 9.700$ V, whereas I, obtained by another method, comes out to 9.705 V.

Of other general regularities in the electronic terms of a molecule, we mention the following. Despite the fact that the number of possible molecular terms must be considerably greater than the number of terms of the atoms of which the given molecule consists (for instance, from the states $^3P + {}^3P$ of two atoms of oxygen or carbon in the ground state there arise 18 molecular states), the number of actually observed molecular terms is ordinarily small. The reason for this is that many of the molecular terms correspond to unstable states of the molecule or to such states that, by virtue of certain selection rules, do not combine with the more accessible terms and, for this reason, escape observation.

Selection rules. As in the case of the atom, all the principal physical and chemical properties of a molecule are determined by the character of its terms. Above all, this applies to the spectroscopic properties of molecules. The structure and peculiarities of molecular spectra will be considered in detail in Secs. 36-41. Here, we shall merely touch on the selection rules necessary for an understanding of the structure of molecular spectra, which rules are obeyed by optical transitions in molecules. Without going into the proofs of the selection rules that are established, as in the case of atoms (see Sec. 28), by calculating appropriate quasi-moments, we confine ourselves to a simple enumeration of these rules. Changes in the quantum numbers Λ, Σ, and Ω obey the following selection rules:

$$\Delta\Lambda = 0, \pm 1, \tag{35.10}$$

$$\Delta\Sigma = 0, \tag{35.11}$$
$$\Delta\Omega = 0, \pm 1. \tag{35.12}$$

According to the first rule, only the following terms can combine: $\Sigma \leftrightarrow \Sigma$, $\Pi \leftrightarrow \Pi$, $\Delta \leftrightarrow \Delta$, $\Sigma \leftrightarrow \Pi$, $\Pi \leftrightarrow \Delta$; the combinations $\Sigma \leftrightarrow \Delta$, $\Pi \leftrightarrow \Phi$ are forbidden. In the same way, according to rule (35.12) the combinations $0 \leftrightarrow 0$, $1 \leftrightarrow 1$, $2 \leftrightarrow 2$, $0 \leftrightarrow 1$, $1 \leftrightarrow 2$, are possible and $0 \leftrightarrow 2$, $1 \leftrightarrow 3$ are forbidden. Rule (35.11) and the analogous rule

$$\Delta\mathfrak{S} = 0 \tag{35.13}$$

(Hund's case b) are essential for an understanding of the peculiarities of the fine structure of molecular spectra.

Further, we give the rule

$$\Delta S = 0,$$

which is identical to the rule (28.19), according to which combinations are forbidden between terms of different multiplicity (intercombinations). We saw that, for atoms, prohibition of intercombination is rigorously fulfilled only in the case of those with small nuclear charges when multiplet splitting is slight. The same occurs in the case of molecules.

Also very essential are the selection rules connected with the kind of symmetry of the molecular terms. These rules state that: *positive terms* (+) *combine only with negative* (—) *and even terms* (*g*) *combine only with odd terms* (*u*).

Other important selection rules will be dealt with in the sections that follow. Also, we shall not here examine the selection rules that refer to combinations of terms of complex molecules. The only thing that need be said is that, in part, these combinations obey the same rules as those given above (for instance, the rule $\Delta S = 0$, $g \leftrightarrow u$) and the like.

Terms of complex molecules. Up till now we have considered mainly the electron terms of diatomic molecules. Naturally, the theory of polyatomic molecules is much less developed than that of diatomic molecules. Without going into details, we note that, in complete agreement with experiment, we can deduce from theory the existence of discrete electronic levels of polyatomic molecules, similar to the levels of diatomic molecules or atomic levels.

The problem of systematics of terms of complex molecules is somewhat simplified by the fact that the principal features of the systematics of diatomic molecules are, to some extent, retained also in the case of complex molecules. Primarily, this has to do with linear molecules such as CO_2, CS_2, N_2O, C_2H_2, C_2N_2, etc. Since the molecule has an axis, the quantum numbers here Λ and Ω, generally speaking, retain their meaning, and so the systematics of terms of linear complex molecules can be constructed on the same basis as the systematics of diatomic molecules. Thus, for example, the terms of complex linear molecules are designated by the same symbols, Σ, Π, Δ, ..., as the terms of diatomic molecules.

The situation of all complex molecules possessing *axial symmetry* (the molecules NH_3, NCl_3, CH_3I, and others, for instance) is roughly the same as that of linear molecules because, due to the axis of symmetry, the numbers Λ and Ω retain their meaning, approximately.

In large measure, the electronic levels of polyatomic molecules are determined by the properties of molecular symmetry, which play the main part also in the systematics of molecules. From this viewpoint, Mulliken examined various types of complex molecules in numerous studies devoted to problems of systematics of molecular terms. Without going into details, we note that in the Mulliken classes of symmetry of the terms of complex molecules we have certain analogues of positive and negative and also even and odd terms of diatomic molecules.

It may also be added that irrespective of the form of the complex molecule, the quantum number S retains its physical meaning; S takes on the values $S = S_1 + S_2 + \ldots$, $S_1 + S_2 + \ldots - 1$, $S_1 + S_2 + \ldots - 2$, etc., where S_1, S_2, ... are the spin quantum numbers of the atoms comprising the molecule. The number S determines the *multiplicity* of terms of complex molecules as in the case of diatomic molecules and atoms.

36. Rotational Terms

Rotational terms of diatomic molecules. Rotation of a molecule is manifested in the heat capacity of gases and in the structure of molecular spectra. The so-called fine structure of these spectra indicates that this molecular motion is quantised. The same result is obtained from a solution of the wave equation that describes rotational molecular motion.

In a mechanical sense, the problem of rotation of a diatomic molecule is identical with that of the rotation of an electron and nucleus about their common centre of gravity in the hydrogen atom. For this reason, the rotational motion of a diatomic molecule (on condition of separation of variables in the wave equation) is described by the Schrödinger equation of the same type as in the case of the hydrogen atom, i.e., an equation of the form *

* Like equation (23.4), this equation is obtained directly from wave equation (23.3) by substitution of $\lambda = \hbar/\mu r\omega$ (the de Broglie relation) and $E = \mu r^2\omega^2/2$ (ω is the angular velocity of the atoms).

$$\frac{\partial^2\psi}{\partial x^2}+\frac{\partial^2\psi}{\partial y^2}+\frac{\partial^2\psi}{\partial z^2}+\frac{2\mu}{\hbar^2}E_{rot}\psi=0 \quad (36.1)$$

where μ is the reduced mass of the molecule equal to

$$\mu=\frac{m_1 m_2}{m_1+m_2}$$

(m_1 and m_2 are the masses of the atoms) and x, y, z are the relative coordinates of the nuclei ($x=x_1-x_2$, $y=y_1-y_2$, $z=z_1-z_2$) connected with the internuclear distance r by the relation

$$r^2=x^2+y^2+z^2.$$

To a first approximation, it may be considered that the distance between the nuclei remains unchanged when the molecule rotates (*rigid rotator*) and is equal to the equilibrium distance r_0. Introducing the spherical coordinates r_0, ϑ, φ, which are connected with the rectangular coordinates x, y, z by the relations

$$x=r_0\sin\vartheta\cos\varphi,\ y=r_0\sin\vartheta\sin\varphi,\ z=r_0\cos\vartheta,$$

and designating the constant $\frac{\hbar}{4\pi\mu r_0^2}=\frac{\hbar}{4\pi I_0}$ (I_0 is the moment of inertia of the molecule equal to $I_0=\mu r_0^2$) by

$$B_0=\frac{\hbar}{4\pi I_0}, \quad (36.2)$$

we transform equation (36.1) to the form

$$\frac{1}{\sin\vartheta}\frac{\partial}{\partial\vartheta}\left(\sin\vartheta\frac{\partial\psi}{\partial\vartheta}\right)+\frac{1}{\sin^2\vartheta}\frac{\partial^2\psi}{\partial\varphi^2}+\frac{E_{rot}}{\hbar B_0}\psi=0. \quad (36.3)$$

It will readily be seen that this equation is identical with equation (24.4) and may be obtained from it by substituting ψ in place of function S and $E_{rot}/\hbar B_0$ in place of the constant λ. Whence it follows that the solutions of equation (36.3) are

$$\psi=\Theta(\vartheta)\,\Phi(\varphi),$$

which, after taking into account the functional relationships of Θ and Φ, are written as follows:

$$\psi_{rot}=\psi_{JM}=(1-x^2)^{\frac{|M|}{2}}\frac{d^{|M|+J}}{dx^{|M|+J}}(x^2-1)^J e^{iM\varphi},\quad x=\cos\vartheta \quad (36.4)$$

(cf. (24.8) and (24.10)). Here, J and M are integers, and from (36.4) it follows that $M\leqslant J$.

The energy values E_{rot} that correspond to the fundamental functions (36.4) are of the form

$$E_{rot} = hB_0 J(J+1). \qquad (36.5)$$

It will be noted that this formula may be obtained without solving equation (36.3). Indeed, noting that the number J plays the part of number l, which appears via a solution of the Schrödinger equation for the H atom, and substituting $l = J$ and $\lambda = E_{rot}/\hbar B_0$ into equality (24.9), which, obviously, holds true also in the given case, we arrive directly at expression (36.5).

The number J, which takes on the values 0, 1, 2, ..., is called the *rotational quantum number* and according to (36.5) determines the rotational energy of the molecule. The number M characterises the magnitude of the projection of vector **J** on a given direction ($\vartheta = 0$), and $M = \pm J, \pm(J-1), \ldots, 0$. If this direction is specified by an external magnetic field, M is the magnetic quantum number (cf. p. 251). Since, in the absence of an external field, each rotational state of a molecule represents $2J+1$ states with the same energy, which states are characterised by appropriate values of M, the *statistical weight* of the given rotational state is equal to $2J+1$.

Designating the angular momentum vector of a rotating molecule by $\mathfrak{M}$, we can represent the energy of rotation as

$$E_{rot} = \frac{\mathfrak{M}^2}{2I_0}.$$

Comparing this expression with expression (36.5), we get, for the angular momentum,

$$\mathfrak{W} = \hbar\sqrt{J(J+1)}$$

(cf. (24.20)).

As follows from (36.5), the rotational energy of a molecule is a quantised quantity; on the basis of this expression for rotational terms

$$T_{rot} = \frac{E_{rot}}{h} = B_0 J(J+1) \qquad (36.6)$$

we get the following values:

J	0	1	2	3	4	5	...
T_{rot}	0	$2B_0$	$6B_0$	$12B_0$	$20B_0$	$30B_0$	...

The corresponding levels are shown in Fig. 77.

Expression (36.5) for the rotational energy of a molecule is obtained on the assumption that the internuclear distance remains constant (rigid rotator). In reality, however, due to a centrifugal force the molecule is somewhat stretched, and the equilibrium distance is dependent on the quantum number J. In this case, calculation of the rotational energy of a molecule (to a second approximation) leads to the expression

$$E_{rot} = hB_0 J(J+1) + hD_0 J^2 (J+1)^2 \qquad (36.7)$$

where D_0 is a constant ($D_0 \ll B_0$). Due to the smallness of D_0, the difference between the more precise expression (36.7) and expression (36.5) is not essential for not too large J.

Fine structure of rotational terms. The rotational energy of a molecule is expressed by formula (36.5) only in the relatively rare case when the total angular momentum of the molecule **J** is completely determined by the rotation of the nuclei. In the general case, however, the vector **J** is composed (in addition to the angular momentum vector of nuclei $\mathfrak{M}$) of vectors that characterise the motion of the electrons in the molecule, as may be seen from Fig. 74. Thus, for the three cases (Hund's cases a, b, and c) considered in the previous section, we have:

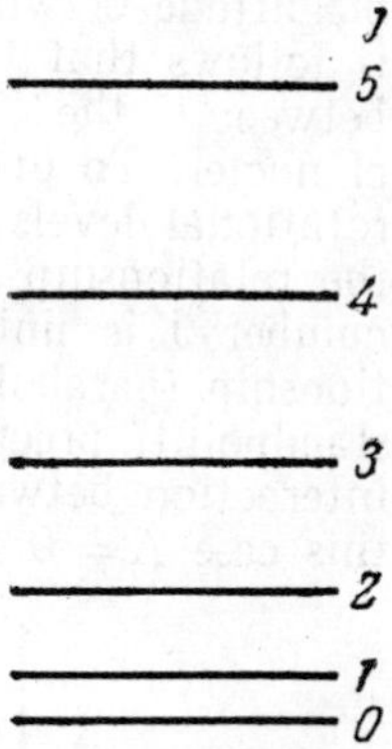

Fig. 77. Rotational terms of diatomic molecule

a) $\mathbf{J} = \mathfrak{M} + \Omega$,
b) $\mathbf{J} = \mathfrak{M} + \Lambda + \mathbf{S} = \mathbf{K} + \mathbf{S}$,
c) $\mathbf{J} = \mathfrak{M} + \Omega$.

Accordingly, for the rotational energy of nuclei

$$E_{rot} = \frac{\mathfrak{M}^2}{2I_0}, \text{ we get *:}$$

$$\left.\begin{aligned} &\text{a) } E_{rot} = hB_0 [J(J+1) - \Omega^2], \\ &\text{b) } E_{rot} = hB_0 [K(K+1) - \Lambda^2], \\ &\text{c) } E_{rot} = hB_0 [J(J+1) - \Omega^2]. \end{aligned}\right\} \qquad (36.8)$$

We note that in the case of $\Lambda = 0$ and $S = 0$, i.e., in the case of $^1\Sigma$-terms (and also 0-terms) all three expressions for E_{rot} pass into (36.5).

From equality (36.8) there follows the following important limitation for the quantum numbers J and K, namely, due to $E_{rot} \geqslant 0$, the conditions $J \geqslant \Omega$ and $K \geqslant \Lambda$ must be fulfilled. And so the values $J = 0$ (in the case of integral J) and $K = 0$ are possible only when $\Omega = 0$ and, consequently, when $\Lambda = 0$. But

* The squares of the vectors **J** and **K** are equal to $\hbar^2 J(J+1)$ and $\hbar^2 K(K+1)$, respectively; whereas the squares of Ω and Λ, which are projections of vectors **L** + **S** and **L** on the axis of the molecule, are equal to $\hbar^2\Omega^2$ and $\hbar^2\Lambda^2$.

when $\Omega > 0$, $\Lambda > 0$, the minimum values of J and K are determined by the values of Ω and Λ (for example, for term $^1\Delta K_{min} = 2$); here, the numbering of rotational terms must begin with these minimum values of J and K.

Now let us turn directly to the problem of the *fine structure* of rotational terms. Experiment shows that in most cases the rotational terms exhibit a peculiar splitting (fine structure), the magnitude of which increases with J (or K). From this fact alone it follows that this splitting must be connected with interaction between the motion of electrons and the rotation of nuclei. To prove this we give the following facts. Splitting of rotational levels is not observed in the case of terms $^1\Sigma$, where the relationship between the rotational energy and the quantum number J is uniquely determined by formula (36.5). This relationship (parabola) is graphically shown in Fig. 78a. From this standpoint, precisely in the case of term $^1\Sigma$ there should be no interaction between electron motion and nuclear rotation, since in this case $\Lambda = 0$ and $S = 0$.

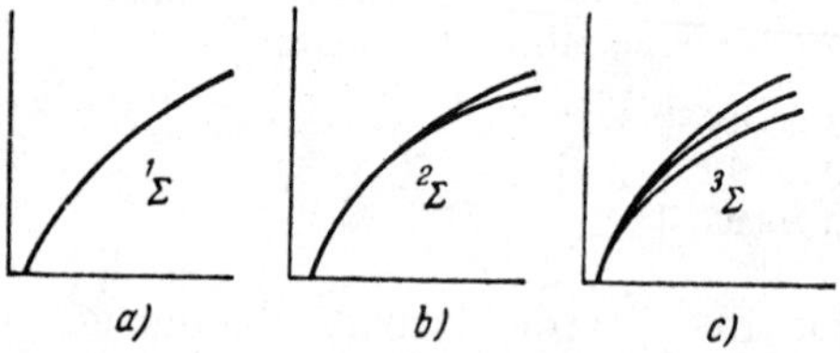

Fig. 78. Rotational energy of molecule as a function of the rotational quantum number in the case of electron terms $^1\Sigma$ (a), $^2\Sigma$ (b), $^3\Sigma$ (c)

Further, experiment shows that the rotational levels, in the case of term $^2\Sigma$, exhibit splitting into two components, the magnitude of which increases with J. In this case the dependence of E_{rot} upon J is graphically expressed by two parabolic branches (Fig. 78 b). In the case of the terms $^3\Sigma$ we have three such branches (Fig. 78c). Obviously, in the two latter cases one can only speak of interaction between the vectors **S** and $\mathfrak{M}$ (**S**, $\mathfrak{M}$), because here $\Lambda = 0$, as in the first case. We can visualise this interaction as follows. In a magnetic field imposed by rotation of nuclei, vector **S** is oriented in accord with the laws of space quantisation, i.e., the number of different orientations of **S** and, hence, the number of splitting components is equal to $2S+1$. Applying this rule to the terms $^1\Sigma$, $^2\Sigma$, and $^3\Sigma$, for which S is equal to 0, 1/2, and 1, respectively, we find, for the number of components of the fine structure of rotational levels, 1, 2, and

3 — in complete agreement with experiment. Increase in the magnitude of splitting with J is associated with increase in the magnetic interaction of vectors S and 𝔐; this increase is due to a build-up of the intramolecular magnetic field with rotation of the molecule.

Let us examine some more facts. In the case of terms that correspond to values $\Lambda > 0$, we find splitting of each rotational level into two components, irrespective of the multiplicity of the term, as is shown in Fig. 79 a, b, and c for $^1\Pi$-, $^2\Pi$- and, $^3\Pi$-terms. Here, the magnitude of splitting also increases with J (or K). The fact, observed in these cases, that the character of

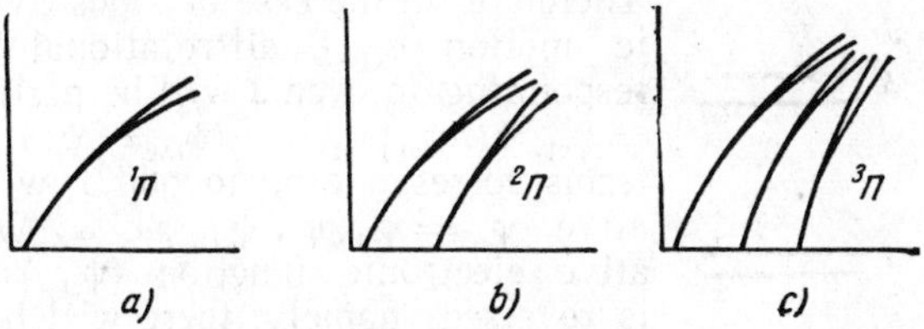

Fig. 79. Rotational energy of molecule as a function of the rotational quantum number in the case of electron terms $^1\Pi$ (a), $^2\Pi$ (b), $^3\Pi$ (c)

splitting is independent of the multiplicity of the term (i.e., of S) is an indication that the splitting here should be due to interaction between vectors Λ and 𝔐. The growth of the magnitude of splitting with rotation of the molecule (J) indicates, further, a magnetic type of interaction.

As has already been pointed out (p. 325), all terms that correspond to values $\Lambda > 0$, are doubly degenerate due to the fact that the same energy corresponds to the values $+\Lambda$ and $-\Lambda$. For this reason, when there arises an intramolecular magnetic field due to the rotation of the molecule, each such term is split into two components (+ and —) as is the case when an external magnetic field is superposed on an electric field (see p.268). This type of splitting of rotational terms (see above) is called Λ-type *doubling*.

As regards the interaction of S and 𝔐 in the case of Π-, Δ-, etc., terms, we find that here, in the case of weak rotation (small J), there is strong interaction between S and Λ, which leads to term splitting independent of rotation (multiplet structure of a term similar to the natural splitting of atomic terms). As the rotation increases the (S, 𝔐) interaction becomes stronger; this, however, leads only to closer approaching of the components of the multiplet term (Fig. 79b and c).

Properties of symmetry of rotational terms. Let us consider the extremely important properties of rotational terms associated with the *symmetry* of appropriate wave functions. If ψ_{el} denotes the electronic wave function and ψ_{rot}, the rotational wave function, their product, $\psi = \psi_{el}\psi_{rot}$, is the wave function that characterises the rotational term belonging to the corresponding electronic state of the molecule. Each of the functions ψ_{el} and ψ_{rot} may be *positive* or *negative* depending on whether the sign of the function changes with a change in sign of all coordinates of electrons and nuclei (ψ_{el}) and with change of the sign of the coordinates of the nuclei alone, i.e., when the sense of rotation is reversed (ψ_{rot}). It then turns out that the functions ψ_{rot} corresponding to even values of the number J are positive, and to odd J, negative.

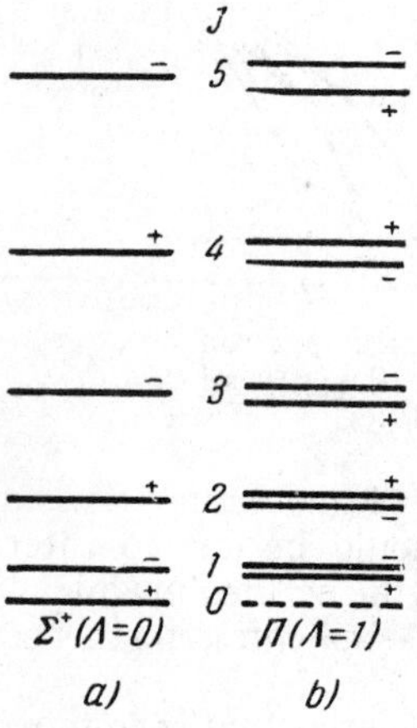

Fig. 80. Positive and negative rotational terms in the case of electron terms Σ^+ (a) and Π (b)

Therefore, in the case of a positive electronic function (ψ_{el+}), all rotational terms corresponding to even J will be positive: $\psi_+ = \psi_{el+}\psi_0, \psi_{el+}\psi_2, \ldots (\psi_{rot} = \psi_J)$, while the terms corresponding to odd J, will be negative: $\psi_- = \psi_{el+}\psi_1, \psi_{el+}\psi_3, \ldots$ With a negative electronic function (ψ_{el-}), the case is reversed, namely: there will be negative rotational terms for even J: $\psi_- = \psi_{el-}\psi_0, \psi_{el-}\psi_2, \ldots$, and positive for odd J: $\psi_+ = \psi_{el-}\psi_1, \psi_{el-}\psi_3, \ldots$ Thus, in the case of Σ-terms, the corresponding rotational terms will alternately be positive (+) and negative (—) as is shown in Fig. 80a for the term Σ^+.

In the case of Π-, Δ-, etc., terms, one of the components of Λ-type doubling of each rotational term will be positive and the other, negative (Fig. 80 b).

Unlike molecules with different nuclei, in the case of molecules with *identical* nuclei, a change in sign of the coordinates of the nuclei alone (transposition of nuclei) is possible in addition to a change in sign of the coordinates of electrons and nuclei, which changes lead to positive and negative electronic wave functions (ψ_{el+} and ψ_{el-}) and, accordingly to "+" and "—" electronic terms. As has been pointed out above (p. 326), this leads to even (g) and odd (u) electronic terms of a molecule. If the molecule is in rotation, we distinguish *symmetric* (s) and *antisymmetric* (a) rotational terms, the symmetric being all positive and even or all negative and odd terms, while the antisymmetric are all positive and odd or negative and even terms. Thus, rotational terms that correspond to this electronic term become symmetric (s) and antisymmetric (a) in alternation:

$$\psi_{el+g}\psi_{0,2}, \ \ldots, \ \psi_{el-u}, \ \psi_{0,2}, \ \ldots, \ \psi_{el+u}\psi_{1,3}, \ \ldots, \ \psi_{el-g}\psi_{1,3}, \ \ldots \longrightarrow s,$$
$$\psi_{el+g}\psi_{1,3}, \ \ldots, \ \psi_{el-u}\psi_{1,3}, \ \ldots, \ \psi_{el+u}\psi_{0,2}, \ \ldots, \ \psi_{el-g}\psi_{0,2}, \ \ldots \longrightarrow a.$$

The components of Λ-type doubling Π-, Δ-, etc., terms have different symmetry (s and a). To illustrate the properties of symmetry of rotational terms, Fig. 81 gives level-diagrams of the Σ^+-term for cases when the positive terms (Fig. 81 a) and the negative terms (Fig. 81 b) are symmetric.

Selection rules. A rotational quantum number obeys definite selection rules, like the quantum numbers that determine the energy states of atoms. Since J determines the wave function of the same type as the orbital quantum number l, the selection rules for both numbers must be the same. Thus, for J we have

$$\Delta J = \pm 1 \qquad (36.9)$$

(cf. $\Delta l = \pm 1$, p. 237).

However, the selection rule (36.9) holds only in the case of $\Lambda = 0$. For $\Lambda \neq 0$,

$$\Delta J = 0, \ \pm 1. \qquad (36.10)$$

We also note that in the case of spectra of so-called Raman scattering of light (Sec. 39), the quantum number J can also change by ± 2.

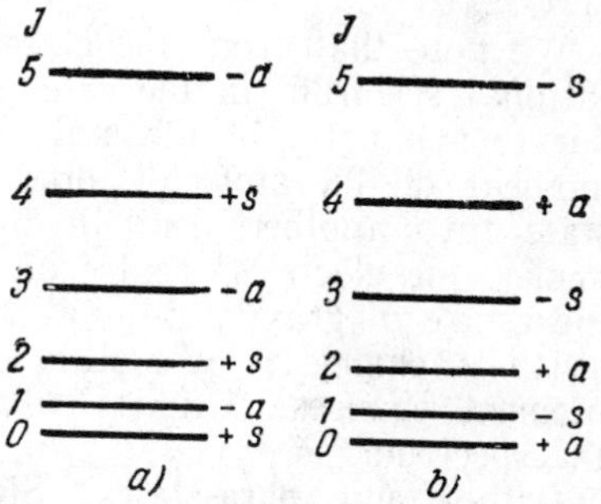

Fig. 81. Properties of symmetry of rotational terms of the same nuclei in the case of Σ-states ($\Lambda = 0$)

Another important selection rule is the rule for combining positive and negative rotational terms, according to which transitions with radiation or absorption of light can occur only between positive and negative terms, i.e., only the following radiative transitions are possible:

$$+ \leftrightarrow - \text{ and } - \leftrightarrow + \qquad (36.11)$$

Fig. 81a shows that this rule does not contradict rule $\Delta J = \pm 1$ (36.9). Moreover, from Fig. 81b it follows that to each transition $J+1 \longrightarrow J$ in the rotational spectrum (see Sec. 38) of a diatomic molecule there will correspond not four components but two ($+ \longrightarrow -$ and $- \longrightarrow +$).

For the Raman spectra we have the reverse selection rule, namely, $+ \leftrightarrow +$ and $- \leftrightarrow -$, while combinations between positive and negative terms are forbidden. This is also in agreement with the selection rule $\Delta J = 0, \ \pm 2$ for Raman scattering of light (see p. 381).

In the case of molecules with the same nuclei, on the basis of the selection rule $+ \leftrightarrow -$ (36.11) and $g \leftrightarrow u$ (see p. 337) we also have the following selection rule: *only symmetric-symmetric and antisymmetric-antisymmetric combinations of terms are possible:*

$$s \leftrightarrow s \text{ and } a \leftrightarrow a. \qquad (36.12)$$

Following directly from the selection rule (36.12) in accordance with the fact that the rotational terms of a molecule are alternately symmetric and antisymmetric is the impossibility of combination of rotational terms of a molecule with identical nuclei. Consequently, such molecules as H^1H^1, $O^{16}O^{16}$, $Cl^{35}Cl^{35}$, etc., cannot exhibit a rotational spectrum, in contrast to the molecules HD, $O^{16}O^{18}$, $Cl^{35}Cl^{37}$, etc.

We note that from the classical viewpoint the absence of a rotational spectrum in the case of molecules with identical nuclei is due to symmetry of the molecule, as a result of which the dipole moment of the molecule does not change when passing from one state into another. But in the case of molecules with different nuclei, the electrical centre of the molecule does not coincide with the centre of gravity so that when the state of the molecule changes (with a change in the state of rotation, for example) its dipole moment changes. This is what leads to the nonzero intensity of the spectrum.

Ortho- and para-states. Since the combinations $s \leftrightarrow a$ and $\Delta J > 1$ are forbidden, the rotational terms of a molecule having identical nuclei are divided into two groups of terms that do not combine (s and a). Taking into account *nuclear spin*, we must assign to each group of terms *different statistical weights*. Indeed, for a complete characterisation of the rotational term of a molecule it is necessary that we take into account also the wave function ψ_1 that corresponds to nuclear spin (spin function). Allowing for separation of variables in the wave equation, we can write the total wave function of a molecule in the form $\Psi_s\psi_1$ or $\Psi_a\psi_1$, where Ψ_s and Ψ_a are wave functions that correspond to its symmetric and antisymmetric states.

Having in view a molecule whose nuclei have spin 1/2 (such, for example, is the hydrogen molecule H_2) and introducing, for a description of the state of a nucleus corresponding to a positive value of the projection of spin (+1/2), the spin function α, and for a state with negative projection of spin (−1/2), the spin function β, we will have the following four functions (cf. p. 201) representing the general spin factor of the total wave function:

$$\psi_0 = \alpha(1)\beta(2) - \alpha(2)\beta(1),$$
$$\psi_1 = \alpha(1)\beta(2) + \alpha(2)\beta(1),$$

$$\psi_1 = \alpha(1)\alpha(2),$$
$$\psi_1 = \beta(1)\beta(2).$$

Obviously, the first of these functions is antisymmetric (since it reverses its sign upon transposition of nuclei) and the other three (ψ_1) are symmetric. Consequently, the total wave function will be symmetric for combinations $\Psi_s\psi_1$ and $\Psi_a\psi_0$, and antisymmetric for combinations $\Psi_s\psi_0$ and $\Psi_a\psi_1$. However, since only such states of the molecule are possible that correspond to antisymmetric total wave functions, the first two combinations are not realised and only the combinations $\Psi_s\psi_0$ and $\Psi_a\psi_1$ remain. Here, combination $\Psi_s\psi_0$ corresponds to rotational terms of a molecule with even J (in the case of H_2) that are symmetric terms, while combination $\Psi_a\psi_1$ corresponds to terms with odd J (antisymmetric terms). And since to function ψ_0 there corresponds the value of total nuclear spin 0 of the molecule and, hence, the statistical weight of the appropriate state 1, while to function ψ_1 there corresponds spin 1 and statistical weight 3, the rotational terms will alternately have a statistical weight of unity and three.

Terms with greater statistical weight (in the case at hand they are the antisymmetric terms) are called *ortho-terms*, while the terms with lower statistical weight (the symmetric terms of the H_2 molecule) are called *para-terms*. This is the origin of the ortho- and para-hydrogen modifications that differ in a number of physical properties. For instance, due to the difference in statistical weights, there is a difference in the heat capacity of the two modifications (it is particularly great at low temperatures). This was how the modifications were discovered.

We also point out the manifestation of ortho- and para-modifications of hydrogen in a peculiar alternation of line intensity in its spectrum: due to a difference in the statistical weights of the symmetric and antisymmetric rotational states, the lines of ortho-hydrogen are three times more intense than the lines of para-hydrogen. We shall return, in Sec. 40, to the problem of variable intensities of spectral lines due to the presence of ortho- and para-terms.

Rotational terms of complex molecules. In the general case, a polyatomic molecule has three moments of inertia that correspond to its three principal axes* and are expressed by the formula

---

* The principal axes are the three mutually perpendicular axes that pass through the same point (usually the centre of gravity); relative to these axes the moments of inertia of the molecule have maximum or minimum values. Plotting on the principal axes quantities that are reciprocals of the square roots of these moments of inertia, we obtain the *ellipsoid of inertia* of the molecule.

$$I_i = \sum_k m_k r_k^2 \tag{36.13}$$

where m_k is the mass of the *k*th atom and r_k is its distance from the respective axis. These moments of inertia are called *principal moments of inertia*. In the case of symmetric molecules, the principal axes are always *axes of symmetry*, while the *plane of symmetry* is always perpendicular to one of the principal axes.

As in the case of the diatomic molecule, the principal moments of inertia of polyatomic molecules are the main parameters that determine their rotational energy. Depending on the geometrical structure of the molecule, we obtain different expressions for the rotational energy. The simplest case is that of *linear* polyatomic molecules. Here, as for diatomic molecules, when the projection of the momentum of the electrons on the axis of the molecule is zero ($\Lambda = 0$, Σ-state), the moment of inertia relative to this axis may be considered equal to zero, and the expression for the rotational energy has the form of (36.5). We note that the ground states of all known linear polyatomic molecules are Σ-states. For states having $\Lambda \neq 0$, the rotational energy is expressed by formula (36.8) a) or b). In the case of a linear molecule, the quantities r_k in the expression of the moment of inertia (36.13) that enters into the rotational constant (36.2) are distances of the atoms from the centre of gravity of the molecule.

Equation (36.5) also expresses the rotational energy of those symmetric molecules, all three moments of inertia of which are equal. Such, for example, are the molecules CH_4, CCl_4, P_4, SF_6, etc. It is to be noted, however, that by virtue of certain specific properties of symmetry the statistical weight of the rotational levels of these molecules (called *spherical top molecules*) is not given by the formula $2J + 1$, which is valid in the case of diatomic and linear polyatomic molecules, but has a more involved expression that differs for different types of symmetry of rotational levels.

Next in structural complexity of rotational levels of polyatomic molecules is the *symmetric top molecule*. Molecules that belong to this type of symmetry have two different moments of inertia (the moments of inertia relative to the principal axes, normal to the axis of the molecule, coincide). The symmetric-top type includes, among others, all molecules with axes of symmetry of an order above two, for instance, BCl_3 (planar molecule), NH_3, PCl_3 (pyramidal molecules), CH_3Cl, and others. The rotational energy of these molecules is expressed by the formula

$$E_{rot} = hBJ(J+1) + h(A - B)K^2. \tag{36.14}$$

Here, A and B are the rotational constants, equal to

$$A=\frac{\hbar}{4\pi I_A} \quad \text{and} \quad B=\frac{\hbar}{4\pi I_B}, \tag{36.15}$$

I_A is the moment of inertia relative to the axis of the molecule, I_B is the moment of inertia relative to the axes that are perpendicular to the axis of the molecule, J and K are the rotational quantum numbers, and

$$J=K,\ K+1,\ K+2,\ \ldots, \tag{36.16}$$
$$K=0,\ 1,\ 2,\ 3,\ \ldots \tag{36.17}$$

Finally, in the most general case we have molecules with *three* noncoinciding moments of inertia. Such molecules belong to the *asymmetric-top* type. In the case of the asymmetric top, solution of the wave equation leads to polynomials to the power $2J+1$ (J is the rotational quantum number), from which it is possible to calculate the rotational energy of the molecule as a function of its three moments of inertia. Thus, the rotational energy of an asymmetric top molecule may be represented by a definite formula only in the case of small J. To each value of J there correspond $2J+1$ values of rotational energy, hence, $2J+1$ rotational levels. It is common to designate these levels by the symbols J_τ, where $\tau=J,\ J-1,\ \ldots\ 0,\ \ldots,\ -J+1, -J$. The lowest level is J_{-J}, the highest, $-J_J$.

In addition to the rotation of a molecule as a whole, in certain cases the rotation of one part of the molecule relative to another is possible. Such *internal rotation* is evident from the existence of what is known as *rotational isomerism* of molecules with simple bonding, and also from a number of other physico-chemical properties of molecules with simple bonds (σ-bonds). Theoretical and experimental investigations into internal rotation show that it is practically never completely free: due to a certain potential barrier that separates different equilibrium positions of the rotating parts of the molecule and is conditioned by the fact that, ordinarily, the axis of symmetry is an axis of a finite (mostly, third) order, internal rotation is always, to one degree or another, hindered (restricted).

Calculations of the energy of internal rotation show that it is quantised like the energy of rotation of the molecule as a whole. Thus, in the simplest case of a symmetric or nearly symmetric top molecule (such, for example, is the molecule CH_3OH) and on the assumption of free rotation, we have the following expression for the energy of internal rotation:

$$E_{\text{int rot}}=h\,\frac{A_1A_2}{A}\left(k_1-k\,\frac{A}{A_1}\right)^2 \tag{36.18}$$

where k and k_1 are quantum numbers that assume the following values:

$$k = \pm K \text{ and } k_1 = 0, \ \pm 1, \ \pm 2, \ \ldots,$$

and A, A_1, and A_2 are rotational constants equal to

$$A = \frac{\hbar}{4\pi I_A}, \quad A_1 = \frac{\hbar}{4\pi I_A^{(1)}} \text{ and } A_2 = \frac{\hbar}{4\pi I_A^{(2)}}. \tag{36.19}$$

Here, I_A is the moment of inertia of the molecule relative to its axis, while $I_A^{(1)}$ and $I_A^{(2)}$ are moments of inertia of parts of the molecule rotating one relative to the other about the same axis. Thus, the total energy of rotation of a symmetric top is expressed by the sum

$$E_{rot} = hBJ(J+1) + h(A-B)K^2 + h\frac{A_1A_2}{A}\left(k_1 - k\frac{A}{A_1}\right)^2. \tag{36.20}$$

Free rotation is one limiting case of the internal rotation of a molecule. Another limiting case is totally restricted rotation, which, essentially, is *torsional oscillations* (see below, p. 361). A theoretical investigation of internal rotation shows that as the height of the potential barrier rises above zero (free rotation) to a sufficiently large value, which increase leads to complete restriction of rotation, the levels of free rotation (36.18) gradually pass into levels of torsional oscillations. Thus, energy levels that correspond to internal rotation, which, as has already been pointed out, is always, to one degree or another, hindered (restricted), are levels that are intermediate between those of free rotation and those of torsional oscillations.

37. Vibrational Terms

Natural vibration frequencies of molecules. In the least-energy state, the atoms of a molecule occupy certain equilibrium positions characterised by specific internuclear distances, which are called *equilibrium* distances (r_e and r_0). If this equilibrium is upset the atoms perform vibrational motion. If the amplitude of the atomic vibrations a is small (small vibrations), variation of interatomic distances with time obeys the law

$$r - r_e = a \sin 2\pi\omega t \tag{37.1}$$

(harmonic oscillations), where ω is the vibrational frequency of the molecule. If for the sake of simplicity we take a diatomic molecule and expand its potential energy in a power series of the small quantity $r - r_e$:

$$U = U_0 + \left(\frac{\partial U}{\partial r}\right)_{r=r_e}(r - r_e) + \frac{1}{2}\left(\frac{\partial^2 U}{\partial r^2}\right)_{r=r_e}(r - r_e)^2 + \ldots, \quad (37.2)$$

in the case of small vibrations we can confine ourselves to the first three terms of the expansion. Since $\left(\frac{\partial U}{\partial r}\right)_{r=r_e} = 0$ (the condition of equilibrium), the second term in this expression disappears and the interaction force of the atoms becomes

$$f = -\frac{\partial U}{\partial r} = -\left(\frac{\partial^2 U}{\partial r^2}\right)_{r=r_e}(r - r_e) = -k(r - r_e) \quad (37.3)$$

(quasi-elastic force). Substituting (37.3) into the equation of motion

$$\mu \frac{d^2(r - r_e)}{dt^2} = f,$$

it will readily be seen that the solution of this equation can be represented as (37.1). From this solution we get the following expression for the vibrational frequency:

$$\omega = \frac{1}{2\pi}\sqrt{\frac{k}{\mu}}. \quad (37.4)$$

The quantity k is called the quasi-elastic (force) constant.

The mechanical problem of small vibrations can be solved in the case of a polyatomic molecule as well. From the solution of this problem it follows that in the general case a molecule consisting of N atoms has $3N - 6$ different vibrational frequencies. This number can also be obtained from the following reasoning. An N-atomic molecule has 3N degrees of freedom, of which 3 are degrees of freedom of translational motion of the molecule as a whole and 3 are rotational degrees of freedom. Deducting these six degrees of freedom, we get $3N - 6$ vibrational degrees of freedom and, hence, in the general case, $3N - 6$ different frequencies. In the case of a linear molecule with only two rotational degrees of freedom, the number of vibrational frequencies is $3N - 5$. Further, in the case of symmetric molecules, such as CO_2, CH_4, CCl_4, etc., certain frequencies coincide (degeneracy) and the total number of different frequencies is less than that calculated from previous equations. To take an example, in the case of CO_2, the *normal vibrations** of which are depicted in Fig. 82, these coincident frequencies are the two frequencies ω_2 that correspond to vibrations

* Normal vibrations are simple (linear) oscillatory motions representing components of the complex vibrational motion of the molecule as a whole.

of the molecule in two mutually perpendicular planes (bending vibrations). This vibration is, therefore, degenerate.

To a doubly degenerate bending vibration of a linear symmetric triatomic molecule there corresponds a simple (nondegenerate) vibration of a symmetric triatomic molecule of triangular shape, such

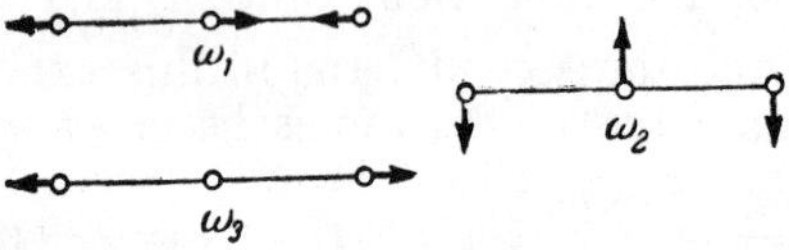

Fig. 82. Vibrations of linear triatomic molecule

as the molecule of water H_2O. Such a molecule has three rotational degrees of freedom and, hence, $3\times3-6$, or three (and not four) vibrational degrees of freedom. Three normal vibrations of the

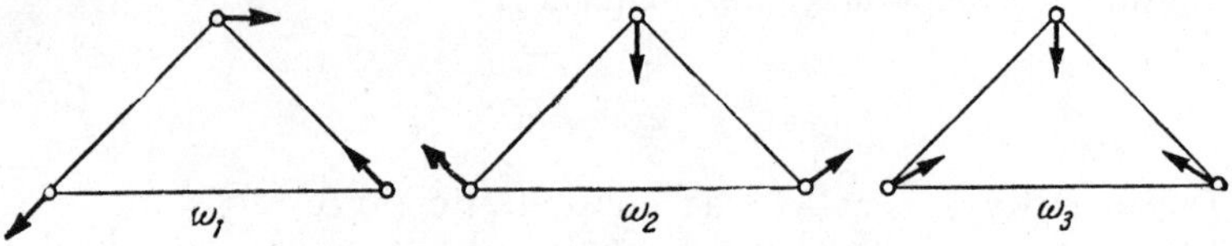

Fig. 83. Vibrations of symmetric triatomic molecule of triangular shape

molecule YXY of triangular shape are shown in Fig. 83. Of nine normal vibrations of molecule CH_4 (or, in the general case, any tetrahedral molecule of type XY_4), one is simple, one is doubly degenerate (two normal vibrations) and two are triply degenerate (six normal vibrations). And so in place of nine we have only four different frequencies.

We note that to a simple vibration there corresponds a statistical weight of 1, to a doubly degenerate vibration, 2, etc. Fig. 84 gives 12 normal vibrations of a planar molecule of type X_2Y_4 (for example, C_2H_4 or C_2D_4).

Vibrational terms of a diatomic molecule. The vibrational energy of a molecule, which is a quantised quantity, may be determined from experimental, mostly spectroscopic, data. The quantised vibrational energy is also obtained theoretically, from a solution of the wave equation describing the vibrational motion of the molecule. In the simplest case of a diatomic molecule (upon assumption of separation of variables), the wave equation for vibrations has the form

$$\frac{d^2\psi(r)}{dr^2}+\frac{2\mu}{\hbar^2}[E_{vib}-U(r)]\psi(r)=0 \qquad (37.5)$$

or

$$\frac{d^2\psi(\varrho)}{d\varrho^2}+\frac{2I_e}{\hbar^2}[E_{vib}-U(\varrho)]\psi(\varrho)=0 \qquad (37.5a)$$

where

$$\varrho=\frac{r-r_e}{r_e}$$

represents the relative change in interatomic distance and I_e is the moment of inertia of the molecule. We shall call function

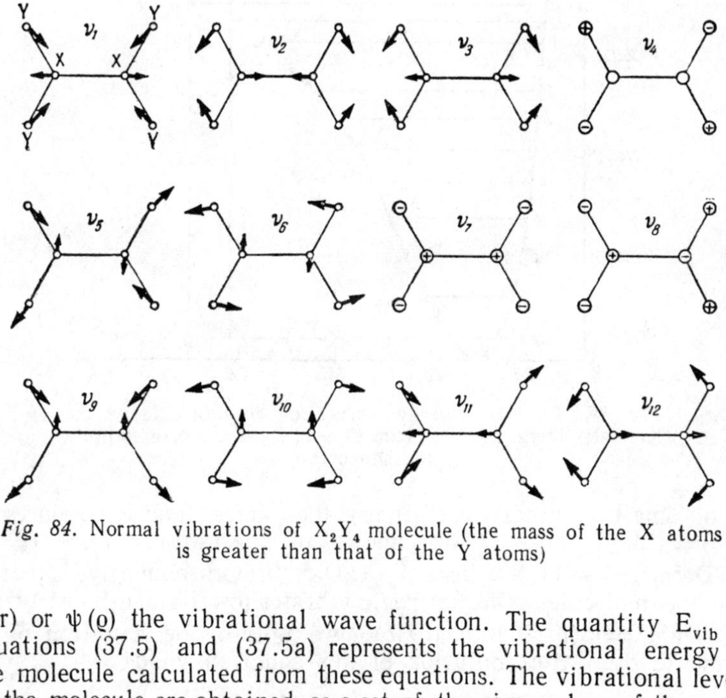

Fig. 84. Normal vibrations of X_2Y_4 molecule (the mass of the X atoms is greater than that of the Y atoms)

$\psi(r)$ or $\psi(\varrho)$ the vibrational wave function. The quantity E_{vib} in equations (37.5) and (37.5a) represents the vibrational energy of the molecule calculated from these equations. The vibrational levels of the molecule are obtained as a set of the eigenvalues of the problem of molecular vibrations.

To solve this problem we can take advantage of the following expression of potential energy $U(\varrho)$ proposed by Morse (*Morse function*):

$$U(\varrho)=D(1-e^{-a\varrho})^2. \qquad (37.6)$$

The Morse function gives a rough idea of the dependence of potential energy of a molecule on the interatomic distance, as may be seen from a correlation of the dashed potential-energy curve of the H_2 molecule (Morse function) and the solid curve calculated by means of more precise methods (Fig. 85). As is evident from Fig. 85, and also from (37.6), the difference $U(\infty)-U(0)=D$, whence it follows that parameter D is the *dissociation energy* of the molecule.

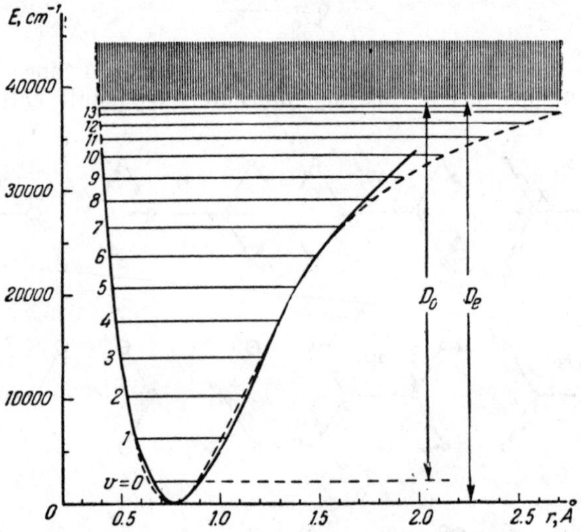

Fig. 85. Potential-energy curves of H_2 molecule by the Klein-Rydberg method (curve) and by the Morse formula (dashed curve)

For small ϱ (small vibrations) the Morse function reduces to $U(\varrho)=Da^2\varrho^2$, which is the potential of quasi-elastic force $f=-2Da^2\varrho/r_e=-kr_e\varrho$ where $k=2Da^2/r_e^2$. Consequently, in this case the molecule is an harmonic vibrator (oscillator). Substituting $U=Da^2\varrho^2=kr_e^2\varrho^2/2$ into (37.5a) we obtain the equation of an harmonic oscillator. Solution of this equation yields

$$E_{vib}=h\omega\left(v+\frac{1}{2}\right) \qquad (37.7)$$

where

$$\omega=\frac{1}{2\pi}\sqrt{\frac{k}{\mu}}=\frac{a}{2\pi}\sqrt{\frac{2D}{I_e}} \qquad (37.8)$$

is the natural frequency of the oscillator. The number v, which takes on the values 0, 1, 2, ..., is called the *vibrational quantum number*.

From equation (37.7) it follows that the vibrational terms of an harmonic oscillator

$$T_{vib}=\omega\left(v+\frac{1}{2}\right) \tag{37.9}$$

are a system of equidistant terms, the difference of two adjacent terms being equal to the frequency ω (see Fig. 86, dashed lines).

Further, according to (37.7) the minimum value of vibrational energy of a diatomic molecule is equal to $E_{vib}(0)=h\omega/2$. $E_{vib}(0)$ is called the *zero vibrational energy*.

In Fig. 86, the dashed curve is the parabolic potential of an harmonic oscillator. This curve is close to the Morse curve only at small values of ϱ. It therefore follows that equation (37.7) for the vibrational energy of a molecule is roughly correct only for small ϱ. A more precise expression for the vibrational energy of a diatomic molecule is obtained by substituting the Morse function (37.6) into the wave equation. In this case the oscillations are no longer harmonic (*anharmonic oscillator*) and from a solution of the wave equation we get the following expression for the vibrational terms:

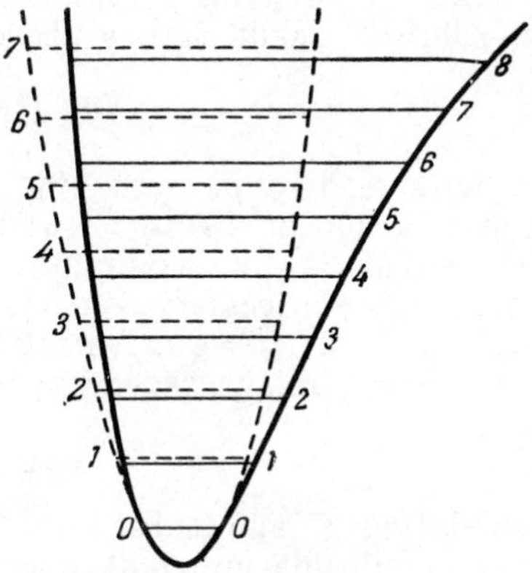

Fig. 86. Vibrational terms of a diatomic molecule; the dashed lines are the harmonic oscillator, the solid lines, the anharmonic oscillator (after Morse)

$$T_{vib}=\omega\left(v+\frac{1}{2}\right)-x\omega\left(v+\frac{1}{2}\right)^2. \tag{37.10}$$

In this expression, the constant x, called the *anharmonicity constant*, is

$$x=\frac{h\omega}{4D}. \tag{37.11}$$

The main steps in the solution of equation (37.5) are as follows. By means of the Morse function, this equation transforms as ($y=e^{-a\varrho}$)

$$\frac{d^2\psi}{dy^2}+\frac{1}{y}\frac{d\psi}{dy}+\frac{2I_e}{a^2\hbar^2}\left(\frac{E_{vib}-D}{y^2}+\frac{2D}{y}-D\right)\psi=0.$$

We then represent function ψ in the form $\psi = f(y)/\sqrt{y}$ and, computing ψ' and ψ'', we transform the equation obtained to

$$f'' + \lambda^2\left(\frac{Q}{y^2} + \frac{2D}{a^2 y} - \frac{D}{a^2}\right) f = 0$$

where

$$\lambda^2 = \frac{2I_e}{\hbar^2} \text{ and } Q = \frac{E_{vib} - D}{a^2} + \frac{1}{4\lambda^2}.$$

Let us first find the asymptotic solution of the latter equation. This solution holds for any high value of y. Since, in this case, we can ignore terms containing y in the denominator, the sought-for solution should satisfy the differential equation

$$f'' - D\frac{\lambda^2}{a^2} f = 0.$$

As will readily be seen, the solution to this equation has the form $f_{as} = e^{\beta y}$ or $f_{as} = e^{-\beta y}$ where $\beta^2 = (\lambda^2/a^2) D$. Obviously, only the second of the asymptotic solutions ($f \to 0$ when $y \to \infty$) satisfies the necessary requirement of finiteness of function f throughout the range of variation of the variable y (cf. p. 178).

Appealing to the general solution of the equation for function f, we get

$$f = C(y) e^{-\beta y}.$$

Calculating f'' and substituting f and f'' into this equation, we get the following differential equation for $C(y)$:

$$C'' - 2\beta C' + \lambda^2\left(\frac{Q}{y^2} + \frac{2D}{a^2 y}\right) C = 0.$$

As we can readily see by means of simple substitution, the solution of the latter equation has the form

$$C = \sum_k b_k y^{\nu+k}.$$

Substituting this polynomial into our differential equation, we get

$$\sum b_k (\nu + k)(\nu + k - 1) y^{\nu+k-2} - 2\beta \sum b_k (\nu + k) y^{\nu+k-1} + \\ + 2\beta^2 \sum b_k y^{\nu+k-1} + \lambda^2 Q \sum b_k y^{\nu+k-2} = 0,$$

whence, by equating the coefficients of $y^{\nu+k-1}$, we find the following recurrent equation for the coefficients of the polynomial:

$$[(\nu + k + 1)(\nu + k) + \lambda^2 Q]\, b_{k+1} = [2\beta(\nu + k) - 2\beta^2]\, b_k.$$

Again taking into account the necessary condition of finiteness of the polynomial C, we limit it by the conditions $b_0 = 0$ and $b_{v+2} = 0$. On the basis of these conditions, we obtain (from the recurrent equation) $v(v+1)=-\lambda^2 Q$ and $v+v+1=\beta$ or, eliminating v,

$$-\lambda^2 Q=(\beta-v)(\beta-v-1)=\beta^2-2\beta\left(v+\frac{1}{2}\right)+v(v+1).$$

Substituting, into the latter equality, the value of Q and noting that $\beta^2=(\lambda^2/a^2)D$, we find

$$E_{vib}=2\beta\frac{a^2}{\lambda^2}\left(v+\frac{1}{2}\right)-\frac{a^2}{\lambda^2}\left(v+\frac{1}{2}\right)^2,$$

whence, due to (37.8) and (37.11), we get

$$E_{vib}=h\omega\left(v+\frac{1}{2}\right)-h\omega x\left(v+\frac{1}{2}\right)^2$$

and, hence, arrive at (37.10).

As can be seen from expression (37.10), the terms of the anharmonic oscillator are no longer equidistant; the distance between two adjacent terms is equal to

$$\Delta T_{vib}=\omega-2x\omega(v+1), \tag{37.12}$$

i.e., it diminishes with increasing quantum number v. The terms of the anharmonic oscillator are shown in Fig. 86 (solid lines).

As will be seen from equations (37.10) and (37.12), the terms of the anharmonic oscillator converge to a certain limit which is determined by the condition:

$$\Delta T_{vib}=\omega[1-2_x(v_{max}+1)]=0$$

or

$$v_{max}=\frac{1}{2x}-1.$$

Substituting this value of v_{max} into formula (37.10) and using (37.11), we obtain the following expression for the maximum vibrational energy of a diatomic molecule:

$$hT_{max}=\frac{h\omega}{4x}(1-x^2)=D(1-x^2),$$

which, since $x^2\ll 1$ (see below), turns into the expression

$$hT_{max}=\frac{h\omega}{4x}=D. \tag{37.13}$$

From this expression it follows that the vibrational energy of a diatomic molecule cannot exceed its energy of dissociation. It may be added that the thermal dissociation of molecules is connected with excitation of vibrations which, upon attainment of v_{max} (convergence limit of vibrational terms), leads to decomposition of the molecule.

The approximate nature of the Morse function is evident from the fact that the actual terms of a diatomic molecule can be represented by formula (37.10) only for small v. From spectroscopic data it follows that the best approximation is the formula

$$T_{vib}=\omega\left(v+\frac{1}{2}\right)-x\omega\left(v+\frac{1}{2}\right)^2+y\omega\left(v+\frac{1}{2}\right)^3+\ldots \quad (37.14)$$

The quantities x, y, etc., in this formula ordinarily satisfy the relation $1 \gg x^2 \gg y^2 \gg \ldots$

Fig. 87, for states with $v=0, 1, 2, 3, 4$, and 10, gives the eigenfunctions that represent solutions of the wave equation (37.5a) in the case of an harmonic oscillator (dashed line), and also functions $\psi\psi^*$, which determine the probability of finding atoms at a distance r from one another (solid curves). In the simplest case of a zero vibrational state, function $\psi_0\psi_0^*$ is expressed by the following formula (with an accuracy to the normalising factor):

$$\psi_0\psi_0^*=\psi_0^2=e^{-\alpha\rho^2},$$

that is to say, it is a Gauss error function. As can be seen from Fig. 87, in the states with $v>0$, the function $\psi\psi^*$ has two main maxima; these maxima correspond to turning points, i.e., points at which the relative velocity of motion of the atoms in a classical oscillator reverses sign when passing through zero, and signify that the appropriate interatomic distances are most frequently realised.

Vibrational terms of polyatomic molecules. For vibrational terms of a triatomic molecule, various authors, by solution of the appropriate wave equation, obtained an expression of the form

$$\begin{aligned}T(v_1, v_2, v_3)=&\omega_1\left(v_1+\frac{1}{2}\right)+\omega_2\left(v_2+\frac{1}{2}\right)+\omega_3\left(v_3+\frac{1}{2}\right)+\\&+x_{11}\left(v_1+\frac{1}{2}\right)^2+x_{22}\left(v_2+\frac{1}{2}\right)^2+x_{33}\left(v_3+\frac{1}{2}\right)^2+\\&+x_{12}\left(v_1+\frac{1}{2}\right)\left(v_2+\frac{1}{2}\right)+x_{13}\left(v_1+\frac{1}{2}\right)\left(v_3+\frac{1}{2}\right)+\\&+x_{23}\left(v_2+\frac{1}{2}\right)\left(v_3+\frac{1}{2}\right)+\ldots \quad (37.15)\end{aligned}$$

Here, v_1, v_2, and v_3 are vibrational quantum numbers, ω_1, ω_2, and ω_3 are frequencies of normal vibrations and x_{ik} are constants of anharmonicity and constants of mutual coupling of vibrations: the constants x_{11}, x_{22}, and x_{33} correspond to the anharmonicity constant x of a diatomic molecule, the others characterise the mutual coupling of vibrations of the molecule. To illustrate

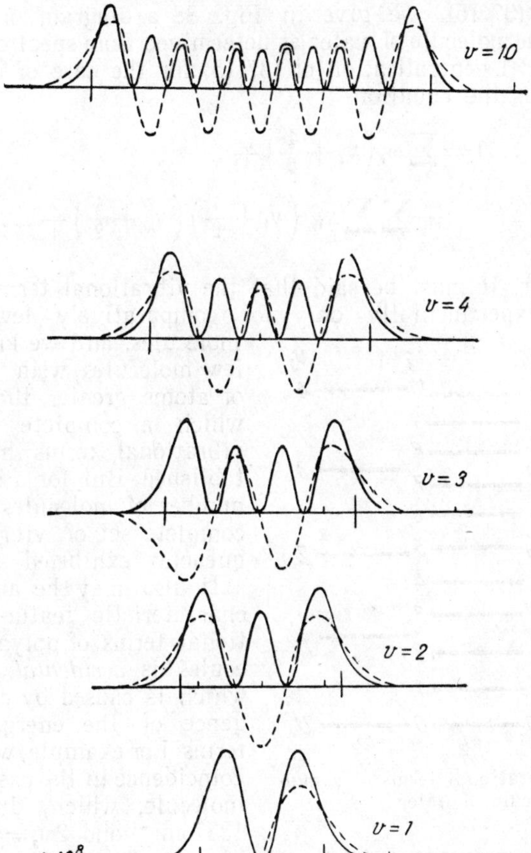

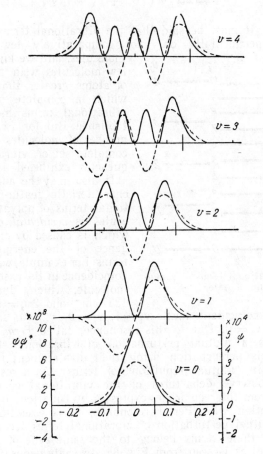

Fig. 87. Eigenfunctions (dashed lines) and probability densities (solid curves) of a harmonic oscillator for v = 0, 1, 2, 3, 4, and 10

equation (37.15), we give in Fig. 88 a diagram of vibrational terms of a molecule of water as determined from spectroscopic data.

A natural generalisation of (37.15) for the case of an N-atomic molecule is the equation

$$T(v_1, v_2, \ldots) = \sum_i \omega_i \left(v_i + \frac{1}{2}\right) + \\ + \sum_i \sum_k x_{ik} \left(v_i + \frac{1}{2}\right)\left(v_k + \frac{1}{2}\right) + \ldots . \quad (37.16)$$

However, it must be said that the vibrational terms have been studied experimentally only for comparatively few triatomic molecules, and we know of very few molecules with the number of atoms greater than three for which a complete diagram of vibrational terms has been established. But for a rather large number of molecules we have a complete set of vibrational frequencies exhibited in spectra.

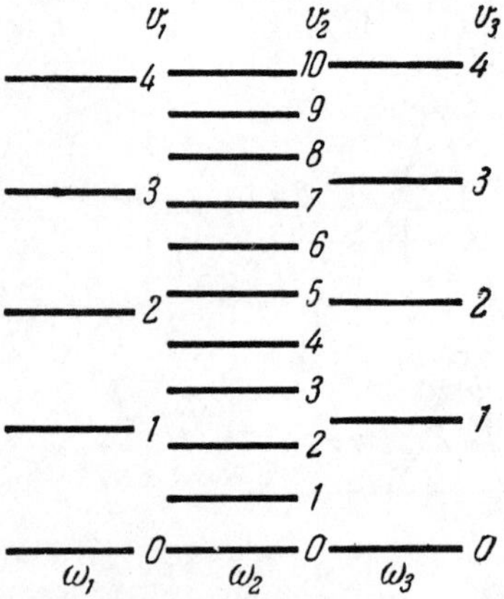

Fig. 88. Vibrational terms of a molecule of water.

It also may be added that a characteristic feature of vibrational terms of polyatomic molecules is *accidental degeneracy*, which is caused by close coincidence of the energies of two terms. For example, we have such coincidence in the case of the CO_2 molecule, which, due to $\omega_1 = 1337\ cm^{-1}$ and $2\omega_2 = 1334\ cm^{-1}$, has nearly coincident levels $v_1 = 1$, $v_2 = 0$, $v_3 = 0$, and $v_1 = 0$, $v_2 = 2$ and $v_3 = 0$. Due to this resonance, called *Fermi resonance*, there occurs a mutual perturbation of vibrational terms, the effect of this perturbation being their displacement in opposite directions (in "mutual repulsion" of terms). As a result of this shift, we observe departures of the vibrational energy of the molecules from the regularities expressed by equations like (37.15).

In connection with Fermi resonance, it is essential to point out that mutual perturbation of vibrational terms occurs only in cases when these terms belong to the same type of symmetry. For instance, as is seen from Fig. 88, two vibrations of the molecule H_2O have close frequencies ($\omega_1 = 3614\ cm^{-1}$ and $\omega_3 = 3709\ cm^{-1}$); however, by virtue of the fact that these vibrations belong to different types of symmetry, Fermi resonance is not observed here. In contradistinction to these two states ($v_1=1$, $v_2=0$, $v_3=0$, and $v_1=0$, $v_2=0$, $v_3=1$), all states of the molecule H_2O v_1, v_2, v_3 (with $v_1>2$) and v_1-2, v_2, v_3+2 having the same symmetry mutually perturb each other, according to Darling and Dennison.

Fermi resonance was also detected in the case of COS, CS_2, COSe, ICN, C_2H_2, and other molecules.

Torsional oscillations. As has already been poined out (p. 350), restricted rotation of one part of a molecule relative to another leads to torsional oscillations that appear when the atoms in a molecule form configurations separated by minima of potential

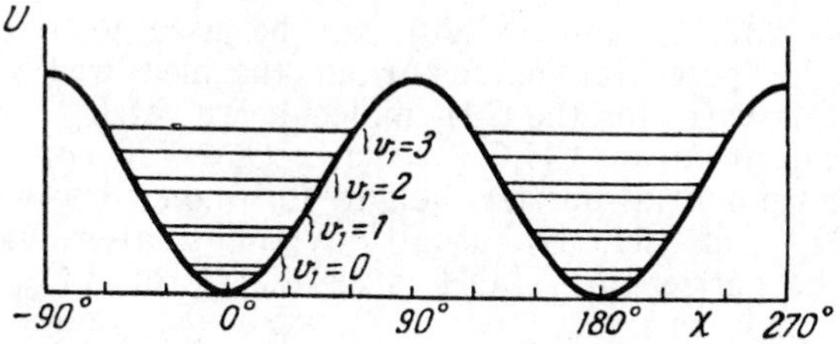

Fig. 89. Potential energy as a function of the torsion angle in molecules of the ethylene type C_2H_4

energy. Such, for example, are two energetically identical configurations of the molecule C_2H_6 or CH_3OH, etc. The dependence of the potential energy of an ethylene-type molecule upon the angle of torsion χ is given in Fig. 89. This figure also gives the levels of torsional oscillations (the splitting of each level into two components is due to the finite probability of passage through the potential barrier).

When the potential function of torsional oscillations has the form shown in Fig. 89, it is usually represented in the form

$$U=\frac{1}{2}U_0(1-\cos n\chi) \qquad (37.17)$$

where n is the number of identical minima and U_0 is the height of the potential barrier separating these minima. The levels of torsional oscillations lying significantly below the barrier and, hence, corresponding to small oscillations are the levels of an harmonic oscillator; to them corresponds the formula

$$T=\omega\left(v+\frac{1}{2}\right), \qquad (37.18)$$

because in the case of small oscillations, i.e., small χ, $\cos n\chi$ may be represented as $1-{}^1/_2 n^2\chi^2$; then the potential function assumes the form $U_0(n\chi/2)^2$, i.e., the form of a potential of quasi-elastic force. In this case, for the frequency of torsional oscillations we get the following formula:

$$\omega = n\sqrt{\frac{U_0 A_1 A_2}{A}} \tag{37.19}$$

where A, A_1, and A_2 are rotational constants with the same values as those given on p. 350. For a symmetric molecule of the type C_2H_4 or C_2H_6 (since $A_1 = A_2 = 2A$), (37.19) becomes

$$\omega = 2n\sqrt{U_0 A}. \tag{37.20}$$

Equations (37.19) and (37.20) can be used to determine the height of the potential barrier from the measured values of ω and A. In this way, for the C_2H_4 molecule we get $U_0 = 8700$ cm^{-1}, for the molecule trans-$CH_3CH=CHF$, $U_0 = 770$ cm^{-1}. Calculations of the potential-barrier height for molecules with simple bonds (C_2H_6 and CH_3OH) usually yield smaller values. For example, the barrier in CH_3OH is 388 cm^{-1}, in H_2O_2, 113 cm^{-1}, in CH_3NO_2, 2.1 cm^{-1}.

Due to the finite probability of the tunnel process, the transition of a molecule from one position to another, which corresponds to the adjacent minimum of potential energy, is possible also at values of energy of torsional oscillations that are less than the height of the potential barrier. Given an inverse relationship between the vibrational energy and the barrier height, torsional oscillations pass into free rotation. For the molecules considered (C_2H_4, etc.) that contain the same atoms in rotating groups, the different interconverting configurations are indistinguishable. But in molecules containing different atoms, for instance, in the molecule C_2ABXY, the configuration ABC=CXY and the configuration ABC=CYX derived from it have different properties that correspond to two different tautomeric modifications of the given substance. In such cases, the rate of tautomeric transformation can serve as a measure of the probability of transition of a molecule from one configuration to another.

Inversion. In the cases that we have considered, the transition of a molecule from one configuration to another is a result of mutual rotation of parts of the molecule. Cases are possible when one configuration passes into another not as a result of rotation but due to *inversion*, or transformation, which might also be called a mirror reflection. An example is the molecule NH_3 (XY_3), for which two configurations are possible that intertransform by inversion and that correspond to two possible positions of the atom N (X) with respect to the plane in which the three H (Y) atoms are situated. To these two configurations there correspond two potential-energy minima separated by a potential barrier as shown in Fig. 90. This figure also shows the vibrational levels of the molecule which are associated with vibrations of the atom N (X) relative to H_3 (Y_3). Due to the finite height of the potential barrier, we have resonance splitting of vibrational levels (similar to the splitting of levels of

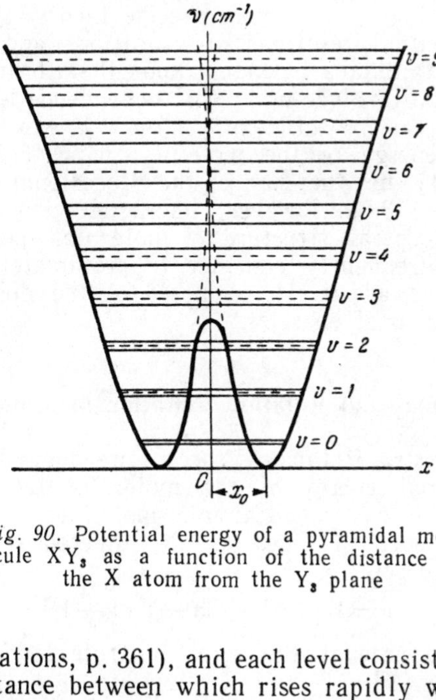

Fig. 90. Potential energy of a pyramidal molecule XY_3 as a function of the distance of the X atom from the Y_3 plane

torsional oscillations, p. 361), and each level consists of two components, the distance between which rises rapidly with increase in the quantum number v. Here, the magnitude of doublet splitting is directly related to the probability of transition of the molecule from one configuration to another, which enables one to calculate the probability of the inversion process from the measured doublet splitting. For the ground state of the NH_3 molecule, this calculation leads to a mean time of inversion equal to 2.5×10^{-11} sec. This time is 700 times that of the vibrational period of the N atom relative to the plane of H_3. A similar calculation for the molecule PH_3 yields a time of 1.1×10^{-7} sec, which is greater than the oscillation period of the atom P relative to the plane of H_3 by a factor of 3.3×10^6. The time of inversion must be particularly great in the case of heavy atoms because the probability of the tunnel transition diminishes drastically with increase in the mass of the atom.

Up to now we have assumed that the vibrational and rotational motions of molecules are independent of one another. In reality, however, as a result of vibrations (just as in the case of rotation of the molecule) changes occur in the mean distances between the atoms, as a result of which both types of internal motion of the molecule cease to be independent of one another. Accordingly, in a more precise theory that takes into account the mutual relations of vibrations and rotation, the rotational constants are dependent upon the vibrational quantum number. For small values of v, this dependence leads to a slight correction, whereas for sufficiently large v it exerts a significant effect on the energy of the molecule, which can no longer be expressed simply by the sum of the vibrational and rotational energies (see Sec. 38). However, having in view only an elucidation of the general structure of molecular spectra, in future we shall more frequently consider (approximately) the energy of a molecule as additively composed of the electronic, vibrational, and rotational energies.

38. Rotational and Rotation-Vibration Molecular Spectra

Rotational spectra. Rotational spectra are due solely to changes in the rotational energy of the molecule. Let us first consider the simpler case of diatomic molecules. Calculating the frequencies of spectral lines as the differences of rotational terms (36.6), we get

$$\nu = B\,[J'(J'+1) - J(J+1)] \tag{38.1}$$

or, taking into account the selection rule for the rotational quantum number $\Delta J = \pm 1$,

$$\nu = 2B\,(J+1). \tag{38.2}$$

From (38.2) it follows, to a first approximation, that the rotational spectrum of a diatomic molecule is (since we identify the molecule with a rigid rotator) a series of equidistant lines with the spacing of adjacent lines

$$\Delta\nu = 2B\,[(J+1+1) - (J+1)] = 2B. \tag{38.3}$$

If we determine 2B experimentally, we can, from (36.2), calculate the moment of inertia of molecule I_e and the equilibrium interatomic distance r_e. For example, from the distance between the lines of the rotational spectrum of HCl, equal to 20.68 cm^{-1}, we find $B_e = 10.34$ cm^{-1}, which, from (36.2), yields $I_e = 2.71 \times 10^{-40}$ g cm^2 and, since $\mu = 1.63 \times 10^{-24}$ g, then $r_e = 1.29 \times 10^{-8}$ cm.

Knowing the moment of inertia of the molecule (or at least its approximate value), one can solve the inverse problem, that of calculating the distance between the lines of a rotational spectrum and the absolute values of the frequencies, i.e., find the region of the spectrum in which the rotational spectrum of the given molecule lies. We find that, depending on the moment of inertia of the molecule, this spectrum can lie within a broad range of wavelengths measured in tens and hundreds of microns, right up to millimetres and centimetres (the far infrared).

The distribution of intensity between the separate lines of the rotational spectrum is directly related to the distribution of molecules in rotational levels. If this distribution is an equilibrium one (thermal), then the number of molecules in the *J*th level is determined by the Boltzmann distribution law

$$n(J) = \frac{(2J+1)\, e^{-\frac{hBJ(J+1)}{kT}}}{\sum (2J+1)\, e^{-\frac{hBJ(J+1)}{kT}}}\, n, \tag{38.4}$$

where n (J) is the number of molecules in the *J*th rotational level, and n is the total number of molecules. The sum in the denominator, which is called the rotational sum of states, obviously depends only on the rotational constant B and on the absolute temperature T, but is independent of the number J. We shall henceforward designate this sum Z_B:

$$Z_B = \sum_{J=0}^{J=\infty} (2J+1)\, e^{-\frac{hBJ(J+1)}{kT}}. \tag{38.5}$$

A measure of the line intensity in the absorption spectrum is its absorption coefficient $\mu = \mu^\circ n(J)$, which enters into the formula

$$I = I_0 e^{-\mu d}. \tag{38.6}$$

Here, I_0 and I are, respectively, the intensities of incident and transmitted light and d is the thickness of the absorbing layer. Since μ° is practically constant for all lines, from $\mu = \mu^\circ n(J)$ it follows that in the case of thermal equilibrium the distribution of intensity between separate lines of the rotational spectrum is determined by the Boltzmann law.

Rotational spectra of complex molecules are determined by the molecular structure. Linear molecules have the simplest structure;

the structures of their rotational spectra are in no way different from those of the spectra of diatomic molecules. Next in complexity come the rotational spectra of molecules belonging to the symmetric-top class. From (36.14), which expresses the rotational energy of a molecule of this class, and from the selection rules $\Delta J=0, \pm 1$ and $\Delta K=0$, we get a formula (for line frequencies of the rotational spectrum) that coincides with (38.2); the rotational spectrum of a symmetric top then consists of equidistant lines just as the spectrum of a linear or diatomic molecule. However, due to the fact that in reality each line in the spectrum of a symmetric top molecule consists of $J+1$ ordinarily merging lines, given insufficient resolution (these lines

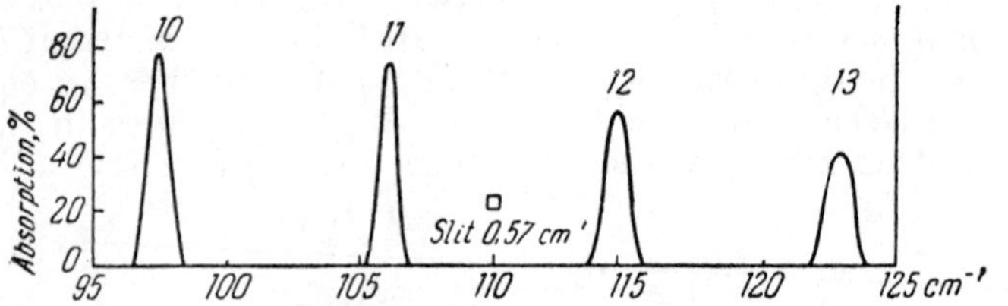

Fig. 91. Part of the rotational spectrum of a PH_3 molecule (after Wright and Randall)

are obtained from the more exact equation for the rotational energy, which takes into account the stretching of the molecule under the action of a centrifugal force) the intensities of equidistant unresolved lines observed in the spectrum are no longer determined by the Boltzmann law, but depend on the rotational quantum number in a more complicated way. Fig. 91 shows the rotational absorption spectrum of a PH_3 molecule which belongs to the symmetric-top type.

Unlike the spectra of diatomic and polyatomic linear molecules and also the spectra of symmetric-top molecules, the rotational spectra of asymmetric-top molecules have a very complex structure due to the complex dependence of the rotational energy upon the rotational quantum number (p. 348). To illustrate the structural complexity of the rotational spectrum of an asymmetric-top molecule, we indicate that, for example, when combining two systems of levels characterised by the quantum numbers $J=3$ and $J=4$, respectively, 32 allowed lines are possible: 6 in combinations of different sublevels 3_τ ($J=3$, different τ), 10 in combinations of different sublevels 4_τ and 16 in combinations of different 3_τ with different 4_τ. The structural complexity of the rotational spectra of asymmetric-top molecules explains why these spectra have been studied only in a very limited number of cases, including the water molecule. A detailed analysis of the rotational spectrum of H_2O was given by Mecke, who obtained the following values for the three moments of inertia of the H_2O molecule: $I_1 = 0.995 \times 10^{-40}$, $I_2 = 1.908 \times 10^{-40}$, and $I_3 = 2.980 \times 10^{-40}$ g cm^2.

As has already been pointed out, rotational spectra are observed in the far infrared. Until recently, this was one of the most inaccessible regions of the spectrum, and only during recent years with the application of radio methods has substantial progress been made in the study of molecular spectra. The infrared is now just as accessible as the photographic region of the spectrum. During these years, many radiospectroscopic studies devoted to investigations of rotational spectra and determinations of various molecular constants have been made.

Rotation-vibration spectra. The distances between adjacent lines of a rotational spectrum, which distances we shall, for the sake of convenience, call rotational quantum, are quantities of the order of $2B_0$, i.e., of the order of 1 to 10 cm^{-1}, while the distances between adjacent vibrational levels (vibrational quanta), which are measured by the vibrational frequency of the molecule, are of the order of magnitude of 100-1000 cm^{-1}. And so, whereas rotational spectra can be observed in pure form, the excitation solely of vibrations appears possible only in extremely rare and special cases. In almost all cases there is a simultaneous change in the vibrational and rotational states of the molecule. The spectrum produced by change in both forms of internal energy of the molecule is called a *rotation-vibration spectrum.*

Disregarding the interaction of vibrations with rotation (see above), we express the total energy of the molecule by the additive formula

$$E = E_{el} + E_{vib} + E_{rot}$$

where E_{el} designates electronic, E_{vib} vibrational, and E_{rot} rotational energy of the molecule. In the case of a rotation-vibration spectrum, the electronic energy of the molecule does not change, and for the line frequencies of this spectrum we get the expression

$$\nu = \frac{E'_{vib} - E_{vib}}{h} + \frac{E'_{rot} - E_{rot}}{h} = \nu_{vib} + \nu_{rot}. \tag{38.7}$$

The prime here corresponds to the upper rotational and vibrational states, while ν_{vib} denotes the frequencies of the "pure" vibrational spectrum. Since, from the foregoing, the difference between the rotational terms $\nu_{rot} = T'_{rot} - T_{rot}$ is two to three orders of magnitude less than ν_{vib}, on the basis of (38.7) one should conclude that rotation does not disturb the vibrational structure of a molecular spectrum. As a result of the superposition of small rotational quanta on vibrational quanta, the lines of the vibrational spectrum are converted into *bands*, groups of rotational lines. That is how we get the *linear-band structure* of the rotation-vibration spectrum.

Disregarding the rotation of the molecule, let us first find out the nature of the band (vibrational) structure of the spectrum. Describing each band by the frequency ν_{vib}, we get the vibrational spectrum of the molecule as a set of these frequencies.

The vibrational structure of a spectrum is simplest in the case of diatomic molecules. A necessary condition for the appearance of vibrational bands in the spectra of these molecules is the presence of a dipole moment or, more precisely, variation of dipole moment associated with appropriate quantum transitions of the molecule. Whence it follows that diatomic molecules consisting of the same atoms cannot have rotation-vibration spectra. In this case, the vibrational frequencies are called *optically inactive*.

However, it is possible to observe optically inactive frequencies at high pressures when, due to collisions, the symmetry of the molecule is upset. For example, at pressures of 150 atm and higher we observe absorption bands $v=0 \rightarrow v'=1$ for H_2, N_2, and O_2. In the same way, at pressures up to 25 atm the absorption spectrum of acetylene C_2H_2 exhibits an optically inactive band $\omega_2 = 1974$ cm^{-1}, which corresponds to symmetric vibration of the molecule, at which its dipole moment does not change. The intensity increase of this band in proportion to the square of the gas density indicates that its appearance is due to deformation of the C_2H_2 molecule in collisions.

It will be noted that according to the data of a number of authors, optically inactive frequencies (for example, the above-mentioned frequency of H_2) are also observed during the adsorption of gases on solid surfaces. This effect is undoubtedly also associated with the appearance of a dipole moment due to deformation of the molecule in adsorption.

Calculation of transitional moments that correspond to various changes in the vibrational quantum number (Δv) lead, for an harmonic oscillator, to the following selection rule: $\Delta v = \pm 1$. However, any values of Δv are possible for an anharmonic oscillator. As has already been pointed out (p. 357), real molecules are anharmonic oscillators, so that any combinations of $v \leftrightarrow v'$ are permissible. However, due to comparatively weak anharmonicity of vibrations ($x^2 \ll 1$), band intensities in rotation-vibration spectra, as a rule, diminish rapidly with growth of Δv.

For vibrational frequencies $\nu_{vib} = T'_{vib} - T_{vib}$, from (37.10) we get the following expression:

$$\nu_{vib} = \omega(1 - x)(v' - v) - \omega x(v'^2 - v^2). \qquad (38.8)$$

According to this expression, the vibrational spectrum of a diatomic molecule appears as a set of *series* of bands that correspond to the transition of the molecule from the given vibrational level to adjacent levels. Such, for example, is the series resulting from a transition from the zero vibrational level ($v = 0$) to higher-lying levels (absorption spectrum). In the case of this *(zero)* series, (38.8) takes the form

$$\nu_{vib}(0, v') = \omega(1 - x)v' - \omega x v'^2, \qquad (38.9)$$

and we get the following set of lines (bands):

$$\nu_1 = \omega(1 - 2x), \quad \nu_2 = 2\omega(1 - 3x), \quad \nu_3 = 3\omega(1 - 4x),$$

etc. The spacing of two adjacent lines diminishes with increasing v' and, hence, with the frequency, as is seen from the differences: $\nu_2 - \nu_1 = \omega(1 - 4x)$, $\nu_3 - \nu_2 = \omega(1 - 6x)$, etc. All the other series have a similar structure. The lines ν_{vib} of each series of the vibrational spectrum *converge* to a certain limit, which corresponds to similar convergence of vibrational levels of the molecule (cf. p. 357). This convergence limit corresponds to dissociation of the molecule.

The series structure is also characteristic of vibrational (rotation-vibration) spectra of polyatomic molecules. Due to the complexity of the scheme of vibrational levels of these molecules (see (37.15) and (37.16), and also Fig. 88), the vibrational structure here is naturally more complex. For example, due to the simultaneous excitation of a large number of different levels (combination frequencies) the series structure in these spectra is ordinarily not so clearcut.

Inasmuch as the intensity of the infrared bands is entirely due to change in the dipole moments of molecules, there is a definite possibility of finding the dipole moments of bonds from measurements of the intensities in infrared spectra. This possibility was first pointed out by Mecke, who was also the first to attempt to determine the dipole moments of certain bonds from spectroscopic data (see p. 455).

When considering the *rotational structure* of rotation-vibration spectra, we must, in the general case, proceed from the expression for the energy of a *simultaneously* rotating and vibrating molecule. This expression can be obtained by solving the general wave equation for the function $\psi(r, \vartheta, \varphi)$, i.e., without resorting to an approximation associated with allowance for separation of variables that reduces the problem to the solution of two equations: the wave equation for function $\psi_{vib}(r)$ and the wave equation for function $\psi_{rot}(\upsilon, \varphi)$. Weizel obtained the following expression for the energy of a diatomic molecule, on the well-known assumption concerning the form of function of potential energy U and by solving the general equation:

$$E = E_{el} + h\left[\omega\left(v + \frac{1}{2}\right) - \omega x\left(v + \frac{1}{2}\right)^2 + \omega y\left(v + \frac{1}{2}\right)^3 + \ldots\right] + \\ + h\left[B_v J(J+1) + D_v J^2 (J+1)^2 + \ldots\right], \quad (38.10)$$

where

$$B_v = B_0 - \alpha v + \gamma v^2 + \ldots = B_e - \alpha_e\left(v + \frac{1}{2}\right) + \\ + \gamma_e\left(v + \frac{1}{2}\right)^2 + \ldots \quad (38.11)$$

and

$$D_v = D_0 + \beta v + \ldots = D_e + \beta_e\left(v + \frac{1}{2}\right) + \ldots, \quad (38.12)$$

Expression (38.10) can, provisionally, be rewritten in the form

$$E = E_{el} + E_{vib} + E_{rot};$$

however, unlike the analogous additive formula that we have already used, the rotational energy

$$E_{rot} = h\left[B_v J(J+1) - D_v J^2 (J+1)^2 + \ldots\right] \quad (38.13)$$

is in this case dependent not only on the rotational quantum number J, but, according to expressions (38.11) and (38.12), which take into account the interaction of vibrations and rotation, also on the vibrational quantum number v, i.e., it is a complex function of the numbers J and v. This dependence of the rotational energy of a molecule on both quantum numbers, which is due primarily to change in the moment of inertia of the molecule when the vibrations are excited (because then there is a change in the equilibrium distance between nuclei), is the reason for there being no additivity of vibrational and rotational energies of the molecule.

But in order to determine the general nature of the rotational structure of molecular spectra we can take advantage of a still simpler equation:

$$\nu = \nu_{vib} + B_0\left[J'(J'+1) - J(J+1)\right], \quad (38.14)$$

which is derived by substitution of (38.1) into (38.7) and which assumes additivity of the vibrational and rotational energies and also rigidity of the molecule ($D_v=0$). It should be pointed out that due to the smallness of the quantities D_0, α, β, γ, ..., disregarding them leads to an appreciable distortion of the true structure of the spectrum only for sufficiently large values of the quantum numbers v and J.

To study the arrangement of rotational lines in a band characterised by definite values of numbers v and v′, i.e., $\nu_{vib}=\text{const}$, we take the second term of (38.14), which determines the *fine* rotational structure of the band. In the simplest case of Σ-states, according to the selection rule for the rotational quantum number (36.9), we have $J'=J\pm1$. When $J'=J+1$, from equality (38.14) we get a group of lines

$$\nu_{+1}=\nu_{vib}+2B_0(J+1), \tag{38.15}$$

which is characterised by the values $\nu>\nu_{vib}$. This group of lines is called the *positive*, or *R-branch* of the band. $J'=J-1$ yields a group of lines with $\nu<\nu_{vib}$,

$$\nu_{-1}=\nu_{vib}-2B_0J, \tag{38.16}$$

called the *negative*, or *P-branch*.

The lines of the latter group begin with $J=1$, because $J=0$ corresponds to $J'=J-1=-1$, which is meaningless physically. We thus obtain the following lines that form R- and P-branches of the given band:

J	0	1	2	3	...
R	$\nu_{vib}+2B$	$\nu_{vib}+4B$	$\nu_{vib}+6B$	$\nu_{vib}+8B$	...
P	—	$\nu_{vib}-2B$	$\nu_{vib}-4B$	$\nu_{vib}-6B$	...

i.e., a series of equidistant lines with a zero-gap ν_{vib} (called the *zero line* of the band) and the distance between adjacent lines equal to $\Delta\nu=2B$.

The set of lines thus obtained is graphically represented in Fig. 92 (for the sake of clarity, only every other line is shown), where two straight lines denote the R- and P-branches. In reality, due to interaction between rotation and vibration these straight lines become curved. Indeed, substituting into (38.7) the values of rotational energy (38.13) and ignoring the constant D (and also terms with higher powers of J), we get the following expression for the frequency of the rotational lines of the given band:

$$\nu=\nu_{vib}+B_{v'}J'(J'+1)-B_vJ(J+1), \tag{38.17}$$

from which we find

$$\nu_{+1}=\nu_{vib}+(B_{v'}+B_v)(J+1)+(B_{v'}-B_v)(J+1)^2 \tag{38.18}$$

and

$$\nu_{-1} = \nu_{vib} - (B_{v'} + B_v) J + (B_{v'} - B_v) J^2. \quad (38.19)$$

It is readily seen that the dependence of ν_{+1} and ν_{-1} upon J obtained from these formulas corresponds to parabolic branches of the second order. They are depicted in Fig. 92 by the dashed lines.

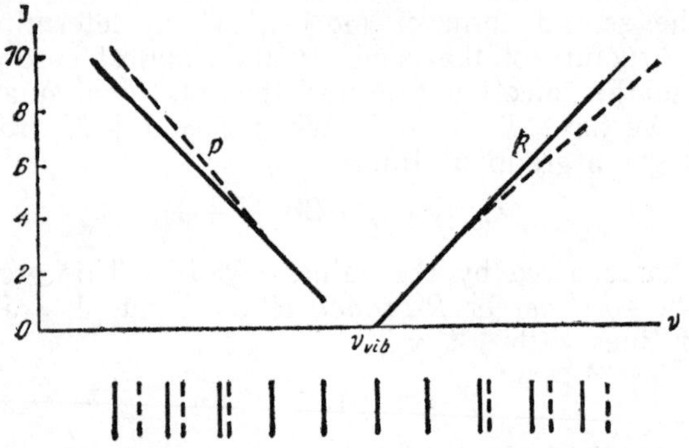

Fig. 92. Distribution of lines of P- and R-branches in the band of a vibration-rotation spectrum without regard for (solid lines) and with regard for (dashed lines) interaction between rotation and vibration

Fig. 93 shows an absorption band of HCl λ 3.5μ (v = 0 → v′ = 1). A striking thing here is the uniform distribution of approximately equidistant rotational lines,* a characteristic minimum of inten-

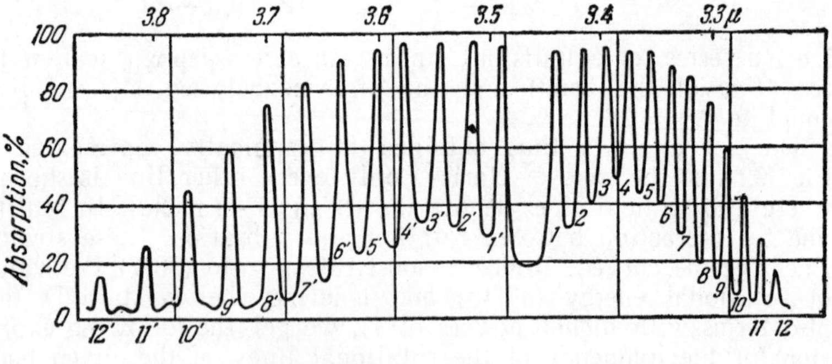

Fig. 93. Absorption band of HCl λ 3.5 μ (0 → 1′)

* From formula $\Delta\nu = \frac{c}{\lambda^2}\Delta\lambda$ it follows that in passing from the wavelength scale (Fig. 93) to the scale of frequencies, the distances between rotational lines should differ less.

sity at the point of the zero line (ν_{vib}), and two maxima of intensity (one in each of the R- and P-branches).

Intensity distribution in bands (absorption spectrum). These maxima are due to the intensity distribution of rotational lines of the band, which in turn are determined by the Boltzmann distribution of molecules according to rotational levels and the probabilities of appropriate transitions.

Distribution of molecules in rotational levels is expressed by equation (38.4) (p. 365), while the measure of intensity of the line in the absorption spectrum is its absorption coefficient, which can be represented in the form

$$\mu = \mu^0 n(J) = \mu^0 \frac{(2J+1)\, e^{-\frac{hB_0 J (J+1)}{kT}}}{Z_B} n \qquad (38.20)$$

where μ^0 is a constant proportional to the probability of the appropriate quantum transition. Here we are interested in the *relative* probabilities of transitions, which can be determined theoretically with comparative ease.

These probabilities are determined with particular ease in the case of the terms $^1\Sigma$. In this case, two transitions ($J \rightarrow J+1$ and $J \rightarrow J-1$) are possible from each level with a definite J value (with the exception of $J=0$). We denote the total probability of these transitions by A_0 and the probability of each of them separately, by A_+ and A_-; obviously $A_0 = A_+ + A_-$. Calculations show that the A_0 remains approximately constant within the limits of a given band. Ordinarily, to characterise the relative probabilities of transitions we introduce the so-called *intensity factor* i, which is determined from the equality $iA_0 = (2J+1)A$, whence it follows that

$$\sum i = i_+ + i_- = 2J + 1. \qquad (38.21)$$

Introducing the intensity factor into the expression for the absorption coefficient (38.20), we obtain

$$\mu \sim \frac{e^{-\frac{hB_0 J (J+1)}{kT}}}{Z_B} in. \qquad (38.22)$$

The values of intensity factors for various transitions in the case of $^1\Sigma$-terms can be obtained on the basis of the following reasoning. To the transitions $J \rightarrow J'$ and $J' \rightarrow J$ there correspond the same values of intensity factors because the numbers J and J' enter symmetrically into the expressions of the appropriate quasi-moments. For this reason (see also (38.21)), we must assign to transitions $0 \rightarrow 1'$ and $1' \rightarrow 0$, $i(0) = i_+(0) = 1$ (i_- in this case is zero), and to transitions $1 \rightarrow 0'$ and $0' \rightarrow 1$, $i(1) = i_-(1) = 1$.

But in the latter case, the transition $1 \longrightarrow 2$ is also possible from the level $J=1$. Designating the appropriate intensity factor by $i_+(1)$, we find, from equality (38.21), $i_+(1)=3-1=2$. Consequently, for the transition $2 \longrightarrow 1'$ we also have $i_-(2)=2$. Whence, for the transitions $2 \longrightarrow 3'$ and $3 \longrightarrow 2'$ we obtain, by means of (38.21), $i_+(2)=i_-(3)=5-2=3$, etc. Generalising the results of these calculations, we arrive at the following equations for the intensity factors of lines belonging to the R- and P-branches of the band:

$$\left.\begin{aligned} R&: \; i_+(J)=J+1, \\ P&: \; i_-(J)=J. \end{aligned}\right\} \tag{38.23}$$

Taking advantage of equations (38.23), we can, from expression (38.22), find the value of J and, consequently, the frequency (or wavelength) to which, at the given temperature, there corresponds a *maximum* of intensity in each branch of the band. Differentiating (38.22) with respect to J, we obtain the following condition of maximum:

$$\frac{di}{dJ}=i(2J+1)a, \quad a=\frac{hB_0}{kT},$$

which for the R- and P-branches will be written in the form: $2J_+^2+3J_++1=1/a\,(R)$ and $2J_-^2+J_-=1/a\,(P)$. Solving these equations, we find the values of J_+ and J_-, by means of which we can determine the frequencies ν_+ and ν_- that correspond to the maximum intensity.

We calculate the distance between maxima $\Delta\nu_{max}$. From (38.15) and (38.16) we find, for the quantity $\Delta\nu_{max}$,

$$\Delta\nu_{max}=\nu_+-\nu_-=2B_0(J_++J_-+1).$$

Solving the quadratic equations for J_+ and J_- we obtain $J_++J_-+1=2/a$* and, hence, $\Delta\nu_{max}=2B_0\sqrt{2/a}$. Substituting here the quantities $a=hB_0/kT$ and $B_0=\hbar/4\pi I_0$, we get

$$\Delta\nu_{max}=\frac{1}{\pi}\sqrt{\frac{kT}{I_0}}. \tag{38.24}$$

A formula identical to (38.24) was proposed by Bjerrum for determining the moment of inertia of a molecule (I_0) from the distance between the maxima of the bands $\Delta\nu_{max}$:

$$I_0=\frac{kT}{(\pi\Delta\nu_{max})^2}.$$

* This simple formula is obtained on the assumption that $a \ll 2$, which is always the case at room and higher temperatures. For different molecules at room temperature, a ranges between 0.1 and 0.001.

For this reason, bands with a double maximum in rotation-vibration spectra are sometimes called *Bjerrum doublets.*

The Bjerrum formula is important in that with its help one can determine the moment of inertia of a molecule without analysing the fine structure of the bands. True, it must be said that the accuracy of this determination is usually not high, due to insufficient accuracy of measurement of $\Delta\nu_{max}$. However, the Bjerrum method is sometimes useful for obtaining tentative data.

Let us compute $\Delta\lambda_{max}$ for the λ 3.5 μ band of HCl given in Fig. 93. Substituting into (38.24) $I_0 = 2.71 \times 10^{-40}$ g cm² (see p. 365) and $T = 273°$K, we find: $\Delta\lambda_{max} = 0.15\ \mu$. Approximately the same quantity $\Delta\lambda_{max}$ is obtained from experiment (see Fig. 93).

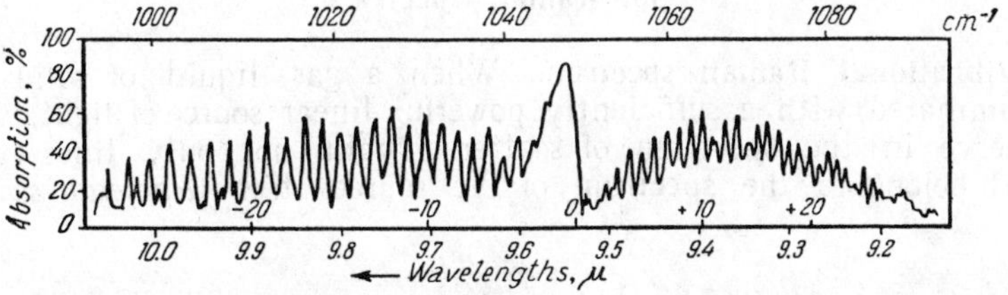

Fig. 94. Fine structure of band λ 9.55 μ CH_3F (after Benett and Meyer)

As for the rotational structure of the spectra of complex molecules, suffice it here to say that the structure of these spectra is, as a rule, far more complicated than the structure of the spectra of diatomic molecules. However, in some (true, comparatively rare) cases, the rotational structure of the spectrum of a complex molecule is just as simple as that of a diatomic molecule. A simple spectrum (with respect to its rotational structure) is, for example, that of molecules that belong to the symmetric-top type, such as NH_3, CH_3X (X = F, Cl, Br, I), and also the spectrum of CH_4 (spherical top molecule). In this case, when the direction of the electric moment of the molecule coincides with its axis, the rotation-vibration spectrum exhibits bands with even distribution of approximately equidistant rotational lines similar to the spectra of diatomic molecules. However, unlike, for instance, the above-considered spectrum HCl (Fig. 93), we have, here, also a zero line (ν_{vib}) associated with the transitions $\Delta J = 0$, as a result of which we ordinarily get a group of lines that are close to the ν_{vib} line. This group of lines forms the Q-branch of the band. Such, for example, is the fine (rotational) structure of the λ 9.55 μ band of the molecule CH_3F, given in Fig. 94, in which the Q-branch is just as prominent as the R- and P-branches. We note that the Q-branch is also observed in the case of diatomic molecules with $\Lambda > 0$, for which, according to the selection rule (36.10), there are R-, P-, and Q-branches. The NO molecule whose ground state is the state $^2\Pi\ (\Lambda = 1)$ is an instance of these molecules.

The spectrum of a symmetric top molecule has a far more complex structure when the electric moment does not coincide with the axis of the molecule. The complex rotational structure of the bands is also characteristic of asymmetric-top molecules. This can be seen even from the complexity of the structure of the rotational spectrum of water (see p. 366).

39. Raman Spectra

Vibrational Raman spectrum. When a gas, liquid or solid is illuminated with a sufficiently powerful linear source of light, we observe in the spectrum of scattered light not only lines (ν_0) that belong to the spectrum of the source itself (*Rayleigh scat-*

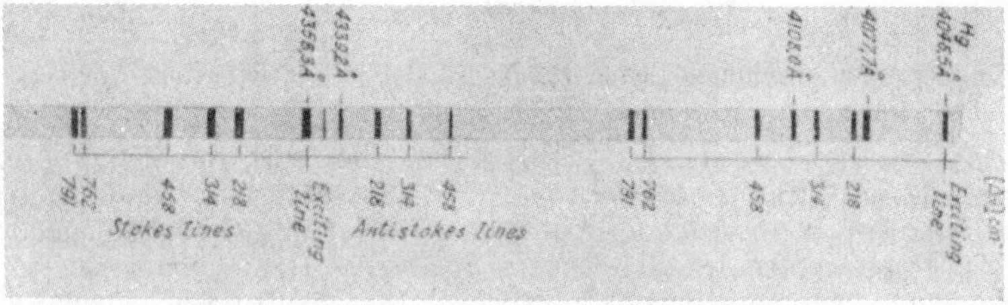

Fig. 95. Scattering spectrum of CCl_4 (after Glockler). The numbers under the spectrum designate Raman-line frequencies

tering of light) but new lines displaced from the lines of the source. This phenomenon, discovered by Raman in India and, simultaneously, by Landsberg and Mandelshtam in Moscow in 1928, became known as *Raman scattering* or the *Raman effect* (in the Russian literature, *combination scattering*). The displaced lines are called *Raman lines* (ν_p). Fig. 95 gives the Raman spectrum of carbon tetrachloride CCl_4.

The very first studies of Raman spectra showed that in most cases the differences in the frequencies of displaced and undisplaced lines, $\nu_0 - \nu_p$, coincide with the frequencies of the normal vibrations of the molecules of the scattering substance (more precisely, with the frequencies that correspond to the vibrational quanta of the molecule, which in the case of diatomic molecules are equal to $\omega=\omega_0(1-2x)$, i. e.,

$$\nu_0-\nu_p=\omega. \tag{39.1}$$

The lines of Raman scattering are frequently arranged symmetrically on both sides of the Rayleigh line, as, for example, certain lines of CCl_4 (Fig. 95). The lines with frequencies less than that of ν_0, i.e., the lines $\nu_p^s=\nu_0-\omega$ are called *Stokes lines*, while the lines with frequencies $\nu_p^a=\nu_0+\omega$ are *anti-Stokes lines*. Thus, the process of the Raman scattering of light may be formally represented by the following scheme:

$$\text{s: } h\nu_0+M(0)\rightarrow h\nu_p^s+M(1),$$
$$\text{a: } h\nu_0+M(1)\rightarrow h\nu_p^a+M(0),$$

where M(0) denotes a molecule of the scattering substance on a zero vibrational level ($v=0$), M(1) is the same molecule possessing one vibrational quantum. On this scheme, the Raman scattering of light shows a peculiar interaction of light and matter, as a result of which in the first case (s) a vibrating molecule of energy $h\omega$ and a scattered light quantum $h\nu_p^s$ are generated at the expense of the energy of the quantum $h\nu_0$. In the second case (a), the interaction of the primary quantum $h\nu_0$ with the vibrating molecule yields a molecule in the zero vibrational state and a scattered light quantum with a correspondingly higher energy $h\nu_p^a=h\nu_0+h\omega$.

Further, since the intensity of the scattered light must be proportional to the number of molecules of the scattering substance, and the number of molecules M(1) and M(0), on the condition of thermal equilibrium, are related as $e^{-h\omega/kT}:1$, one should expect that the ratio of intensities of anti-Stokes and Stokes lines of Raman scattering will vary with the temperature according to the law

$$\frac{I^a}{I^s}=e^{-\frac{h\omega}{kT}}.$$

This dependence of the intensities of both types of lines upon the temperature of the scattering substance is actually observed experimentally. Thus, by raising the temperature one observes anti-Stokes lines that are absent at lower temperatures. Besides, one very often finds that lines which correspond to small vibrational quanta are observed both as Stokes and anti-Stokes lines, whereas lines corresponding to large quanta are observed only as Stokes lines.

The theory of Raman scattering of light. In classical optics, Raman scattering of light is interpreted as follows. Under the action of the electric vector of a light wave

$$\mathfrak{E} = \mathfrak{E}_0 \sin 2\pi\nu_0 t,$$

a dipole moment is induced in a molecule; this moment vibrates with the frequency of the incident light ν_0. These forced vibrations of the molecular dipole are the cause of ordinary Rayleigh scattering of light. However, by virtue of specific dynamic conditions, a change can occur in the polarisability of the molecule, this change being due to a certain participation also of nuclei in the vibrations of the dipole. From the standpoint of the electron-nuclear structure of the molecules, these dynamic conditions are due to a force coupling of electrons and nuclei, as a result of which the forced vibrations of the electrons (with frequency ν_0) cause vibrations of the nuclei. The vibrations of the latter, which are much slower than those of electrons (because of the great difference in the electron and nuclear masses), are what lead to a change in the polarisability of the molecule. It will readily be seen that this latter factor alters the frequency of the light being scattered, i.e., gives rise to the lines of Raman scattering. Indeed, designating the polarisability of a molecule (given vibrations of frequency ω) by

$$\alpha = \alpha_0 + \alpha^0 \sin 2\pi\omega t \tag{39.2}$$

where α_0 is the polarisability of a nonvibrating molecule and α^0 is the amplitude of change in polarisability during vibrations, we have, for the induced dipole moment of the molecule,

$$P = \alpha_0 \mathfrak{E}_0 \sin 2\pi\nu_0 t + \alpha^0 \mathfrak{E}_0 \sin 2\pi\omega t \sin 2\pi\nu_0 t.$$

Transforming this expression, we get

$$P = \alpha_0 \mathfrak{E}_0 \sin 2\pi\nu_0 t + \frac{1}{2} \alpha^0 \mathfrak{E}_0 [\cos 2\pi(\nu_0 - \omega)t - \cos 2\pi(\nu_0 + \omega)t]. \tag{39.3}$$

As is seen from (39.3), when polarisation of the molecule is changed, the scattered light will be emitted not only with the frequency of the incident light ν_0 (Rayleigh scattering), but also with the combined (Raman) frequencies $\nu_0 + \omega$ and $\nu_0 - \omega$. Thus, on the classical theory each primary line of frequency ν_0 in the scattered-light spectrum will have two satellites with frequencies $\nu_0 \pm \omega$.

Classical theory, however, cannot solve the problem of intensity of the lines ν_p^s and ν_p^a. What is more, as follows from the foregoing, both types of lines must have the same intensity, which contradicts experiment. Again in conflict with experiment is the continuous nature of the spectrum (that follows from classical theory) of Raman scattering caused by rotation of the molecular dipole in the electric field of the light wave; in actuality, this spectrum has a discrete linear structure. Only quantum mechanics gives a quantitatively correct description of the phenomenon of combination (Raman) scattering.

The quantum-mechanical theory of Raman scattering is based on the Kramers-Heisenberg theory of light dispersion. Corresponding to the forced oscillations of the molecular dipole of classical theory, we have, in quantum theory, transitions of electrons to certain (virtual) energy levels of the molecule. Light scattering, in the quantum-mechanical interpretation, can also be visualised as a transition of the molecule to all possible energy levels with a subsequent return to one of the lower levels.* If the final level coincides with the initial level we have Rayleigh scattering, otherwise, Raman scattering. Thus, designating arbitrarily the energy of the higher energy levels of the molecule that participate in scattering by E_x, the energy of the initial level, by E_0, and the final, by E, the process of light scattering can, provisionally, be divided into two stages:

$$h\nu_0 = E_x - E_0 \text{ and } E_x - E = h\nu.$$

Summing them we have

$$\nu_0 - \nu = \frac{E - E_0}{h}. \qquad (39.4)$$

In the case of $E = E_0$ we will have Rayleigh scattering, and if $E \neq E_0$ we get Raman scattering.

This scheme is a pictorial representation of the process of light scattering and has the advantage that it reveals a number of peculiarities characteristic of Raman spectra. For example, in the case of symmetric diatomic molecules, such as H_2, N_2, Cl_2 that do not have rotation-vibration infrared spectra due to the optical inactivity of their vibrational frequencies (cf. p. 368), we observe intense lines of Raman scattering that correspond to these frequencies. On the foregoing two-stage scheme, excitation of optically inactive frequencies in light scattering is readily accounted for: in this case, excitation of vibrations involves allowed electronic transitions that are possible for any molecule. For this reason, forbiddenness of purely vibrational (or rotation-vibration) transitions is not essential here.

The possibility of detecting and measuring optically inactive frequencies is particularly important for complex molecules. As

---

* These transitions cannot be identified with transitions that correspond to ordinary light absorption; in the latter case, the absorbed quantum is exactly equal to the difference between the respective energy levels.

has been pointed out above, these frequencies are either totally absent in infrared spectra or are masked by combination frequencies (cf. p. 369). But in Raman spectra, as follows from intensity calculations, the lines that correspond to these frequencies are the most intense, in complete agreement with experiment. To summarise, then, Raman spectra significantly supplement infrared spectra and simplify the problem of analysing the vibrational terms of complex molecules.

Along with measuring the natural frequencies of molecules, very important are investigations of the *degree of depolarisation* of scattered light. By degree of depolarisation ϱ we understand the ratio of the intensity of scattered light polarised in a plane parallel to the plane of polarisation of the incident light, to the intensity of the scattered light that is polarised in the perpendicular plane. The degree of polarisation of scattered light is directly related to the form of the molecule (more precisely, to the form of the *polarisability ellipsoid* of the molecule (see p. 431) and to the symmetry of vibrations participating in the scattering event. For example, in the case of symmetric molecules of type CH_4 where the polarisability ellipsoid degenerates into a sphere, completely symmetric vibrations (in the CH_4 molecule, the symmetric vibrations of the H atoms relative to the C atom) cannot lead to depolarisation of scattered light, i.e., in this case $\varrho = 0$. But as regards asymmetric vibrations of the molecule, the degree of depolarisation must differ from zero. It is evident from what has been said that investigations into the degree of depolarisation of Raman lines is very important in establishing the type of appropriate vibrations and, in the final analysis, the molecular structure.

Rotational Raman spectra. Along with Raman lines that correspond to definite natural frequencies of the molecules of the scattering substance, the scattering spectrum (given sufficient dispersion) also exhibits lines that correspond to the rotational quanta of the molecules. Thus, due to the Raman effect, studies of the structure of rotational terms of molecules are moved from the far infrared to the photographic region of the spectrum.

The structure of rotational Raman lines is determined by appropriate selection rules for the rotational quantum number; these rules can readily be established by means of a two-stage scheme of the process. Indeed, considering the transition $E_0 \rightarrow E_x$ and making use of the selection rule $\Delta J = \pm 1$, we get two possible values for the rotational quantum number of the transitional state (J_x), namely, $J_x = J_0 \pm 1$ (J_0 refers to the initial state of the molecule). Upon transition to the final state ($E_x \rightarrow E$) the rotational quantum number of the latter must be $J = J_x \pm 1 =$

$=(J_0 \pm 1) \pm 1 = J_0,\ J_0 \pm 2$. Thus, unlike the infrared spectrum, where the selection rule is $\Delta J = \pm 1$ (in the case of Σ-terms), for the rotational Raman spectrum we get $\Delta J = 0,\ \pm 2$.

On the basis of equations (39.4) and (36.5), for the rotational lines we have

$$\nu_p = \nu_0 - B_0 [J'(J'+1) - J(J+1)]. \qquad (39.5)$$

Having in view the case that corresponds to selection rule $\Delta J = 0,\ \pm 2$, we obtain from (39.5) the following formulas for the

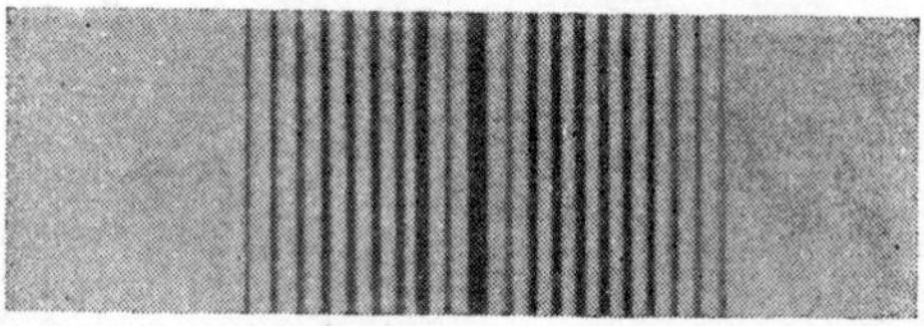

Fig. 96. Rotational Raman spectrum in oxygen (after Rasetti)

two branches of the rotational band (these are called S- and O-branches):

$$\text{S:}\ \nu_p^s = \nu_0 - 2B_0 (2J+3),$$
$$\text{O.}\ \nu_p^a = \nu_0 + 2B_0 (2J-1)$$

(and, in addition, the line $\nu = \nu_0$, which corresponds to $\Delta J = 0$). According to these formulas, the separation of adjacent lines in the band is equal to $\Delta\nu = 4B_0$, in place of $\Delta\nu = 2B_0$ in the infrared spectrum. Fig. 96 is a photograph of the rotational Raman spectrum of oxygen.

For molecules with $\Lambda > 0$, and also for symmetric-top molecules, we have $\Delta J = 0,\ \pm 1$ (for the infrared spectrum). It can easily be shown, by means of the same two-stage scheme of the scattering process, that in this case the rotational Raman spectrum has, in addition to S- and O-branches, the usual R- and P-branches ($\Delta J = \pm 1$), i.e., for the Raman spectrum in this case we have the selection rule $\Delta J = 0,\ \pm 1,\ \pm 2$. The frequencies belonging to the P- and R-branches of the lines are expressed by the formulas:

$$\text{P:}\ \nu_p^s = \nu_0 - 2B_0 (J+1),$$
$$\text{R:}\ \nu_p^a = \nu_0 + 2B_0 J.$$

The selection rule $\Delta J = 0,\ \pm 1,\ \pm 2$ also occurs in the case of an asymmetric top molecule.

Let it also be mentioned that the rotation-vibration Raman spectrum usually has the form of separate lines that correspond to the first bands of the zero series (or their combinations). Investigation of the fine structure of these lines shows that in reality they are narrow bands that correspond to the Q-branch, which due to superposition of the closely spaced rotational lines has an apparent intensity in considerable excess of that of the other branches of the band. That is why the latter ordinarily escape detection.

In addition to the vibrational and rotational (and also rotation-vibration) Raman spectra, there may also occur a spectrum in which the difference $\nu_0 - \nu_p$ represents the energy of electronic exsitation of the molecule. A spectrum of this kind was found in the case of NO, where, besides the lines $\nu_p = \nu_0 \pm \omega$ we find the lines $\nu_p = \nu_0 \pm ({}^2\Pi_{3/2} - {}^2\Pi_{1/2})$. It will be noted that the direct combination of terms ${}^2\Pi_{3/2}$ and ${}^2\Pi_{1/2}$, which are components of the ground term of the NO molecule ${}^2\Pi$, is forbidden by the selection rule $\Delta\Sigma = 0$. Here, as in the case of the rotational and vibrational terms of symmetric molecules the general rule is valid according to which two terms that combine with a third do not ordinarily intercombine.

Since the discovery of Raman scattering, a large number of papers have been published in this field covering an enormous number of organic and nonorganic compounds. Due to simplicity of technique, studies of Raman spectra have many advantages over infrared spectra. From the Raman spectra we find the natural frequencies of molecules (vibrational spectra) and their moments of inertia (rotational spectra). The possibility of detecting directly the frequencies of optically inactive vibrations makes the method of Raman scattering particularly valuable. This method is likewise very important for studying the structure of molecules and the structural alterations that molecules undergo during changes in the aggregate state of matter (association, solvation, dissociation, etc.), and also in studies of chemical equilibria, for analysing complex mixtures, for identifying compounds, etc.

40. Electronic Spectra of Molecules

Vibrational structure of the spectrum. Electronic spectra are spectra associated with a simultaneous change both of the vibrational and rotational, and electronic state of the molecule. On p. 370 we derived an expression for the total energy of a molecule that included also the energy of the electronic state (E_{el}). We shall here consider the electronic spectra to the same approximation that we considered the rotation-vibration spectra of molecules. Assuming additivity of the three types of energy, the frequencies of the separate lines of the electronic spectrum are represented by the formula

$$\nu = \frac{(E'_{el} + E'_{vib} + E'_{rot}) - (E_{el} + E_{vib} + E_{rot})}{h} = \nu_{el} + \nu_{vib} + \nu_{rot} \quad (40.1)$$

where

$$\nu_{el} = \frac{E'_{el} - E_{el}}{h}, \quad \nu_{vib} = \frac{E'_{vib} - E_{vib}}{h} \text{ and } \nu_{rot} = \frac{E'_{rot} - E_{rot}}{h}.$$

Here, ν_{vib} characterises the vibrational (band) structure of the spectrum, ν_{rot} the rotational, or fine structure of the bands. The quantity ν_{el}, which determines the change in electronic energy of the molecule, is usually far in excess (tens of times) of ν_{vib} and exceeds ν_{rot} by a factor of thousands. For this reason, the electronic spectrum of a molecule is displaced with respect to its rotation-vibration spectrum towards the short wavelengths, ordinarily into the visible or ultraviolet regions of the spectrum.

In the case of the *diatomic molecule*, we have from (36.6) and (37.10)

$$\nu_{vib} = \omega'\left(v' + \frac{1}{2}\right) - \omega' x'\left(v' + \frac{1}{2}\right)^2 - \omega\left(v + \frac{1}{2}\right) + \omega x\left(v + \frac{1}{2}\right)^2 \quad (40.2)$$

and

$$\nu_{rot} = B'_0 J'(J' + 1) - B_0 J(J + 1) \quad (40.3)$$

(the primed quantities refer to the upper energy states). Comparing expressions (40.2) and (40.3) with the analogous expressions (38.14) and (38.8), we see that the former contain two different frequencies ω and ω' (in place of one) and two rotational constants B_0 and B'_0. The large number of constants (to the same degree of approximation) is due to the fact that here we have two electronic states, each of which is characterised by a definite frequency ω, also an anharmonicity constant ωx, and a definite equilibrium distance r_0 between atoms, i. e., a definite value of B_0.

Without taking into consideration ν_{rot}, let us first determine the peculiarities of the vibrational structure of the electronic spectrum of a diatomic molecule. For the *zero line* (see below) of each band of this spectrum we have the following expression, on the basis of (40.1) and (40.2):

$$\nu = \nu_{el-v} = \nu_{el} + \omega'\left(v' + \frac{1}{2}\right) - \omega' x'\left(v' + \frac{1}{2}\right)^2 - \omega\left(v + \frac{1}{2}\right) + \omega x\left(v + \frac{1}{2}\right)^2. \quad (40.4)$$

This formula, in the form

$$\nu = \nu_0 + \omega_0' v' - \omega_0' x_0' v'^2 - \omega_0 v + \omega_0 x_0 v^2 \tag{40.5}$$

was first derived empirically by Deslandres and is known as the *Deslandres formula.* From a comparison of (40.5) and (40.4), we get the following relations between the constants that enter into them:

$$\left.\begin{aligned} \nu_0 &= \nu_{el} + \frac{\omega'}{2}\left(1 - \frac{x'}{2}\right) - \frac{\omega}{2}\left(1 - \frac{x}{2}\right), \\ \omega_0 &= \omega(1 - x), \\ \omega_0' &= \omega'(1 - x'), \\ \omega_0 x_0 &= \omega x, \\ \omega_0' x_0' &= \omega' x'. \end{aligned}\right\} \tag{40.6}$$

Assigning to each frequency (band) the indexes vv' ($\nu_{vv'}$), we can represent the entire *system of bands* expressed by the Deslandres formula in the following table (Table 35). We see that the bands that form this system are distributed in definite series (progressions) that correspond to the horizontal rows and vertical columns of Table 35. The former are called v progressions and the latter, v′ progressions.

Table 35

Deslandres system of bands of a diatomic molecule

v' \ v	0	1	2	3	4	...
0	ν_{00}	ν_{10}	ν_{20}	ν_{30}	ν_{40}	...
1	ν_{01}	ν_{11}	ν_{21}	ν_{31}	ν_{41}	...
2	ν_{02}	ν_{12}	ν_{22}	ν_{32}	ν_{42}	...
3	ν_{03}	ν_{13}	ν_{23}	ν_{33}	ν_{43}	...
4	ν_{04}	ν_{14}	ν_{24}	ν_{34}	ν_{44}	...
.	.	.	.	.	.	...
.	.	.	.	.	.	...
.	.	.	.	.	.	...

The v′ progressions correspond to $v = \text{const}$ and can be expressed as

$$\nu = \nu_{0v} + \omega_0' v' - \omega_0' x_0' v'^2, \tag{40.7}$$

derived from (40.5). According to (40.7), the v′ progressions are a group of bands that converge to a certain limit in the region of high frequencies. This series is obtained in transitions from a definite vibrational level v that corresponds to a lower electronic state of the molecule, to all possible vibrational levels v′ of an upper state (or vice versa). The v′ progressions are characteristic of absorption spectra. They are clearly distinguishable in the absorption spectra of I_2, Br_2, N_2, O_2, NO, CO, O_3, SO_2, H_2CO, C_6H_6, etc. Illustrative of such a spectrum is the absorption spectrum of CO in the Schumann region ($\lambda < 2000$ A) given in Fig. 97.

The v progressions, on the contrary, are expressed by

$$\nu = \nu_{0v} - \omega_0 v + \omega_0 x v^2 \tag{40.8}$$

and are associated with transitions from a definite vibrational level of an upper electronic state of the molecule to all possible lower vibrational levels (or vice versa). These progressions are characteristic of emission spectra, in particular for a fluorescence spectrum. For example, when iodine vapour is excited by the green line of mercury 5461 A, we observe a series of bands in the fluorescence

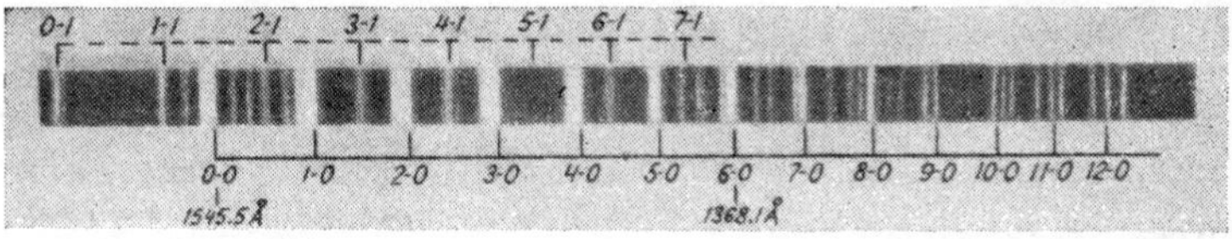

Fig. 97. Absorption spectrum oɪ CO in the Schumann region (after Hopfield and Birge). The figures 0 — 0, etc,, denote the vibrational quantum numbers of the upper and lower quantum states, respectively

spectrum that correspond to transitions $v' = 26 \rightarrow v = 1, 2, 3, 4, \ldots$ Similar progressions are also observed in the fluorescence spectra of O_2, S_2, NO, SO_2, etc.

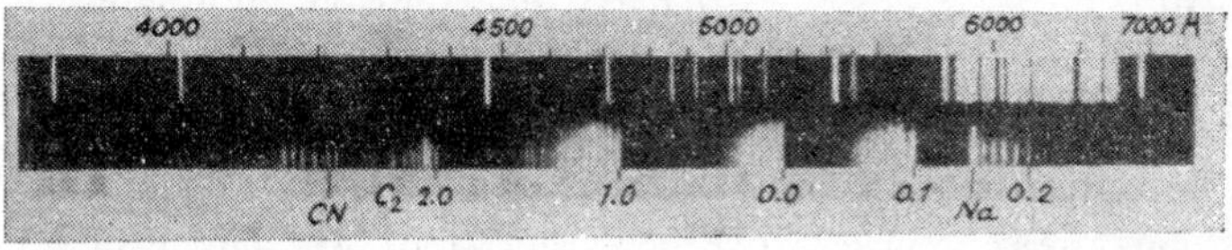

Fig. 98. Part of spectrum obtained in the passage of a shock wave through a mixture of acetylene and argon. It contains bands of CN and of C_2 (Swan bands) (after Gaydon)

In the case of excitation of emission spectra under the complex conditions of an electric discharge, and also in temperature and chemical (chemiluminescence) excitations, the various progressions ordinarily overlap and the pattern of the spectrum becomes very complicated. Very often, when different progressions overlap, separate groups of bands in the spectrum segregate; these correspond to the *diagonal progressions* of Table 35, for instance, the progressions ν_{00}, ν_{11}, ν_{22}, etc., or ν_{10}, ν_{21}, etc. Such progressions are characteristic of spectra of C_2, N_2, CO, CN, etc. Fig. 98 shows a portion of a spectrum obtained during the passage of a shock wave through a mixture of acetylene and argon. The spectrum contains bands of CN and bands of C_2 (*Swan bands*).

The characteristic constant of each system of bands is the band ν_{00} (to be more exact, the zero line of this band), which corresponds to the combination $v'=0 \leftarrow\rightarrow v=0$ and is called the *zero band*. As follows from (40.6), the frequency of the zero line of the zero band does not coincide with the frequency ν_{el} because of the zero vibrational energy of the molecule.

Intensity distribution in the Deslandres system of bands. When we considered the rotation-vibration spectra we pointed out that the band intensity rapidly falls off with increasing Δv. Besides, this spectrum is absent in molecules the dipole moment of which is zero. In contrast to rotation-vibration spectra, the bands (in electronic spectra) that correspond to different values of Δv have a comparable intensity in a large range of Δv, irrespective of the presence of a dipole moment.

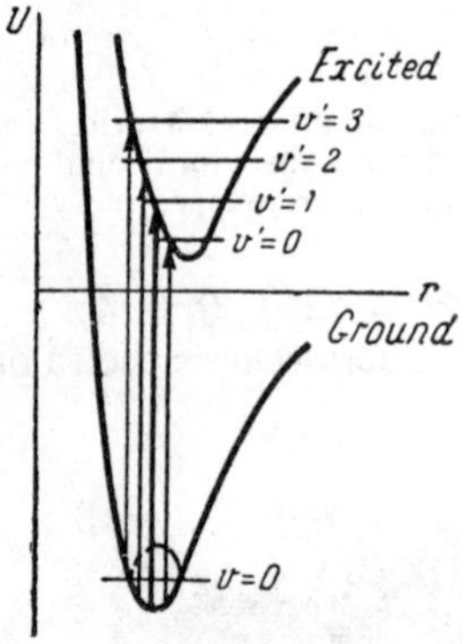

Fig. 99. Probabilities of transition after Franck and Condon

The reason for this is that the probabilities of transitions in electronic spectra are determined by variation of the transition moment of the molecule, which is due to its electron configuration. For this reason, in the case of an allowed electronic transition, any values of Δv are, generally speaking, possible.

Intensity distribution in the Deslandres band system can be explained on the basis of the *Franck-Condon principle*. Franck expressed the view that those bands have greatest intensity that are associated with quantum transitions in which there is *no change* either in the internuclear distances or in the nuclear momenta. This assumption is based on the fact that when the molecule absorbs or emits light, the electronic transitions occur so rapidly that neither the positions nor the velocities of the nuclei have time to change perceptibly during the time of a transition, and transitions occur for the practically constant internuclear distance r. Let us examine Fig. 99, which shows the potential-energy curves of a diatomic molecule in the ground and excited states. Excitation of the molecule (transition from ground to excited state) occurs, according to Franck, with unchanged distance between nuclei r (vertical arrows). As a result of this transition, the potential energy of the excited molecule is equal to U'. However, since to this energy there corresponds the internuclear distance $r'=r$, which, generally speaking, differs from the equilibrium distance r'_e of the excited molecule, the positions of the nuclei at the instant of excitation will not be in equilibrium and the molecule will begin to vibrate. The energy of these vibrations E'_{vib} will obviously be equal to the difference $U' - U'_0$. The vibrational quantum number v' (which determines this energy) together with the number v of the lower state (in the case that corresponds to the heavy arrow in Fig. 99, $v=0$) will describe this band, which is associated with the given transition.

However, on the Franck view, it is not clear how, in addition to this band, there can appear other bands of the series $v=\text{const}$ ($v=0$), though this is actually what occurs. This difficulty is eliminated by a quantum-mechanical interpretation of the Franck principle as given by Condon.

In quantum mechanics, the probability of the combination $v \leftrightarrow v'$ is determined by the value of the quasi-moment that corresponds to the given transition

$$q_{v'v} = \int \psi_{v'}(r)\, q\, \psi_v(r')\, d\tau. \qquad (40.9)$$

The functions $\psi_{v'}$ and ψ_v that enter into this expression have the form shown in Fig. 87. It is seen that the vibrational wave functions have a perceptible magnitude in a certain interval of values r. Due to this diffuseness they overlap in the interval Δr, and this, according to (40.9), leads to the possibility of a transition from the given level v' not only to the higher-lying level v but also to adjacent levels, as is shown in Fig. 99. Here, the vertical arrows of various thickness depict possible transitions $v=0 \rightarrow v'$ ($0 \rightarrow 0'$, $0 \rightarrow 1'$, $0 \rightarrow 2'$, $0 \rightarrow 3'$). The thickness of the arrow is in accord with the relative probability of the given transition, i.e., with the intensity of the respective band.

It will be noted that (as follows from Fig. 87) the quantity $\psi_0^2(r)$, which is shown in Fig. 99 by the dashed curve and which determines the probability of finding nuclei at a given distance r when $r \neq r_e$, is nonzero and is evidence (from the corpuscular point of view) of motion of nuclei that does not cease even in the zero vibrational state of the molecule. The energy of this motion represents zero vibrational energy.

Fig. 99 refers to the particular case when the zero vibrational level ($v=0$) is the initial state of the molecule. In this case, in the series $v=\text{const}$, we find one maximum of intensity (in the case that refers to Fig. 99 band 01′ is strongest). It will readily be seen that in the case of $v \neq 0$ in v progressions there are, as a rule, *two* bands with maximum intensity that correspond to the maxima of the function $\psi_{v'}$ at two turning points of the nuclei (Fig. 87). That is why we will have two intensity maxima in these series.

The same goes for the case when the initial level is the v′ level (emission); to each value of the number v′ (for $v'>0$) there will be two values of v that correspond to two of the strongest bands of the v progressions. At $v'=0$, we will have a series with one intensity maximum.

By drawing a line through the bands of maximum intensity on the diagram of the band system (Table 35), we obtain a curve whose shape is determined by the relative positions of the potential-energy curves of the upper and lower states of the molecule. On the basis of figures like Fig. 100, it is easy to see that when r_e' differs but slightly from r_e, the values of v_1' and v_2',

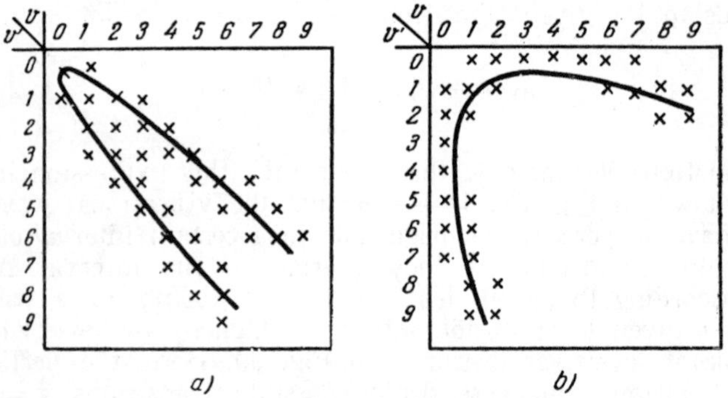

Fig. 100. Intensity distribution in the Deslandres band system (Condon parabolas)

which correspond to each given value of v, must differ very little and the curve of maximum intensities (*Condon parabola*) degenerates almost into a straight line. This curve is shown in Fig. 100 a, where the crosses indicate the strongest bands. In this case, the spectrum should exhibit a prominent diagonal progression. On the contrary, when there is a large difference between r_e' and r_e, the numbers v_1' and v_2' differ greatly and we get a curve like that shown in Fig. 100 b. Thus, on the basis of the shape of these curves we can judge the type of change in the equilibrium distance in a given quantum transition, and, hence, also the relative positions of the appropriate potential-energy curves of the molecule. We can add that the curves of maximum intensity are a reliable criterion of the validity of the Deslandres formula, by means of which the experimentally found bands are expressed.

Fine (rotational) structure of spectra. Turning to a consideration of the rotational structure of electronic spectra of diatomic molecules, let us select some band that is characterised by definite values of vibrational quantum numbers v and v'. The frequencies of the individual rotational lines of this band can be represented by the approximate formula

$$\nu = \nu_{el-v} + B_{v'} J' (J' + 1) - B_v J (J + 1), \qquad (40.10)$$

derived from (40.1)—(40.4). Formula (40.10) is very similar to (38.17), differing from it only in the constant ν_{el-v} (that replaces the constant ν_{vit}), and also by the fact that the constants B in (38.17) refer to the same electronic state of the molecule, and in (40.10), to different electronic states.

Due to the similarity of equations (40.10) and (38.17), we can obviously derive from (40.10), in the general case, three parabolas that are expressed by formulas similar to (38.18) and (38.19)*:

$$\left.\begin{aligned} &R: \nu_R = \nu_{el-v} + (B_{v'} + B_v)(J+1) + (B_{v'} + B_v)(J+1)^2, \\ &Q: \nu_Q = \nu_{el-v} + (B_{v'} - B_v) J + (B_{v'} - B_v) J^2, \\ &P: \nu_P = \nu_{el-v} - (B_{v'} + B_v) J + (B_{v'} - B_v) J^2. \end{aligned}\right\} \qquad (40.11)$$

Such parabolas that refer to the band AlH λ 4241 A are shown in Fig. 101. As is seen from this figure, which is commonly called a *Fortrat diagram*, the lines become closely spaced (to the left) near a certain sharp limit (called the band *head*) and become widely spaced at the other end of the band (to the right). This decline in total intensity away from the head (resulting from such a line distribution in the band) is called *shading* of the band. The band in Fig. 101 is shaded towards long wavelengths; in this case one speaks of *red shading* of the band (in contradistinction to *violet shading*).

The band head is due to a turning point in one of the parabolas (the R-branch in Fig. 101). The question of which of the branches (R or P) has a turning point is solved by the sign of the quadratic term in equations (40.11), that is, by the ratio between $B_{v'}$ and B_v. It is readily seen that the turning point on the R-branch is obtained when $B_v > B_{v'}$ and on the P-branch when $B_v < B_{v'}$. Further, since according to (36.2) the quantities B are inversely proportional to the corresponding moments of inertia, i.e., inversely proportional to r^2, red shading indicates an increase in the equilibrium distance with excitation of the molecule and, conversely, violet shading of the band (turning point on the

* Here we also give the equation for the Q-branch that results when $\Delta J = 0$.

P-branch) is an indication of a decrease in the equilibrium distance, i.e., a strengthening of the molecule, with its excitation.

It may be added that in many cases there is no head. This occurs when the difference between $B_{v'}$ and B_v is slight.

A characteristic band constant is its *zero line* ν_{el-v}, which is absent from the spectra of diatomic molecules. The absence of the zero line in the R- and P-branches was proved on p. 377. In the Q-branch this line is absent due to the selection rule $J' = 0 \leftrightarrow J = 0$. The position of the zero line in a band can frequently be deter-

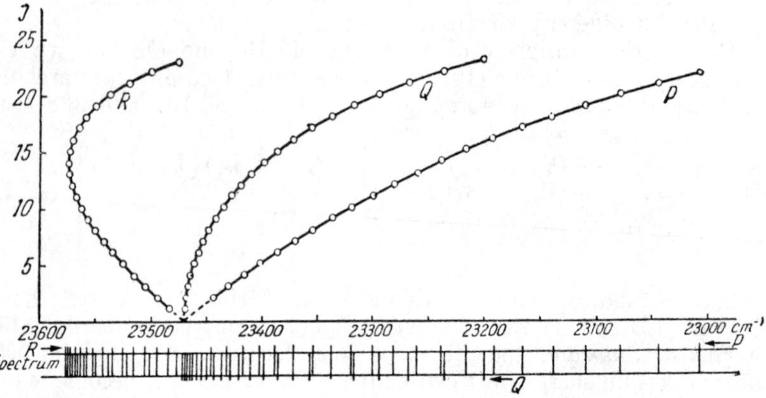

Fig. 101. Fortrat diagram of band AlHλ4241 A (after Bengtsson-Knave)

mined from the characteristic gap that disrupts the line sequence (see, for example, Fig. 93). The exact value of ν_{el-v} is obtained from a detailed analysis of the rotational structure of the bands.

The set of values of ν_{el-v} found in this way permits establishing the Deslandres formula for a given system of bands, i.e., determining the constant ν_{el} and also the vibrational constants ω and x for both combining electronic terms.

Let us dwell in somewhat more detail on an analysis of the rotational structure of bands. The object of this analysis is primarily to determine the rotational terms and, consequently, the rotational constants of the molecule B_v and $B_{v'}$ which permit expressing the frequencies of separate lines in the band by means of equations similar to (40.11). This analysis is simplified by the possibility of setting up definite relations between frequencies of the rotational lines, thus making it possible to isolate individual rotational terms of the molecule. Denoting the rotational term by

T (J) and rewriting (40.10) in the form

$$\nu_P(J)=\nu_{el-v}+T'(J-1)-T(J),$$
$$\nu_Q(J)=\nu_{el-v}+T'(J)-T(J),$$
$$\nu_R(J)=\nu_{el-v}+T'(J+1)-T(J),$$

it will readily be seen that the following relations obtain for the separate lines:

$$\left.\begin{aligned}\nu_Q(J)-\nu_P(J)=\nu_R(J-1)-\nu_Q(J-1)=\\=T'(J)-T'(J-1)=2B_{v'}J,\\\nu_Q(J-1)-\nu_P(J)=\nu_R(J-1)-\nu_Q(J)=\\=T(J)-T(J-1)=2B_vJ.\end{aligned}\right\}\quad(40.12)$$

Consequently, the frequency difference of two lines in a band is repeated *twice* and is a quantity that is a multiple of $2B_v$ or $2B_{v'}$. For this reason, the starting point in an analysis of the rotational structure of a band is ordinarily to determine the differences that satisfy relations (40.12). Whence, we directly find the values of the constants B_v and $B_{v'}$ of the molecule and its rotational terms.*

The foregoing reasoning is schematic because our initial expression (40.10) is an approximate one. Even if we consider the molecule unstretchable, i.e., if we disregard constant D, we can consider expression (40.10) as valid only in the case of combination $^1\Sigma\leftrightarrow{}^1\Sigma$. However, here, due to the selection rule $\Delta J=\pm1$ the Q-branch is absent and we only have branches R and P.

The simplest case when also the Q-branch appears is the combination of terms $^1\Sigma$ and $^1\Pi$. However, here we must take into account the Λ-doubling of the Π-term, and since change in energy associated with Λ-doubling in (40.11) was not taken into account, these formulas and also the relations (40.12) derived from them cannot, obviously, hope to be accurate. And despite the Λ-doubling of the Π-term the number of parabolas in the band remains equal to 3. Indeed, above (p.344) we pointed out that the rotational Σ-terms are alternately positive and negative, while the components of Λ-doubling of the Π-term (ordinarily designated by the symbols Π_a and Π_b) also have different signs. And so, on the basis of the selection rules $\Delta J=0, \pm1$ and $+\leftrightarrow-$ we obtain only three combinations of each rotational $^1\Sigma$-term, i.e., three simple branches.

---

* Thus, from (40.12) for $J=1$ we have: $T'(1)-T'(0)=T'(1)=2B_{v'}$, and $T(1)-T(0)=T(1)=2B_v$. These relations straightway yield the constants B_v and $B_{v'}$ and the terms $T(1)$ and $T'(1)$. For $J=2$ we get $T'(2)-T'(1)=4B_{v'}$ and $T(2)-T(1)=4B_v$, whence $T(2)$, $T'(2)$, etc.

These combinations can be schematically represented in the following form:

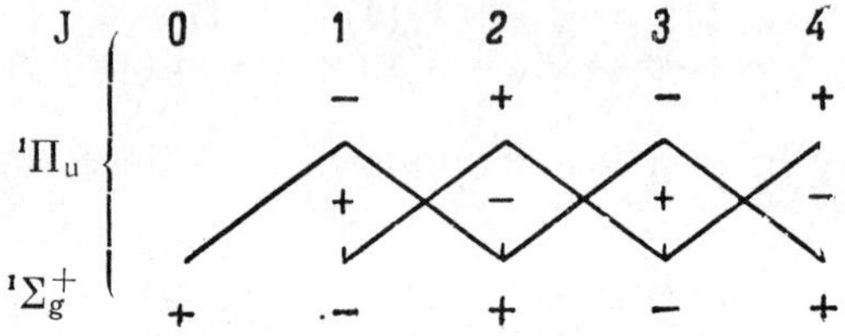

The rotational structure of bands in the combination of other terms is considerably more involved. Without going into details, we can state that, for example, in the case of combinations $^1\Pi \leftrightarrow {}^1\Pi$ and $^1\Pi \leftrightarrow {}^1\Delta$ we have six parabolas or branches (two R-, two Q- and, two P-branches), in the case of the combinations $^2\Sigma \leftrightarrow {}^2\Sigma$ 4 branches (two R- and two P-branches), and in the case of $^2\Sigma \leftrightarrow {}^2\Pi$ 12 branches, etc.

Let us also add that the electronic spectra of complex molecules are characterised by a larger number of constants and, for this reason, naturally, have a more complicated vibrational and rotational structure than that of the spectra of diatomic molecules. In particular, this has to do with asymmetric-top molecules. Only in the case of symmetric linear molecules (for instance, CO_2^+) does the rotational structure of the bands come close to the band structure of diatomic molecules. Due to complexity of structure, the analysis of electronic spectra of complex molecules has as yet been carried out only in an extremely limited number of cases.

The isotope effect in spectra. One of the extremely important properties that apply equally to molecular spectra with electronic excitation and to infrared spectra and Raman spectra is the *isotope effect* in these spectra. We differentiate between the *vibrational effect*, due to a difference in natural frequencies of the isotopic molecules, and the *rotational effect*, due to the difference in their moments of inertia. Let us first consider the vibrational isotope effect in the spectra of diatomic molecules.

Since, according to (37.8) and (37.11), the natural frequencies, like the anharmonicity constants, are inversely proportional to the square root of the reduced mass of the molecule $\mu = m_1 m_2/(m_1 + m_2)$ (m_1 and m_2 are the masses of the atoms that comprise the molecule), by introducing the quantity

$$\varrho = \sqrt{\frac{\mu'}{\mu}}$$

(μ and μ' refer to two isotopic molecules), for the magnitude of isotope shift of the zero lines ($\Delta\nu_0$) in the spectrum of these molecules we get, from the Deslandres formula,

$$\begin{aligned}\Delta\nu_0 = (\varrho - 1)\left[\omega'\left(v' + \frac{1}{2}\right) - \omega\left(v + \frac{1}{2}\right)\right] - \\ - (\varrho^2 - 1)\left[\omega'x'\left(v' + \frac{1}{2}\right)^2 - \omega x\left(v + \frac{1}{2}\right)^2\right]\end{aligned} \quad (40.13)$$

or, approximately (disregarding anharmonicity),

$$\Delta\nu_0 = (\varrho - 1)\left[\omega'\left(v' + \frac{1}{2}\right) - \omega\left(v + \frac{1}{2}\right)\right]. \quad (40.14)$$

Let us calculate $\varrho - 1$ for two isotopic molecules of oxygen, O_2^{16} and $O^{16}O^{18}$. Designating the masses of the atoms 0^{16} and 0^{18} by m and m', respectively, we find in this case $\varrho - 1 = \sqrt{\frac{2m'}{m + m'}} - 1$ or, approximately (due to the smallness of $\Delta m = m' - m$ as compared with m),

$$\varrho - 1 = \frac{\Delta m}{4m}. \quad (40.15)$$

Substituting here $\Delta m = 2$ and $m = 16$, we get $\varrho - 1 = 0.03$.

The isotope effect in oxygen was, for example, detected in the so-called atmospheric bands ($^3\Sigma - {}^1\Sigma$). In this case, $\omega' = 1432.6$ and $\omega = 1580.3$ cm^{-1}. Substituting these values of frequencies together with $\varrho - 1 = 0.03$ into (40.14), we get, for the various bands of the series $v = 0$, the following values of isotope shift $\Delta\nu_0$: -2.3 (00'), 42.5 (01'), 87.2 (02') cm^{-1}, etc. These quantities can easily be measured even when the spectral instrument gives a slight dispersion. Thus, the vibrational isotope effect is a clearcut effect easily detected in molecular spectra. In Fig. 102 the vibrational isotope effect is shown in the case of the Swan bands of C_2.

Superposition, on the vibrational effect, of the rotational, isotope effect gives rise to an additional shift of the rotational lines. This shift is expressed as the product of $\varrho^2 - 1$ by the difference of the rotational terms, which difference is considerably less than that of the vibrational terms. For this reason, the rotational isotope effect is small compared with the vibrational effect; nevertheless, it, too, leads to a measurable line shift.

The isotope effect in molecular spectra gives a sensitive and precise method of identifying isotopes and measuring their relative abundances (by measuring intensities in the spectrum). It may be noted that a number of isotopes were discovered in this way, i.e., spectroscopically: H^2(D), C^{13}, N^{15}, O^{17}, O^{18}.

The isotope effect is also observed in the spectra of complex molecules. Theoretically (to a first approximation), one should expect an isotope shift of those lines (or bands) which are associated with vibrations and rotation that occur with the participation of the isotope. This conclusion is completely confirmed by experiment.

Nuclear spin and intensity alternation in spectra. In addition to the isotope shift, the spectra of isotopic molecules exhibit the

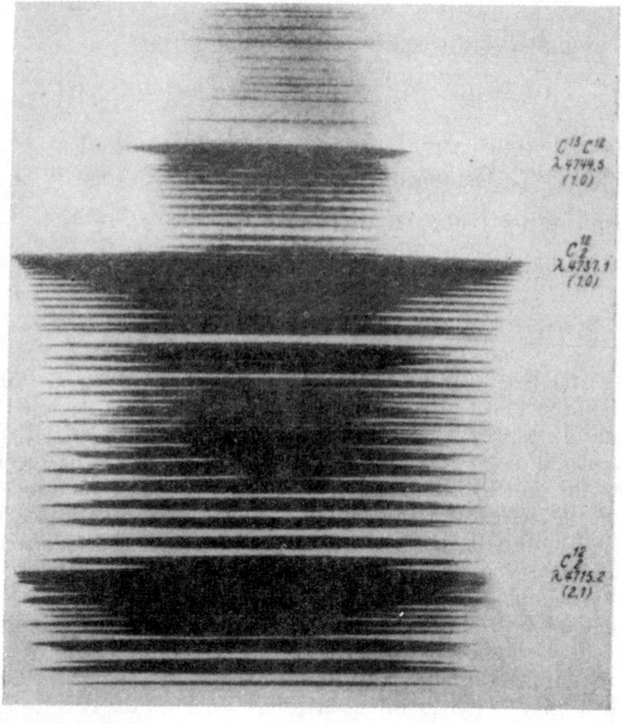

Fig. 102. Isotope effect in C_2 spectrum (Swan bands), after King and Birge

following characteristic difference. As we have already seen (p.346), the terms of molecules composed of the same atoms are divided into two non-intercombining groups that possess different statistical weights: ortho- and para-terms. The lines of the ortho-modification with its greater statistical weight are more intense than the lines of the para-modification. As a result we get a peculiar *alternation of intensities* in spectra of the molecules under consideration, which alternation is absent in molecules that consist of different atoms. This difference is particularly prominent when the nuclear moment is zero: in this case the statistical weight of the para-terms becomes zero, i.e., the para-terms are simply absent, and in the spectrum of molecules consisting of the same atoms every other line drops out (the lines of the para-modification). Such, for instance, is the spectrum of the $O^{16}O^{16}$ molecule. Unlike this spectrum, the spectra of molecules $O^{16}O^{17}$ and $O^{16}O^{18}$ exhibit all lines permitted by the selection rule for the number J. To illustrate, Fig. 103 gives the 01′ band of the molecules $O^{16}O^{16}$ and $O^{16}O^{18}$ (absorption spectrum of the terrestrial atmosphere). Besides the intensity differences of the lines of these isotopic molecules, which differences are due to the different content of isotopes O^{16} and O^{18} in ordinary oxygen, we see that whereas in band $O^{16}O^{16}$ there are only lines (doublets) * with even values of the rotational quantum number, in the band $O^{16}O^{18}$ there are lines both with even and with odd J. A certain unevenness in distribution of intensity in the bands of both isotopes and also the presence of weak intermediate lines not indicated by arrows are due to the superposition on the oxygen spectrum of other spectra, mainly the lines of iron and water vapour (the light source in this case is the sun).

Table 36

Nuclear spin and the ratio of line intensities of the ortho- and para-modifications in the spectra of diatomic molecules

Molecule	Intensity ratio	Nuclear spin	Molecule	Intensity ratio	Nuclear spin
H_2	3:1	$^1/_2$	O_2^{16}	∞	0
D_2	2:1	1	P_2^{31}	3:1	$^1/_2$
He_2	∞	0	S_2^{32}	∞	0
Li_2^7	1.67:1	$^3/_2$	Cl_2^{35}	1.4:1	$^5/_2$
C_2^{12}	∞	0	Se_2^{80}	∞	0
N_2^{14}	2:1	1	I_2^{127}	1.4:1	$^5/_2$

* The doublet structure of the lines is due to interaction of spin with the rotation of the molecule. This structure results if we take it that in the given case (transition $^3\Sigma_g^- \longrightarrow {}^1\Sigma_g^+$) the selection rule $\Delta J = 0, \pm 1$ operates and not $\Delta J = 0, \pm 1, \pm 2$; since the latter rule results for quadrupole radiation, it therefore follows that the atmospheric bands O_2 are associated not with quadrupole radiation, but with magnetic dipole radiation.

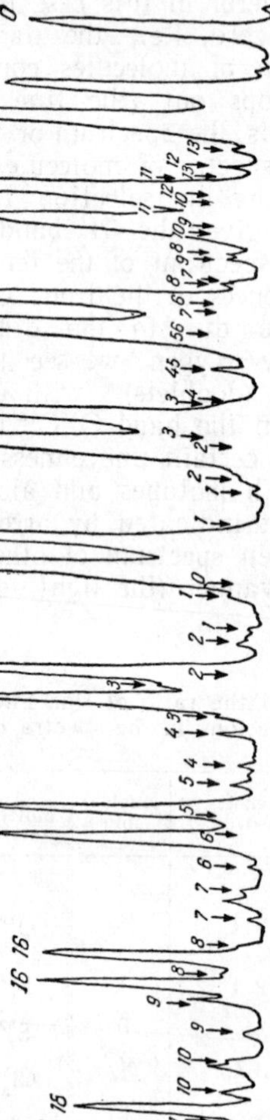

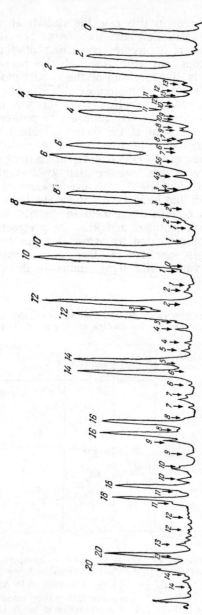

Fig. 103. Band (01') of isotopic molecules $O^{16}O^{16}$ and $O^{16}O^{18}$ in the absorption spectrum of the terrestrial atmosphere. The lines of the $O^{16}O^{18}$ molecule are denoted by arrows. Intense doublets represent the P-branch of this band of $O^{16}O^{16}$.

It may be shown that the ratio of statistical weights of ortho- and para-modifications and, hence, the ratio of intensities of the corresponding lines in the spectrum of a molecule that has identical nuclei should be equal to

$$\frac{I_o}{I_p} = \frac{i+1}{i} \tag{40.16}$$

where i is the quantum number that characterises the nuclear moment of the atom. And so from intensity measurements it is possible to find the nuclear moment or the appropriate value of i. In Table 36 we give the ratios of line intensities of the ortho- and para-modifications of different molecules and the values of i found from them.

41. Continuous and Diffuse Spectra

Continuous spectra. In addition to molecular spectra that have a more or less marked discrete linear-band structure, we very often (particularly in the case of complex molecules) observe *continuous* spectra. We can suggest two basic reasons for the absence of a fine structure in the spectrum. One, purely external, amounts to a broadening of the spectral lines ordinarily due to high temperature (Doppler effect) or high pressure (impact broadening). When the pressure is increased, the width of the separate rotational lines can exceed the width of the interval between adjacent lines in the band, and this will result in the fine structure of the band disappearing. With sufficiently high pressures the broadening can cover also the intervals between the separate bands, in which case we get a completely continuous spectrum. However, such a conversion of a discrete spectrum into a continuous spectrum can be expected only at very high pressures (and temperatures) that do not occur under ordinary conditions. Yet experiment shows that continuous spectra are very often observed at low pressures and low temperatures.

These spectra can, obviously, be due only to internal causes. From theory it follows that one of the causes is the absence of quantisation of vibrations and rotation in the case of at least one of the combining electronic terms of the molecule. To take an instance, a continuous spectrum appears when one of the combining states is unstable. The absence of discrete vibrational and rotational levels in this case is what gives rise to the continuous character of the spectrum.

However, even for combination of stable states the spectrum can also be continuous under certain conditions. Indeed, the mutual arrangement of potential-energy curves that correspond to two combining states of the molecule may be such that for a given quantum transition the potential energy of the molecule will turn out more than its energy of dissociation D′, i.e.,

$$U' - U_0' \geqslant D'$$

where U_0' is the energy corresponding to the minimum of the potential-energy curve of the molecule in an excited state. In this case the arrangement of potential energy curves is as given in Fig. 104. The attained excited state cannot be stable, and the process of absorption of light will end in *dissociation* of the molecule (*photodissociation*), with the surplus energy $U' - U_0' - D'$ converting into the kinetic energy of the atoms that fly apart. Due to the absence of discrete levels of energy on the segment of the "excited" curve (Fig. 104) lying above the asymptote $U_0' + D'$ (dashed line), the spectrum in this case will be continuous.

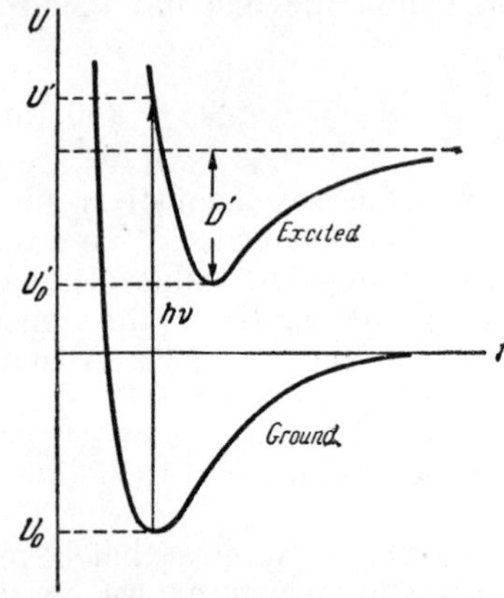

Fig. 104. Photodissociation of diatomic molecule (origin of continuous absorption spectrum)

Experiment shows that in a number of cases the continuous spectrum adjoins the convergence limit of the bands, which are v′ progressions, and the spectrum as a whole is of the form schematically shown in Fig. 105. The origin of this spectrum is clear from the foregoing: both its discrete (band) part and the continuous portion of the spectrum are due to transitions to one and the same potential-energy curve ("excited"), the only difference being that the discrete bands appear in transition to the part of the curve lying below the asymptote $U_0' + D'$, while the continuous region, to the part of the curve lying above this asymptote. Such spectra are observed for Cl_2, Br_2, I_2, O_2, ClO_2, etc. The convergence limit of the bands (the boundary between the continuous and discrete regions of the spectrum) makes it possible, in this case, to determine with great accuracy the energy of dissociation of molecules (see Sec. 49).

Fig. 105. Absorption spectrum containing discrete and continuous portions

Most frequent are the cases when in the absorption spectrum, there is either one discrete region (v progressions break off much before the limit of their convergence) or one continuous region. The first case is observed when the equilibrium distances in the ground and excited states of the molecule differ but slightly, as a result of which transition of the molecule to a portion of the "excited" curve that lies above asymptote U'_0+D' (Fig. 104) has a negligibly small probability.

When r'_e considerably exceeds r_e, so that transitions from all levels v (accessible under the conditions of the experiment) of the "ground" curve (Fig. 104) lead to the portion of the "excited" curve lying above the asymptote U'_0+D', the absorption spectrum is continuous throughout its extent. As has already been pointed out, the spectrum is completely continuous also when the "excited" curve corresponds to the unstable state of the molecule (repulsion curve).

Continuous absorption spectra are observed for diatomic molecules of type HX, MeX (where X is the halogen atom), and also in the case of a large number of more complex molecules, such as N_2O, Cl_2O, COS, XCN, H_2O, H_2S, H_2O_2, SO_3, the molecules of saturated hydrocarbons, alcohols, ethers, acids, etc. We note that in the case of complex molecules, the ratios between equilibrium distances and the energy of the molecule are, of course, far more complicated; but a large part of the foregoing reasoning is approximately applicable also to these molecules.

Our examination of continuous spectra has up to now mainly dealt with absorption spectra. Yet quite often we find cases of continuous emission spectra. Such, for example, are the spectra of temperature luminescence of halogens; they originate as a result of *recombination* of atoms. These spectra are an *inversion* of continuous absorption spectra of molecules X_2, just as the process of recombination $X+X'=X_2+h\nu$ is an inversion of the process of photodissociation $X_2+h\nu=X+X'$ (X' denotes an excited halogen atom).

A continuous emission spectrum is also observed in the bombardment of H_2 molecules with electrons. This spectrum, which extends from 5000 A to 1600 A, is connected with transition of the molecule from a stable triplet state $1s\sigma 2s\sigma\,{}^3\Sigma_g^+$, excited by electronic impact, to the unstable state $1s\sigma 2p\sigma\,{}^3\Sigma_u^+$, which corresponds to the repulsion curve. As a result of this transition the H_2 molecule disintegrates into two normal atoms. Absence of a continuous spectrum of H_2 underexcitation by light (fluorescence) is due to the fact that the levels ${}^1\Sigma_g^+$ (ground state of H_2) and ${}^3\Sigma_g^+$ (like any triplet level of H_2) do not intercombine. However, due to the possibility of electron *exchange* (the free electron changes places with one of the electrons of the molecule), which may be represented by the scheme

$$\overset{1}{\underset{e}{\uparrow}} + \underset{H_2(^1\Sigma)}{\overset{2\,3}{\downarrow\uparrow}} \rightarrow \underset{H_2(^3\Sigma)}{\overset{1\,3}{\uparrow\uparrow}} + \overset{2}{\underset{e,}{\downarrow}}$$

the prohibition of intercombinations is removed and the level $1s\sigma 2s\sigma\, {}^3\Sigma_g^+$ may be excited; following this is the emission of a continuous spectrum, $1s\sigma 2s\sigma\, {}^3\Sigma_g^+ = 1s\sigma 2p\sigma\, {}^3\Sigma_u^+ + h\nu$. The origin of continuous emission spectra of helium, xenon, and certain other gases is similar to that of the continuous spectrum of H_2.

A number of continuous spectra have a peculiar structure exhibiting alternating maxima and minima of intensity. Such are the spectra of Hg_2, Cd_2, Zn_2 observed both in absorption and emission, and also absorption spectra of the vapours of halogen salts of alkali metals. The latter have been subject to particularly careful study; according to Kuhn, the structure of these spectra is accounted for as follows. The lower state is the ground state of the MeX molecule to which there corresponds a potential-energy curve with a deep minimum. Corresponding to the upper state is the repulsion curve, which throughout $r' > r_0$ is nearly a straight line parallel to the axis r (this is due to superposition, on forces that determine the normal course of the repulsion curve, of polarisation van der Waals forces of attraction). Because of this shape of the upper curve, the energy of the molecule in the excited state should be practically constant (equal to U_0'). Expressing the energy of the molecule for different vibrational levels of the ground state in the form $U = U_0 + E_{vib}(v)$, we will have, for the frequencies of the corresponding transitions,

$$\nu = \nu_{el\text{-}v} = \nu_0 - \omega\left(v + \frac{1}{2}\right) + \omega x\left(v + \frac{1}{2}\right)^2. \quad (41.1)$$

Since the upper state of the molecule is not quantised, to these transitions there will correspond broad maxima. This accounts for the earlier indicated periodicity of intensity distribution in the continuous absorption spectra of MeX molecules.

As is seen from expression (41.1), the intensity maxima should converge to a certain limit lying in the region of long wavelengths (cf. the v′ progressions). The distance between the first two (shortest wavelength) maxima should be approximately equal to the quantity ω. This conclusion is in rather good agreement with the data on natural frequencies of MeX molecules.

As follows from the foregoing, we may expect the appearance of such intensity maxima only when one of the potential-energy curves is more or less horizontal. However, if the repulsion curve, on the contrary, rises steeply, the separate maxima will merge into a continuous spectrum with uniform distribution of intensity. It is, apparently, to this circumstance that we must attribute the fact that the periodic distribution of intensity in continuous spectra is relatively infrequent. For instance, intensity maxima are absent in the continuous spectra of NaCl, NaBr, and KCl.

Predissociation. One of the most important peculiarities of molecular spectra is associated with the phenomenon of *predissocia-*

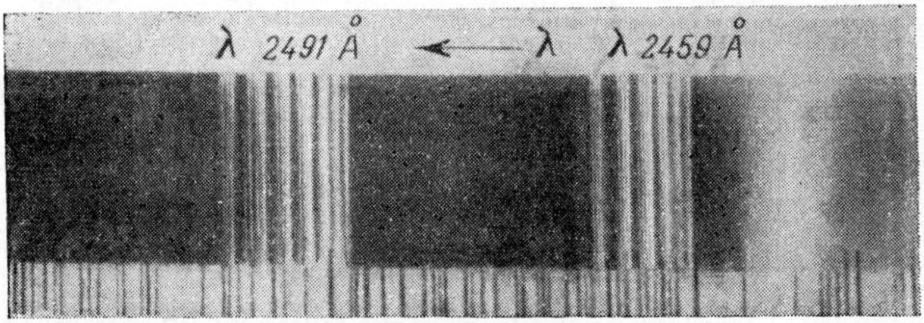

Fig. 106. Predissociation in the ultraviolet absorption spectrum of NO_2 (after Harris). Below, comparison spectrum

tion. This phenomenon is most frequently detected by diffuse bands in the absorption spectra of gases due to the anomalous broadening of rotational lines. In some cases the line width and, consequently, the diffuseness of the bands in the absorption spectrum build up slowly with diminishing wavelength; in other cases, the bands become diffuse suddenly, and between the bands with fine structure and the diffuse bands (which ordinarily belong to the same series) we find a sharp boundary (the *predissociation limit*). An example is predissociation in the short-wave region of the absorption spectrum of NO_2 (Fig. 106).

The phenomenon of dissociation, discovered by Henri in 1928 and theoretically explained in the works of Bonhoeffer, Farkas, Kronig, and Herzberg, is a quantum-mechanical effect similar to the Auger effect in atomic spectra. The Auger effect occurs when discrete energy levels of the atom are overlapped by an energy continuum, as shown in Fig. 107. In such cases, transition is possible of an excited atom to an unstable state (ionisation). In the case of ordinary photoionisation, the absorption of light by the atom and its ionisation represent a single elementary event, whereas ionisation of the atom in the Auger effect occurs in two stages:

first, absorption of light leads to excitation of the atom, then the excited atom passes from the discrete to an unstable state (i.e., becomes ionised). While in the excited state, the atom can emit light with a certain probability and can be ionised with a probability $1-\alpha$. In determining the probability of each of these processes as a mathematical expectation (frequency) of the process divided by the sum of the mathematical expectations of both processes, i.e., $\alpha=\frac{\nu_1}{\nu_1+\nu_2}$ and $1-\alpha=\frac{\nu_2}{\nu_1+\nu_2}$, and introducing the lifetimes (which are their reciprocals) for the processes under consideration and the total lifetime of the atom τ, which is connected with the quantities τ_1 and τ_2 by the relation

$$\frac{1}{\tau}=\frac{1}{\tau_1}+\frac{1}{\tau_2}, \qquad (41.2)$$

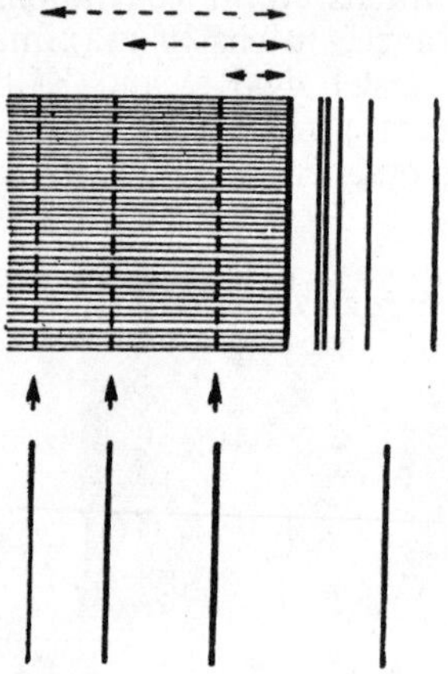

Fig. 107. Auger effect (autoionisation of atom) (after Herzberg)

we obtain $\tau=\alpha\tau_1=(1-\alpha)\tau_2$. Noting that τ_1 is the total lifetime of an ordinary excited state of the atom (in the absence of the Auger effect), i.e., is of the order of 10^{-8} sec, we conclude, on the basis of the relationship $\tau=\alpha\tau_1$, that the smaller α is, i.e., the greater the probability of spontaneous ionisation of the atom $1-\alpha$, the smaller is the lifetime of an excited atom. This shortening of the lifetime of an excited atom gives rise to the experimentally observed broadening of the corresponding spectral lines, because from the uncertainty relation

$$\Delta\nu\times\tau=\hbar \qquad (41.3)$$

the line width $\Delta\nu$ must be inversely proportional to the lifetime.

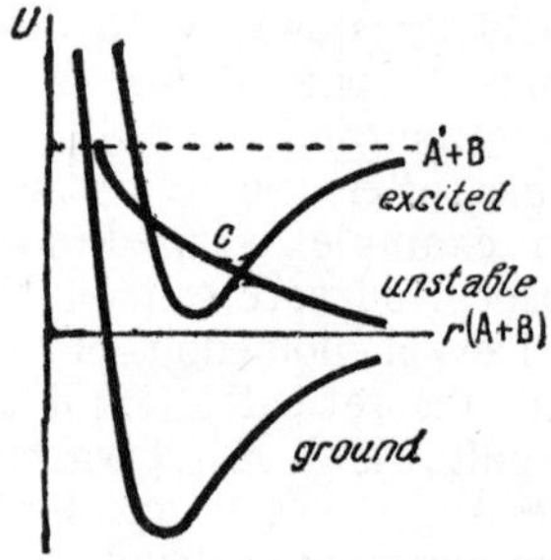

Fig. 108. Predissociation of a diatomic molecule

In the case of molecules, the overlapping of discrete energy levels by the energy continuum is observed with particular frequency. For instance, the vibrational levels of excited states of a molecule are frequently overlapped by the continuum that corresponds to an unstable state arising out of the ground states of the atoms. An instance of this kind is given in Fig. 108 for a diatomic molecule: the overlapping states here are the stable state of the excited molecule and the unstable state. Transition of the molecule from a stable state to an unstable state, expressed by the transition from the "excited" curve to the "unstable" curve, is precisely what predissociation is.

According to the Franck-Condon principle, which holds also for radiationless transitions (these are transitions not accompanied by the emission or absorption of light), when a molecule passes from one state to another there are no substantial changes in the distance between the atoms or in their relative velocities. It follows that a predissociation transition from one curve to another is possible only near the point of intersection of the curves; this point must lie below the initial level of excitation.

Predissociation transitions also obey definite selection rules that partly coincide and partly differ from the selection rules for radiative transitions. For example, a radiationless transition is possible only in the case of a constant total momentum of the molecule ($\Delta J = 0$), when $\Delta\Lambda = 0, \pm 1$, when $\Delta S = 0$. The combining terms must both be positive or both negative, in contradistinction to radiative transitions, in which only positive and negative terms can combine. In the case of a molecule consisting of the same atoms, both terms must be either symmetric (s) or antisymmetric (a).

Predissociation, the spontaneous decay of an excited molecule, is observed when transition to an unstable state is not associated with violation of any selection rule. However, also in the case of forbidden transitions predissociation may be possible under the action of some external factor that removes the quantum prohibition; in this case it is called *induced*. Up till now, cases have been observed of predissociation induced by a magnetic field (I_2) and by molecular collisions (I_2, Br_2, N_2, NO, S_2, Se_2, Te_2); the latter is of particular interest in understanding the mechanism of photochemical reactions.

A quantum-mechanical treatment of different transitions (including predissociation transitions) in a molecule shows that interaction of overlapping states leads to splitting and shifting of levels, which are manifested in distortion of potential-energy curves. When selection rules are not fulfilled, the mutual perturbation of the terms is slight; however, here too it is frequently observed in molecular spectra. Most often it disturbs the rotational structure of the bands; more rarely, it leads to disturbances in the vibrational structure of the spectra. In both cases we speak of *perturbations* in spectra. Fig. 109 shows a perturbation of the rotational structure in band CN (11, 11′) λ 3921 Å, where there is a clearcut violation of the regular sequence of rotational lines both in the R- and P-branch. In the P-branch, the perturbation appears as a sudden increase in doublet splitting (for $K=12$) that passes through a maximum and diminishes to a small value (when $K>16$).

Disturbances of the vibrational structure of spectra are due to distortion of the potential-energy curves that results in two new curves in place of the two intersecting curves. This disturbance is particularly great when the selection rules are not violated. The ICl molecule is an example of such transformation of potential-energy curves; the potential-energy curves for the ground and excited states of this molecule (these curves are constructed on the basis of an analysis of its spectrum) are shown in Fig. 110. We note

Fig. 109. Perturbation of rotational structure in CN band λ 3921 A (after Jenkins)

that the "mixed" origin of the vibrational levels of the upper curve is evident from their diffuseness, which leads to the diffuse nature of the absorption bands in the ICl spectrum.

Transformation of the potential curves, like that shown in Fig. 110, gives a vivid picture of the predissociation decomposition of the molecule. The molecule, which due to the absorption of light gets into one of the vibrational levels lying above the point of intersection of the original curves, will have the opportunity, after a time of the order of half a cycle of vibration, to pass to the repulsion curve, i.e., to dissociate. The energy of the products of dissociation is then equal to the height of the initial excitation level above the asymptote of the repulsion curve.

Due to the predissociation decomposition of the molecule, its lifetime is shortened and this causes the absorption spectrum to be diffuse. Indeed, in ordinary radiative excitation that does not lead to dissociation of the molecule, for instance in the transition to one of the vibrational levels lying below the point of intersection of the stable-state curve and the repulsion curve, the time the molecule is in the excited state is ordinarily of the order of

$\tau_1 = 10^{-8}$ sec. During this time the molecule will execute $10^{-8}:10^{-13} = 10^5$ vibrations (10^{-13} sec is the period of vibration) and about $10^{-8}:10^{-11} = 10^3$ rotations (10^{-11} sec is the period of rotation). In this case the absorption spectrum is an ordinary system of bands with fine (rotational) structure. But in the region of predissociation the duration of the excited state of the molecule,

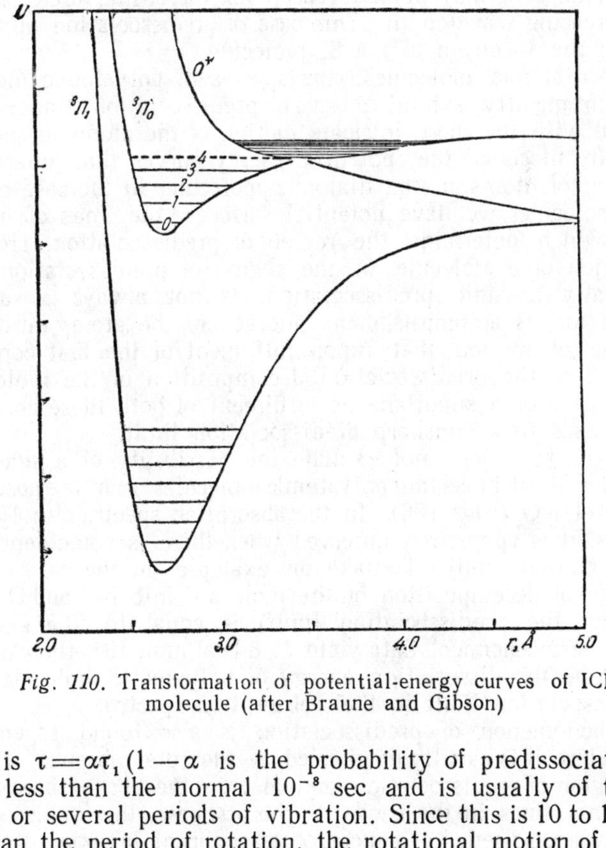

Fig. 110. Transformation of potential-energy curves of ICl molecule (after Braune and Gibson)

which is $\tau = \alpha\tau_1$ ($1 - \alpha$ is the probability of predissociation), becomes less than the normal 10^{-8} sec and is usually of the order of one or several periods of vibration. Since this is 10 to 100 times less than the period of rotation, the rotational motion of the molecule (as quantised periodic motion) can, obviously, no longer occur, and consequently the fine structure of the bands will be absent: the bands become diffuse.

The predissociation diffuseness of the bands in the absorption spectra of diatomic molecules sets in suddenly, i.e., beginning with a certain definite wavelength, the bands of a given series become diffuse. In this case, one speaks of a *sharp predissociation limit*. Sometimes, the absorption spectra of diatomic molecules exhibit a gradual increase in the predissociation diffuseness of the bands with diminishing wavelength, that is, the predissociation limit is not sharp. In part this may be due to the tunnel effect. The probability of the latter increases with decreasing distance of the initial vibrational level from the point of intersection of the curves, and this may be the reason for increasing predissociation with decreasing wavelength. This case of predissociation apparently occurs in the spectrum of the S_2 molecule.

Unlike diatomic molecules, the spectra of polyatomic molecules rather infrequently exhibit a sharp predissociation limit; this is connected with the more intricate motion of the atoms in such molecules. In place of the potential-energy curves that characterise interaction of atoms in the diatomic molecule, in the case of polyatomic molecules we have potential surfaces, the lines of intersection of which determine the region of predissociation. However, the location of a molecule in the region of predissociation, i.e., energetically possible predissociation, is not always a sufficient condition for its accomplishment. Moreover, the atoms must be in the phase of motion that (upon fulfilment of the first condition) could lead to the predissociation decomposition of the molecule.* The necessity of a simultaneous fulfilment of both these conditions is what leads to a nonsharp predissociation limit.

However, this does not exclude the possibility of a sharp predissociation limit in certain polyatomic molecules, as in the absorption spectrum of NO_2 (Fig. 106). In the absorption spectra of polyatomic molecules, it is apparently observed when there is coincidence with the dissociation limit. To take an example, in the case of NO_2, the energy of decomposition of the molecule into NO and O (calculated from the predissociation limit) is equal to 70.8 kcal/mol, whereas thermochemical data yield 71.8 kcal/mol. It is thus possible to determine the dissociation energy of polyatomic molecules from the predissociation limit in their absorption spectra.

The phenomenon of predissociation is also found in emission spectra. Here it is usually manifested in the total absence of bands in the region of predissociation, and also in the abrupt breaking-off of rotational lines in the bands. In the first case, the predissociation limit is characterised by a more or less abrupt breaking-off of the spectrum and is readily detected. This type of breaking-off is observed in the emission spectra of S_2, NO, N_2, and others for certain values

* The insufficiency of the energy condition alone is already obvious from the fact that, unlike a diatomic molecule, a polyatomic molecule can be stable even when the vibrational energy exceeds its energy of dissociation. It may be noted that in this case the concentration of vibrational energies on definite bonds can lead to a unimolecular decomposition of the molecule.

of the quantum numbers v and J determined for each series of bands (v) and for each band(J). It is interesting to note that in some cases (S_2) at high pressures the region of predissociation exhibits bands that are absent at low pressures. This fact is, apparently, to be interpreted in the sense that the mean lifetime of a predissociating molecule becomes comparable with the time interval between two quenching collisions of an excited molecule with other molecules.

Fig. 111 shows the 0,0′ emission band of CaH λ 3533.6 A. We see the abrupt breaking-off of the rotational structure that occurs at K=9 in the R-branch and at K=11 in the P-branch. A curious

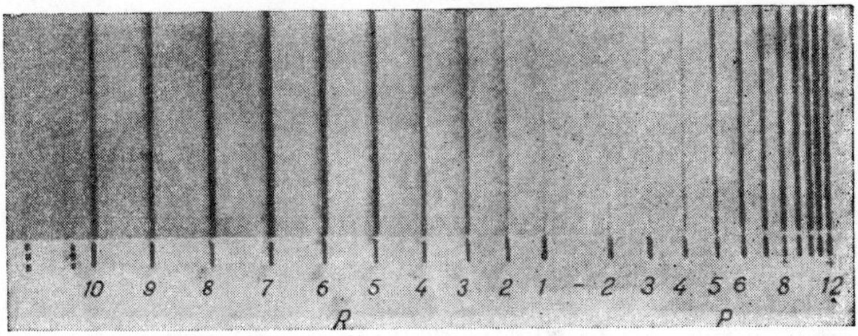

Fig. 111. Abrupt breaking off of emission band of CaH at λ 3533.6 A due to predissociation (after Mulliken)

breaking-off of the spectrum is observed in the case of HgH, where it occurs also at definite values of the quantum number K (K_{max}) for each band, namely: in bands corresponding to v=0, $K_{max}=31$, v=1—24, v=2—17, v=3—9, v=4—6. According to Oldenberg, the reason for the sudden breaking-off of the rotational band structure is, in this case, the break-up of the molecule under the action of the centrifugal force produced by rotation of the molecule (predissociation by rotation).

42. Some Applications of Molecular Spectroscopy

Molecular spectral analysis. Besides the great importance of molecular spectroscopy for the physics and chemistry of atoms and molecules, we must also point out its vast practical value. Of the applications of molecular spectroscopy we shall here consider analytical applications and those in the field of thermodynamics.

The aim of molecular spectral analysis is the *identification* of chemical compounds and the measuring of their *concentrations*. The first problem is solved both by absorption spectra and by emission spectra; the necessary condition for identifying a given substance is a discrete spectrum characteristic of the given substance.

The principal problem is that of the *limit of sensitivity* of the spectroscopic method of identification. Let us first examine *absorption spectra*. In these investigations the common procedure is to use light sources with a continuous spectrum. In this case, the sensitivity of the method is determined by the portions of radiant energy absorbed in a given spectral interval, i.e., by the quantity

$$\Delta = \frac{I_0 - I}{I_0} \tag{42.1}$$

where I_0 is the intensity of the incident light and I is the intensity of the light transmitted through the absorbing layer. In the case of diatomic molecules, Δ may be represented by the following approximate formula:

$$\Delta = \frac{1}{40} \frac{\lambda_0^3}{\pi c} AFln \tag{42.2}$$

where λ_0 is the wavelength of the absorbed light, A is the probability of transition (emission), F is the resolving power of the spectral instrument, l is the length of the absorbing layer, and n is the gas concentration (number of molecules per cubic centimetre). This equality may be used to determine the order of the minimum concentration n from the absorption spectrum.

Considering the limiting measurable absorption equal to 5%, i.e., $\Delta = 0.05$ and substituting into equality (42.2) $\lambda_0 = 4000$ Å (the boundary between the visible and ultraviolet regions of the spectrum), $A = 10^8$ sec^{-1} (the usual order of magnitude of the mathematical expectation of emission), $F = 10^4$ (the theoretical resolving power of an average spectral device) and $l = 1$ cm, we find $n = 10^{13}$, or $p = 10^{-4}$ mm Hg (at 300°K). Thus, the limiting measurable gas density (from the electronic spectrum of absorption) for a 1cm length of absorbing layer corresponds to a partial pressure of the order of 10^{-4} mm Hg.

It may be shown that the limiting sensitivity of detecting a given gas on the basis of its absorption spectrum in the visible or ultraviolet regions when using instruments of high resolving power (diffraction gratings) is approximately one order of magnitude above the computed value.

The figures obtained must, however, be regarded as the upper limit of sensitivity of the described method for the identification of chemical compounds. In reality, however, due to imperfections in the optical system of the spectral instruments in use (primarily because of the more or less wide slit) which reduce their resolving power; also, due to a reduced probability of A, which frequently is greatly different from the maximum probability that we take 10^8 sec^{-1} (particularly in the infrared); and, finally, due to the fact that at high temperatures and also in the case of polyatomic molecules with their large number of rotational and vibrational degrees of freedom, the number of molecules capable of absorbing light of wavelength λ_0 make up only a small part n, the limit of sensitivity rarely exceeds a magnitude corresponding to partial pressures of the order of $10^{-1}-10^{-3}$ mm Hg.

As has already been pointed out, due to the smallness of A, in the infrared the sensitivity is usually much lower than that in the visible and ultraviolet regions. For this reason, infrared absorption spectra are commonly used for identifying chemical compounds only in the case of condensed substances (liquid and solid).

A decisive factor that puts a limit on the sensitivity of the second spectroscopic method of identification (based on *emission spectra*) is the sensitivity of the method of recording radiation. Given proper time for adjustment, the human eye is capable of registering radiation intensity of several tens of quanta per second. The sensitivity limit of electrical methods of registration of radiation based on the use of photoelectric devices is apparently 10^5 to 10^7 quanta per second (depending on the spectral region). This limit may be reduced by several orders of magnitude by means of photomultiplying. Finally, the most sensitive types of photographic plates record a radiation density corresponding to 10^{10}-10^{11} quanta per square centimetre. Taking into account the possibility of utilising the time factor in the photographic method (in contrast to the electric and visual methods) and assuming an exposure of several hours, we get, from the foregoing figures, recorded intensities of the order of 10^6-10^7 quanta per second per square centimetre.

The number of emitted quanta recorded by a given method does not allow us to judge of the actual concentration of a substance, because it is determined by the concentration of the excited molecules, which may differ greatly from that of the nonexcited particles. In the general case, we have the following relationship between the concentration of excited n′ and nonexcited n molecules of a given substance:

$$n' = fn. \tag{42.3}$$

We may call the quantity f the *excitation factor*. This quantity is a complex function of the conditions of excitation and, in each separate case of radiative (fluorescence), electrical (gas discharge), or chemical (chemiluminescence) excitation it may be determined only by experiment. An exception here is the case of thermal radiation where the ratio between the concentration of excited and nonexcited particles is given by the Boltzmann distribution. In the simplest case of atomic radiation the factor of thermal excitation is

$$f = \frac{g'}{g} e^{-\frac{E}{kT}} \tag{42.4}$$

where g' and g are the statistical weights of the excited and nonexcited states of the atom and E is its excitation energy.

By way of illustration, let us consider the radiation of sodium under the conditions of an ordinary flame ($T = 2000°K$). In this case, from the excitation energy of the D-lines, which amounts to 48.1 kcal/gm-atom, and from the statistical weights of the states $^2P_{3/2}$ and $^2S_{1/2}$ we find $f = 10^{-5}$. We determine the order of magnitude of the limiting, photographically recordable concentration of sodium atoms in the flame. The intensity of sodium radiation of 1 cm^3 of the flame zone as measured by the number of quanta emitted in one second is obviously equal to

$$I = An' \tag{42.5}$$

where A is the probability of radiation of an excited atom of Na. The density of radiation i may be set equal to $i = \frac{I}{4\pi R^2}$, where R is the distance of the photographic plate from the centre of the flame. Thus, to determine the concentration of sodium atoms in the flame we have the equality

$$n = 4\pi R^2 \frac{i}{Af}. \tag{42.6}$$

Substituting $R = 50$ cm, $f = 10^{-5}$, $i = 10^7$ (see above), and $1/A = 1.4 \times 10^{-8}$ sec, we find for the limiting concentration of sodium atoms in the flame a magnitude of the order of 10^9 (or a partial pressure of the order of 10^{-7} mm Hg). This is substantially less than the minimum quantities of a substance that are usually necessary for their detection by the photographic method. Indeed, from the limiting concentration of sodium atoms, for the quantity of sodium in grams we get a value of the order of 10^{-14} gm, whereas usually the absolute sensitivity of the method for metals (and also for molecular gases) rarely exceeds that of a concentration of the order of 10^{-10} gm/cm^3.

It must be said that the factor of excitation in radiative, electrical, and chemical excitations is, as a rule, considerably above the thermal factor. For this reason, the limit of sensitivity of the spectroscopic method of identification based on emission spectra is higher than that of the absorption method.

Solution of the second problem of molecular spectral analysis — that of measuring the concentrations of chemical compounds — involves almost exclusively the absorption method; with very few exceptions, determinations may be made of the concentrations of chemically stable substances. Here, it is possible to establish an empirical relationship between the coefficient of absorption for a given substance and its concentration by means of pre-graduated measurements of absorption spectra. Ordinarily, the accuracy of these measurements does not exceed several per cent of the quantity being measured. With regard to certain gases, the spectroscopic method of emission may be used to determine concentrations up to 10^{-4} per cent.

We shall not dwell on other optical methods of measuring concentrations (refractometry, polarimetry, etc.). Of other extremely important methods of molecular spectral analysis, special mention should be made of Raman scattering and radiospectroscopy as exceedingly effective and simple methods of analysis. If small amounts of gas are to be analysed, the radiospectroscopic method is far more sensitive than the ordinary spectroscopic method.

Let us touch briefly on one of the basic results of spectral analysis that led to the establishment of definite characteristic frequencies possessed by individual radicals or groups of atoms that comprise a given molecule (*chromophoric groups* or *chromophores*) and also by individual bonds inside the molecule. Definite frequencies that change but slightly from molecule to molecule were established for the radicals OH, NH_2, NO_2, CO, C_6H_5, etc. (see p. 526). Therefore, the presence of these radicals in a molecule may easily be established on the basis of specific bands in the infrared or of appropriate lines of Raman scattering. In exactly the same way, the presence of different intramolecular bonds, such as the bonds C—C, C=C, C≡C, C=O, C—H, etc., is established on the basis of frequencies characteristic of these bonds (see Sec. 50).

Due to the development of molecular spectroscopy that has led to the establishment of these characteristic frequencies, it has become possible to analyse complex mixtures of hydrocarbons and other substances of great practical importance.

As a rule, chromophores also exhibit specific, characteristic spectra associated with electronic excitation. This property of chromophores and, hence, of the molecules that contain them is very important for the synthesis of dyes, for biological spectral analysis, etc.

Thermodynamic applications of molecular spectroscopy. Molecular spectroscopy finds one of its most important practical applications in thermodynamics. An analysis of molecular spectra leads to the establishment of molecular constants (natural frequencies of molecules, their moments of inertia, the heats of dissociation, electronic and nuclear moments, etc.) that define the various thermodynamic functions of a given gas. Among the most important thermodynamic functions are the heat capacity, entropy, and free energy. Using the latter one, we can compute the constants of equilibrium that determine the partial pressures of gases in thermodynamic equilibrium.

In calculating thermodynamic functions, the starting point is the following expression for the energy of a single gram-molecule of gas:

$$E = E_0 + \sum N_i \varepsilon_i \quad (42.7)$$

where E_0 is the energy of the gas at absolute zero and N_i is the number of molecules possessing energy ε_i. Representing N_i in the form

$$N_i = \frac{N_a}{Z} g_i e^{-\frac{\varepsilon_i}{kT}}$$

where g_i is the statistical weight of the ith state of the molecule, Z is the partition function,

$$Z = \sum g_i e^{-\frac{\varepsilon_i}{kT}}, \quad (42.8)$$

and N_A is Avogadro's number, it may readily be shown that the sum $\sum N_i \varepsilon_i$ can be represented as

$$\sum N_i \varepsilon_i = RT^2 \frac{d\ln Z}{dT}$$

whence it follows that

$$E = E_0 + RT^2 \frac{d\ln Z}{dT}. \quad (42.9)$$

The partition function Z may be represented in the form of a product of the sum of states Z_{tr} corresponding to the translational motion of the molecule, and Z_{in}, the partition function that is associated with its internal energy,

$$Z = Z_{tr} Z_{in}.$$

Quantum statistics for Z_{tr} yields the following expression:

$$Z_{tr} = \frac{V}{h^3} (2\pi mkT)^{3/2} \quad (42.10)$$

where V is the volume of the gas and h is Planck's constant. From expression (42.10) we find

$$\frac{d\ln Z_{tr}}{dT} = \frac{3}{2} \frac{1}{T}$$

whence it follows that

$$E=E_0+\frac{3}{2}RT+RT^2\frac{d\ln Z_{in}}{dT}. \qquad (42.11)$$

From the latter formula we obtain the following expression for the *molar heat capacity of the gas* (for a constant volume):

$$C_v=\frac{dE}{dT}=\frac{3}{2}R+R\frac{d}{dT}\left(T^2\frac{d\ln Z_{in}}{dT}\right). \qquad (42.12)$$

Formula (42.7), or formula (42.9) which is its equivalent, is also the starting point for calculating the entropy and free energy of the gas. In the case of a reversible process proceeding at constant volume, the entropy is determined as

$$dS=\frac{dE}{T}.$$

Noting that $\frac{dE}{T}=\frac{dE}{dT}\frac{dT}{T}=\frac{C_v dT}{T}$ and substituting C_v (42.12) into this expression, we obtain for the molar entropy of the gas S (accurate to the constant of integration):

$$S=R\left(\ln Z+T\frac{d\ln Z}{dT}\right). \qquad (42.13)$$

Finally, for the *free energy* of one gram-molecule of gas $F=E-TS$, from (42.9) and (42.13) we get (also accurate to the constant term)

$$F=E_0-RT\ln Z. \qquad (42.14)$$

In the general case, the partition function Z_{in} can approximately (without taking into account the interaction between vibrations and rotation of the molecule, and also the dependence of the vibrational and rotational energy upon the electronic energy) be represented as the product

$$Z_{in}=Z_{rot}Z_{vib}Z_{el}Z_{nuc}$$

where Z_{rot} is the rotational, Z_{vib} the vibrational, Z_{el} the electronic, and Z_{nuc} the nuclear partition function.

In the simplest case of a diatomic molecule with different nuclei and in the state $^1\Sigma$ (HCl, N_2, CO, NaCl), the quantity Z_{rot} is expressed by the formula

$$Z_{rot}=\sum_{J=0}^{J=\infty}(2J+1)e^{-\frac{hBJ(J+1)}{kT}}. \qquad (42.15)$$

When $hB\ll kT$, which practically always occurs already at room temperature, Z_{rot} can be approximately represented in the form

$$Z_{rot}=\frac{kT}{hB} \qquad (42.16)$$

whence for the heat capacity C_v (42.12) we get the ordinary expression $C_v = \frac{5}{2}R$ (without the vibrational part of the heat capacity).

The vibrational partition function of a diatomic gas is expressed as

$$Z_{vib} = \sum_{v=0}^{v=v_{max}} e^{-\frac{E_{vib}(v)}{kT}} \approx \sum_{v=0}^{v=\infty} e^{-\frac{E_{vib}(v)}{kT}} \tag{42.17}$$

where E_{vib} is the vibrational energy of the molecule and v is the vibrational quantum number. Considering the vibrations harmonic, to a first approximation, we have $E_{vib} = h\omega\left(v + \frac{1}{2}\right)$, where ω is the natural frequency of the molecule. Substituting this expression into the formula for Z_{vib}, we can rewrite it in the form

$$Z_{vib} = e^{-\frac{h\omega}{2kT}} \sum_{v=0}^{v=\infty} e^{-\frac{h\omega v}{kT}} = \frac{e^{-\frac{h\omega}{2kT}}}{1 - e^{-\frac{h\omega}{kT}}}. \tag{42.18}$$

From this expression, for the vibrational part of the heat capacity of a diatomic gas we get

$$C_{v\,vib} = R\left(\frac{h\omega}{kT}\right)^2 \frac{e^{-\frac{h\omega}{kT}}}{\left(1 - e^{-\frac{h\omega}{kT}}\right)^2}, \tag{42.19}$$

and, consequently, for the total heat capacity we have

$$C_v = \frac{5}{2}R + R\left(\frac{h\omega}{kT}\right)^2 \frac{e^{-\frac{h\omega}{kT}}}{\left(1 - e^{-\frac{h\omega}{kT}}\right)^2}. \tag{42.20}$$

It is readily seen that when $h\omega \ll kT$, i.e., at a sufficiently high temperature, the vibrational part of the heat capacity tends to the value R and the total heat capacity to 7/2 R (equidistribution of energy over the degrees of freedom).

The electronic partition function has the form

$$Z_{el} = \sum g_i e^{-\frac{E_i}{kT}}. \tag{42.21}$$

Here, E_i is the energy of the *i*th electronic state of the molecule with respect to its lowest state, i.e., the difference between the energies of the *i*th and ground states, and g_i is the statistical weight of the appropriate electronic state. The quantities E_i are ordinarily considerably greater than kT.

For this reason, the preceding expression for Z_{el} is of the form

$$Z_{el}=g_0 \tag{42.22}$$

where g_0 is the statistical weight of the ground state of the molecule. For the terms $^1\Sigma$, $^2\Sigma$, $^3\Sigma$, ... g_0 has the values 1, 2, 3, ...

Finally, the nuclear partition function is

$$Z_{nuc}=(2i_1+1)(2i_2+1) \tag{42.23}$$

where i_1 and i_2 are quantum numbers that characterise the nuclear spins of the atoms that comprise the molecule.

In the case of molecules consisting of the same atoms, the rotational terms are divided into two nonintercombining groups (see p.346 et seq.), having different statistical weights. The terms with greater statistical weight are called ortho-terms, with less, para-terms. When the nuclear spin is zero the para-terms are absent; this is seen, for instance, in the fact that half the spectral lines (every other line) drop out in each parabola of the band. The rotational partition function in this case contains members either with even or odd J.

In the case of nuclear spin, however, we have

$$Z_{rot}Z_{nuc}=g_{ortho}\sum_{ortho}(2J+1)e^{-\frac{hBJ(J+1)}{kT}}+ \\ +g_{para}\sum_{para}(2J+1)e^{-\frac{hBJ(J+1)}{kT}}. \tag{42.24}$$

For example, in the case of hydrogen, due to the fact that $i=\frac{1}{2}$, the ortho-terms have a statistical weight $g_{ortho}=3$, the para-terms, $g_{para}=1$, the odd J corresponding to the former, the even, to the latter. Consequently, the partition function (42.24) in this case will be written as

$$Z_{rot}Z_{nuc}=3\sum_{J=1,3,5,\ldots}(2J+1)e^{-\frac{hBJ(J+1)}{kT}}+ \\ +\sum_{J=0,2,4,\ldots}(2J+1)e^{-\frac{hBJ(J+1)}{kT}}. \tag{42.25}$$

On the condition that $hB \ll kT$, i.e., for sufficiently high temperatures ($T>100°$ K), each of the sums of this expression can approximately be put equal to $\frac{kT}{2hB}$, whence, on the basis of (42.12), we find $C_v=5/2\,R$ for the heat capacity of both modifications of hydrogen. However, at low temperatures, due to the different dependence of each of the two sums upon the temperature, the heat capacities themselves of both modifications of hydrogen will differ, as well as their temperature variation. Since ordinary hydrogen is a mixture of three parts of the ortho- and one part of the para-modification, its total heat capacity, the rotational component of which is defined by the formula

$$C_{rot}=\frac{3C_{v\ rot,\,ortho}+C_{v\ rot,\,para}}{4},$$

exhibits a peculiar temperature variation that radically differs from the ordinary trend which corresponds to (42.12). This "anomaly" in the heat capacity of hydrogen was the first experimental fact that led to the discovery of its ortho- and para-modifications.

For polyatomic molecules, the sums of states naturally have considerably more complicated expressions than those for diatomic molecules. In this case, approximate formulas are ordinarily used to compute the thermodynamic quantities. They also have to be used in the case of diatomic molecules when the accuracy of calculations requires that account be taken of the anharmonicity of vibrations, the interaction of vibrations and rotation, spin and rotation, etc. At times, in place of closed expressions and series, we use the values of rotational and vibrational terms taken directly from spectral measurements.

CHAPTER 9

ELECTRICAL AND MAGNETIC PROPERTIES OF ATOMS AND MOLECULES

The electrical structure of atoms and molecules consisting of nuclei and electrons is vividly manifested in their electrical and magnetic properties. These properties consist in the possibility of ionisation of atoms and molecules, that is to say, in the appearance of electrically charged free atomic and molecular ions, or in the polarisation of atoms and molecules in an external electric field, in an electric molecular field, or in the electric field of a light wave. The electrical structure of atoms and molecules is also manifested in the presence of electric and magnetic moments and in the peculiarities of their interaction associated thereto.

43. Ionisation of Atoms and Molecules

Thermal ionisation of gases. We begin a consideration of the electrical properties of atoms and molecules with their ionisation. In the normal state, atoms (or molecules) are electrically neutral with the number of electrons equal to the charge of the nucleus expressed in units of elementary charge (Z). However, due to external effects, atoms and molecules are capable of losing some of their electrons and of converting into positively charged ions. This process always involves an expenditure of energy, which is usually measured by the *ionisation potential*. Depending upon the nature of the ionising factor, one speaks of thermal ionisation, which is due to the thermal energy of the atoms and molecules, and photoionisation, caused by the action of light. In an electric discharge, ionisation occurs due to the impacts of fast electrons and ions. Finally, solutions exhibit ionisation caused by interaction of the dissolved molecule with the molecules of the solvent, as a result of which the molecule dissociates into oppositely charged parts — cation and anion (electrolytic dissociation). Having in view the ionisation processes in gases, we shall consider only the first three cases of ionisation.

In contrast to the positive ionisation of atoms and molecules, their negative ionisation, associated with saturation of *electron affinity*, does not ordinarily require the expenditure of energy. The existence, in a number of atoms, of a positive electron affinity is an indication that in a neutral atom the electric field of the nucleus is not completely saturated, and so the negative ion has energy less than that of the separately taken atom and electron. Such, for example, is the case of the fluorine atom, where total saturation of the nuclear charge sets in when one electron is added to form (together with the seven outer electrons of the neutral F atom) a closed eight-electron L-group of the F^- ion.

Besides atomic ions, we also encounter molecular negative ions whose stability is due to the same causes as that of the former. Such for instance is the hydroxyl ion HO^-. From the viewpoint of general electronic structure, the radical HO (with seven outer electrons) should be similar to the F atom (see p. 334); this accounts for the similarity of various properties (including electrical) of HO and F.

We now turn to the *thermal ionisation* of atoms and molecules. In terrestrial conditions, thermal ionisation is most often encountered in flames. It may be taken that under conditions of thermal equilibrium, ionisation is caused by the collision of atoms and molecules, as a result of which their thermal energy passes into the work of ionisation. However, since the mean energy per degree of freedom at the temperature of the flame (2000-3000° K) is only about 0.1 eV, it is evident that there will be a perceptible percentage of ionised atoms or molecules only when the ionisation potential is sufficiently small. This condition is satisfied by the atoms of alkaline elements and accounts for the appreciable conductivity of flames containing these metals.

According to Saha, the degree of ionisation of a gas in a flame can be computed from the temperature equilibrium.* Considering the equilibrium

$$A \rightleftarrows A^+ + e$$

and regarding the electrons as a one-atom ideal gas, we obtain from thermodynamics the following expression for the *constant of ionisation equilibrium* (without account taken of the possible electronic levels of the atom A and the ion A^+):

$$K = \frac{x^2}{1 - x^2} p = \left(\frac{2\pi m}{h^2}\right)^{3/2} (kT)^{5/2} e^{-\frac{eI}{kT}} \tag{43.1}$$

where x is the degree of ionisation equal to the ratio of the partial pressure of ions to the sum of the pressures of the ions and the

* In the zone of maximum temperature of the flame occupying the greatest volume.

neutral atoms, p is the total pressure, m the electron mass, and I the ionisation potential.

The theory of ionisation equilibrium permits computing the electric conductivity of flames as determined by the electron concentration in the flame, which is approximately equal to the ion concentration.* On the other hand, measurements of the electric conductivity allow us, on the basis of the theory of ionisation equilibrium, to compute the ionisation potential of atoms, the ionisation of which gives rise to electric conductivity in flames. In Table 37 we give the values of ionisation potentials of atoms of the alkaline elements obtained by Noyes and Wilson from the electric conductivity of flames, together with the exact values taken from spectroscopic data.

Table 37

Ionisation potentials (I) computed from the electric conductivity of flames, and the spectroscopic values of ionisation potential (I_{sp})

Element	Li	K	Rb	Cs
I, V	5.46	4.35	4.26	4
I_{sp}, V	5.35	4.32	4.15	3.87

The close coincidence of ionisation potentials computed from the electric conductivity of flames and the spectroscopic values of ionisation potentials corroborates the theory of ionisation equilibrium. This theory has also proved extremely fruitful in application to ionisation in stellar processes.

Ionisation by electron and ion impact. A large number of investigations in the field of ionisation of gases is devoted to the study of processes of ionisation of atoms and molecules under electron and ion impacts. These investigations are aimed at measuring the ionisation potentials and determining the probability (cross-section) of ionisation for various energies of the bombarding particles. In most cases, the procedure consists in measuring the ionic current produced in the rarefied space filled with the gas under study when a beam of electrons or ions of specific velocity is passed through it.

Electrons are the only suitable bombarding particles for measuring ionisation potentials. Indeed, applying the laws of conservation of energy and momentum to the collision of a bombarding particle and of the atom or molecule undergoing ionisation (we consider the atom and molecule as stationary), it can readily be shown that the minimum energy of a fast particle K_0 must be connected with the ionisation potential I by relation (19.1) (p. 122), from which it follows that only in the case of an electron ($m \ll M$)

* In view of the low mobility of ions due to their large masses, the electric conductivity of flames is determined almost exclusively by free electrons.

does K_0 practically coincide with the ionisation potential. In the case of ions, the minimum energy is always greater than I. Besides, as was noted by J. Franck, in ionisation by ion impact one has to take into account the Coulomb repulsion of the bombarding and newly produced ions—this repulsion is not included in equation (19.1).

The accuracy of measurement of ionisation potentials in the best studies reaches several hundredths and even thousandths of a volt. By means of the electron-impact method it has been possible to measure the ionisation potentials of a large number of atoms and molecules.

Along with simple ionisation, in the case of molecules we very often encounter ionisation accompanied by dissociation of the molecule, as a result of which some of the products of dissociation are ionised. The mass-spectroscopic method is used to study this *dissociative ionisation*. Measurement of the minimum potential difference of the electric field that accelerates the bombarding electrons (at which potential difference ions of a given type appear) yields the ionisation potential corresponding to a given type of ionisation of the molecule. We note that the mass-spectroscopic method is also one of a series of effective methods for measuring the bond-dissociation energy in molecules (see Sec. 49).

The probability of ionisation is ordinarily expressed as the *cross-section for ionisation* σ, which enters into the formula

$$\frac{dN}{dT} = \sigma n u_{el} \qquad (43.2)$$

which is the number of ionisation events performed by one electron in 1 sec in 1 cubic centimetre of gas containing n atoms or molecules with the electron velocity u_{el}. The quantity σ has the dimensions of [cm^2] and can be expressed by the formula $\sigma = \pi r^2$, where r is the effective radius of an ionised atom or molecule. To characterise the probability of ionisation, use is also frequently made of the product σn_1, where n_1 is the number of gas molecules in 1 cm^3 at normal temperature and at a pressure of 1 mm Hg equal to 3.54×10^{16} cm^{-3}; σn_1 has the dimensions of [cm^{-1}].

The cross-section for ionisation by electron impact rises rapidly from zero at electron energy $K_{el} = eI$, reaches a maximum at a certain energy that is usually between 50 and 150 eV, after which it slowly diminishes. The maximum ionisation cross-section for various gases is ordinarily of the order of 10^{-16}-10^{-15} cm^2, which is of the order of the gas-kinetic cross-section.*

The foregoing figures refer to *single ionisation*, i.e., to processes of the type $e + He = He^+ + 2e$ or $e + O_2 = O_2^+ + 2e$. But when

* The gas-kinetic cross-section is determined from the transport equations (see p. 475).

we have double or triple ionisation, the maximum is displaced towards higher electron energies, and the maximum cross-section falls. For example, the maxima of ionisation of the mercury atom that correspond to processes $e + Hg = Hg^{+} + 2e$ (single ionisation), $e + Hg = Hg^{++} + 3e$ (double ionisation) and $e + Hg = Hg^{+++} + 4e$ (triple ionisation) lie at 50, 155 and 210 eV, respectively, while the maximum cross-sections are 5.85×10^{-16}, 0.90×10^{-16}, and 0.20×10^{-16} cm².

Likewise, the ionisation cross-section of atoms and molecules by fast-ion impact rises from zero at a certain ion energy, reaches a maximum, and then declines. However, whereas the maximum of ionisation by electron impact, as has been stated above, occurs at an electron energy of the order of 100 eV, the ion-impact ionisation maximum ordinarily corresponds to appreciably greater energy. For instance, the maximum cross-section for ionisation of argon by electron impact lies at 50 eV, the maximum ionisation of argon by impact of the K^{+} ion is at 4000 eV. And the maximum cross-sections themselves (multiplied by n_1) are close: 10.3 cm⁻¹ (e) and 8.5 cm⁻¹ (K^{+}).

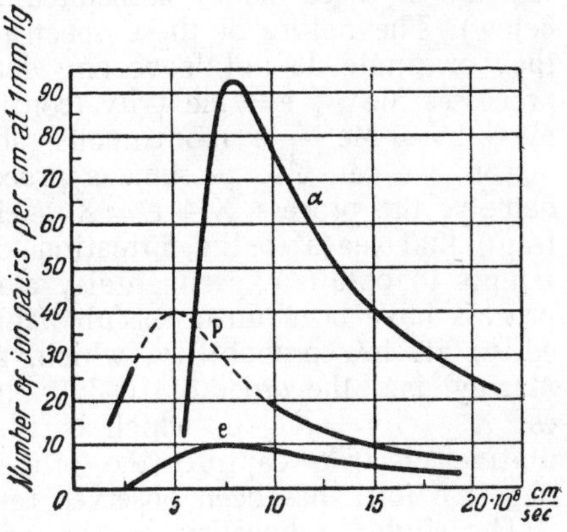

Fig. 112. Cross-section for ionisation of air by electrons (e), protons (p), and α-particles (α) (after Engel and Stenbeck)

In the preceding example, the values of energy corresponding to maximum σ differ by two orders of magnitude. The corresponding velocities of electron and K^{+} ion, which are 4.2×10^{8} cm/sec and 1.4×10^{7} cm/sec, differ by only one order of magnitude. The close values of ionisation maxima, when passing from the energy of the bombarding particle to its velocity, are still more striking in the case of ionisation of air by the impact of an electron, proton, and alpha-particle. Here, the energy values are 110 eV (e), 1.3×10^{5} eV (p) and 1.8×10^{6} eV (α), i.e., they differ, respectively, by three and four orders of magnitude, while the velocities are 7.5×10^{8} cm/sec (e), 5.0×10^{8} cm/sec (p), and 8.0×10^{8} cm/sec (α), in other words, they are of one order of magnitude (Fig. 112). Thus, we may conclude that the position of maximum probability of ionisation by the impact of a fast particle is determined more by its velocity than by its energy.

Up till now we have considered the formation of positive ions upon the collision of an electron (or ion) with an atom or molecule. By mass-spectroscopic techniques it is also possible to observe negative ions, for instance, the ions H^-, Cl^-, Br^-, I^-, HO^-, CCl_3^-, SF_6^-, etc. The formation of a negative ion from an appropriate atom and electron is like the neutralisation of an atomic positive ion upon its recombination with an electron. The latter process has actually been observed by Mohler and others in the case of alkali metals. For instance, at high current densities, Mohler observed, in the emission spectrum of a discharge in the vapours of alkali metals, the usual linear spectrum and also a continuous spectrum like the continuous absorption spectra of the vapours of these metals associated with their photoionisation (see below). The nature of these spectra and the conditions under which they originate do not leave any doubt that they are caused by the processes $Me^+ + e = Me + h\nu$ (continuous emission spectrum) and $Me + h\nu = Me^+ + e$ (continuous absorption spectrum). For this reason, we can also presume a process similar to the first of them, namely, the process $X + e = X^- + h\nu$ (continuous emission spectrum) that leads to the formation of negative ions. However, attempts to obtain experimentally a spectrum corresponding to this process have been unsuccessful *; this, apparently, may be attributed to its low probability, which, according to the calculations of Massey, is of the order of 10^{-7}.** It may be noted that the process $X^- + h\nu = X + e$, which is the reverse of the process of radiative electron capture (the process of photoneutralisation of a negative ion), has been observed repeatedly (see below).

The slight probability of the process of radiative electron capture explains the fact that negative ions ordinarily arise nonradiatively, in other words, not as a result of the direct recombination of an atom or molecule with an electron accompanied by the emission of light. The following is a well-studied radiationless process of the formation of negative ions:

$$X_2 + e = X + X^-$$

(X is a halogen atom) or

$$HX + e = H + X^-.$$

Similar processes have also been observed in the case of O_2, NO, CO, H_2O, H_2S, H_2Se, NH_3, SF_6 etc. Some of them (for instance, I_2) are accomplished with the participation of thermal electrons, in

* Here, the apparent exception is the process $H + e = H^- + h\nu$, observed by Fuchs in a spark in hydrogen at high temperature and pressure.

** The probability of this process is determined by the ratio of the cross-section (corresponding to it) to the gas-kinetic cross-section of the atom (or molecule).

other cases considerable electron energy is required. In all cases, the process of molecular splitting with the formation of a negative ion is accomplished in a narrow interval of electron energies and has a pronounced probability maximum. A typical curve of the cross-section of the process versus the electron energy is given in Fig. 113, where the left-hand curve gives the yield of O^- ions that form in the process $e+O_2=O+O^-$. Negative O^- ions, the yield of which is shown by the right-hand curve, are formed by the process $e+O_2=O^+ +O^- +e$.

The maximum probability of splitting of the molecule O_2 into O and O^- is 1.2×10^{-3}. The maximum splitting probabilities of halogen molecules are: $Cl_2 - 5\times 10^{-3}$ (at 1.5 eV), $Br_2 - 6.3\times 10^{-3}$ (at 1.8 eV), and $I_2 \sim 1$ (at 0.34 eV). To summarise then: with the exception of the latter case, the maximum probabilities of splitting a molecule by an electron with the formation of a negative ion come out to the order of 10^{-3}-10^{-2}.

The characteristic relation of probability of dissociation of a molecule versus electron energy in the process $e+AB=A+B^-$ is accounted for by means of potential-energy curves like those shown in Fig. 114 a and b. Here, the curves AB are potential-ener-

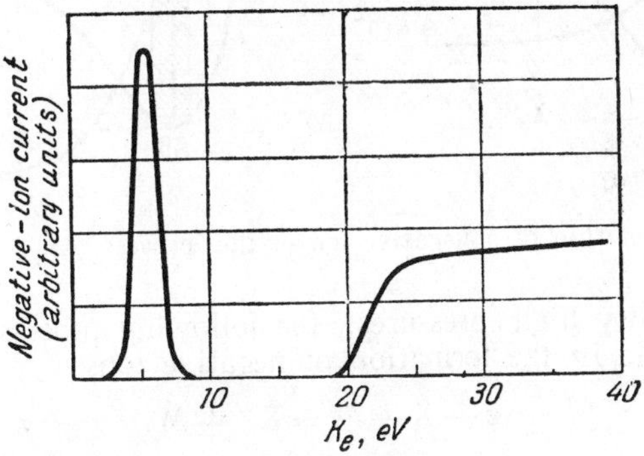

Fig. 113. Formation of negative O^- ions in collision of electron with O_2 molecule as a function of electron energy (after Messi)

gy curves of the molecule AB, the curves AB^- are curves of the molecular ion AB^-. The decomposition of the molecule AB in this scheme may be regarded as its transition, through the action of an electron, to the state of the AB^- ion with subsequent dissociation of the latter into $A+B^-$. If the transition $AB \rightarrow AB^-$ occurs from the zero vibrational state of the AB molecule (low temperatures), then the maximum cross-section of the process will correspond to electron energy determined by the distance along the vertical (vertical potential of the process) of the curve AB^- from the minimum of curve AB (heavy arrow in Fig. 114). In accordance with the form of the wave function of the zero vibrational state (see Fig. 87, p. 359), the transition region $AB \longrightarrow AB^-$ is determined by the cross-hatched band in Fig. 114 and is bounded on the low-energy side by a short arrow and on the high-energy side by a long arrow. It is to this region that the left-hand curve of O^- ion yield in Fig. 113 corresponds.

When the electron affinity of atom B exceeds the heat of dissociation of molecule AB, curve AB^- can intersect curve AB near its minimum (Fig. 114 b). When curve AB^- intersects curve AB at its minimum, the splitting process is already possible at thermal-electron energy and the maximum probability of the process will occur at electron energy equal or close to zero. This case is apparently accomplished in the splitting of I_2 by thermal electrons.

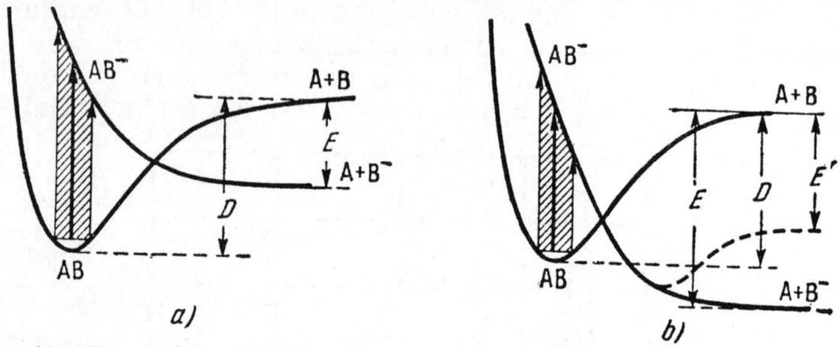

Fig. 114. Formation of a negative ion in the process $AB + e = A + B^-$

At sufficiently high pressures, the following process can play a significant role in the formation of negative ions:

$$e + X + M = X^- + M$$

where M is any molecule (third particle). The probability of this process is apparently close to unity, i.e., every gas-kinetic triple collision is effective.

Photoionisation of gases. In the absorption spectra of a large number of gases we find regions of continuous absorption that adjoin the convergence limit of the Rydberg series. Such, for example, are the absorption spectra of the vapours of alkali metals. Since the energy corresponding to the series limit is equal to the respective ionisation potential of the atom or molecule, the quanta absorbed in the region of the continuous spectrum must satisfy the condition

$$h\nu \geqslant eI. \tag{43.3}$$

For this reason, a continuous absorption spectrum is indicative of the process

$$M + h\nu = M^+ + e$$

(M designates an atom or molecule), i.e., of the possibility of photoionisation of gases.

Photoionisation, or the photoelectric effect, in gases was detected in a number of cases directly by the appearance of a photocurrent upon irradiation of the gas with light of sufficiently short wavelength. The atoms of alkali metals which have the lowest ionisation potentials are capable of being ionised by light of a wavelength corresponding to the relatively near ultraviolet. For the limit of the photoelectric effect of vapours of Li, Na, K, Rb, and Cs, we find the following wavelengths from the ionisation potentials of these elements using formula (43.3): 2299 A (Li), 2412 A (Na), 2856 A (K), 2968 A (Rb), and 3188 A (Cs). With few exceptions (Al, Ba, Ca, Ga, In, Sr, Tl), the other vapours can be ionised only in the vacuum region of the spectrum ($\lambda < 2000$ A).*

Table 38 gives the ionisation potentials of a number of gases measured both on the basis of photoionisation and spectroscopically—by the limit of the Rydberg series in the absorption spectrum of the appropriate gas. From the table it will be seen that both methods yield practically coincident results (the error of the photoionisation method is ± 0.01 eV, that of the spectroscopic method, somewhat less).

Table 38

Ionisation potentials of certain molecules measured by the photoionisation method and spectroscopically (in volts)

Molecule	Photoionisation	Spectroscopically	Molecule	Photoionisation	Spectroscopically
CO	14.01	14.013	C_2H_5I	9.33	9.345
H_2O	12.59	12.61	C_2H_4	10.516	10.51
H_2S	10.46	10.473	C_4H_6	9.07	9.063
CO_2	13.79	13.79	C_2H_2	11.41	11.41
CS_2	10.08	10.079	H_2CO	10.87	10.88
N_2O	12.90	12.72	CH_3CHO	10.21	10.228
CH_3Cl	11.28	11.22	$(CH_3)_2CO$	10.69	10.705
CH_3Br	10.53	10.541	C_6H_6	9.245	9.240
CH_3I	9.54	9.538	$CH_3C_6H_5$	8.82	8.82

* Here, we do not consider the processes of secondary photoionisation when an atom or molecule absorbs a quantum of radiant energy and passes into an excited state and is ionised only as a result of the absorption of a second quantum or by collision with another excited particle. In this case, it is obvious that condition (43.3) is not obligatory for every absorbed quantum.

Above (p. 422) we pointed to the possibility of photoneutralisation of a negative ion, that is, the possibility of the process

$$X^- + h\nu = X + e.$$

On the basis of this process, Branscomb developed an experimental method for measuring electron affinity; it consists in measuring the minimum frequency of light which, when used to irradiate a beam of negative ions, produces electrons.

Photoionisation is also characteristic of X-rays and gamma rays. In this case, the ionisation differs from ordinary ionisation in that the atom or molecule undergoing ionisation loses one of the inner electrons and not one of the outer, weakly bound ones.

44. Polarisation of Electronic Shells

Polarisation is one of the most important properties of atoms and molecules. It has extremely diversified manifestations. Associated with it are the dielectrical and optical properties of matter. The polarisation of molecules is very important for the geometry and energy of molecules. The polarisation of scattered light and the phenomenon of double refraction (bi-refringence) is due to molecular polarisability. Polarisation forces are of importance in the interaction of molecules.

In this section we shall confine ourselves to a consideration of polarisation in an isolated molecule or in a sufficiently rarefied gas as related to certain macroscopic properties of gases. We shall have in view nonpolar gases, that is, gases whose molecules do not have a permanent dipole moment. We begin with polarisation of a gas in a constant electric field.

Polarisation in a constant electric field. In the simplest case, molecular polarisability is characterised by the *polarisation coefficient* α, which is equal to the dipole moment induced in the molecule by an electric field of unit intensity. The dipole moment induced in a molecule by an external electric field of intensity $\mathfrak{E}$ may be represented by the formula

$$p = \alpha \mathfrak{E}. \tag{44.1}$$

Connected with molecular polarisability are the dielectric properties of the medium characterised by the *dielectric constant* ε. There is a unique relationship between α and ε which is expressed by the *Clausius-Mosotti equation*:

$$P = \frac{4\pi}{3} N_A \alpha = \frac{\varepsilon - 1}{\varepsilon + 2} \frac{M}{\varrho}. \tag{44.2}$$

Here, N_A is the Avogadro number, M the molecular weight, and ϱ the density. P is called the *molar polarisation*.

Thus, on the basis of (44.2) the coefficient of polarisation α may be found from measurements of the dielectric constant.

The coefficient of polarisation thus determined fully characterises the molecular polarisability only in the case of *isotropic molecules*: molecules, the polarisability of which is the *same* in all directions. In the more general case of an *anisotropic molecule*, its polarisability is determined by three, generally different, axes of the *polarisability ellipsoid* that correspond to polarisation of the molecule in the direction of these axes. In this case, the quantity α in expression (44.2) is only the *mean coefficient of polarisation of the molecule*. In an anisotropic molecule, the direction of the induced dipole moment coincides, in the general case, with that of the electric field. This anisotropy is particularly marked in optical phenomena associated with polarisation of molecules in the rapidly alternating electric field of a light wave. For this reason, optical measurements (in particular refraction measurements) play an important part in studies of the polarisation of molecules.

Polarisation in an alternating field. Refraction. According to Maxwell, the dielectric constant of a nonpolar gas ε is equal to the square of its refractive index r^2. And so equation (44.2) can be represented as

$$R=\frac{4\pi}{3}N_A\alpha=\frac{r^2-1}{r^2+2}\frac{M}{\varrho} \tag{44.3}$$

(the *Lorentz-Lorenz relation*). The quantity R defined by this equation is called *molar refraction*. Consequently, the earlier introduced molar refraction P can also be called molar refraction at a field frequency equal to zero (constant electric field). However, since molar refraction is usually found from measurements of the refractive index for visible light, i.e., at frequencies of the order of 10^{15} sec^{-1}, whereas the dielectric constant is measured in alternating fields (the frequency of which is small relative to the frequency of light) it is necessary to extrapolate R to $\nu=0$ when computing molar polarisation from measurements of the refractive index. This extrapolation is ordinarily carried out by means of the following equation:

$$\frac{1}{\alpha}=\frac{1}{\alpha_0}\left(1-\frac{\nu^2}{\nu_0^2}\right) \tag{44.4}$$

where α_0 is the polarisation coefficient for $\lambda=\infty$ $(\nu=0)$, $\nu_0=\frac{e}{\sqrt{4\pi m\alpha_0}}$. We find $\alpha_0(R_0)$ from equation (44.4) by measuring $\alpha(R)$ for several values of λ.

The occasional divergence of values of $R=R_0$ and molar polarisation P computed in this manner is to be explained by the fact that polarisation is partially due to a shift (in the external electric field) of atoms and groups of atoms in the molecule, which shift can hardly be accounted for when extrapolating R. However, this shift is usually small and can often be disregarded.

As is evident from (44.2) and (44.3), molar polarisation and molar refraction of a gas mixture are additive quantities insofar as the polarisability α of each molecule may be considered independent of the surrounding molecules, which is fully permissible in the case of gases. What is more, experiment shows that molar refraction is but very slightly dependent on the temperature, pressure (concentration), and alterations (associated with the latter) of the aggregate state (association, condensation). Finally, from experiment it follows that molar refraction of a complex chemical compound may be represented approximately as the sum of refractions of the component atoms or ions:

$$R_M = \sum R_A \tag{44.5}$$

R_M is the molar and R_A are the *atomic* or *ionic refractions*).

This formula is most precise in the case of ionic compounds; the ionic refractions (or polarisation coefficients of the ions), which are determined for a given ion from the molar refractions of various compounds, differ but slightly. Therefore, refraction, or polarisability, of an ion is a constant that describes a given ion in any compound that contains it. The polarisation coefficients (polarisabilities) of a number of ions are given in Table 39.

Table 39

Polarisabilities of ions (in $cm^3 \times 10^{24}$)

	O^{--}	S^{--}	Se^{--}	Te^{--}
	2.74	8.94	11.4	16.1
H^-	F^-	Cl^-	Br^-	I^-
10.18	0.96	3.60	5.0	7.60
Li^+	Na^+	K^+	Rb^+	Cs^+
0.03	0.19	0.89	1.50	2.60
Be^{++}	Mg^{++}	Ca^{++}	Sr^{++}	Ba^{++}
0.008	0.10	0.55	1.02	1.86

For investigations into the field of ionic refractions we are indebted primarily to Fajans and his school. The work of this school deals mainly with aqueous solutions. Measurements of the refraction of solutions with account taken of that of water, and also alterations of the latter (they are due to the action of ions) lead to the possibility of determining ionic refractions through the use of (44.5).

A similar method was applied by Born and Heisenberg for calculating the ionic refractions from measured molar refractions of NaCl-type salt crystals. They also attempted to calculate R_A from the atomic terms. This possibility follows from the fact that the Rydberg and Ritz corrections that enter into the expression of atomic terms of alkali metals are directly determined by the polarisation coefficient α of the ions of these metals (see p. 157). Finally, the refraction of ions with the electronic structure of a noble gas was obtained by Pauling theoretically (on the basis of quantum mechanics). All the foregoing methods yield close values of ionic refractions.

In the case of atomic molecules (unlike ionic compounds), the refraction of separate atoms determined from the molar refraction of various compounds by means of (44.5) yield significantly *different values*, depending on the *type of bond* of the respective atom in the molecule. For example, the atomic refraction of carbon is different depending on whether a given C atom is connected with the other atoms in the molecule by single, double, or triple bond. In the same way, the hydroxyl, ether, and carbonyl oxygens have different atomic refractions. Change in atomic refraction with the bond type of a given atom appears to be quite natural if one takes into account that the refraction of lightweight atoms is in large measure due to the outer electrons: when passing from one type of bond to another, there is a change in the bond rigidity of the valence electrons in the molecule, and this is detected from the change in atomic refraction.

In addition, a definite part of refraction is also taken up by double and triple bonds; only by taking this into consideration when calculating the molar refraction from corresponding atomic refractions is it possible to obtain satisfactory agreement with the measured value. Table 40 gives the empirical values of refractions of some atoms together with the refractions that are formally attributed to C=C and C≡C bonds.

Table 40

Atomic refractions (for D-lines of sodium)

Atom (bond)	Refraction	Atom (bond)	Refraction
H	1.100	O hydroxyl	1.525
F	0.997	O ether	1.643
Cl	5.967	O carbonyl	2.211
Br	8.865	N primary	2.322
I	13.900	N secondary	2.502
C	2.418	N tertiary	2.840
Double C, C bond	1.733	N nitrile	3.118
Triple C, C bond	2.398		

By way of illustrating the computation of molar refraction from the refraction of the atoms that comprise the molecule (this is very important for determining the structure of chemical compounds), let us compute the molar refraction of ethyl alcohol C_2H_5OH. Here, we have two carbon atoms, six H atoms, and one hydroxyl atom O connected by single bonds. From Table 40 we get $2R_C + 6R_H + R_{O_{hyd}} = 4.836 + 6.600 + 1.525 = 12.961$, whereas direct measurements give 12.78. In exactly the same way, computing the molar refraction of acetacetic ester

$$
\begin{array}{ccccccccc}
 & H & & O & & H & & O & & & & H & & H \\
 & | & & \| & & | & & \| & & & & | & & | \\
H- & C & - & C & - & C & - & C & - & O & - & C & - & C & -H \\
 & | & & & & | & & & & & & | & & | \\
 & H & & & & H & & & & & & H & & H
\end{array}
$$

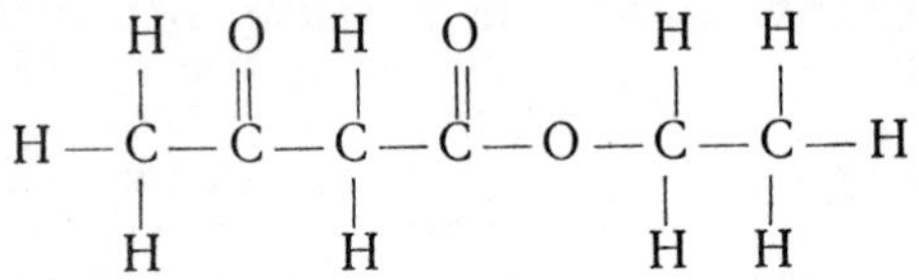

with six C atoms, ten H atoms, two carbonyl O atoms, and one ester atom, we get $R_M = 14.508 + 11.000 + 4.422 + 1.643 = 31.573$, instead of the measured molar refraction 32.00.

There is however another possible method of representing molar refraction. Namely, we can assign definite values of refraction not to individual atoms but to the separate *bonds* in the molecule, as is done in Table 41.

Table 41

Refractions of bonds

H — H	2.08	C = C	4.15	C — F	1.60
C — H	1.705	C ≡ C	6.025	C — Cl	6.57
N — H	1.87	N — C	1.55	C — Br	9.47
O — H	1.88	O — C	1.42	C — I	14.51
C — C	1.209	O = C	3.42		

The refractions of bonds given in this table are related to the atomic refractions (Table 40) as follows (after Steiger and Smyth):

$$R_{C-H} = \frac{1}{4}R_C + R_H, \qquad R_{C\underset{H}{\overset{\diagdown}{}}O} = \frac{1}{4}R_C + R_H + R_{O_{hyd}}$$

$$R_{C-C} = \frac{1}{2}R_C, \qquad R_{C\underset{C}{\overset{\diagdown}{}}O} = \frac{1}{2}R_C + R_{O_{eth}}$$

$$R_{C=C} = R_C + I=, \qquad R_{C=O} = \frac{1}{2}R_C + R_{O_{car}}$$

$$R_{C\equiv C} = \frac{3}{2}R_C + I\equiv, \qquad R_{C-X} = \frac{1}{4}R_C + R_X.$$

Here, the symbols $I=$ and $I\equiv$ designate the atomic refraction due to double and triple carbon bonds, $R_{O_{hyd}}$, $R_{O_{eth}}$, and $R_{O_{car}}$ are atomic refractions of the hydroxyl, ether, and carbonyl atoms of oxygen and X = F, Cl, Br, and I.

The good coincidence of calculated and measured values of molar refraction that is observed in most cases shows that the molar refraction of various chemical compounds can be pre-calculated to a high degree of accuracy. This accuracy permits taking advantage of refractometric measurements as a method of studying molecular structure. Molar refraction permits establishing the presence and number of complex bonds in a molecule, the nature of the oxygen bond, etc. This accounts for the great role played by refractometry in structural chemistry, in particular in organic chemistry and in the chemistry of complex compounds, and also in the study of solutions.

The following simple instance will illustrate the use of refractometric data in establishing the type of bonds in a molecule. Assuming that the CO_2 molecule is an ionic molecule, i.e., that it consists of a C^{+4} ion and two O^{--} ions, from the refraction of these ions (0.0034 and 9.88) we get for the molar refraction of CO_2 the number 19.76, which is three times the actual value of $R_{CO_2}=6.71$ In contrast to this result, calculation of R_{CO_2} on the assumption of the atomic structure of the CO_2 molecule yields practically complete coincidence of calculated (6.84) and measured values, as will readily be seen from the data given in Tables 40 and 41. Whence there follows the inevitable conclusion as to the atomic structure of CO_2.

Refractometric measurements are also very important for molecular energetics. Since we are able to assign to each bond a definite portion of refraction, it is possible to judge of the strength of the bonds in a molecule from the magnitude of the respective refractions. The stronger the bond, the more rigidly fixed in the molecule are the electrons, and hence, the less should be the refraction they are responsible for.

It should be pointed out that in conjugated and aromatic systems we notice perceptible deviations of molar refraction from additivity. These deviations indicate that the compounds are exceedingly strong; they are called *exaltation* of refraction.

Anisotropy of polarisability and molecular structure. One of the manifestations of anisotropy of polarisability is the *depolarisation of scattered light*. Measurements of the degree of polarisability permit us, in certain cases, to determine the principal polarisabilities of a molecule that characterise its polarisability ellipsoid. The degree of depolarisation Δ is determined by the ratio of intensities (in a scattered ray) that correspond to oscillations parallel and perpendicular to the direction of the oscillations of the exciting ray:

$$\Delta=\frac{I_{\parallel}}{I_{\perp}}.$$

In the classical theory of Tyndall, which does not take into account rotation of the molecules, the intensities $I_{\parallel}$ and $I_{\perp}$ are calculated as follows. We introduce a coordinate system fixed in the molecule ξ, η, ζ, the directions of the axes of which coincide with the directions of its principal polarisabilities α_1, α_2, α_3, and a fixed coordinate system x, y, z. Let the electrical vector E of the exciting linearly polarised ray be directed along the z axis. Then for the moments induced in the molecule in the direction of its principal electrical axes we will have

$$p_\xi = \alpha_1 E \cos(\xi, z), \quad p_\eta = \alpha_2 E \cos(\eta, z), \quad p_\zeta = \alpha_3 E \cos(\zeta, z).$$

Obviously, the components of the moments along the axes z and x are

$$p_z = p_\xi \cos(\xi, z) + p_\eta \cos(\eta, z) + p_\zeta \cos(\zeta, z),$$
$$p_x = p_\xi \cos(\xi, x) + p_\eta \cos(\eta, x) + p_\zeta \cos(\zeta, x).$$

To simplify calculations, in the case of a molecule with an axis of symmetry ($\alpha_2 = \alpha_3$) we may consider the axis η as lying in the plane xy, whence it follows that $\cos(\eta, z) = 0$.

Introducing the designations $\angle(\eta, y) = \varphi$ and $\angle(\zeta, z) = \vartheta$ we will have

$$\cos(\xi, z) = \sin\vartheta, \quad \cos(\zeta, z) = \cos\vartheta, \quad \cos(\xi, x) = \cos\varphi \, \cos\vartheta,$$
$$\cos(\eta, x) = \sin\varphi, \quad \cos(\zeta, x) = -\cos\varphi \, \sin\vartheta.$$

Substituting these values of cosines into the expressions for the components of the induced moments, we get

$$p_z = (\alpha_1 \sin^2\vartheta + \alpha_2 \cos^2\vartheta)\, E \text{ and } p_x = (\alpha_1 - \alpha_2) \sin\vartheta \cos\vartheta \cos\varphi \cdot E.$$

The intensities of the scattered light are proportional to the squares of the respective moments. We find the mean intensities as

$$I_{\parallel} \sim \frac{\int_0^{\pi/2}\int_0^{\pi/2} p_x^2 \sin\vartheta \, d\vartheta \sin\varphi \, d\varphi}{\int_0^{\pi/2}\int_0^{\pi/2} \sin\vartheta \, d\vartheta \sin\varphi \, d\varphi}, \qquad I_{\perp} \sim \frac{\int_0^{\pi/2} p_z^2 \sin\vartheta \, d\vartheta}{\int_0^{\pi/2} \sin\vartheta \, d\vartheta}.$$

Substituting here the above-obtained expressions for p_x and p_z and integrating, we get

$$\Delta = \frac{(\alpha_1 - \alpha_2)^2}{3\alpha_1^2 + 4\alpha_1\alpha_2 + 8\alpha_2^2}. \qquad (44.6)$$

If the exciting light is natural, an analogous computation for the degree of depolarisation yields

$$\Delta = \frac{2(\alpha_1 - \alpha_2)^2}{4\alpha_1^2 + 2\alpha_1\alpha_2 + 9\alpha_2^2}. \qquad (44.7)$$

Finally, in the case of a molecule that does not have an axis of symmetry ($\alpha_2 \neq \alpha_3$), the expression for the degree of depolarisation of natural light, when it is scattered, has the form

$$\Delta = \frac{2(\alpha_1^2 + \alpha_2^2 + \alpha_3^2 - \alpha_1\alpha_2 - \alpha_2\alpha_3 - \alpha_3\alpha_1)}{4(\alpha_1^4 + \alpha_2^4 + \alpha_3^2) + (\alpha_1\alpha_2 + \alpha_2\alpha_3 + \alpha_3\alpha_1)}. \qquad (44.8)$$

Inasmuch as account of the rotation of molecules leads to the same expressions for the degree of polarisability of scattered light, the foregoing equations may be considered general.

Firstly, from these equations it follows that in the case of a symmetric isotropic molecule ($\alpha_1 = \alpha_2 = \alpha_3$) the degree of depolarisation must equal zero. In another extreme case of a totally anisotropic molecule ($\alpha_2 = \alpha_3 = 0$), the degree of depolarisation of linearly polarised light should equal $\frac{1}{3}$ and of natural light $\frac{1}{2}$.

To determine the principal polarisabilities of a molecule α_1, α_2, α_3, we have the following equations. First of all, from (44.3) for the mean polarisability of the molecule,

$$\alpha = \frac{\alpha_1 + \alpha_2 + \alpha_3}{3},$$

we get the expression

$$\alpha_1 + \alpha_2 + \alpha_3 = \frac{9}{4\pi n}\frac{r^2 - 1}{r^2 + 2}$$

which may be represented approximately (due to $r^2 \approx 1$) in the form

$$\alpha_1 + \alpha_2 + \alpha_3 = \frac{3(r-1)}{2\pi n} \qquad (44.9)$$

(n is the number of molecules in 1 cm^3). The second equation is (44.8), which may be rewritten as

$$\frac{10\Delta}{6 - 7\Delta} = \frac{(\alpha_1 - \alpha_2)^2 + (\alpha_2 - \alpha_3)^2 + (\alpha_3 - \alpha_1)^2}{(\alpha_1 + \alpha_2 + \alpha_3)^2}$$

or, because of (44.9),

$$(\alpha_1 - \alpha_2)^2 + (\alpha_2 - \alpha_3)^2 + (\alpha_3 - \alpha_1)^2 = \frac{45\Delta}{6 - 7\Delta}\frac{(r-1)^2}{2\pi^2 n^2}. \qquad (44.10)$$

To summarise, then, we have two equations, (44.9) and (44.10), to determine the three unknowns α_1, α_2, and α_3. Whence it follows that, alone, the measurements of the degree of polarisation and refractive index permit determining α_1, α_2, and α_3 only for molecules having an axis of symmetry when the missing equation is obtained from the symmetry of the molecule, namely, equation $\alpha_2 = \alpha_3$. Table 42 gives the values of the principal polarisabilities of certain symmetric molecules found in this manner.

Table 42

Principal polarisabilities of a number of molecules (in $cm^3 \times 10^{24}$)

Molecule	α_1	α_2	Molecule	α_1	α_2
N_2	2.38	1.45	C_2H_4	5.61	3.59
O_2	2.35	1.21	C_2H_6	6.35	12.31
CO	2.60	1.63	C_6H_{12}	8.90	11.90

The third equation * that is missing in the general case of an asymmetric molecule may be obtained by taking into account the *Kerr effect*. The essence of this effect lies in the fact that isotropic substances, when placed in an electric field, become *bi-refringent*, i.e., light rays passing through them are polarised parallel and perpendicular to the field and acquire different velocities. The result is a difference in the paths of the rays. This difference, according to the Kerr law, is

$$\delta\lambda = K \frac{r}{\lambda} l E^2 \qquad (44.11)$$

where K is the Kerr constant, r and λ are the refractive index and the length of the light wave in the absence of a field, l is the geometrical path of the rays in a bi-refringent substance, and E is the field intensity. Designating the refractive indexes of the two rays by $r_\parallel$ and $r_\perp$, we can represent the optical difference of path as $\delta\lambda = \frac{(r_\parallel - r_\perp) l}{\lambda}$, whence we get the following expression

* It is possible, in principle, to determine the quantities α_1, α_2 and α_3 also on the basis solely of measurements of Δ and r, since, according to the foregoing, the degrees of depolarisation of linearly polarised and natural light are different; this gives the third equation. However, in the case of gases (because of great difficulties in measuring the degree of depolarisation and the considerable concomitant errors) measurements in polarised excited light are practically impossible. When measuring Δ the rule is to use bright sunlight, that is, natural light.

for the Kerr constant:

$$K=\frac{r_{\parallel}-r_{\perp}}{r}\frac{1}{E^2}. \qquad (44.12)$$

The theory of the Kerr effect in a nonpolar gas was given by Langevin and subsequently generalised to a polar gas by Born. We do not intend to give a detailed account of the theory but will confine ourselves to a brief examination of its underlying concepts and its chief results.

In view of the equal probability of all directions in the absence of an electric field, a gas consisting of optically anisotropic molecules is an isotropic medium. In an electric field there arises a certain directed molecular orientation, which is what leads to anisotropy of the gas as seen in the Kerr effect. In the case of a nonpolar gas, this directivity is due to polarisation of molecules in an electric field; in a polar gas there is, in addition to polarisation, an orientation effect of permanent dipoles. Because of the directivity of the total dipole moment of a molecule in an electric field, its polarisability in the direction of the field ($\alpha_{\parallel}$) will differ from that perpendicular to the field ($\alpha_{\perp}$). When computing the mean polarisabilities $\alpha_{\parallel}$ and $\alpha_{\perp}$, one can represent them as a function of the following quantities: the principal polarisabilities of the molecule in the electric field of a light wave α_1, α_2, α_3, the principal polarisabilities in an electrostatic field a_1, a_2, a_3, the components of the electric moment of the molecule p, i. e., the projections of p on the coordinate axes ξ, η, ζ (fixed in the molecule), p_1, p_2, p_3, the square of the electric field intensity E^2, and, finally, the absolute temperature of the gas. On the other hand, $\alpha_{\parallel}$ and $\alpha_{\perp}$ may be represented as

$$\frac{4}{3}\pi n\alpha_{\parallel}=\frac{r_{\parallel}^2-1}{r_{\parallel}^2+2} \text{ and } \frac{4}{3}\pi n\alpha_{\perp}=\frac{r_{\perp}^2-1}{r_{\perp}^2+2}$$

thus making it possible to express the Kerr constant (44.12) in terms of α_1, α_2, α_3, a_1, a_2, a_3, p_1, p_2, p_3 and the temperature T. By virtue of equalities (44.2) and (44.3) we should have the following relationship between the quantities a_1, a_2, a_3 and α_1, α_2, α_3:

$$\frac{a_1}{\alpha_1}=\frac{a_2}{\alpha_2}=\frac{a_3}{\alpha_3}=\frac{\varepsilon-1}{\varepsilon+2}:\frac{r^2-1}{r^2+2}. \qquad (44.13)$$

Further, the Kerr constant may be represented as the sum of two terms: K_1, which is associated with pure polarisation of the molecules, and K_2, which is determined by the orientation of the permanent dipoles (dipole member). For the first of them (at $r\approx1$)

we get from theory the following expression:

$$K_1 = \frac{\pi}{15} \frac{n}{kT} \frac{\varepsilon - 1}{r^2 + 2} [(\alpha_1 - \alpha_2)^2 + (\alpha_2 - \alpha_3)^2 + (\alpha_3 - \alpha_1)^2], \quad (44.14)$$

which, in view of (44.11) and also $P = nkT$ (ideal gas), may be represented in the form

$$K_1 = \frac{3}{4\pi} \frac{1}{P} (\varepsilon - 1)(r - 1) \frac{\Delta}{6 - 7\Delta}. \quad (44.15)$$

From (44.15) it follows that the constant K_1 is practically independent of the temperature of the gas.

For K_2 the following general expression is obtained:

$$K_2 = \frac{\pi}{15} \frac{n}{k^2 T^2} [(p_1^2 - p_2^2)(\alpha_1 - \alpha_2) + (p_2^2 - p_3^2)(\alpha_2 - \alpha_3) + (p_3^2 - p_1^2)(\alpha_3 - \alpha_1)], \quad (44.16)$$

which, in case of coincidence of the direction of the dipole moment of the molecule with the direction of one of its electrical principal axes (for instance, the ζ axis), takes on a simpler form:

$$K_2 = \frac{\pi}{15} \frac{n}{k^2 T^2} p^2 (2\alpha_3 - \alpha_2 - \alpha_1). \quad (44.17)$$

Expression (44.17) can serve as the missing third equation, which, together with equations (44.9) and (44.10), permits determining the constants α_1, α_2 and α_3 for any polar molecule on the condition that $p = p_3$, $p_1 = p_2 = 0$. The dipole moment of the molecule should then be known. However, in the case of nonpolar molecules, which always have at least one axis of symmetry, it is sufficient to have two equations to determine the polarisability ellipsoid: (44.9) and (44.10) or (44.9) and (44.14). It may be noted that due to the greater accuracy in measuring the Kerr constant, it is usual to take the second pair of equations to determine the principal polarisabilities.

As has already been pointed out, a determination of the optical polarisability ellipsoid of molecules is exceedingly important for finding the geometrical molecular structure. We shall consider here several of the simplest cases that illustrate this method of establishing molecular structure. Thus, for the molecules SO_2 and H_2S we may, generally speaking, conceive of both linear and bent (equilateral triangle) molecular structures. Measurements of α_1, α_2, and α_3 for SO_2 yield 54.9×10^{-25}, 27.2×10^{-25}, and 34.9×10^{-25} cm^3 and for H_2S 42.0×10^{-25}, 32.1×10^{-25}, and 39.3×10^{-25} cm^3. The different values of all three polarisabilities in both cases compel us to exclude the linear structure of the molecule, for then, due to an electrical axis of symmetry, the two polarisabilities would coincide. The bent structure is also obtained for molecules of alcohols, esters, ketones, etc. In contrast, in the case of the N_2O molecule, measurements yield $\alpha_1 = 53.2 \times 10^{-25}$ and $\alpha_2 = \alpha_3 = 18.3 \times 10^{-25}$ cm^3, that is, the structure is linear. Similar results also point to a linear structure of the molecules HCN, CO_2, CS_2, C_2H_2, C_2N_2. Further, from the fact that within experimental error all three principal polarisabilities of the molecules CCl_4 and $SnCl_4$ are the same, it follows that these molecules are of tetrahedral symmetric structure.

On the mutual interaction of atoms in molecules. Polarisation of molecules is also extremely important as one of the essential conditions for conveying the mutual interaction of atoms or atomic groups in a molecule. One of the most common types of mutual effect is that which Markovnikov characterised as follows: "The effect ... diminishes with their (atoms — Kondratyev) recession from one another in the overall chain of chemical action." In the language of electronic concepts, this type of mutual interaction became known as the *induction* type.

When an atom or atomic group is replaced by another one, a redistribution of density occurs in the electron cloud of the molecule. This distortion of the electron cloud is greatest near the replaced (functional) group and rapidly falls off with recession from it. Acetic acid is one of numerous instances of the induction effect:

$$H_3C - C\!\!\!\diagup^{\displaystyle O}_{\displaystyle OH}.$$

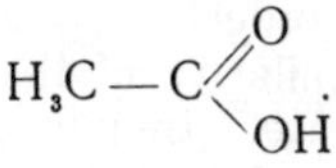

When one of the H atoms in the methyl group is replaced by a halogen atom (X), we have an induction shift of the electron density in the direction of the electronegative atom (as indicated by the arrows):

$$\begin{array}{c} H \\ | \\ X \leftarrow C \leftarrow C \leftarrow O \leftarrow H. \\ | \quad\;\; \| \\ H \quad\; O \end{array}$$

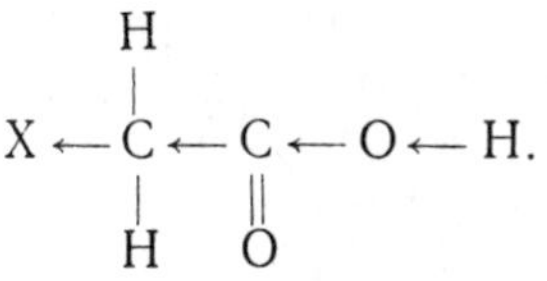

As a result of this shift, the O—H bond in the hydroxyl group becomes more polar or more electrovalent; this is manifested in a more ready ionisation of the bond, i.e., the proton in solution is more easily split off. In full correspondence with theoretical concepts, it follows from experiment that the more electronegative the halogen, the easier the proton is split off; further, in the series of carbonic acids, variation of proton mobility upon replacement of the H atom in the extreme methyl group by a halogen becomes less and less as the chain length increases.

The induction effect does not in any way exhaust the types of mutual effect of atoms. A special type of mutual effect is characteristic of so-called *conjugated systems*, i.e., molecules containing alternating single and double bonds. This, for instance, is the structure of molecules with polymethine chains, such as the hexadiene molecule $H_3C-CH=CH-CH=CH-CH_3$. A characteristic feature of conjugated bonds is their greater or lesser similarity, which is due to a certain smoothing of the differences between single and double bonds. This is evident from both chemical experiments and physical measurements, in particular, measurements of interatomic distances and bond strength, elastic forces acting between the atoms and determining the vibrational frequencies of the molecule. All these data lead to the conclusion that the electron-cloud density (corresponding to a single bond) in a conjugated system of bonds is greater than the electron-cloud density in an isolated single bond and less than in an isolated double bond, thus being intermediate between them. The degree of similarity of bonds in the conjugated chain systems is the greater the longer the chain; this must be due to the greater uniformity of elements of long-chain molecules. For this reason, in the benzene molecule, which consists of six similar CH elements, the bonds are in every way similar and the molecule has a high degree of symmetry (axis of symmetry of the sixth order).

Connected with the similarity of the electron density in conjugated systems is their greater strength over systems with isolated bonds. For this reason, the transition from molecules with isolated bonds to molecules with a system of conjugated bonds is ordinarily accompanied by the release of energy. A good example is the Zelinsky reaction:

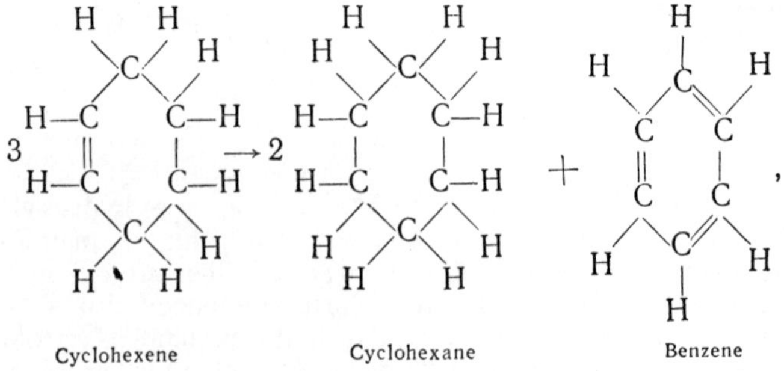

in which 19.8 kcal are released per gram-molecule of benzene.

From the point of view of quantum chemistry, the similarity of single and double bonds in conjugated and aromatic systems may be associated with the great mobility of the electron cloud of π-bonds. The partial overlapping of the p-clouds of double bonds separated by a single bond leads to the formation of "bridges" between the double bonds; these bridges strengthen the single bonds between them and, at the same time, weaken the double bonds (Fig. 115). From this standpoint, the chemical bonds in conjugated systems should be regarded as a special type of bond. Indeed, whereas in molecules with ordinary isolated single or double bonds each valence electron together with the electron of an adjacent atom forms a cloud that corresponds only to a definite bond, in conjugated systems one valence electron can simultaneously be shared by the clouds of two adjacent bonds. Considering aromatic bonds as the limiting case of conjugated bonds, we may assume that the chemical linkage here is, to a certain extent, very

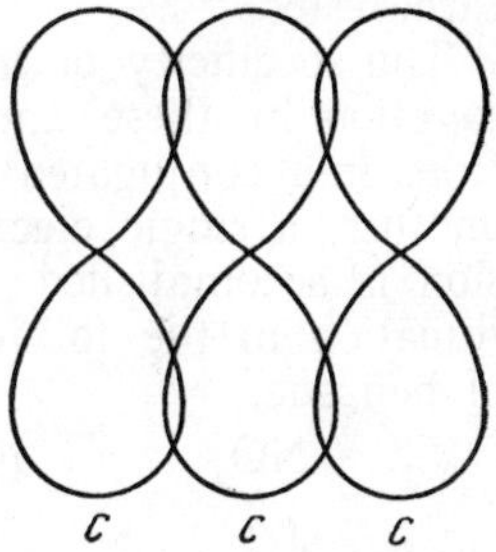

Fig. 115. Overlapping of p-clouds in a conjugated system of π-bonds (all C, C-bonds are equalised)

close to the linkage in metals, i. e., to linkage between atoms in the crystal lattice of a metal, where each electron binds many atoms. And just as the valence electrons in a metal do not actually belong to any one atom and form a single electron cloud, so, for instance, in the benzene molecule the six electrons of the π-bonds should be considered as being shared by all six atoms of carbon.

The peculiarities, characteristic of conjugated systems, in the transmission of mutual interaction of atoms are accounted for by special properties of chemical linkage in these systems. In contrast to the rapidly attenuating induction effect, the mechanism of its transfer in conjugated systems is such that the effect is transmitted along the chain of conjugation almost without any attenuation. By way of illustration, let us examine the case of crotonic and sorbic esters

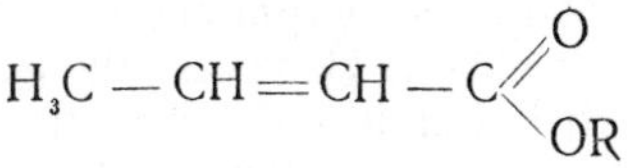

$$H_3C - CH = CH - C \diagup^{O}_{\diagdown OR}$$

and

$$H_3C - CH = CH - CH = CH - C \diagup^{O}_{\diagdown OR}$$

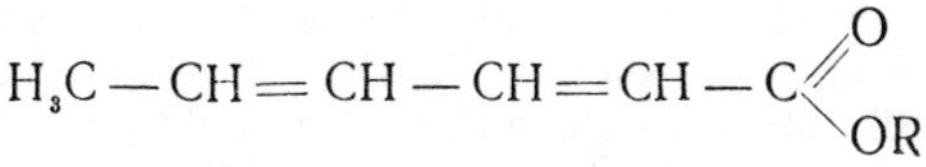

Despite the great distance of the methyl group from carboxyl oxygen, the specific influence of the latter on this group persists in the molecules of these esters just as in the molecule of acetic ester,

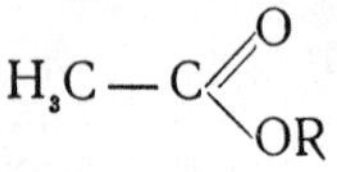

which follows from the close properties of the methyl group in all three esters.

The specificity of transmission of an effect along a chain of conjugation in these and other cases is due to the fact that all π-electrons in a conjugated or aromatic system form, to one degree or another, a single electron cloud, by means of which the transmission is accomplished. The correctness of this mechanism finds confirmation in the following data. Of the following five derivatives of benzene,

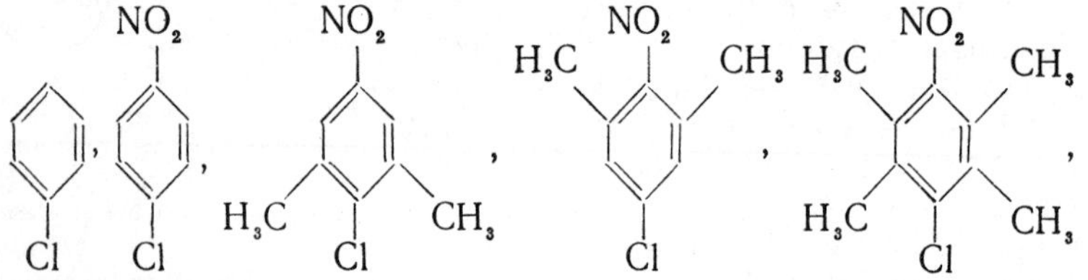

the first (chlorobenzene) has a typical aromatic chlorine atom of low mobility. In the next two (parachloronitrobenzene and meta-dimethyl-parachloronitrobenzene) the chlorine atom is mobile due to the influence of the nitro group, which influence is transmitted via the benzene nucleus. In the last two derivatives (orthodimethyl-parachloronitrobenzene and 2, 3, 5, 6-tetramethyl-4-chloronitrobenzene) the chlorine atom is again of low mobility as in chlorobenzene. At the same time, the nitro group in the last two derivatives is pulled out of the plane of the ring by two adjacent CH_3 groups; this disrupts the cloud of π-electrons and, thus, precludes the transmission of influence of the nitro group via the benzene nucleus.

As is evident from the foregoing examples and from other numerous chemical and physical data, some types of mutual interaction of atoms and groups of atoms are explainable in terms of the electronic concepts of quantum chemistry. However, the problem of mutual effect taken as a whole still requires further theoretical development, particularly as regards the establishment of quantitative regularities.

The peculiarities of the mutual interaction of atoms and groups of atoms (this finds expression in a redistribution of density of the electron cloud of the molecule and in the polarity of the covalent bonds, in a tendency of bonds to become similar in conjugated systems, in changes of the strength of individual bonds, and in other effects) lead to a great diversity of properties of chemical compounds. The necessity for systematisation of vast experimental material gave rise to the systems of organic and inorganic chemistry. All the compounds were arranged in separate classes characterised by definite features of chemical structure. However, even within the limits of a single class, the compounds frequently differ greatly as to chemical structure. The reason lies in changes in the electron cloud of the molecule under the influence of a variety of atomic groups To illustrate, let us consider the derivatives of carbonic acid expressed by the formula

$$\begin{matrix} RO \diagdown \\ \quad C=O, \\ RO \diagup \end{matrix}$$

where R is an H atom or group of atoms. From the capacity for hydrolysis, i.e., for the reaction

$$\begin{matrix} RO \diagdown \\ \quad C=O \end{matrix} + 2HO^- \rightarrow ROH + CO_3^{--},$$
$$RO \diagup$$

it follows that the R—O bond in these compounds is more or less electrovalent. The greater the difference in electronegativity of the R group and the O atom, the greater the tendency for hydrolysis. In the limiting case, a compound of this kind will have a structure corresponding to the formula

$$\begin{matrix} R^+O^- \diagdown \\ \quad C=O \\ R^+O^- \diagup \end{matrix}$$

in contradistinction to another limiting case of a purely homopolar compound, the structure of which corresponds to the formula

$$\begin{matrix} RO \diagdown \\ \quad C=O. \\ RO \diagup \end{matrix}$$

However, the foregoing formula of an ionic compound does not express the true structure of a molecule of a derivative of carbonic acid even in the limiting case because it does not take into account the mutual effect of the RO groups and the carbonyl group. In reality, however, as follows from the symmetric structure of the CO_3^{--} ion (this structure indicates complete similarity of all three bonds between the atoms C and O) the electron cloud of the C=O bond should be shifted towards the oxygen atom and impart to it a certain negative charge and there should be a simultaneous displacement of the negative charge of oxygen of the RO group in the direction of the C atom. The true structure of the molecule under consideration is given by the following formula (by means of curved arrows that indicate the direction of shift of the negative charge):

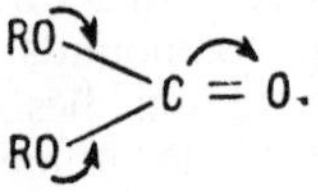

From the foregoing it follows that the true structure of the derivatives of carbonic acid does not correspond either to the limiting ionic or the limiting covalent formulas, in the same way as, for example, the true structure of the HF molecule cannot be expressed by the limiting formulas

$$H-F \text{ and } H^+F^-.$$

The HF molecule is neither purely atomic nor purely ionic, but has a structure *intermediate* between these extreme forms. As has been pointed out earlier (see (33.9)), the wave function of such a molecule is expressed, to a first approximation, by the sum of two terms that correspond to the two limiting structures: atomic and ionic.

The above examples of changes in the mobility of individual atoms under the influence of substitutes depending upon the structure of the molecules are an illustration of Butlerov's concept of the mutual relationship between the structure and reactivity of chemical compounds. The degree of mobility of a given atom or atomic group may be regarded as a certain relative measure of the reactivity of the molecule. The relativity of this measure is evident from the fact that the reactivity of a given molecule is significantly affected not only by its structure but by the nature of the particles interacting with it, and the conditions in which the reaction proceeds—the medium, temperature, and other factors. During the reaction the reacting particles form a single complex in which the same mutual interactions of atoms obtain as in an isolated molecule. The mutual interactions in a reacting system, which may be called *dynamic* (in contrast to the *static* ones that occur in isolated molecules), find expression in a redistribution of electron density, which ultimately leads to a redistribution of bonds in accord with the structure of the newly formed substances—the reaction products. Dynamic effects explain the specific peculiarities of various reactions of addition and substitution, the phenomena of transfer of the reaction centre of a molecule from one atom to another, phenomena of orientation in a benzene ring, and many other regularities of chemical reactions.

To illustrate, we take the case of a dynamic effect relating to the reaction of butadiene with hydrogen chloride in an acid medium. The overall equation of this reaction is given in the form

$$H_2C{=}CH-CH{=}CH_2+HCl \rightarrow H_3C-CH{=}CH-CH_2Cl.$$

According to the mutual-interaction theory, in the initial stage of the reaction (which involves the attack on a butadiene molecule by an H^+ ion) there is a displacement of the electron cloud in the direction of the attacking charge in the nonpolar molecule of butadiene:

$$H^+ \quad H_2C = CH - CH = CH_2.$$

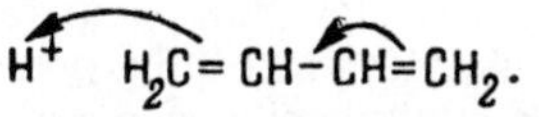

This results in the cation $H_3C - CH = CH - CH_2^+$ which, by adding a chlorine ion (at the end of the chain), converts into the reaction product

$$H_3C - CH = CH - CH_2^+ + Cl^- \longrightarrow H_3C - CH = CH - CH_2Cl.$$

A peculiar manifestation of the mutual interaction of atoms in separate molecules or during the interaction of molecules is exhibited in the so-called *hydrogen bond*. This bond is effected between a hydrogen atom (which is chemically connected with one of the atoms in the molecule, usually with an atom of O or N) and some other atom (usually an atom of O, N, or F) of the same or of a neighbouring molecule. In the former instance one speaks of an *internal*, or *intramolecular*, bond, in the latter, of an *external*, or *intermolecular*, hydrogen bond.

An example of a compound with an intramolecular hydrogen bond is acetylhydroperoxide. Because of the hydrogen bond (designated by dots) there are two forms of this compound:

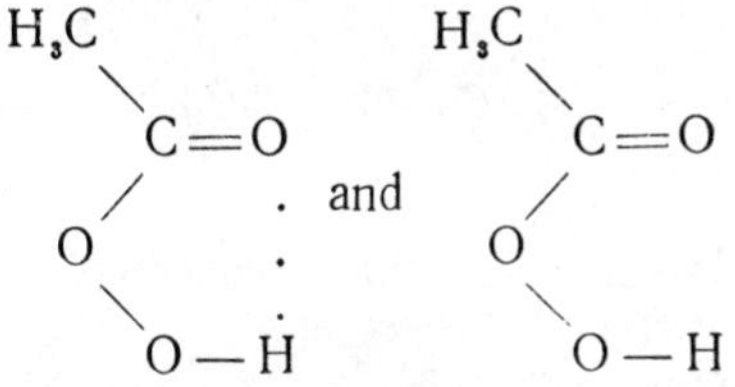

that are stable at different temperatures. A similar example is the molecule of acetacetic ester (enol form), the structural formula of which is

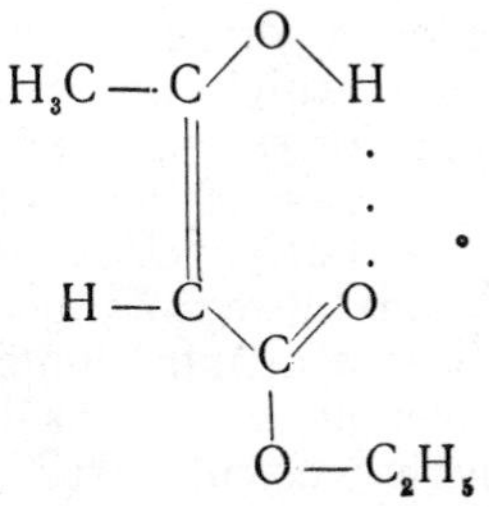

The intramolecular hydrogen bond imparts to the molecule specific physico-chemical properties. The formation of a hydrogen bond with the participation of hydroxyl hydrogen involves "masking" the hydroxyl group; this is seen in the absence of the hydroxyl band in the infrared absorption spectrum of the compound (λ 2.7 μ). The hydrogen bond also accounts for the comparatively weak solubility in water, the anomalous electric conduction of solutions, etc. The presence or absence of a hydrogen bond essentially alters the reactivity of the molecule.

The strength of hydrogen bonds is usually measured in energies of 4 to 8 kcal/mol.

45. Intermolecular Forces in Gases

Intermolecular hydrogen bond. The intermolecular hydrogen bond is most frequently expressed in the *association* of molecules, for example, in the dimerisation of carbonic acids and other compounds. To illustrate, the formic acid molecule, which is dimeric in the liquid and gaseous states and also in solutions in nonpolar solvents, may be represented in the form

$$
\begin{array}{c}
\text{O}\cdots\text{H—O} \\
\diagup\quad\quad\quad\diagdown \\
\text{H—C}\quad\quad\quad\quad\text{C—H.} \\
\diagdown\quad\quad\quad\diagup \\
\text{O—H}\cdots\text{O}
\end{array}
$$

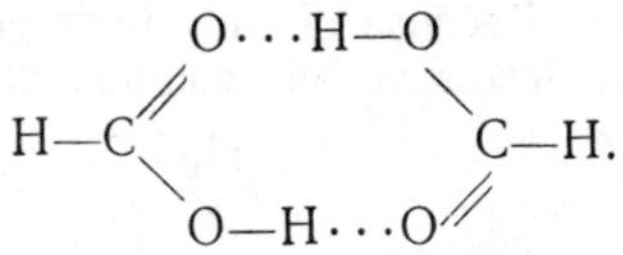

It is essential to point out that according to electronographic measurements the distances O—H and O $\cdots$H in the dimers both of formic and other carbonic acids are different.

Association of molecules accomplished by means of the hydrogen bond is a type of intermolecular interaction which to some extent approaches the ordinary chemical interaction of molecules. Indeed, the intermolecular hydrogen bond is frequently seen to have stoichiometric ratios, which are characteristic of chemical interaction due to valence forces. As a result of the fulfilment of stoichiometric ratios in the case of the aforementioned association, molecules that tend to the latter possess features characteristic of radicals. For instance, if one disregards the mechanism of molecular interaction, one notices a certain similarity between the above-considered molecules of formic acid HCOOH, which, as a result of association, form the dimeric molecules $(HCOOH)_2$, and, for example, the NO and NO_2 molecules that dimerise into $(NO)_2$* and $(NO_2)_2$. At the same time, intermolecular interaction due to the hydrogen bond has certain features of similarity with the nonvalent van der Waals interaction of molecules.

This type of interaction is determined by the forces of mutual attraction of molecules that give rise to the difference between real and ideal gases, to the condensation of gases, molecular association, solvation (in solutions), and, finally, to interaction between different parts of the same molecule that are not directly (chemically) connected. The interaction energy that corresponds to van der Waals forces operating between neutral molecules is of the order of magnitude of molecular heats of evaporation. Many of the aforementioned phenomena may be due either to van der Waals forces or to hydrogen bonds. It has been pointed out that the distinguishing feature of van der Waals forces is that they do not satisfy stoichiometric ratios in molecular interaction.

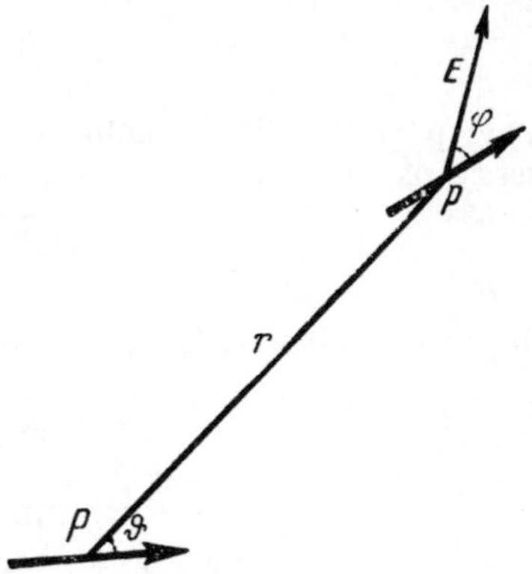

Fig. 116. Orientation interaction of dipoles

The nature of van der Waals forces. Underlying the theory of van der Waals forces are the following concepts of intermolecular interactions. It may be assumed that in polar substances there operate *orientation forces* between molecular electric dipoles; these forces tend to bring the interacting system (which in the simplest case is a pair of molecules) into a position of minimum potential energy. Further, both in the interaction of two dipoles and of a dipole with a nonpolar molecule we have *polarisation* of one particle in the electric field by another, which leads to mutual attraction. Finally, for nonpolar molecules the main part is played by the so-called *dispersion forces*, which correspond to the interaction of momentary electric dipoles that arise in molecules due to the rotational motion of the electrons. As we shall see, dispersion

---

* According to roentgenographic measurements, the dimer $(NO)_2$ has the following structure:

$$r_1 \begin{array}{c} r_2 \\ N-O \\ | \quad | \\ O-N \end{array}$$

$(r_1 = 1.10$ A and $r_2 = 2.38$ A).

forces likewise play an important part in the interaction of polar molecules. Let us consider each of the three types of van der Waals forces, first calculating the potential of the orientation forces.

Fig. 116 shows two dipoles separated by a distance r. Here, ϑ is the angle between the direction of r and the axis of the first dipole, and φ is the angle between the direction of the electric field E produced by the first dipole and the axis of the second dipole. Considering the dipoles identical and the magnitude of r great as compared with the dimensions of the dipoles, we will have

$$E=\frac{\sqrt{1+3\cos^2\vartheta}}{r^3}\,p$$

where p is the dipole moment. Whence, for the mutual potential energy of the dipoles $U=pE\cos\varphi$, we get

$$U=\frac{\sqrt{1+3\cos^2\vartheta}}{r^3}\,p^2\cos\varphi.$$

The mean value of U is determined by the expression

$$\bar{U}=\frac{\int_0^\pi\int_0^\pi e^{-\frac{U}{kT}}\,U\sin\vartheta\,d\vartheta\,\sin\varphi\,d\varphi}{\int_0^\pi\int_0^\pi e^{-\frac{U}{kT}}\sin\vartheta\,d\vartheta\,\sin\varphi\,d\varphi}.$$

At sufficiently high temperatures, i.e., at $U\ll kT$, this expression yields

$$\bar{U}=-\frac{2}{3}\frac{p^4}{kTr^6}. \tag{45.1}$$

The existence of dimers in the vapours of alkali-halogen salts, $(NaF)_2$ for instance, must be attributed to orientation interaction; however, dispersion interaction should also play a significant role as well (see p. 449).

To compute the potential of polarisation forces let us consider the interaction of a dipole and a nonpolar molecule. In this case, the mutual potential energy of the particles is

$$U=-\frac{\alpha E^2}{2},$$

where α is the polarisation coefficient of the nonpolar molecule and E is the electric field intensity of the dipole. Substituting into this expression $E=\frac{\sqrt{1+3\cos^2\vartheta}}{r^3}\,p$ and computing the mean value of the potential U $\left(\cos^2\vartheta = \frac{1}{3}\right)$, we get

$$\bar{U} = -\frac{\alpha p^2}{r^6}. \qquad (45.2)$$

The quantum-mechanical theory of van der Waals forces in the case of nonpolar molecules was developed by London. Below we give a simplified derivation of the potential energy of molecular interaction due to Born. The motion of a single electron is con-

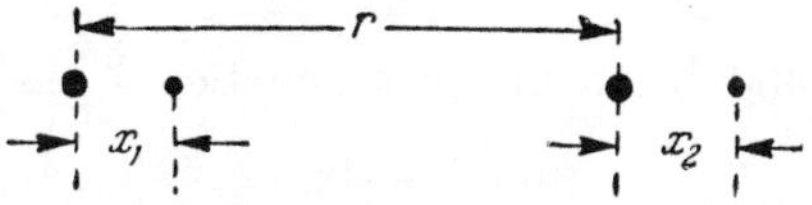

Fig. 117. Model representation of dispersion interaction of molecules (after Born)

sidered in the Coulomb field of the nucleus. The instantaneous relative position of nuclei and electrons of two such "molecules" is shown in Fig. 117. Here, r is the internuclear distance, x_1 is the distance between the nucleus and the electron of the first molecule, and x_2, of the second one. The potential energy of the system that corresponds to Fig. 117 is, obviously,

$$U = \frac{e^2}{r + x_2 - x_1} + \frac{e^2}{r} - \frac{e^2}{r + x_2} - \frac{e^2}{r - x_1}.$$

Expanding this expression in a series of powers of the small quantities x/r

$$U = \frac{e^2}{r}\left[1 - \frac{x^2 - x_1}{r} + \frac{(x_2 - x_1)^2}{r^2} - \ldots + 1 - 1 + \right.$$
$$\left. + \frac{x^2}{r} - \frac{x_2^2}{r^2} + \ldots - 1 + \frac{x_1}{r} - \frac{x_1^2}{r^2} + \ldots\right] = -\frac{2e^2 x_1 x_2}{r^3} + \ldots$$

and confining ourselves to the first term of the series, we find

$$U = -\frac{2e^2 x_1 x_2}{r^3}.$$

Considering each molecule separately as a harmonic oscillator, we represent the quasi-elastic force that gives rise to the oscillations of the electron as $F = fx$, where f is the quasi-elastic bond constant. It will be noted that the constant f may be expressed in terms of the polarisability of the molecule α: writing the instantaneous value of the dipole moment of the molecule $ex = \alpha E$, where E is the electric field intensity equal to $E = F/e$, we have $ex = \frac{\alpha f}{e}x$, i. e.,

$f=\frac{e^2}{\alpha}$. From the expression for a quasi-elastic force we get $U=\frac{fx^2}{2}$ for the potential energy of the oscillator.

Adding to U the kinetic vibrational energy $T=\frac{m\dot{x}^2}{2}=\frac{p^2}{2m}$ ($p=m\dot{x}$ is the momentum corresponding to the coordinate x, m is the electron mass), we get the Hamiltonian function

$$H=\frac{p^2}{2m}+\frac{fx^2}{2}$$

from which we find the oscillation equation $\frac{dp}{dt}=-\frac{\partial H}{\partial x}$ or

$$m\ddot{x}=-fx.$$

Solving this equation we find the oscillation, frequency of the oscillator

$$\omega=\frac{1}{2\pi}\sqrt{\frac{f}{m}}.$$

In the given case of two interacting oscillators, the Hamiltonian function will be written in the form

$$H=\frac{1}{2m}(p_1^2+p_2^2)+\frac{f}{2}(x_1^2+x_2^2)-\frac{2e^2x_1x_2}{r^3}.$$

Introducing new variables

$$X_1=\frac{1}{\sqrt{2}}(x_1+x_2) \text{ and } X_2=\frac{1}{\sqrt{2}}(x_1-x_2),$$

we can rewrite the Hamiltonian function as

$$H=\frac{1}{2m}(P_1^2+P_2^2)+\left(\frac{f}{2}-\frac{e^2}{r^3}\right)X_1^2+\left(\frac{f}{2}+\frac{e^2}{r^3}\right)X_2^2.$$

Solving the oscillation equations of the system that are obtained from this expression

$$m\ddot{X}_1=-\left(f-\frac{2e^2}{r^3}\right)X_1 \text{ and } m\ddot{X}_2=-\left(f+\frac{2e^2}{r^3}\right)X_2,$$

we get, for the oscillation frequencies,

$$\omega_1=\frac{1}{2\pi}\sqrt{\frac{1}{m}\left(f-\frac{2e^2}{r^3}\right)} \quad\text{and}\quad \omega_2=\frac{1}{2\pi}\sqrt{\frac{1}{m}\left(f+\frac{2e^2}{r^3}\right)}.$$

Expanding these expressions in a power series of $1/r$,

$$\omega_1=\omega\left(1-\frac{e^2}{fr^3}-\frac{e^4}{2f^2r^6}-\ldots\right) \quad\text{and}\quad \omega_2=\omega\left(1+\frac{e^2}{fr^3}-\frac{e^4}{2f^2r^6}+\ldots\right)$$

$\left(\text{here } \omega=\frac{1}{2\pi}\sqrt{\frac{f}{m}}\right)$ and discarding terms that contain the higher powers of $1/r$, we get the following expression for the zero vibrational energy of the system (see p. 355):

$$\frac{h\omega_1}{2}+\frac{h\omega_2}{2}=h\omega\left(1-\frac{e^4}{2f^2r^6}\right).$$

We see that as a result of the interaction of momentary dipoles the zero vibrational energy of the system diminishes by

$$U=-\frac{h\omega e^4}{2f^2r^6} \qquad (45.3)$$

which is thus the potential of the van der Waals forces that correspond to this interaction. Since $\omega=\frac{1}{2\pi}\sqrt{\frac{f}{m}}$ and $f=\frac{e^2}{\alpha}$, expression (45.3) can be transformed to

$$U=-\frac{he\alpha^{3/2}}{2\pi\sqrt{m}r^6}. \qquad (45.4)$$

Expressions (45.3) and (45.4) were generalised by Slater and Kirkwood for the case of spherically symmetric molecules having n outer electrons. The expression they obtained for the potential of van der Waals forces is of the form

$$U=-0.68\frac{he\alpha^{3/2}\sqrt{n}}{2\pi\sqrt{m}\,r^6}. \qquad (45.5)$$

Comparing (45.1), (45.2) and (45.5), we see that in all cases of interaction the potential of van der Waals forces is inversely proportional to the sixth power of the intermolecular distance r and, consequently, may be expressed as

$$U=-\frac{A}{r^6}. \qquad (45.6)$$

For various cases of interaction, A has the form: $A_1=\frac{2}{3}\frac{p^4}{kT}$ (orientation effect), $A_2=\alpha p^2$ (polarisation effect), and $A_3=0.68\frac{he\alpha^{3/2}\sqrt{n}}{2\pi\sqrt{m}}$ (dispersion effect).

For an approximate comparative appraisal of these three effects, we calculate the values of A_1, A_2, and A_3, putting $p=10^{-18}$, $\alpha=10^{-24}$, $n=8$, and $T=290°K$. This calculation yields: $A_1=1.7\times10^{-57}$, $A_2=1\times10^{-60}$, and $A_3=3\times10^{-57}$. We thus see that even in the case of polar molecules the dispersion effect is comparable with the orientation effect, while the polarisation effect may, apparently, be ignored in all cases.

Van der Waals molecules. The negative sign of the potential of van der Waals forces (45.6) shows that all molecules mutually attract, irrespective of their chemical nature. However, in the case of saturated molecules or molecules that are not capable of establishing a chemical bond between themselves, chemical forces of repulsion are superposed on the van der Waals forces of attraction. For this reason, the mutual potential energy of these molecules may be represented to a first approximation as the sum of two terms:

$$U = U_0 - \frac{A}{r^6} \quad (45.7)$$

where U_0 is the potential of repulsive forces ($U_0 > 0$). Computations of U_0 for H and He atoms show that in this case it can approximately be represented by an exponential function of the form

$$U_0 = Be^{-Cr} \quad (45.8)$$

where B and C are constants. Extending this expression to other atoms and molecules, * we rewrite expression (45.7) in the form

$$U = Be^{-Cr} - \frac{A}{r^6}. \quad (45.9)$$

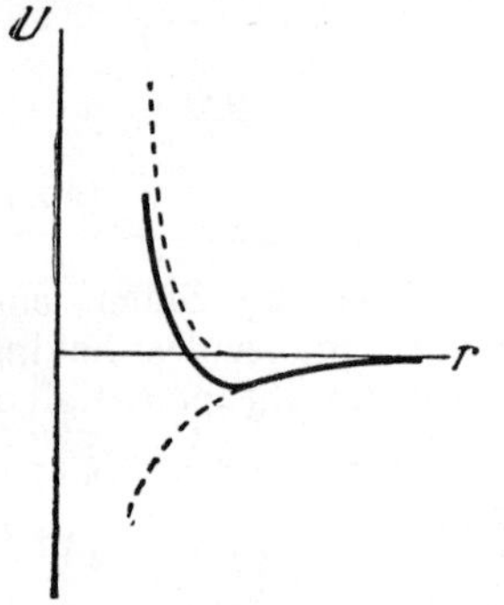

Fig. 118. Potential-energy curve of van der Waals molecule

From (45.9) it follows that as a result of the superposition of the van der Waals force potential on the positive potential of repulsive forces, the ordinary repulsion curve can have a shallow minimum which will account for a certain stability in the associated, or, as it may be called (after J. Franck), van der Waals molecule. This type of potential-energy curve is shown in Fig. 118, which also gives the original repulsion curve and the curve of van der Waals potential (dashed). Differentiating U (45.9) with respect to r and equating the derivative to zero, we get an expression for determining the equilibrium distance r_0 between the atoms in a van der Waals molecule. Experimental and theoretical data show that r_0 is of the order of several Angstroms, which is several times greater than the equilibrium distance between atoms in ordinary molecules (see Sec. 48). Now the energy of dissociation of van der Waals molecules, which is equal to the distance of the minimum of the potential-energy curve from the axis r (Fig. 118), is usually

* It may be noted that in addition to expression (45.8), U_0 is frequently represented as $U_0 = B/r^{12}$ or $U_0 = B/r^m$, $m > 6$.

measured in tens and hundreds, and sometimes even in thousands of cal/mol, which is from 100 to 1000 times less than the heats of dissociation of ordinary molecules. To illustrate we give the values of r_0 and the heats of dissociation D of van der Waals molecules of neon, argon, and krypton:

Element	Ne	Ar	Kr
r_0, A	3.0	3.8	4.1
D, cal/mol	80	240	335

The heats of dissociation of some van der Waals molecules have also been determined spectroscopically. Due to the low interaction energy of the atoms in diatomic van der Waals molecules, the energy levels of the latter differ but slightly from the levels of the respective atoms. For instance, in the case of potassium, Kuhn found weak absorption lines, which he attributed to van der Waals K_2 molecules. These bands are located near the atomic absorption lines at a distance of several Angstroms. Unlike the quasi-molecule spectrum (see p. 318), the bands of van der Waals molecules exhibit a *fine structure* characteristic of stable molecules. Such bands are observed also in the case of the molecules Hg_2, Cd_2, Zn_2, HeH, NeH, ArH, etc.; these bands are invariably associated with certain atomic lines, which is an indication of the proximity of the respective molecular and atomic energy levels. The heats of dissociation (determined from spectra) of the van der Waals molecules Hg_2 and Cd_2 came out to 1840 and 2000 cal/mol, respectively.

We further point out the possibility of calculating the constant a in the van der Waals equation

$$\left(p+\frac{a}{v^2}\right)(v-b)=RT$$

on the basis of the van der Waals force potential. Such calculations were first carried out by Slater and Kirkwood for Ne, Ar, Kr, Xe, H_2, N_2, O_2, and CH_4. The results of their calculations are given in Table 43, which also gives the directly measured values of a for comparison. It will be seen that the calculated values are in satisfactory agreement with the measured values.

Table 43

Calculated and measured values of the van der Waals constant for certain gases (in erg cm³)

Gas	Ne	Ar	Kr	Xe	H_2	N_2	O_2	CH_4
$a \times 10^{-12}$ (calc)	0.37	1.67	2.33	3.70	0.55	1.58	1.64	2.32
$a \times 10^{-12}$ (meas)	0.21	1.29	2.07	3.86	0.20	1.34	1.49	2.28

It may also be noted that attempts were made to connect the mutual influence of separate atomic groups in the molecule with their van der Waals attraction.

Sec. 46. Dipole Moments of Molecules

The presence of a permanent dipole moment in a molecule is the result either of a difference in electrical properties or of a certain asymmetry in the arrangement of the atoms in the molecule. All diatomic molecules consisting of different atoms have a dipole moment, in contrast to the molecules H_2, N_2, O_2, Cl_2, etc., the dipole moments of which are zero. The bent shape of the molecules, which upsets their symmetry, accounts for dipole moments in the molecules H_2O, $(CH_3)_2O$, $(CH_3)_2S$, etc. The asymmetrical arrangement of atoms in the linear molecule of nitrogen oxide NNO is likewise the cause of the finite value of its dipole moment. We thus have a direct relationship between the dipole moment of a molecule and its geometrical structure; hence the great importance of measuring dipole moments for determining molecular structure.

Measuring dipole moments. The experimental determination of dipole moments has, until just recently, been based exclusively on measurements of molar polarisation and molar refraction, i.e., ultimately, on measurements of the dielectric constant and the index of refraction of the substance under study.

In the case of a nonpolar gas (zero molecular dipole moment), molar polarisation is entirely due to molar polarisability in an electric field; polarisability is characterised by the polarisation coefficient α. Between α and the dielectric constant of the medium ε there is a unique relationship expressed by the Clausius-Mossotti equation (44.2):

$$P = \frac{\varepsilon - 1}{\varepsilon + 2}\frac{M}{\varrho} = \frac{4\pi}{3} N_A \alpha,$$

on the basis of which the coefficient α may be obtained from measurements of ε.

However, this equation does not suit the case of a polar gas because in addition to polarisation of molecules in an electric field we have to take into account the orientation of dipoles with respect to the field direction. Disregarding thermal motion, we will have, for the molar polarisation contributed by each molecule, a magnitude equal to its dipole moment p (plus the induced dipole moment due to polarisation of the molecule in an electric field). In reality, however, the thermal motion disorients the molecular dipoles that tend to align with the field. As a result we measure a certain effective value of the dipole-moment projection of the molecules on the field direction.

In the molecular theory of paramagnetism (Sec. 47), too, we shall encounter a similar phenomenon: the orienting action of the field and — its opposite — the disorienting action of thermal motion. In this theory classical concepts yield the following expression for the average projection of the magnetic moment of the molecule on the field direction: $\mu^1 = \mu^2/3kT$ (for the field intensity $H = 1$). Insofar as quantum effects are inessential for orientation of molecular dipoles in an electric field, this expression may be applied in full to the case of dipoles; for this we rewrite it in the form

$$p' = \frac{p^2}{3kT} \tag{46.1}$$

where p' denotes the average value of the dipole-moment projection of the molecule on the direction of the electric field. Substituting into (44.2) the sum $p' + \alpha$ in place of α, we get the following expression for the molar polarisation of a polar gas:

$$P = \frac{\varepsilon - 1}{\varepsilon + 2}\frac{M}{\varrho} = \frac{4\pi}{3} N_A \left(\alpha + \frac{p^2}{3kT}\right) \tag{46.2}$$

This expression was first derived by Debye and is called the *Debye equation.*

The Debye equation serves as the basis for one of the methods of determining dipole moments. By measuring the dielectric constant of a given substance at different temperatures, the results of these measurements (according to equation (46.2)) may be represented graphically as a straight line $P = a + \frac{b}{T}$ (in coordinates P and $1/T$). The magnitude of the moment is determined from the angle of inclination of this line to the axis $1/T$, the tangent of which is $b = \frac{4\pi}{9}\frac{N_A}{k} p^2$,

$$p = 0.0127 \sqrt{b} \times 10^{-18} \text{ absolute unit.} \tag{46.3}$$

In the particular case of $p = 0$, the dielectric constant (like the polarisation P) is independent of temperature; in this case, the straight line $P = a$ is parallel to the abscissa axis. Dipole moments are customarily expressed in debyes, 1 debye $= 10^{-18}$ absolute unit.

The accuracy of measurement of the dipole moment by means of the foregoing method is determined by the precision with which the angle of inclination of the straight line $P = a + \frac{b}{T}$ is found. Whence it follows that to obtain accurate results it is necessary to perform the measurements in a sufficiently broad temperature interval; in a number of cases this involves considerable experimental difficulties. Besides, temperature variations may involve changes in the substance under study (processes of dissociation and association, etc.) which distort the measurement results. For this reason, one often resorts to another method that permits measuring the dipole moment at a constant temperature. It consists in the simultaneous measurement of molar polarisation and molar refraction expressed by the Lorents-Lorenz relation (44.3):

$$R = \frac{r^2 - 1}{r^2 + 2} \frac{M}{\varrho} = \frac{4\pi}{3} N_A \alpha.$$

From (46.2) and (44.3) it follows that

$$P - R = \frac{4\pi}{9} \frac{N_A}{kT} p^2$$

or

$$p = 0.0127 \sqrt{(P - R) T} \times 10^{-18} \text{ absolute unit.} \qquad (46.4)$$

Thus, by measuring the index of refraction of the given substance and its dielectric constant for a certain (constant) temperature, we find the appropriate values of molar refraction and molar polarisation, substitution of which into (46.4) gives p.

In addition to the above-considered two methods, a new experimental method has in recent years been successfully employed to determine dipole moments; it is based on measurements of microwave radio-frequency spectra, which ordinarily are rotational (less frequently rotation-vibrational) spectra. In an electric field, the individual rotational lines are displaced relative to their position in the spectrum in the absence of an electric field because of displacement and splitting of the energy levels of the molecule, and there appear new lines associated with transitions between components of electrical splitting of the rotational levels. In this process, the frequencies of lines observed in the presence of an electric field are dependent upon the field intensity and the electric moment of the molecule. Frequency measurements of the microwave spectra of molecules in an electric field as a function of the field intensity enable us to determine dipole moments.

The advantages of the microwave method over other methods of measuring dipole moments are its high accuracy and sensitivity, which makes measurements possible with small quantities of material. The latter is especially significant in the case of low-volatile substances whose dipole moments either could not at all be determined by the old methods (because it was impossible to measure the dielectric constant and index of refraction of these substances due to the low vapour pressure) or could be measured only in a solution, which frequently entails errors caused by interaction of the molecules of the substance under study with the solvent. This interaction distorted the dipole moment. It may be noted that the microwave method (in a modification of it consisting of measurements in a molecular beam and closely resembling the magneto-resonance method, see p. 225) was used to measure the dipole moments of the molecules of such low-volatile substances as the halogen salts of alkaline elements (see Table 27, p. 282).

All the foregoing methods of determining dipole moments yield the moment of the molecule as a whole. Yet of particular interest in clarifying the various peculiarities of molecular structure—distribution of electron density in the molecule, the character of intramolecular bonds, the mutual interaction of the atoms, and the reactivity of the molecule—are the dipole moments of *individual bonds* in the molecule. In certain cases the latter may be evaluated on the basis of a vector dipole model of the molecule (see below). This evaluation, however, is extremely crude.

An experimental method for determining the dipole moments of intramolecular bonds has been proposed by Mecke (already mentioned on p. 369); it consists in measuring the intensities of infrared vibrational spectra. According to quantum mechanics, the intensity of the absorption band that corresponds to the transition $v \longrightarrow v'$ (v and v' are vibrational quantum numbers) is determined by the square of the respective quasi-moment $M_{vv'}$ (see p. 387) which may be expressed as follows:

$$|M_{vv'}|^2 = \frac{3hc}{8\pi^2\nu}\int \mu_\nu \, d\nu = \frac{\left|\int \psi_v p \psi^*_{v'} dr\right|^2}{\int |\psi_v|^2 dr \int |\psi_{v'}|^2 dr}. \tag{46.5}$$

Here, $\int \mu_\nu \, d\nu$ is the area of the absorption band (μ_ν is the absorption coefficient and ν is the frequency), $\psi_v(r)$ and $\psi_{v'}(r)$ are wave functions that correspond to the combining vibrational states of the molecule, and p is the electric moment of the chemical bond whose valence vibrations give rise to the given absorption band. It is thus fundamentally possible to determine the electric moment of the bonds from the experimentally measured area of the appropriate absorption band, on the condition that we know the wave functions $\psi_v(r)$ and $\psi_{v'}(r)$ and the variation of the dipole transition moment versus the interatomic distance r, i.e., the form of the function $p(r)$.

The wave functions can be found by solving the wave equation for normal vibrations of the molecule. The question of the dependence of p upon r requires special investigation and at the present stage of development of quantum chemistry can, apparently, be solved only semi-empirically, i.e., by correlating the computed values of the dipole moment (on the assumption of a certain p-r relationship) with the directly measured values of the moments of the simplest molecules (including diatomic). The presently available experimental data are insufficient to decide on the fitness of such an assumption and on the possibility of representing the p (r) relation in various molecules by means of a function of some one type. We may note that Mecke, in development of this view, recently proposed an empirical formula that represents the dipole transition moment as a sum of the ionic, polar, and inductive components.

From measurements of intensities in the infrared spectra of HCl, H_2O, and $CHCl_3$, Mecke calculated the values of the dipole moments of the bonds Cl—H, O—H, and C—H. In this way, a number of workers have also determined the moments of the C—F and Si—F bonds in CF_4 and SiF_4, respectively, the moments of C—H and C—D bonds in C_2H_2 and in C_2D_2, and others.

A vector dipole model of a molecule.* Table 44 gives the measurements of the dipole moments of a number of simple molecules, and can serve as a basis for certain definite conclusions regarding the structure of these molecules. For instance, by comparing the dipole moments of type AB_2 triatomic molecules we conclude that the molecules H_2O, H_2S, SO_2 are triangular, in contradistinction to the molecules CO_2 and CS_2, to which we should assign a linear structure due to $p=0$. This is in complete agreement with all other data relating to these molecules. Further, the presence of a dipole moment different from zero in the case of the molecules NH_3, PH_3, AsH_3, and $(C_2H_5)_3N$ excludes a planar structure and compels us to assign to them the structure of a trihedral pyramid. The fact that CH_4 and CCl_4 have zero dipole moments is equally compatible with a symmetrical planar structure and with a tetrahedral structure. However, the entire assemblage of data referring primarily to the optical and electrical

Table 44

Molecular dipole moments (in debyes)

Molecule	p	Molecule	p
H_2O	1.84	CO_2	0
H_2S	0.93	CS_2	0
SO_2	1.61	CH_4	0
NH_3	1.46	CCl_4	0
PH_3	0.55	PCl_5	0
AsH_3	0.16	C_2H_6	0
$(C_2H_5)_3N$	0.83	C_2H_4	0
$(CH_3)_2O$	1.30	C_2H_2	0
$(CH_3)_2CO$	2.73	C_6H_6	0

* The theory given here is simplified; it does not take into account, for instance, the atomic dipole moments (see p. 462).

properties of the CH_4 and CCl_4 molecules is in favour of a tetrahedral structure. Further, the C_6H_6 molecule is symmetrically planar and the C_2H_6, C_2H_4, and C_2H_2 molecules are symmetrical, and the latter one is linear. Since the dipole moment of $(CH_3)_2O$ is different from zero, we must assign to it a triangular structure. The fact that the dipole moment of $(CH_3)_2CO$ is different from zero and also the fact of directed carbon valences compel us to assign to it the structure

$$\begin{matrix} H_3C \diagdown \\ C = O. \\ H_3C \diagup \end{matrix}$$

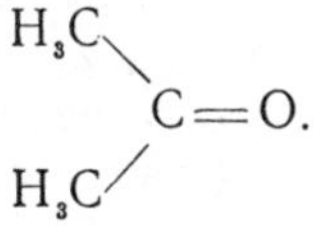

It is interesting to note that unlike PCl_5 the dipole moment of BrF_5 is not zero but 1.51 debyes. Whence we can conclude that the BrF_5 molecule has the shape of a square prism, whereas PCl_5 is a symmetrical trigonal bipyramid. A study of isotope exchange between PCl_5 and Cl_2 shows that of the five chlorine atoms in PCl_5 three are most readily exchangeable. In the molecule, these three occupy an equatorial position. We thus see that the five P—Cl bonds in PCl_5 are not equivalent.

As has already been pointed out, all diatomic molecules consisting of different atoms are polar, i.e., they have a finite dipole moment. Such, for example, are NO (0.16), CO (0.11), HCl (1.04), HBr (0.79), HI (0.38), ICl (0.50), OH (1.54 debyes), etc.* This compels us to assign a definite moment to each pair of directly bound atoms in a molecule or to each intramolecular bond, on the condition that the atoms are different or are in different valence states. The zero dipole moment of many symmetric polyatomic molecules is due to the *mutual compensation* of the moments of individual bonds.

To illustrate, let us consider the CH_4 molecule. Undoubtedly, each of the four C—H bonds of this molecule has a certain dipole moment different from zero. However, due to the symmetrical tetrahedral structure of the methane molecule, the moments of the individual bonds are mutually compensated. Indeed, if the moments of the C—H (P) bonds are directed along these bonds, as is shown in Fig. 119, we get, for the sum of the projections of the three moments on the direction of the fourth, $3P\cos(HCH) = P$ (because $\cos(HCH) = \cos 109°28' = 1/3$). Thus, the three moments of the C—H bond in the CH_4 molecule are completely compensated for by the fourth.

* An approximate quantum-mechanical calculation gives 1.97 debyes for the dipole moment of the CH molecule (radical). From this calculation it also follows that the $^2\Pi$ state (near which is the $^4\Sigma$ state) is the ground state of CH.

If we replace one of the H atoms in the CH_4 molecule with some other univalent atom or radical, for instance, the Cl atom, we violate the internal compensation of moments of bonds, and the molecule as a whole (the CH_3Cl molecule in the given instance) will acquire a finite dipole moment, obviously equal to the geometrical sum of moments of the individual bonds.

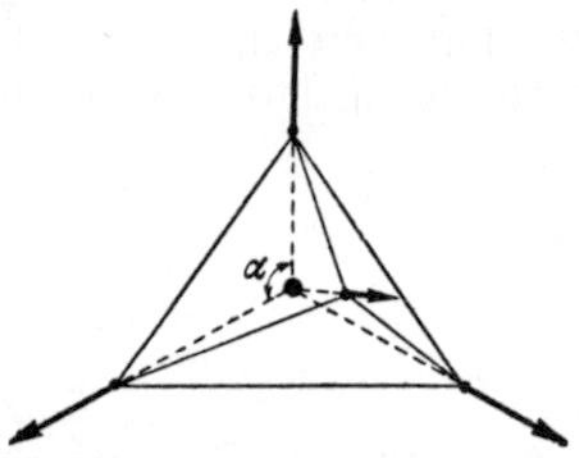

Fig. 119. Vector dipole model of CH_4 molecule

The vector concept of the moments of bonds, or the *vector dipole model of a molecule*, which was first introduced by J. J. Thomson, is very important in elucidating the structural peculiarities of molecules.

Measurements of the dipole moments of different molecules permit of the conclusion that in a large number of molecules the dipole moments corresponding to the bond of a given pair of atoms remain approximately unchanged. For example, if on the basis of the vector model we represent the dipole moment of the water molecule as $2P_{OH}\cos\frac{1}{2}(HOH) = 2P_{OH}\cos 52°30'$, where P_{OH} is the moment of the O—H bond, we find $P_{OH} = 1.51$ debyes. Further, from the dipole moment of dimethyl ester (1.30 debyes), which we represent as $2P_{OCH_3}\cos\frac{1}{2}(H_3COCH_3) = 2P_{OCH_3}\cos 55°30'$, we get $P_{OCH_3} = 1.15$ debyes. Taking advantage of these values of the moments of P_{OH} and P_{OCH_3} we can find the dipole moment of the methyl alcohol molecule CH_3OH. Calculating the latter as the sum $P_{OH}\cos\frac{1}{2}(HOCH_3) + P_{OCH_3}\cos\frac{1}{2}(HOCH_3) = (1.51 + 1.15)\cos 54°$, we get 1.57 debyes in place of the directly measured 1.67 debyes.

A comparison of the dipole moments of different alcohols shows that the difference in dipole moments of the $C-C_nH_{2n+1}$ bonds is not significant. Indeed, from Table 45, which gives the values of the dipole moments of a number of normal alcohols, it is seen that despite the great diversity of alkyl radicals $R = C_nH_{2n+1}$, the dipole moments of homologous alcohols differ but slightly from one another, ranging between 1.60 and 1.70 debyes. A comparison of the dipole moments of the compounds of other classes leads to an analogous conclusion. For example, the dipole moments of ketones of various structure exhibit a surprising constancy which again provides evidence for the small difference in dipole moments of $C-C_nH_{2n+1}$ bonds.

Table 45

Dipole moments of alcohols (in debyes)

Alcohol	p	Alcohol	p
Methyl CH_3OH	1.66	Octyl $C_8H_{17}OH$	1.62
Ethyl C_2H_5OH	1.70	Nonyl $C_9H_{19}OH$	1.60
Propyl C_3H_7OH	1.66	Decyl $C_{10}H_{21}OH$	1.63
Butyl C_4H_9OH	1.66	Undecyl $C_{11}H_{23}OH$	1.66
Hexyl $C_6H_{13}OH$	1.64	Duodecyl $C_{12}H_{25}OH$	1.62

Let us now consider the dipole moments of the ortho-, meta-, and para-dichlorobenzene. Their structural formulas and measured values of dipole moments are:

ortho meta para

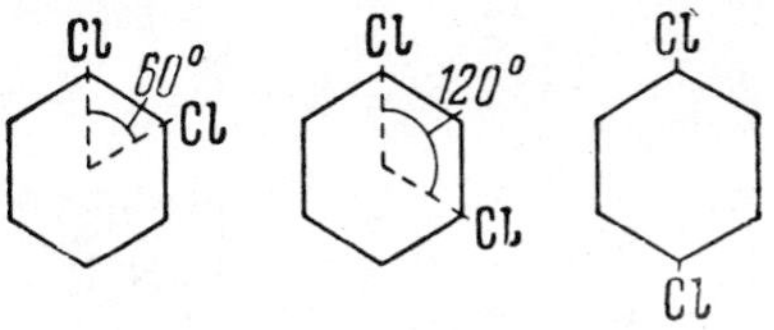

2.27 1.48 0

Expressing the dipole moment of chlorobenzene C_6H_5Cl as the sum $P_{C_6H_5Cl}=P_{C-Cl}+P_{C-H}$, where P_{C-Cl} and P_{C-H} are, respectively, the dipole moments of C—Cl and C—H bonds in the C_6H_5Cl molecule, and calculating the dipole moments of the three dichlorobenzenes from their vector models, we obtain: $P_{ortho}=2(P_{C-Cl}+P_{C-H})\cos 30°$, $P_{meta}=2(P_{C-Cl}+P_{C-H})\cos 60°$, and $P_{para}=2(P_{C-Cl}+P_{C-H})\cos 90°$. Introducing the experimental values of the C_6H_5Cl moment, $P_{C-Cl}+P_{C-H}=1.55$ debyes, $\cos 30°=\frac{\sqrt{3}}{2}$, $\cos 60°=-\frac{1}{2}$, and $\cos 90°=0$, we get $P_{ortho}=2.68$, $P_{meta}=1.55$, and $P_{para}=0$ debyes. Comparing these with the observed values we see satisfactory agreement with experiment. One cannot expect exact quantitative agreement (with experiment) of the results of such calculation because the Cl atoms that replace the H atoms in the benzene ring deform the hydrocarbon core. The magnitude of this deformation is determined both by the properties of the latter and by the electrical properties of the substituting atom. In addition, due to the interaction of the substituting atoms themselves, particularly in the ortho form where these atoms are closer together, the angle between the respective bonds cannot be considered as exactly equal to 60°. However, the possibility of an approximate calculation of the dipole moments of complex molecules on the basis of their vector models shows that in most cases these effects are comparatively slight.

Let us also consider the following examples. Below we give the values of the dipole moments and the positions of the substituting atoms or groups for the following derivatives of benzene:

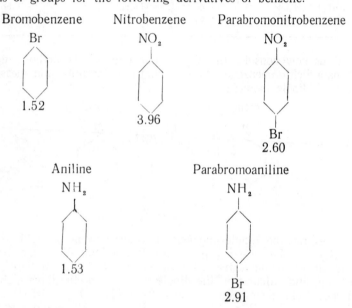

Bromobenzene

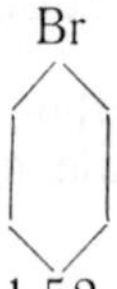

1.52

Nitrobenzene

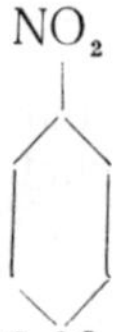

3.96

Parabromonitrobenzene

2.60

Aniline

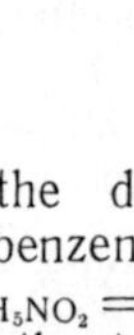

1.53

Parabromoaniline

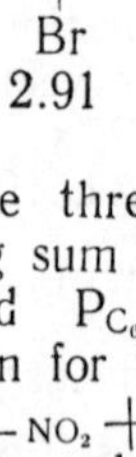

2.91

Expressing the dipole moments of the three monosubstituted compounds of benzene as the corresponding sum $P_{C_6H_5Br} = P_{C-Br} + P_{C-H}$, $P_{C_6H_5NO_2} = P_{C-NO_2} + P_{C-H}$, and $P_{C_6H_5NH_2} = P_{C-NH_2} + P_{C-H}$, from the two first sums we obtain for the dipole moment of parabromonitrobenzene: $P_{NO_2C_6H_4Br} = P_{C-NO_2} + P_{C-H} - P_{C-Br} - P_{C-H} = 3.96 - 1.52 = 2.44$ debyes. This value is in fair agreement with the measured value, 2.60 debyes. Similar calculation of the parabromoaniline dipole moment gives $P_{NH_2C_6H_4Br} = 1.53 - 1.52 = 0.01$ whereas the experimental value is 2.91 debyes. It seems possible to eliminate this discrepancy by assuming that the P_{C-H} moments in C_6H_5Br and $C_6H_5NH_2$, as well as the P_{C-NH_2} and P_{C-Br} moments for parabromoaniline, have different signs, whence it follows, in good agreement with experiment, that $P_{NH_2C_6H_4Br} = P_{C_6H_5NH_2} +$

$+P_{C_6H_5Br} = P_{C-NH_2} - P_{C-H} + P_{C-Br} + P_{C-H} = 1.53 + 1.52 = 3.05$ debyes.

The vector dipole model of a molecule is again useful in explaining the peculiarities of the electrical properties of substances that have isomeric cis and trans forms. Such, for instance, are the disubstituted derivatives of ethylene, an example of which is dichloroethylene. In the trans form $\overset{H}{\underset{Cl}{>}}C=C\overset{Cl}{\underset{H}{<}}$ the moments of the individual bonds are mutually compensated, as a result of which the dipole moment of the molecule is zero. In the cis form $\overset{H}{\underset{Cl}{>}}C=C\overset{H}{\underset{Cl}{<}}$ this compensation is absent, and the molecule gets a finite dipole moment. The dipole moments are thus a sensitive criterion for determining the structure of a given isomer and for distinguishing individual isomers. In the foregoing case of dichloroethylene we have the moments 1.80 and 0 for the cis and trans forms. The third isomer, asymmetric dichloroethylene, with the structure $\overset{H}{\underset{H}{>}}C=C\overset{Cl}{\underset{Cl}{<}}$ very sharply differs from the first two, having a dipole moment of 1.18 debyes.

Calculations of dipole moments on the basis of the vector dipole model of the molecule show that in some cases the calculated results are close to the observed values, while in other cases the discrepancies are rather considerable. The cause may be sought in the mutual influence of atoms or atomic groups, which influence distorts the total moment and may be due both to changes in the valence angles and to the mutual polarisation of polar groups and of the hydrocarbon core. An instance of a molecule where a substantial discrepancy between the calculated and measured moment should be due mainly to the effect of secondary polarisation is that of paranitroaniline $NO_2C_6H_4NH_2$. Computing the dipole moment of this molecule as the sum of moments corresponding to the bonds O_2N-C and H_2N-C, we get $3.96 + 1.53 = 5.49$ debyes, whereas measurements yield 6.2 debyes. Despite the para position of the NO_2 and NH_2 groups (when both substituted groups are at greatest separation), the discrepancy between the calculated and measured values of the moment is rather great; this may be due to the strong inductive effect of the substituting groups. Experiment shows that this influence is particularly great when the substituting groups have radically different electrical properties (this likewise occurs in the case of NO_2 and NH_2) and also when the polarisabilities of these groups are great.

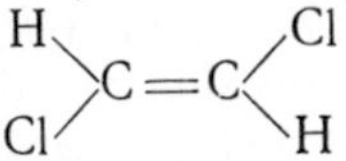

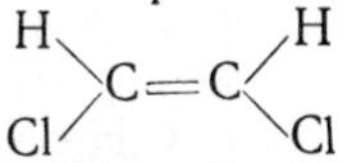

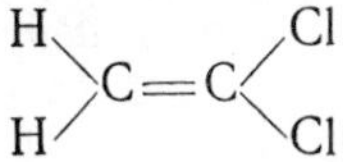

Moreover, it has recently been demonstrated that very often the main part of the electric dipole moment is due (as, for instance, in the molecules H_2O and NH_3) to unshared pairs of electrons of the component atoms of the molecule (*atomic dipole moments*). This still more limits the possibility of assigning definite dipole moments to individual bonds in the molecules of different compounds. In general, investigation into the role of atomic dipole moments has led to a complete revision of all the material on dipole moments of bonds and has actually made it impossible to construct a quantitative vector model of molecules without account of atomic dipole moments.

Especially big changes in the dipole moments are observed in the formation of certain molecular complexes. For example, the complexes of tin tetrachloride $SnCl_4 \cdot (C_2H_5)_2O$ and $SnCl_4 \cdot C_6H_5CN$ have dipole moments of 3.6 and 6.7 debyes, whereas the dipole moments of $(C_2H_5)_2O$, C_6H_5CN, and $SnCl_4$ are 1.1, 3.9, and 0 debyes, respectively. Similarly, the complexes of aluminium trichloride $AlCl_3 \cdot (C_2H_5)_2O$, $AlCl_3 \cdot C_6H_5NH_2$, and $AlCl_3 \cdot C_6H_5NO_2$ have dipole moments 6.7, 6.9, and 9.3 debyes, and the dipole moments of $C_6H_5NH_2$, $C_6H_5NO_2$, and $AlCl_3$ are 1.5, 3.9, and 0 debyes. Here, the changes in the dipole moments can no longer be accounted for by simple deformation of molecules and are a reliable indication of chemical bonds between the molecules forming the given complex.

Summarising the foregoing with respect to vector addition of dipole moments of individual bonds in molecules, we can state that the vector model method is not always reliable quantitatively. However, as a qualitative method it is very important, for it simplifies orientation in the experimental material and systematisation. It also helps to clarify the structural peculiarities of molecules precisely in those cases when there is a very great discrepancy between the calculated and measured values.

Dipole moments and free rotation of polar groups. A substantial supplement to the static molecular vector model is the concept of *free rotation* of the component polar groups that are connected with the remainder of the molecule by simple valence linkage. To illustrate this type of molecule we take the simplest case, H_2O_2, hydrogen peroxide. One of the most probable structures of this molecule is that of a trapezium (Fig. 120a), which in free rotation passes into the shape depicted in Fig. 120b.

Given free rotation, the dipole moment of H_2O_2 may be calculated as follows. Designating the moment of the O—H bond by p and the angle that it forms with the axis of the molecule (—O—O—) by ϑ, we will have, for the momentary value of the moment of the molecule, $2p \sin\vartheta \cos\varphi/2$, where φ is the angle between the planes —O—O—H. In the case of free rotation, all values of angle φ are equally probable, whence for the average square of the effective moment of the molecule we get

$$P^2 = \frac{1}{2\pi}\int_0^{2\pi}\left(2p\sin\vartheta\cos\frac{\varphi}{2}\right)^2 d\varphi = 2p^2\sin^2\vartheta,$$

that is,

$$P = \sqrt{2}\,p\sin\vartheta. \qquad (46.6)$$

Assuming the moment of the O—H (p) bond in the H_2O_2 molecule to be equal to that which we calculated earlier (p. 458) for this bond in the H_2O molecule, $p = 1.51$ debyes, and the angle

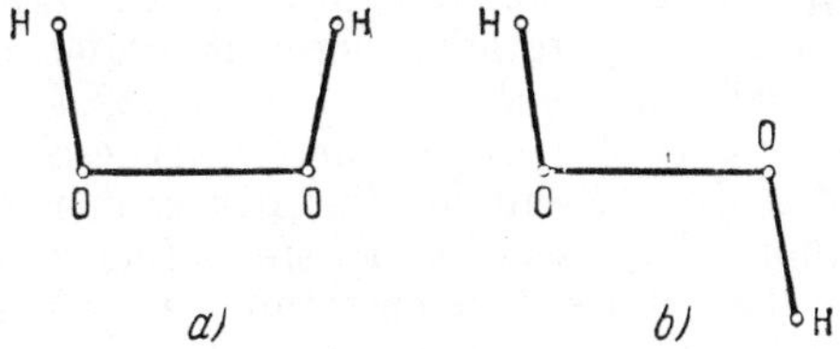

Fig. 120. Two forms of H_2O_2 molecule

between the bonds —O—O— and O—H equal to the valence angle in H_2O, $\angle(HOH) = 105°$, we get 2.06 debyes from (46.6) for the dipole moment of the hydrogen peroxide molecule, whereas the measured value of this quantity is 2.26 debyes. The satisfactory agreement of both values is a weighty argument in favour of the accepted structure of the H_2O_2 molecule.

Like the H_2O_2 molecule, nonzero dipole moments are found in the parasubstitutes of benzene in which the dipole moments of the substituting groups form a certain nonzero angle (due to directed valence) with the axis of the benzene nucleus (such groups are called *irregular* in contrast to *regular* groups, the moments of which are parallel to the axis of the nucleus). Such molecules, for instance, are those of hydroquinone HOC_6H_4OH ($P = 2.47$ debyes) and para-diaminobenzene $H_2NC_6H_4NH_2$ ($P = 1.55$ debyes). But the dipole moment of the disubstitutes of benzene with regular substituents, for example, paraxylene $H_3CC_6H_4CH_3$, paradinitrobenzene $O_2NC_6H_4NO_2$, paradichlorobenzene ClC_6H_4Cl, is zero.

Let us now consider molecules of the XH_2C-CH_2X type which can exist in two isomeric forms, cis and trans; in the cis form the C — X bonds form an angle of $180°00' - 109°30' = 70°30'$ for strictly tetrahedrally directed valences of the C atom, while in the trans form both bonds lie in the same plane forming an angle of 180°. For this reason, the cis form should have a finite dipole moment, whereas this moment in the trans form should be zero. In the case of free rotation of CH_2X groups about the C—C bond (axis of the molecule) one form is constantly passing into the other, and the difference between the two isomers is actually obliterated.

The dipole moment of a molecule of this type (if there is free rotation) is expressed by equation (46.6). Assuming that it is determined by the moments of the C—X bond, we will have, for the cis form,

$$P = 2p \sin \vartheta \cos 30° = \sqrt{3}\, p \sin \vartheta.$$

Substituting into this formula and into (46.6) $p = 1.5$ (X=Cl) and $\vartheta = 70°30'$, we find for the cis form $P = 2.45$ debyes and for the freely rotating form $P = 2.00$ debyes, whereas the measured dipole moment of the 1,2-$C_2H_4Cl_2$ molecule turns out slightly in excess of 1 debye, i.e., considerably less than the calculated values. To account for this discrepancy (on the assumption that the formulas used for P are sufficiently accurate) we have to assume that at room temperature (at which the measured value of the dipole moment of dichloroethane was obtained) there is no free rotation and we have a combination of cis and trans forms. This assumption is confirmed by the observed temperature dependence of the dipole moment: for a rise of temperature from 305° to 554°K the measurements yield an increase from 1.12 to 1.54 debyes. The fact that the temperature coefficient is positive indicates that the nonpolar trans form has less energy than the cis form and the freely rotating form, as a result of which the equilibrium is displaced towards the latter when we have a rise in temperature.

The difficulty of free rotation, which is established on the basis of the temperature dependence of the dipole moment of dichloroethane, is due to the fact that (as in all similar cases as well) two (or more) isomeric modifications are separated by an energy potential barrier. For a sufficiently high barrier the molecule in each state (for instance, cis or trans) can perform only torsional oscillations about the equilibrium position, the amplitude of which increases with the temperature. With increasing temperature, these oscillations pass into free rotation; from calculations by Meyer it follows that the latter is practically realised on the condition $\Delta U < \frac{1}{10} kT$ (ΔU is the barrier height).

The temperature dependence of the dipole moment has also been established in the case of dibromoethane $BrH_2C—CH_2Br$, chlorobromoethane $ClH_2C—CH_2Br$, diacetyl $H_3COC—COCH_3$, etc. In a number of cases, on the basis of an approximate coincidence of calculated (on the assumption of free rotation) and measured dipole moments we can draw the conclusion that there is free rotation for individual substituting groups even at room temperature. Such, for instance, are the groups OH, CH_3, NH_2 in the disubstituted derivatives of benzene. In a number of cases, free rotation has also been established on the basis of measurements of heat capacity, the Kerr constant, and electrono- and roentgenographic studies.

47. Magnetic Properties of Molecules

Diamagnetism. The magnetic moment of an atom or molecule is equal to the geometrical sum of the moments of all electrons in the atom or molecule. In a particular case, as the result of mutual compensation of the components of moments, the total moment of the atom or molecule may be equal to zero; this, obviously, occurs in the case of atoms in the ^1S state, and molecules in the $^1\Sigma$ state. A gas consisting of such atoms or molecules will be *diamagnetic*. Such are the inert gases He, Ne, Ar, Kr, and Xe, and also H_2, N_2, CO, H_2O, CO_2, CH_4, C_6H_6, and many other gases. Otherwise, that is, if the atoms or molecules have a magnetic moment, the gas is *paramagnetic*.

Diamagnetic bodies have negative magnetic susceptibility; this is seen in the repulsion experienced by diamagnetics when introduced into a magnetic field. A pictorial interpretation of the diamagnetic properties of gases may be obtained by the Bohr theory.

From the standpoint of mechanics an electron revolving in orbit is like a top. The stability of a top whose axis of rotation forms a certain angle with the vertical (direction of the force of gravity) is due to the precessional motion of the top's axis about the vertical. The electron orbit follows the same precessional motion about the direction of a magnetic field due to magnetic forces (Larmor precession). Given orbital precession, an electron will experience, in addition to a magnetic force

$$f_H = e[\mathbf{v} \times \mathbf{H}] = evH \sin(\mathbf{v}, \mathbf{H})$$

(v is the electron orbital velocity, H is the magnetic field intensity), the direction of which is perpendicular to the plane **v, H**, also a Coriolis force

$$f_{Cor} = 2m[\mathbf{v} \times \mathbf{o}] = 2mvo \sin(\mathbf{v}, \mathbf{o})$$

(o is the angular velocity of precession). Since vector **o** is parallel to vector **H**, the forces f_H and f_{Cor} are also parallel. Besides these two forces, the electron experiences an additional centrifugal force proportional to o^2 However, since the angular velocity of the electron ω is much greater than that of precession (in ordinary magnetic fields), the centrifugal force may be disregarded in comparison with the first two forces. The equilibrium condition of these forces, which is the condition of stability of motion, has the form $f = f_H + f_{Cor} = 0$, whence for the angular velocity of precession we have

$$\omega = -\frac{1}{2}\frac{e}{m}H. \tag{47.1}$$

The Larmor precession gives rise to an induced magnetic moment that may be calculated in the same way as we earlier (p. 162) calculated the orbital magnetic moment. Representing a current equivalent to a precessing orbit in the form $i = e\omega/2\pi$ and the area over which this current flows, in the form $S = \pi r'^2$, where r' is the projection of the mean orbital radius on the plane perpendicular to the field direction, we get the following expression for the sought-for induced moment $\Delta\mu$:

$$\Delta\mu = iS = \frac{e\omega}{2} r'^2 = -\frac{e^2 H}{4m} r'^2. \tag{47.2}$$

Accordingly, for the atom or molecule with N electrons we have

$$\Delta\mu = -\frac{e^2 H}{4m} \sum_{i=1}^{N} r_i'^2. \tag{47.3}$$

Assuming that all orientations of the orbit to the field direction are equally probable, it can be readily shown that r'^2 is connected with the mean square of the orbital radius r^2 by the relation $r'^2 = \frac{2}{3} r^2$, whence it follows that

$$\Delta\mu = -\frac{e^2 H}{6m} \sum_{i=1}^{N} r_i^2. \tag{47.4}$$

In the case of atoms and molecules with compensated electron moments, $\Delta\mu$ obviously expresses at the same time also the total magnetic moment. In this case, multiplying $\Delta\mu$ by the Avogadro number N_A and dividing by H, we get the following expression for the *molecular susceptibility* χ:

$$\chi = -\frac{e^2 N_A}{6m} \Sigma r_i^2. \tag{47.5}$$

The negative value of magnetic susceptibility points to a diamagnetic effect. Further, in accordance with the empirical regularities established by P. Curie, it follows from expression (47.5) that the diamagnetic susceptibility is independent of the temperature and also (to the extent that the sum Σr_i^2 retains its value) of the aggregate state of the substance. It may be added that Σr_i^2 ordinarily turns out but slightly dependent on the chemical transformations experienced by the atoms.

As follows from the foregoing reasoning, the magnitude and sign of the induced moment are independent of the presence or absence of a permanent moment in the molecule. The diamagnetic effect is, therefore, equally peculiar to dia- and paramagnetic gases. However, for the latter it plays a comparatively secondary part, giving way to the much stronger paramagnetic effect.

Paramagnetism. Underlying modern views on the nature of paramagnetism is the classical theory of Langevin, which treats the paramagnetic effect as the result of a simultaneous orienting action of the field and a disorienting action of molecular thermal motion. Designating the permanent magnetic moment of a molecule by μ, we will have, for the equilibrium number of molecules, the magnetic axes of which form the angle $\vartheta \pm \frac{d\vartheta}{2}$ with the field direction,

$$dn = 2\pi N e^{\frac{\mu H \cos\vartheta}{kT}} \sin\vartheta d\vartheta$$

where $\mu H \cos\vartheta$ is the magnetic energy of the molecule. Calculating the average value of the projection of moment on the field direction μ' (on the assumption that all angles are equally possible) from the equation

$$\overline{\mu'} = \frac{\int \mu \cos\vartheta dn}{\int dn} = \mu \frac{\int_0^\pi e^{\frac{\mu H \cos\vartheta}{kT}} \cos\vartheta \sin\vartheta d\vartheta}{\int_0^\pi e^{\frac{\mu H \cos\vartheta}{kT}} \sin\vartheta d\vartheta}$$

which, for $\mu H \ll kT$ (this is practically always the case), reduces to

$$\overline{\mu'} = \frac{\mu^2 H}{kT} \frac{\int_0^\pi \cos^2\vartheta \sin\vartheta d\vartheta}{\int_0^\pi \sin\vartheta d\vartheta} = \frac{\mu^2 H}{kT} \overline{\cos^2\vartheta} \tag{47.6}$$

we find

$$\frac{\overline{\mu'}}{\mu} = \frac{\mu H}{3kT}. \tag{47.7}$$

Multiplying $\overline{\mu'}$ by the Avogadro number and dividing by H, we obtain for the molecular paramagnetic susceptibility

$$\chi = \frac{\mu^2 N_A}{3kT} = \frac{C}{T}. \tag{47.8}$$

Equation (47.8) expresses the well-known *Curie law*, according to which the magnetic susceptibility of a paramagnetic gas is inversely proportional to its absolute temperature.

A weak point in the classical theory of paramagnetism is the assumption of equal possibility of all angles ϑ. In reality, however, due to the space quantisation of atomic (molecular) elementary magnets in a magnetic field, the projections of the magnetic moment of molecules on the field direction take on discrete values that correspond to definite discrete values of the angle ϑ.

In accord with this quantisation of angle ϑ, and, consequently, of $\cos\vartheta$, there should also be a change in the average value of μ', because $\overline{\cos^2\vartheta}$ in expression (47.6) will no longer be equal to 1/3. Inasmuch as the projection of the magnetic moment on the field direction in the Bohr theory is expressed by the formula $\mu' = \mu_B m_\varphi$ (μ_B is the Bohr magneton), and the quantum number m_φ takes on the values $0, \pm 1, \ldots, \pm(n_\varphi - 1), \pm n_\varphi$, i.e., a total of $2n_\varphi + 1$ values (n_φ is the Bohr azimuthal quantum number), by calculating the average value of $\cos^2\vartheta$ from the formula

$$\overline{\cos^2\vartheta} = \frac{1}{(2n_\varphi + 1)\, n_\varphi^2} \sum_{-n_\varphi}^{+n_\varphi} m_\varphi^2 = \frac{2(1^2 + 2^2 + \ldots + n_\varphi^2)}{(2n_\varphi + 1)\, n_\varphi^2} = \frac{1 + n_\varphi}{3n_\varphi}$$

and substituting it into equality (47.6), we get

$$\frac{\overline{\mu'}}{\mu} = \frac{1 + n_\varphi}{n_\varphi} \frac{\mu H}{3kT}$$

whence, due to $\mu = \mu_B n_\varphi$, we find

$$\overline{\mu'} = \frac{n_\varphi (n_\varphi + 1)}{3kT} \mu_B^2 H. \tag{47.9}$$

Accordingly, for the magnetic susceptibility we get, in place of (47.8),

$$\chi = \frac{\overline{\mu'} N_A}{H} = \frac{n_\varphi (n_\varphi + 1)}{3kT} \mu_B^2 N_A = \frac{C'}{T}. \tag{47.10}$$

We further refine the theory by calculating the average projection of the magnetic moment on the direction of the magnetic field on the basis of quantum mechanics. Proceeding from the quantum-mechanical expression of $\mu' = gm\mu_B$ (30.3), for the square of $\overline{\mu'}$ that enters into expression (47.6), which we rewrite as

$$\overline{\mu'} = \frac{H}{kT} \overline{\mu'^2}$$

we obtain

$$\overline{\mu'} = g^2\mu_B^2 \frac{\sum_{-J}^{+J} m^2}{2J+1} = \frac{g^2J(J+1)}{3}\mu_B^2$$

and, hence,

$$\overline{\mu'} = \frac{g^2J(J+1)}{3kT}\mu_B^2 H. \qquad (47.11)$$

Whence for the paramagnetic susceptibility χ we find

$$\chi = \frac{\overline{\mu'} N_A}{H} = \frac{g^2\mu_B^2 N_A}{3kT} J(J+1). \qquad (47.12)$$

This expression is in excellent agreement with experiment.

Comparing expressions (47.12) and (47.10), we can readily demonstrate that for large n_φ (because of $n_\varphi = l+1$ and $J = l \pm \frac{1}{2}$) (47.10) passes into the exact expression (47.12).

Let us examine in more detail the paramagnetic susceptibility of molecules. The quantum states of the latter, if they belong to Hund's cases a and b (see p. 327) to which we will confine ourselves here, are defined by the quantum numbers Λ and Σ (or S). The simplest case is the term $^1\Sigma$, which corresponds to the ground state of a large number of molecules. Here, since $\Lambda = 0$ and $S = 0$, the magnetic moment is zero, as a result of which all molecules in the $^1\Sigma$ state are diamagnetic.

The spin in molecules in states $^2\Sigma$, $^3\Sigma$, . . . , imparts paramagnetic properties. Such, for example, are the molecules O_2 and S_2, the principal term of which is $^3\Sigma$. For the projection of the magnetic moment of the molecule on the field direction in the case of molecules in Σ-states, we have $\mu' = 2m\mu_B$, where m takes on the values $m = \pm S, \pm(S-1), \ldots$ In the case of molecules O_2 and S_2, $S = 1$ ($^3\Sigma$) and the maximum projection is $2\mu_B$, Studies of the Stern-Gerlach effect in O_2 and S_2 yield experimental confirmation of this conclusion.

Measurements of the paramagnetic susceptibility of oxygen lead to the same coincidence of theory and experiment. To calculate this susceptibility in the case of molecular Σ-terms, we can make use of (47.12), putting $J = S = 1$ and $g = 2$. In this way we get the formula $\chi = \frac{8\mu_B^2}{3kT} N_A$, from which for the specific susceptibility of oxygen (susceptibility of 1 cm^3 of gas) at 760 mm Hg and 20°C, we get 0.142×10^{-6}, whereas measurements under the same conditions yield $(0.1447 \text{ to } 0.1434) \times 10^{-6}$.

In the general case of a molecular term with nonzero Λ and S the projection of magnetic moment of the molecule on the field direction is expressed by the formula

$$\mu' = \mu_B (2\Sigma + \Lambda) \cos\vartheta \tag{47.13}$$

where ϑ is the angle formed by the axis of the molecule with the direction of the magnetic field H. The average value of μ' in this case is

$$\overline{\mu'} = \frac{\mu_B^2 (2\Sigma + \Lambda)^2}{3kT} H$$

whence for the molecular paramagnetic susceptibility we find

$$\chi = \frac{\mu_B^2 (2\Sigma + \Lambda)^2}{3kT} N_A. \tag{47.14}$$

Strictly speaking, this equation is applicable to terms for which strong interaction (S, Λ) is characteristic. And since the latter determines also the magnitude of multiple splitting of a term (natural splitting), we can take the following inequality for the criterion of applicability of (47.14):

$$h\Delta\nu_0 > kT$$

where $\Delta\nu_0$ is the width of the multiplet.

But when $h\Delta\nu_0 < kT$, i.e., when the interaction energy between the spin and the Λ vector is small compared with the mean thermal energy, the spin, to a first approximation, may be regarded as a free vector. In this case, we obtain the magnetic susceptibility as the sum of the expressions

$$\chi = \frac{4\mu_B^2 S(S+1)}{3kT} N_A$$

and (47.14), putting $\Sigma = 0$ in the latter, i.e.,

$$\chi = \frac{\mu_B^2}{3kT}[4S(S+1) + \Lambda^2] N_A. \tag{47.15}$$

All the foregoing cases have referred to isolated molecular terms. Yet there may be cases when another term with different magnetic properties is adjacent to the given term. Such, for instance, is the case of the NO molecule, the principal term of which is $^2\Pi$. Here, the magnetic susceptibility is determined by the components $^2\Pi_{1/2}$ and $^2\Pi_{3/2}$ of term $^2\Pi$, which possesses different magnetic properties; moreover, due to different population of the terms $^2\Pi_{1/2}$ and $^2\Pi_{3/2}$ for different temperatures, the temperature dependence of the susceptibility no longer follows the Curie law. The magnetic susceptibility of NO as a function of temperature was calculated by van Vleck on the basis of the Boltzmann distribution of molecules between the levels $^2\Pi_{1/2}$ and $^2\Pi_{3/2}$. The formula he derived is

$$\chi = \frac{4\mu_B^2}{3kT} \frac{1 - e^{-x} + xe^{-x}}{x + xe^{-x}} N_A \qquad (47.16)$$

where $x = h\Delta\nu_0/kT$, $\Delta\nu_0 = {}^2\Pi_{3/2} - {}^2\Pi_{1/2}$. Experimental verification of this formula leads to a practically complete coincidence of calculated and measured values of χ.

Magnetochemistry. Measurements of magnetic susceptibilities play a significant part in studies of molecular structure (*magnetometric method*). Pascal's investigations showed that the molecular magnetic susceptibilities χ_M (to a first approximation) are *additively* composed of atomic susceptibilities χ_A (*atomic increments*), like molar refraction is composed of atomic refractions (see Sec. 44). In the second approximation, to the sum of atomic increments are added certain "constitutive components" λ_i, which take into account the structural peculiarities of a given molecule (the presence of multiple bonds, etc.). We thus have

$$\chi_M = \Sigma\chi_A + \Sigma\lambda_i. \qquad (47.17)$$

The values of the atomic increments for certain atoms (after Pascal and Klemm) are given in Table 46. The minus sign here indicates diamagnetism and the plus sign, paramagnetism.

Table 46

Atomic increments χ_A ($\times 10^6$ absolute units)

H	—2.93	F	—11.5	Li	— 4.2
C	—6.00	Cl	—20.1	Na	— 9.2
N in open chains	—5.57	Br	—30.6	K	—18.5
N in rings	—4.61	I	—45	Mg	—10
N in monoamides	—1.54	S	—15.0	Ca	—16
N in diamides and imides	—2.11	Se	—23	Al	—13
O	—4.61	Te	—37	Ag	—31
O, bound to C	+1.73	P	—26.3	Zn	—13.5
O in carboxyl group	—3.36	As	—43	Hg	—33

Table 47 gives the constitutive components for certain of the simplest bonds.

To illustrate, let us follow through the method of computing χ_M on the basis of Tables 46 and 47. First we take normal hexane C_6H_{14}. We have 6 C atoms and 14 H atoms with single bonds between them, for which $\lambda = 0$. Therefore, according to (47.17)

$\chi_M = 6\chi_C + 14\chi_H = -(6\times6.00 + 14\times2.93)\times10^{-6} = -77.0\times10^{-6}$, whereas experiment yields -77.1×10^{-6}.

Let us further consider benzoyl chloride $C_6H_5-\underset{\underset{O}{\|}}{C}-Cl$.

In this case, formula (47.17) must obviously be written as $\chi_M = 7\chi_C + 5\chi_H + \chi_O + \chi_{Cl} + 6\lambda C_1 + \lambda C_3 = -(7\times6.00 + 5\times2.93 - 1.73 + 20.1 + 1.44 + 1.29)\times10^{-6} = -77.8\times10^{-6}$ The experimental value of χ_M is -77.9×10^{-6}.

Table 47

Constitutive components λ ($\times10^6$ absolute units)

$>C=C<$	+5.5	$-\overset{\mid}{\underset{\mid}{C}}-Cl$	+3.1
$>C=C-C=C<$	+10.6	$-\overset{\mid}{\underset{\mid}{C}}-Br$	+4.1
$-C\equiv C-$	+0.8	$-\overset{\mid}{\underset{\mid}{C}}-I$	+4.1
$CH_2=CH-CH_2-$	+4.5	$Cl-\overset{\mid}{\underset{\mid}{C}}-\overset{\mid}{\underset{\mid}{C}}-Cl$	+4.3
$-N=N-$	+1.8	$Br-\overset{\mid}{\underset{\mid}{C}}-\overset{\mid}{\underset{\mid}{C}}-Br$	+6.2
$-\underset{\underset{NR}{\|}}{C}-$	+8.2	$>CCl_2$	+1.4
$-N=O$	+1.7		
C_I *	−0.24	C_3 **	−1.29
C_{II} *	−3.1	C_4 **	−1.54
C_{III} *	−4.0	C_3 and C_4 ***	−0.48

* C_I corresponds to the position, in an aromatic compound, of a carbon atom belonging to one ring, C_{II} and C_{III}, to C atoms that are simultaneously components of two and three rings, respectively.

** C_3 and C_4 refer to C atoms connected with three and four other C atoms, respectively (in the positions α, γ, δ, ε). α-, β-, etc., C atoms correspond to their following position in the molecule:

$$R-\underset{\alpha}{C}-\underset{\beta}{C}-\underset{\gamma}{C}-\underset{\delta}{C}-\underset{\varepsilon}{C}-\ldots$$

*** The same, but in position β.

The foregoing examples clearly indicate the importance of magnetometric measurements in determining the structure of a variety of chemical compounds. The procedure in these measurements is based on measuring the force experienced by bodies in an inhomogeneous magnetic field, which force is (in the case of diamagnetic bodies) equal to

$$F=\chi\int H\frac{\partial H}{\partial z}\,dv \tag{47.18}$$

where H is the intensity, $\frac{\partial H}{\partial z}$ the field gradient, and dv is a volume element of the body. By replacing the body under consideration (a gas, for example) with a body of known susceptibility χ_0 and of equal volume and shape, it is frequently possible to avoid difficult measurements of the magnitude of the field gradient. In this case, from a measurement of the force F and the force experienced by a standard body (F_0) we get $\chi=(F/F_0)\chi_0$ on the basis of (47.18).

CHAPTER 10

MOLECULAR CONSTANTS

48. Geometrical Constants

The molecule as a chemical entity is characterised by definite numbers, *molecular constants*. Molecular constants may be divided into two large classes: geometrical constants and energy constants. The geometrical constants characterise the dimensions and structure, the arrangement of atoms in the molecule, and the electric-charge distribution in them. The constants of this class include molecular diameters, distances between atoms in the molecule, angles between bonds, and dipole moments. The class of energy constants, which describe the various energy states of the molecule, its stability in a given energy state, etc., include the energies of molecular terms, the heats of dissociation, average bond energies, etc. The vibrational frequencies of molecules may be put in this class of constants. The present chapter is devoted to a brief survey of these constants and to a description of certain experimental methods of determining them.

Dimensions of molecules. Molecular dimensions represent a certain conventional magnitude. Indeed, each molecule is a more or less complex system of electric charges and is surrounded by a field of force extending to infinity. In quantum theory the infinite extension of the molecular field corresponds to the fact that the density of the electronic cloud of the molecule becomes zero only at infinity. However, the force field of a molecule rapidly falls off with the distance r from its centre, becoming negligibly small at a certain distance r_0 which may arbitrarily be called the *radius* of the molecule. Since the dimensions of molecules are most significant for their interaction, the natural criterion for the strength or weakness of a molecular field at a given distance is the magnitude of interaction energy of the molecules separated by the distance r. For the limiting value of interaction energy we can take the mean energy of relative thermal motion of molecules kT, thus subjecting r_0 to the condition

$$U(2r_0) = kT$$

where $U(2r_0)$ is the energy of interaction of molecules at a distance $2r_0$.

This condition should, in particular, be fulfilled at the critical point when the forces of molecular adhesion are not able to counteract the thermal motion (as a result of which the difference between liquid and gaseous states of the substance vanishes). For this reason, to compute the dimensions of a molecule of a given substance we can take advantage of its critical volume v_{cr}. Representing the molecules as spheres of radius r_0 and proceeding from the most dense packing (to which there corresponds a three-fourths population of the volume), we have

$$\frac{4}{3}\pi r_0^3 N_A = \frac{3}{4}V_{cr} \qquad (48.1)$$

whence we can calculate r_0. It may be noted that due to the known relation between the critical volume and constant b in the van der Waals equation, $V_{cr}=3b$, equation (48.1) yields

$$b=\frac{16}{27}\pi r_0^3 N_A; \qquad (48.2)$$

this also enables us to calculate r_0 from constant b. The values of r_0 obtained from these formulas in the case of molecules that do not have spherical symmetry are obviously certain mean values of molecular radii.

Another method for determining molecular dimensions is based on transfer phenomena (diffusion, thermal conduction, internal friction). Since, according to the kinetic theory of gases, transport phenomena are essentially determined by the mean free path of the molecules λ, which in turn depends upon the molecular diameter $d_0=2r_0$,

$$\lambda=\frac{1}{\sqrt{2}\pi d_0^2 n}\frac{1}{1+\frac{C}{T}}$$

(n is the number of molecules in 1 cm^3, which at normal p and T is 2.69×10^{19}, and C is the Sutherland constant), we have the following relationships between the coefficients of diffusion, thermal conduction, and internal friction, on the one hand, and the diameter d_0, on the other. These relationships permit calculating d_0 from the measured value of any one of the three indicated coefficients. Mostly used is the coefficient of internal friction

$$\eta=0.499\varrho v\lambda \qquad (48.3)$$

(ϱ is the density of the gas, v is the mean square of molecular velocity). Calculating the constant C from the temperature dependence of the internal friction, we find d_0 by (48.3) from the measured η.

We shall not dwell on other methods used to determine molecular dimensions and shall confine ourselves to certain data taken from Stuart (Table 48).

Table 48

Diameters of molecules (in A)

Molecule	Calculated from η	Calculated from V_{cr} or b	Molecule	Calculated from η	Calculated from V_{cr} or b
He	1.96	2.52	NO	3.0	—
Ne	2.35	—	CO	3.2	2.86
Ar	2.92	2.92	HCl	3.0	2.85
Kr	3.2	—	HBr	3.12	—
Xe	3.5	3.1	CH_4	3.34	2.96
H_2	2.47	2.5	CO_2	3.32	2.92
N_2	3.18	2.86	H_2O	2.72	—
O_2	2.98	2.45	N_2O	3.2	—
Cl_2	3.7	—	SO_2	3.38	—
Br_2	4.04	—	CCl_4	3.8	—
I_2	4.46	—	C_6H_6	4.1	—

Intramolecular distances. Unlike the dimensions of a molecule, the distance between the atoms of a molecule is a physically strictly definite magnitude—the equilibrium distance at which the attractive forces experienced by each atom are balanced by the forces of repulsion. Vibrations or rotation of the molecule do not introduce any uncertainty, because any change in the equilibrium distances caused by them can, generally speaking, be taken into account.

An experimental determination of the intramolecular distances does not encounter particular difficulties in the case of diatomic molecules, nor in the case of the simplest (especially symmetric) polyatomic molecules, the structure of which are known on the basis of certain properties of the molecule. Of the methods now in use, most important are the spectroscopic (including microwave spectroscopy), roentgeno- and electronographic methods. In the case of diatomic molecules, all these methods solve the problem of intramolecular distances r_0 quite unambiguously. The spectroscopic method based on an analysis of rotational band structure is the most precise.

As we saw in Chapter 8, the distances between two adjacent lines in a band ($\Delta\nu$) are connected by definite relations with the moment (or moments) of inertia of the molecule. By measuring the quantities $\Delta\nu$, it is not difficult to find the moment of inertia on the basis of these relations:

$$I_0 = \frac{m_1 m_2}{m_1 + m_2} r_0^2$$

whence we can also find r_0 (we, of course, assume that the masses of the atoms in the molecule m_1 and m_2 are known).

Just as simple is the determination of intramolecular distances in the case of symmetric triatomic linear molecules (CO_2, CS_2, and others). Here the moment of inertia, which determines the fine structure of the spectrum, is expressed by

$$I_0 = 2mr_0^2$$

where m is the mass of each of the extreme atoms and r_0 is their distances from the central atom.

In the case of symmetric triangular molecules (H_2O, H_2S, SO_2, etc.), we have the following relations between the principal moments of inertia I_1, I_2, and I_3, which are determined from the rotational structure of the spectra, and the distances r_1 and r_2 (r_1 is the distance between identical atoms, r_2, between different atoms):

$$I_1 = \frac{m}{2} r_1^2,$$

$$I_2 = \frac{2mM}{2m + M} \left[r_2^2 - \left(\frac{r_1}{2} \right)^2 \right],$$

$$I_3 = I_1 + I_2$$

(m is the mass of each of the identical atoms, and M is the mass of the third atom). We thus have two independent equations to determine the two unknowns r_1 and r_2.

The quantities r_0 are uniquely determined from I_0 also in the case of symmetric tetrahedral molecules (CH_4, CCl_4, etc.), whose principal moments of inertia are expressed by the formulas

$$I_1 = I_2 = \frac{m}{2} r_1^2 \quad \text{and} \quad I_3 = mr_1^2$$

(m is the mass of each of the end atoms, r_1 is the distance between these atoms). The distance between the end atom and the central one, i.e., between the vertex and centre of the tetrahedron, is $r_2 = \sqrt{\frac{3}{8}} r_1$.

In all the foregoing cases, the number of unknown intramolecular distances r_i was equal to the number of independent moments of inertia of the molecule, from which it was possible to determine r_i. In the more general case of asymmetric linear triatomic molecules (COS, HCN, etc.), and also in the case of linear tetra-atomic molecules (C_2H_2, C_2N_2, etc.) and more complex molecules, the number of independent moments of inertia is always less than the number of distances r_i, and we need additional data to find them.

By way of illustration, let us consider the linear molecule HCN. Here we have two distances, namely, $r_1 = (C-H)$ and $r_2 = (C-N)$, and one moment of inertia:

$$I = m_H r_1^2 + m_N r_2^2 - \frac{(m_H r_1 - m_N r_2)^2}{m_H + m_C + m_N}$$

(m_H, m_C, m_N are the atomic masses of H, C, and N). In this case, the missing second equation (for a determination of the two unknowns r_1 and r_2) can, for example, be obtained from an analysis of the rotational structure of the spectrum of the DCN molecule. Indeed, because of identical chemical properties of the H and D atom (as in all cases of the isotopes of the same element), the distances (C—H) and (C—D)—and, of course, the distances (C—N)—in the HCN and DCN molecules must be the same. Consequently, for the DCN molecule we have $(C-D) = r_1$ and $(C-N) = r_2$, and

$$I' = m_D r_1^2 + m_N r_2^2 - \frac{(m_D r_1 - m_N r_2)^2}{m_D + m_C + m_N}$$

(m_D is the mass of deuterium). Thus, having determined I and I′ we get two equations to find the unknowns r_1 and r_2. The spectroscopically measured values of the moments of inertia of the molecules HCN and DCN are $I = 18.935 \times 10^{-40}$ g cm^2 and $I' = 23.159 \times 10^{-40}$ g cm^2, whence by means of the previous formulas we get $r_1 = 1.058_7$ A and $r_2 = 1.157_4$ A.

Underlying the roentgeno- and electronographic methods is the scattering of X-rays and electrons by the molecules of the substance under study. These methods of measuring intramolecular distances are particularly suitable for cases when the molecule contains several heavy atoms situated symmetrically with respect to the remainder of the molecule, as in the case of CCl_4, PCl_3, CH_2Cl_2, etc., inasmuch as the diffraction pattern here is less complicated; this makes the calculation more reliable and accurate. In addition, the intensity of the scattered rays that give rise to the diffraction pattern is greater for heavy atoms, and this too simplifies the measurements.

The scattering of X-rays is the result of interaction between a light wave and the electrons that form the electron clouds of the scattering atoms, while the cause of electron scattering is the action of the intramolecular electric field on the electrons being scattered. Outwardly, the scattering of X-rays and electrons appears the same, obeying nearly the same laws: in both cases the diffraction pattern produced by scattering is a system of concentric interference rings. The reason for the identity of both diffraction patterns lies in the wave properties of an electron beam, making it possible to regard the latter as a plane wave.

The calculation of a diffraction pattern (roentgeno- and electronograms) is based on the law of intensity distribution of the scattered rays over the scattering angle ϑ, i.e., over the angle between the directions of the scattered and primary rays.

Let us first consider the scattering of a beam of monochromatic X-rays of wavelength λ by an individual atom. Under the action of the electric vector of the incident wave (E_0) the charges (electrons) contained in the volume element dv perform forced oscillations and emit secondary waves. The amplitude of these waves at the distance R (which is large compared with the size of the atomic nucleus) from the nucleus of the scattering atom will be expressed as

$$\frac{1}{R}\frac{e}{mc^2}\sqrt{\frac{1+\cos^2\vartheta}{2}}\,E_0\varrho\,dv$$

where e and m are the charge and mass of the electron, c is the velocity of light, and ϱ is the density of the electric charges equal to $\varrho = e|\Psi|^2$ (Ψ is the wave function of the atom). On the assumption of spherical symmetry of charge distribution in the atom, i. e., $\varrho = \varrho(r)$, we obtain the following expression for the amplitude of secondary emission of the atom as a whole (as a result of intergration over the whole volume of the atom):

$$\frac{4\pi}{R}\frac{e^2}{mc^2}\sqrt{\frac{1+\cos^2\vartheta}{2}}\,E_0\int_0^\infty \frac{\sin\mu r}{\mu r}|\psi(r)|^2 r^2 dr$$

where

$$\mu = \frac{4\pi}{\lambda}\sin\frac{\vartheta}{2}.$$

The integral in this expression

$$F_R(\vartheta) = 4\pi\int_0^\infty \frac{\sin\mu r}{\mu r}|\psi(r)|^2 r^2\,dr \qquad (48.4)$$

which characterises the effect of the electronic structure of the atom on the intensity of scattered radiation is called the *structural (atomic) factor*. To a certain degree of accuracy, the latter may be determined either theoretically or experimentally. Experimentally, F_R is found from measurements of the intensity of scattered radiation proportional to F_R^2.

Let us examine electron scattering by an atom, in other words, let us attempt to determine the effect of the atomic electric field on the primary electron beam. To do this, we must solve the Schrödinger equation that corresponds to the perturbation problem. Here, the potential energy of the electron being scattered in the field of the atom is the perturbing function. In the case of spherical symmetry of charge distribution in the atom, this energy is expressed by the formula

$$V(r) = -\int \frac{e}{r^2}\left\{4\pi \int_0^r |\psi(r)|^2 r^2 dr - Z\right\} dr. \qquad (48.5)$$

Solving the Schrödinger equation we find the function ψ', which characterises the scattered beam of electrons. Like the amplitude of secondary X-radiation, the function ψ' may be represented in the form of the product of a constant quantity and a certain factor F_E, the square of which yields the distribution of scattered electrons over angle ϑ Mott demonstrated that F_E and F_R are connected by the following relation:

$$F_E(\vartheta) = \frac{e^2}{2mv^2}\{Z - F_R(\vartheta)\} \operatorname{cosec}^2 \frac{\vartheta}{2} \qquad (48.6)$$

(v is the electron velocity). Thus, with the aid of this relation, F, which may be called the *atomic factor for electron diffraction*, can be calculated directly from the atomic factor for X-rays. It will be noted, however, that F_R, which in equality (48.6) has the meaning of a screening term, plays only a secondary part and can frequently be discarded without greatly affecting the accuracy of measurements. Then the expression for F_E reduces to

$$F_E = \frac{e^2 Z}{2mv^2} \operatorname{cosec}^2 \frac{\vartheta}{2}. \qquad (48.7)$$

The principal formulas for calculating the intensity of secondary X-rays scattered by gas molecules were given by Debye and Ehrenfest. Following Debye and considering each atom in a molecule as an independent scattering point-centre, we can calculate the oscillation amplitude of the radiation scattered by a given molecule as the sum of amplitudes of the separate elementary waves scattered by the individual atoms in the molecule (taking into account the phase differences). Calculation of the average square of this total amplitude for all possible orientations of the molecule yields the intensity of the radiation scattered by the molecule. By introducing the atomic factors we take account of the charge distribution in the atoms.

In this way, Debye derived the following equation for the intensity of X-radiation scattered by a gas, the molecules of which contain n atoms separated by the distance r_{ij} and characterised by the atomic factors F_1, $F_2, \ldots, F_n$:

$$I(\vartheta) = k_R \frac{1+\cos^2\vartheta}{2} \sum_{i=1}^{i=n} \sum_{j=1}^{j=n} F_i F_j \frac{\sin \mu r_{ij}}{\mu r_{ij}}. \qquad (48.8)$$

A similar equation for the case of electron scattering has the same form as (48.8) minus the factor $\frac{1+\cos^2\vartheta}{2}$:

$$I(\vartheta) = k_E \sum_{i=1}^{i=n} \sum_{j=1}^{j=n} F_i F_j \frac{\sin \mu r_{ij}}{\mu r_{ij}}. \qquad (48.9)$$

In the case of X-rays, F are expressed by (48.4); but in electron scattering, F represent atomic factors for electron diffraction and are expressed by (48.6). In the latter instance (formula 48.9), λ in the expression $\mu = \frac{4\pi}{\lambda} \sin\frac{\vartheta}{2}$ is the de Broglie wavelength. Besides, these two cases differ in the values of the constant factor k (k_R and k_E).

According to (48.8) and (48.9), the intensity of scattered radiation passes through a series of maxima and minima with variation of the scattering angle ϑ. For this reason, due to the axial symmetry of scattering in the case of a narrow beam of rays, the diffraction pattern, which ordinarily is recorded photographically, presents a system of concentric rings of variable intensity (see Fig. 4, p. 33), which is determined by the values of the respective double sums. The radii of the interference rings depend upon the wavelength λ, the distances r_{ij} between the scattering atoms and also the distances between the scattering entity and the photographic plate (R). Therefore, if we know R and λ, we can find the values of the intramolecular distances r_{ij} from the measured radii of the rings.

The method of interpreting a diffraction pattern usually consists in the following. Having specified a definite molecular structure that appears probable on the basis of certain reasoning, from (48.8) or (48.9) and with the aid of known values of the atomic factors we plot a curve of the relative scattering intensity versus the parameter $x = \mu r_{ij}$. By changing the scale of x this theoretical curve is made to coincide with the curve of intensity distribution over the angle ϑ obtained by photometry of the appropriate roentgeno- and electronograms, and we obtain proof of the proper selection of the molecular model by the coincidence both of intensities and of the arrangement of interference maxima (rings). If the theoretical and experimental curves cannot be made to coincide, this indicates that the selected molecular model is not the right one.

Tables 49 to 51 give some data on intramolecular distances.

Table 49

Intramolecular distances in the molecules of elements (after Herzberg)

Molecule	Distance, A	Molecule	Distance, A
H_2	0.7417	P^{31}_2	1.894
D_2	0.7416	S^{32}_2	1.889
HD	0.7414	Cl^{35}_2	1.988
Li^7_2	2.6723	K^{39}_2	3.923
B^{11}_2	1.589	Se^{80}_2	2.16
C^{12}_2	1.3117	$Br^{79}Br^{81}$	2.284
N^{14}_2	1.094	Te_2	2.59*
O^{16}_2	1.2074	I^{127}_2	2.667
F^{19}_2	1.435*	Hg_2	3.3**
Na^{23}_2	3.079		

* Obtained from electronic diffraction.
** Obtained from data on liquid mercury.

Table 50

Intramolecular distances in diatomic molecules of hydrides (after Herzberg)

Molecule	r_e, A	Molecule	r_e, A	Molecule	r_e, A
Li^7H	1.5953	$Al^{27}H$	1.6459	SrD	2.1448
Li^7D	1.5949	$Al^{27}D$	1.6456	AgH	1.617
Be^9H	1.3431	$Si^{28}H$	1.520	AgD	1.6172
Be^9D	1.3425	$Cl^{35}H$	1.27460	CdH	1.762
$B^{11}H$	1.2325	$Cl^{35}D$	1.275	CdD	1.748
$B^{11}D$	1.231	$K^{39}H$	2.244	InH	1.8376
$C^{12}H$	1.1198	$Ca^{40}H$	2.002	HI	1.604
$C^{12}D$	1.119	$Ca^{40}D$	2.001	$Cs^{133}H$	2.494
$N^{14}H$	1.038	TiH	1.870	BaH	2.2318
$O^{16}H$	0.9706	$Mn^{55}H$	1.73075	$Au^{197}H$	1.5237
$O^{16}D$	0.9699	CoH	1.542	$Au^{197}D$	1.5237
$F^{19}H$	0.9171	NiH	1.475	HgH	1.7404
$F^{19}D$	0.9170	$Cu^{63}H$	1.463	HgD	1.7378
$Na^{23}H$	1.8873	$Cu^{63}D$	1.4625	TlH	1.870
$Na^{23}D$	1.8865	ZnH	1.5945	PbH	1.839
$Mg^{24}H$	1.7306	$Br^{79}H$, $Br^{81}H$	1.414	$Bi^{209}H$	1.809
$Mg^{24}D$	1.7301	RbH	2.367	$Bi^{209}D$	1.805
		SrH	2.1455		

Table 51

Distances between carbon atoms in molecules with single, double, and triple bonds

Molecule	Bond	r, A	Molecule	Bond	r, A
Diamond	C—C	1.54	Cis-2,3-epoxybutane C_4H_8O	C—C	1.54
Ethane C_2H_6	C—C	1.56	Tetrahydrofuran C_4H_8O	C—C	1.54
Propane C_3H_8	C—C	1.54	C_2	C=C	1.31
Isobutane C_4H_{10}	C—C	1.54	Ethylene C_2H_4	C=C	1.34
Neopentane C_5H_{12}	C—C	1.54	Allene C_3H_4	C=C	1.31
Cyclopropane C_3H_6	C—C	1.53	Ketene C_2H_2O	C=C	1.35
Cyclopentane C_5H_{10}	C—C	1.52	Stilbene $(C_6H_5)_2C_2H_2$	C=C	1.33
Cyclohexane C_6H_{12}	C—C	1.51	Benzoquinone $C_6H_4O_2$	C=C	1.32
Butylbromide C_4H_9Br	C—C	1.55	Acetylene C_2H_2	C≡C	1.20
Nonacosane $C_{29}H_{60}$	C—C	1.54	Diacetylene C_4H_2	C≡C	1.20
Paraldehyde $(CH_3CHO)_3$	C—C	1.54	C_2Br_2	C≡C	1.20
Metaldehyde $(CH_3CHO)_3$	C—C	1.54	C_2I_2	C≡C	1.18
Trans-2,3-epoxybutane C_4H_8O	C—C	1.54	HC≡CX	C≡C	1.20

Table 49 gives the values of r_e obtained from the moments of inertia I_e expressed by the formula

$$I_e = \frac{27.994}{B_e} \times 10^{-40} \text{ g cm}^2. \quad (48.10)$$

Unlike r_e, r_0 is computed from the equation

$$I_0 = \frac{27.994}{B_0} \times 10^{-40} \text{ g cm}^2. \quad (48.11)$$

The connection between r_e and r_0 is evident from the following relation:

$$B_0 = B_e - \frac{\alpha_e}{2} \quad (48.12)$$

(cf. (38.11) p. 370). The quantity r_e corresponds to the minimum of the potential curve, whereas r_0 is the mean value of the internuclear distance in the state $v=0$. We may note that the difference between r_e and r_0 is small: for Be O, $r_e = 1.331$ A and $r_0 = 1.335$ A.

The data given in Tables 49-51 exhibit a number of regularities that are particularly marked in the lighter elements (second and third periods). In diatomic molecules of the elements in the Li-F series (Table 49), r_e, which is maximum in the Li_2 molecule, diminishes with increasing atomic number and passes through a minimum in nitrogen. This change in r_e corresponds to a change in the bonding strength from least in Li_2 (single chemical bond) to greatest in N_2 (triple bond). A similar variation of r_e is observed in other periods as well. In the case of hydrogen compounds

(Table 50), there is a regular decrease in r_e in each of the first two periods; apparently, this may be correlated with the decrease in size of the atoms bound to hydrogen and an increase in the stability of the molecule. Also characteristic of A—H bonds is the constant distance between A and H atoms in various compounds, as may be seen from Table 52. This must be attributed to the small change in stability of the respective bond when passing from one compound to the next (see Sec. 49).

Table 52

Length of A-H bond in different molecules

Molecule	Bond	r, A	Molecule	Bond	r, A
CH	C—H	1.12	NH_4Cl	N—H	1.03
CH_4	C—H	1.09	OH	O—H	0.97
HCN	C—H	1.07	H_2O	O—H	0.97
C_2H_2	C—H	1.06			
NH	N—H	1.04	SiH	Si—H	1.52
NH_3	N—H	1.01	SiH_4	Si—H	1.5

The approximate constancy of bond length is also marked in the case of single, double, and triple bonds of carbon atoms (Table 51). As may be seen from this table, to an accuracy of hundredths of an Angstrom, r = 1.54 A corresponds to a single (aliphatic) C—C bond, r = 1.34 A to a double C=C bond, and r = 1.20 A to a triple bond. There is a similar constancy of bond length also in the case of the bonds C—O (1.44 A), C—N (1.4 A), C—Cl (1.7-1.8 A), C=0 (~1.2 A), C≡N (1.16 A), etc. The bond length between two carbon bonds in molecules with conjugated and, particularly, with aromatic bonds differs from the length of the aliphatic C—C bond and the double carbon bond. For instance, in the benzene molecule the length of the carbon-carbon (aromatic) bond is 1.40 A, in C_6Cl_6, 1.42 A and in $C_6(CH_3)_6$, 1.42 A. From these examples, it is seen that the length of an aromatic bond in benzene and its derivatives is intermediate between the lengths of single and double bonds.

Let us further consider the lengths of carbon-carbon bonds in the molecules of butadiene $H_2C{=}CH{-}CH{=}CH_2$, where C—C is 1.46 A and C=C 1.35A; of diacetylene HC≡C—C≡CH, where C—C is 1.36 A for C≡C equal to 1.20 A; of methylacetylene $H_3C{-}C{\equiv}CH$, where the length of the C—C bond is 1.46 A, etc. We see that the lengths of the bonds C—C, C=C, and C≡C in these conjugated-bond molecules differ less than in molecules with isolated carbon-carbon bonds (Table 51). This indicates a certain similarity of bonds in conjugated systems and a complete similarity of bonds in the simplest aromatic compounds.

The above-mentioned regularities, namely, the approximate constancy of distance between a given pair of atoms in different compounds with covalent bonds and the regular decrease in this distance with increasing multiplicity of the bond permit us, in purely formal fashion, to attribute to each atom in its given valence state a *definite radius*, as was proposed by Pauling. The radii of certain atoms computed (after Pauling) from crystallographic structures and also from spectroscopic and electronographic data (these computations are based on the assumption that the distance between adjacent atoms in a crystal or in a molecule is equal to the sum of their radii) are given in Table 53 (for a single bond). Atomic radii for double (r_2) and triple (r_3) bonds are approximately satisfied by the following empirical relations:

$$r_2 = 0.90\, r_1 \text{ and } r_3 = 0.79\, r_1.$$

For the atoms B, C, N, O, and S, the values of r_2 obtained from this relation are, respectively, 0.80, 0.69, 0.63, 0.59, and 0,94 A. Similarly, for r_3 in the case of C and N we find 0.61 and 0.55 A. It will be readily seen that these values are close to those computed from Table 49.

Using r_1, r_2, and r_3, it is possible to find the approximate distances between the atoms in different molecules. In addition, the possibility to assign to the atoms in a molecule definite radii may also be very important for determining the character of the valence bond in various compounds. Let us consider the SO and CO molecules. The close agreement of the value of r calculated on the assumption of a double bond and the observed value in the case of SO (1.53 * and 1.49 A) may serve to indicate that the bond between the atoms S and O in this molecule is indeed a double bond. But in the case of CO the distance between atoms calculated as the sum of the radii of the C and O atoms is 1.28 A** for a double bond, whereas the measured value of this distance comes out to 1.13 A. Whence it may be concluded that the bond in a CO molecule should be stronger than an ordinary double C=O bond; which is actually the case.

Table 53

Covalent radii of atoms for single chemical bonds (r_1) in A

H 0.31						
Li 1.34	Be 1.07	B 0.89	C 0.77	N 0.70	O 0.66	F 0.64
Na 1.54	Mg 1.40	Al 1.26	Si 1.17	P 1.10	S 1.04	Cl 0.99
Cu 1.35	Zn 1.31	Ga 1.26	Ge 1.22	As 1.21	Se 1.17	Br 1.14
Ag 1.53	Cd 1.48	In 1.44	Sn 1.40	Sb 1.41	Te 1.37	I 1.33
Au 1.50	Hg 1.48	Tl 1.47	Pb 1.46	Bi 1.51		

* From the data in Table 49, we get 1.51 A for r_{SO} as the average of r_{O_2} and r_{S_2}.

** From the data in Table 49, we get $r_{C=O} = 1.26$ A.

A number of other properties of the CO molecule (for instance, its great similarity to the nitrogen molecule $N\equiv N$) permits us to consider the bond in CO as close to the triple $C\equiv O$ bond. The sum of the radii of the atoms C and O calculated from the r_1 values given in Table 53 for a triple bond comes out to 1.13 Å, i.e., it coincides with the measured value of the bond length in the CO molecule.

As may be seen from the foregoing, the concept of "atomic radius", unlike that of the interatomic distance (in the molecule), is conventional, just like the concept of *ionic radius*, which is introduced in the case of ionic compounds, ionic crystals for instance. All methods for determining ionic radii proceed from the view of ions as rigid spheres closely packed in the crystal lattice and surrounded by spheres of opposite electric charge. From the directly measured constants of the crystal lattice (these constants give the distance between ions in the crystal, i. e., the sum of their radii) the radius of each ion may be calculated only on the basis of certain simplifying assumptions. To illustrate, in the case of crystals built up of large anions (I^-, for instance) and small cations (Li^+, for example) the dimensions of the latter may be ignored, whence the radius of the anion comes out to half the distance between two anions. Then, from the interionic distances in the lattices built up of this anion and of other cations, it is possible to determine the radii of the latter. Using known cation radii, it is possible from the crystal structure to calculate the radii of other anions. In this way we get a *system of ionic radii* that is used to determine molecular structure, electrical and optical properties, types of crystal lattices, etc.

Ion radii can also be calculated from the properties of the electronic shells of the ions, for instance, from ionic polarisation or from the law for the repulsive force that counteracts further approach of adjacent ions. A common feature to all systems of ionic radii worked out on the basis of different initial data is the fact that they are confined to a comparatively small range of compounds for which the ion radii are indeed certain (though conventional) constants. Outside this range, i.e., when applying this system to other compounds, the additivity of the interionic distances is, as a rule, not fulfilled; whence it follows that the ionic radii are not constant. Further, we have to distinguish ion radii as a function of the type of crystal lattice. This brings the ion radius closer to the "chemical radius" of the atom. However, the concept of approximate constancy of ionic (like atomic) radii turns out to be useful in studies of various properties of atoms and ions, in evaluating interatomic and interionic distances in molecules and in crystals, and in interpreting the structure of a variety of compounds. The radii of ions that have the electronic structure of an inert gas are given in Table 54 (after Rice).

Table 54

Ion radii (in Angstroms)

			H^-	He	Li^+	Be^{++}	B^{3+}	C^{4+}	N^{5+}	O^{6+}	F^{7+}
			2.05	0.92	0.59	0.43	0.34	0.29	0.25	0 22	0.19
C^{4-}	N^{3-}	O^{--}	F^-	Ne	Na^+	Mg^{++}	Al^{3+}	Si^{4+}	P^{5+}	S^{6+}	Cl^{7+}
4.14	2.47	1.76	1.36	1.12	0.95	0.82	0.72	0.65	0.59	0.53	0.49
Si^{4-}	P^{3-}	S^{--}	Cl^-	Ar	K^+	Ca^{++}	Sc^{3+}	Ti^{4+}	V^{5+}	Cr^{6+}	Mn^{7+}
3.84	2.79	2.19	1.81	1.54	1.33	1.18	1.06	0.96	0.88	0.81	0.75
					Cu^+	Zn^{++}	Ga^{3+}	Ge^{4+}	As^{5+}	Se^{6+}	Br^{7+}
					0.96	0.88	0.81	0.76	0.71	0.66	0.62
Ge^{4-}	As^{3-}	Se^{--}	Br^-	Kr	Rb^+	Sr^{++}	Y^{3+}	Zr^{4+}	Nb^{5+}	Mo^{6+}	
3.71	2.85	2.32	1.95	1.69	1.48	1.32	1.20	1.09	1.00	0.93	
					Ag^+	Cd^{++}	In^{3+}	Sn^{4+}	Sb^{5+}	Te^{6+}	I^{7+}
					1.26	1.14	1.04	0.96	0.89	0.82	0.77
Sn^{4-}	Sb^{3-}	Te^{--}	I^-	Xe	Cs^+	Ba^{++}	La^{3+}	Ce^{4+}			
3.70	2.95	2.50	2.16	1.90	1.69	1.53	1.39	1.27			
					Au^+	Hg^{++}	Tl^{3+}	Pb^{4+}	Bi^{5+}		
					1.37	1.25	1.15	1.06	0.98		

Molecular structure. The problem of geometrical molecular structure belongs to the field of *stereochemistry*. Since the time of van't Hoff and LeBel — the founders of this important branch of the science of matter—a vast body of experimental material has been amassed. The principal concepts originated on a purely chemical ground, were subjected to physical verification through experiment and now rest on a firm theoretical foundation. One of these is the concept of directed valency. As was demonstrated in Chapter 7, it follows directly from the quantum-mechanical theory and is thus substantiated theoretically. Earlier examined instances have shown the importance of the theory of directed valency for establishing the geometrical structure of molecules.

Here we shall dwell only on the basic results obtained from an experimental establishment of molecular geometry and also on some of the methods. Some of the results and methods that have already been considered will be omitted.

One of the important physico-chemical methods that played the chief part in an experimental substantiation of the concept of the tetrahedral directivity of carbon-atom valences (van't Hoff) is the *polarimetric method*, which is based on studies of the rotation of the plane of polarisation. It is precisely with this method that the discovery of *optical isomers* — substances that have identical composition but rotate the plane of polarisation in different directions — is connected. As follows from the theory of this phenomenon, the spatial arrangement of atoms (or atomic groups) in optical isomers should be such that one molecule is a mirror image of the other. Such, for example, are the molecules

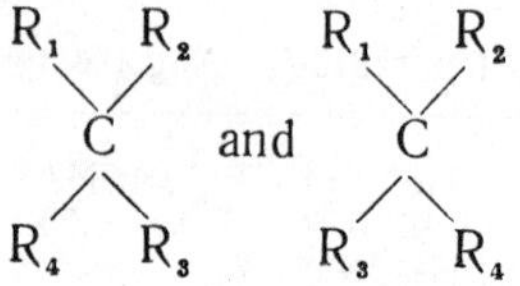

(R_1, R_2, R_3, and R_4 are different atoms or radicals) that are obtained from one another by interchanging two radicals. It will readily be seen that in the case of two *identical* radicals one molecular model passes into the other as a result of simple rotation, and therefore both models have identical structure, i.e., they coincide. Inasmuch as optical isomerism is experimentally observed only in the case of four *different* R_i, these experiments must be regarded as proof of the arrangement of atoms or radicals in the vertexes of a tetrahedron.

One of the manifestations of directed tetrahedral carbon-atom valences is the constancy of the angle between the valence bonds of a tetrahedral C atom. For instance, from measurements of the angles of H—C—Cl or Cl—C—Cl in the molecules CCl_4, CCl_3H, CCl_2H_2, and $CClH_3$ it follows that upon substitution of hydrogen by a chlorine atom these angles undergo a comparatively small change. Yet in the absence of directed valency, for instance in the case of the CCl_2H_2 molecule, one should (for reasons of symmetry) expect an arrangement of Cl atoms in a single straight line, i.e., $\angle$Cl—C—Cl = 180°, whereas in reality we have an angle of 132°.

Cogent proof of the constancy of the valence angle of carbon is given by X-ray studies of normal hydrocarbons, the molecules of which are in the form of an extended chain. These investigations show that the distances between planes of the crystal lattice of normal hydrocarbons vary in proportion to the number of C atoms in the molecule with two other practically unchanged lattice parameters. From this it follows that the axes of the molecules in the crystal are oriented perpendicular to the plane of the lattice. Dividing the measured distances between planes by the number of C atoms in the molecule yields a practically constant value of 1.2 A in all cases. Dividing this number by the distance between the C atoms for an aliphatic bond (this distance is 1.5 A) (see p. 484), we get $\sin\frac{\alpha}{2} = 0.8$, and, consequently, the angle between the bonds C—C—C $\alpha = 107°$ is close to the angle between the axes of a regular tetrahedron, 109°28′. Therefore, the zigzag structure of hydrocarbon chains that follows from these data is a consequence of the constancy of the valence angle of the carbon atom. The constant valence angle of carbon, together with the constancy of interatomic distances between the carbon atoms belong to the fundamental principles of the stereochemistry of carbon, which play a guiding role in modern investigations into the structure of organic compounds.

Theoretically substantiated directed valency occurs also in the case of tri- and bivalent elements. In this respect, trivalent N and P and bivalent O and S have been studied in greatest detail. From the quantum-mechanical theory of atoms with valence p-electrons (such as N, P, O, and S) it follows that in the absence of perturbations the valence bonds must be mutually perpendicular, whence we get 90° for the angle between bonds. In reality, however, due to the interaction of the atoms the valence angle must, to a greater or lesser degree, differ from 90° (exceed it). Theoretically, one should expect triangular molecules of H_2O, H_2S, Cl_2O, $(CH_3)_2O$, etc., and pyramidal molecules of NH_3, PH_3, NCl_3, PCl_3, $N(CH_3)_3$, etc. This conclusion is brilliantly confirmed by extensive experimental material obtained on the basis of diverse methods of research.

By way of illustration, let us consider the PCl_3 molecule. The pyramidal structure of this molecule with the P atom at the vertex of the pyramid and Cl atoms at its base is obtained from various data. First we must point to a dipole moment (1.1 debyes) that is incompatible with the symmetrical planar structure. The Raman spectrum of PCl_3 exhibits four frequencies (510, 480, 257 and 190 cm^{-1}), which is the number to be expected for a symmetric molecule of pyramidal structure (two of these frequencies correspond to doubly degenerate oscillations); if the molecule were planar there would be only three active frequencies in the Raman spectrum. The electronogram of PCl_3 vapour is likewise compatible only with a pyramidal molecule. Its calculation gives the following interatomic distances: Cl—Cl $= 3.18 \pm 0.06$ A and P—Cl $= 2.04 \pm 0.06$ A, from which follows $\angle$Cl—P—Cl $= 102°$. Through the use of the same research methods, the pyramidal structure was established also in the case of NH_3, PH_3, PF_3, PBr_3, AsF_3, $AsCl_3$, and $SbCl_3$.

Interesting from the standpoint of the effect of directed valency on molecular structure is the difference between the molecules C_2H_2 and H_2O_2. The former is in the shape of a stick, the latter, a trapezium. The linear shape of the HC≡CH molecule follows from the directed valence of the ≡C— atom, the trapezoidal structure

O—O
/ \
of the H H molecule likewise directly follows from the theoretical angle of valence of the oxygen atom. As has already been pointed out, this angle is ordinarily somewhat greater than 90°: in the case of H_2O_2 it is close to 105°. The difference in the molecular structure of C_2H_2 and H_2O_2 is evident from the absence of a

dipole moment in the case of acetylene and its presence in hydrogen peroxide. The dipole moment of H_2O_2 (2.26 debyes) is close to that of H_2O (1.84 debyes), whence it may be concluded that the angle $\angle$HOO in H_2O_2 differs but slightly from the angle $\angle$HOH in H_2O. Let it be emphasised that from the viewpoint of the symmetrical arrangement of atoms in the molecule one should expect an identical geometrical structure of the molecules HCCH and HOOH.

Let us consider two more methods of studying the geometrical structure of molecules. The first — the *parachor method* — which is similar to the earlier considered refractometric and magnetometric methods, consists in the following. The parachor is the temperature-independent and constant coefficient P in the empirical formula

$$\sqrt[4]{\sigma} = PD \qquad (48.13)$$

or in the more precise formula

$$\sqrt[4]{\sigma} = P(D - d) \qquad (48.14)$$

that relate the surface tension of a pure liquid σ to its density D (d is the vapour density above the liquid). The parachor is an additive constant (of a given substance) composed of individual elements that characterise the atoms and groups of atoms (radicals) in the molecule — P_i and also various structural peculiarities of the molecule — π_i, i.e..

$$P = \sum P_i + \sum \pi_i. \qquad (48.15)$$

Definite values of P_i and π_i were established from an analysis of experimental material for different structural elements of molecules and these may be utilised for calculating the parachor of a chemical compound (liquid). These values for certain structural elements follow: $P_H = 17.1$, $P_C = 4.8$, $P_N = 12.5$, $P_{CH_2} = 39.0$, $P_{Cl} = 54.2$; for a double bond, $\pi_= = 23.2$; for a triple bond $\pi_\equiv = 46.6$; for a six-member ring $\pi_\diamond = 6.1$.

Let us take advantage of these figures to calculate the parachors of some compounds. In the case of CCl_4 we find $P = P_C + 4P_{Cl} = 4.8 + 4 \times 54.2 = 221.6$ in place of the measured value of 219. For normal heptane C_7H_{16} $P = 7P_C + 16P_H = 307.2$ in place of 309.3. For benzene C_6H_6 $P = 6P_C + 6P_H + 3\pi_= + \pi_\diamond = 207.1$ in place of 206.3.

We see that the calculated values of the parachors practically coincide with the measured values. Thus, by comparing the calculated and measured values of the parachor of a given compound it is possible to judge of the correctness of the structure attributed to the molecules of the compound.

Another method of studying molecular structure is based on the *Ramsauer effect*. The essence of this effect is that when slow electrons (or protons) pass through a gas we observe a peculiar dependence, upon the electron velocities, of the total effective cross-section for the interaction of electrons with the gas molecules. Depending on the nature of the gas, the effective cross-section, which is usually taken as the sum of the cross-sections of the molecules contained in 1 cm^3 at 1 mm Hg and 0°C, varies with the electron velocities in accordance with a curve that is characteristic of the given compound or the given class of compounds. We will not go into the theory of the Ramsauer effect, but will only note that this effect is a diffraction effect since it is caused by the wave properties of electrons and protons.

Figs. 121 and 122 show curves of effective cross-section Q (in cm^{-1}) as a function of the electron velocities in N_2, C_2H_2, and HCN (Fig. 121) and CO_2 and H_2CCCH_2 (Fig. 122). We see that the curves for each class of molecules are charateristic of this class. These data are interesting from the viewpoint of Grimm's law of the displacement of hydrides (Table 34, p. 334) according to which the CH molecule and the N atom, just like CH_2 and O, that have the same number of electrons (isoelectron particles) must in a certain sense be regarded as chemical and physical analogues. This peculiarity is also evident from the shape of the curves under consideration because the substitution of an N atom by a CH group or of an O atom by a CH_2 group does not essentially alter the shape of the respective curve. Hence, the intramolecular field — that acts on the electron and determines the magnitude of the effective cross-section (for a given electron velocity) — in molecules

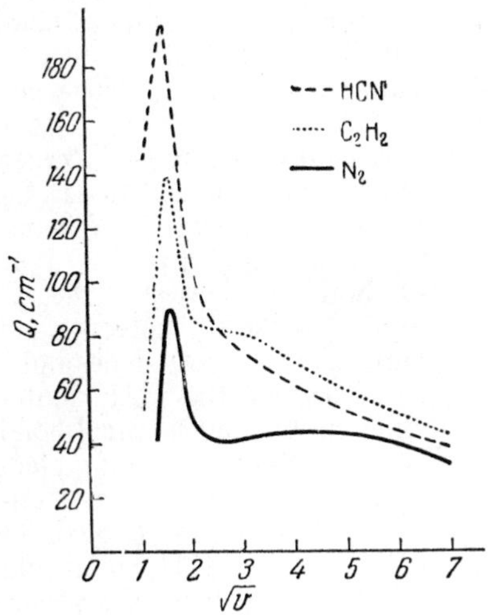

Fig. 121. Effective cross-sections for slow electrons in N_2, C_2H_2, and HCN (after Brueche and Schmieder)

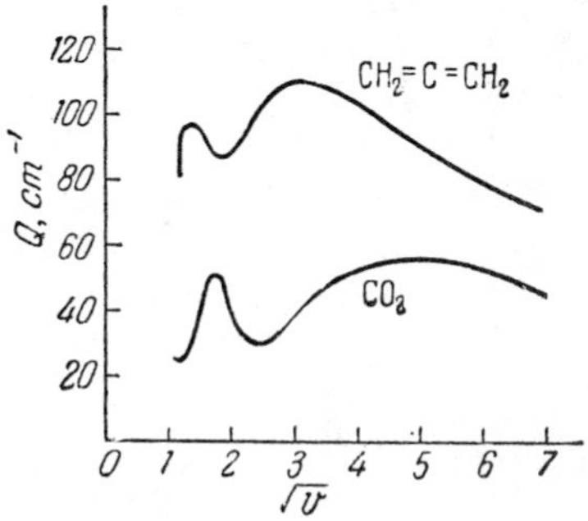

Fig. 122. Effective cross-sections for slow electrons in CO_2 and H_2CCCH_2 (after Brueche and Schmieder)

that belong to each of the two classes under consideration has a similar structure within the limits of a given class. And since this is hardly possible for unlike molecular structure we must conclude that the molecules of each given class have a similar structure peculiar only to the given class. Thus the C atoms in the molecule H_2CCCH_2, like the C and O atoms in the CO_2 molecule, should be situated on a single straight line.

Apparently, Q is also a sensitive indicator of the type of valence bond in a molecule. Interesting in this respect are the curves for the molecules O_2 and $H_2C{=}CH_2$ given in Fig. 123. Despite the same number of electrons in these molecules and the double bond in both, the curves that correspond to them are radically different. However, this difference becomes understandable if one takes into account that oxygen is paramagnetic, whereas ethylene is diamagnetic. Whence we get the different type of bonding between the O atoms in the O_2 molecule and between the methylene radicals CH_2 in the C_2H_4 molecule: in O_2 the chemical bond is accomplished by four electrons, two of which have uncompensated spins ($^3\Sigma$ state) while in the C_2H_4 molecule all electron spins are mutually compensated. This difference in valence bonding undoubtedly exerts its effect on the structure of the field of the molecules under comparison. It is this, therefore, that accounts for the marked difference in the shapes of the respective Ramsauer curves.

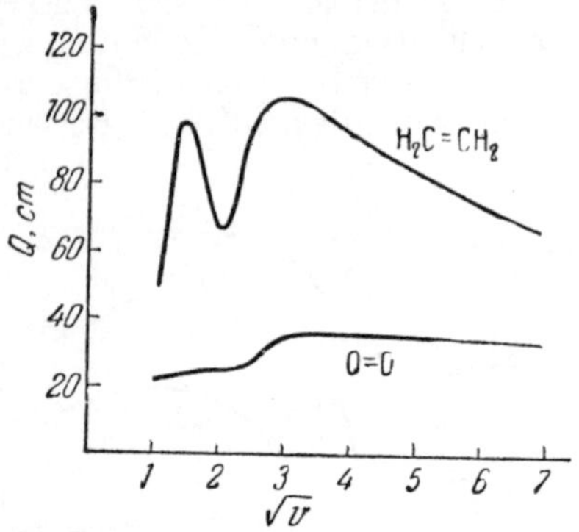

Fig. 123. Effective cross-sections for slow electrons in oxygen and ethylene (after Brueche)

It may be noted that in recent years new methods have emerged in the study of molecular structure. These methods are associated with the development of nuclear physics. One consists in the use of scattering and diffraction of neutrons. On the basis of the scattering of thermal neutrons by the molecules of sulphuric acid, Janik established the presence of OH hydroxyls in the H_2SO_4 molecule. Applying neutron diffraction, Levi and Peterson studied the crystalline structure of NH_4Cl and determined the distance N—H (1.03 ± 0.02 A).

The second in this group of new methods is one that utilises positron-electron interaction to produce positronium. It is capable of measuring the rate of transformation of orthopositronium into para-positronium (by measuring the lifetime of positronium with the help of counters and coincidence circuits). Since this transformation is accomplished with particular ease on free and unpaired electrons in atoms and molecules and since as a result we get, in place of the relatively long-lived ortho-positronium that decays into three gamma-quanta, para-positronium, which is a thousand times more long-lived and decays into two gamma-quanta, it becomes possible to determine the concentration of electrons, atoms, and radicals in the substance. Another possibility of the positron method is connected with observing the annihilation of positrons in their collisions with electrons. This permits studying the distribution of electron density in molecules.

Finally, molecular structure may be studied by a method based on the Mössbauer effect, which consists in the resonance scattering of gamma-quanta by nuclei. Since the resonance-level width of excited nuclei is many orders of magnitude less than the recoil energy obtained by the nucleus due to its emission of a gamma-quantum, resonance scattering of gamma-quanta does not occur in the case of recoil. However, it is observed (this is the Mössbauer effect) if recoil is eliminated. This is achieved by getting the scattering atoms (nuclei) firmly fixed in the crystal lattice at low temperatures. The very slightest external effect (for example, changes in the chemical composition of the scatterer) brings about a displacement (shift) in the nuclear levels. This upsets resonance because of the above-mentioned small width of the resonance levels. Resonance may be restored with the aid of the Doppler frequency shift, which is used to measure the shift in nuclear levels. Studying such shifts in the nuclei of iron Fe^{57} in its various compounds, Kistner and Fynyar made a quantitative determination of the contribution of different electron shells to the valence bonds of iron. Measurements, made by Hanna and others, of the magnitude of the shifts in the case of metallic iron and its oxide Fe_2O_3 have further led to the conclusion that iron nuclei are situated in strong magnetic fields (of the order of hundreds of thousands of oersteds) induced by electron shells. It is very probable that subsequent elaboration of this method will, in the near future, open up great possibilities for studying the fine structure of the electron shells of atoms and molecules.

49. Energy Constants of Molecules

Methods for determining bond energies. Let us first take up the experimental methods of determining the energy of chemical bonds (heats of dissociation). Most widespread are the *thermal methods*, which are based, for example, on measurements of thermodynamic equilibrium. In the simplest case, one of these methods amounts to measuring the pressure of a heated gas or to measuring the concentration (pressure) of the initial gas or its products of dissociation at various temperatures. Having in view to determine the heat of dissociation of a diatomic gas, we can express the constant of equilibrium $X_2 \rightleftarrows 2X$

$$K_p = \frac{p_X^2}{p_{X_2}}$$

(p_X and p_{X_2} are the partial pressures of the atomic and molecular components), on the assumption that both components obey the law of ideal gases, by the following formula:

$$K_p = \frac{4(\Delta p)^2}{p - 2\Delta p} \qquad (49.1)$$

where $\Delta p = p - (T/T_0)\,p_0$, p is the overall pressure at temperature T and p_0 is the initial pressure of X_2 at temperature T_0.* Calculating K_p (49.1) from the values of Δp (measured at various temperatures) by means of equation

$$\frac{d\,ln K_p}{dT} = \frac{Q_p}{RT^2} \qquad (49.2)$$

we find the heat of dissociation $D = Q_p$ at temperature T. The heat of dissociation at absolute zero D^0 may be obtained from the equation

$$D^0 = D - 2\int_0^T C_{p_X} dT + \int_0^T C_{p_{X_2}} dT \qquad (49.3)$$

which is one of the particular expressions of the Kirchhoff formulas.

As may be seen from (49.1), Δp, at a given temperature, is the greater the higher the equilibrium constant K_p, i. e., the less the heat of dissociation D. Therefore, this method of determining the heats of dissociation (due to measuring difficulties at high temperatures and the associated considerable errors) yields the most precise results only in the case of small D when the atom concentration even at relatively low temperatures is appreciable. This method has yielded good results in the case of the halogens Cl_2, Br_2, and I_2. By way of illustration, we give the results of measurements of the heat of dissociation of iodine obtained by Perlman and Rollefson. The values of D^0 computed by these

* At this temperature the partial pressure of the atomic component p_X is practically zero. It will be noted that $p_X = 2\Delta p$.

workers from measurements at different temperatures are: 35.757 (872° K), 35.583 (973° K), 35.528 (1073° K), 35.504 (1173° K), and 35.515 kcal/mol (1274°K). The mean weighted value of 35.514 kcal/mol practically coincides with 35.556 kcal/mol obtained spectroscopically.

It should, however, be noted that during recent years as a result of considerable refinement in methods of measuring temperatures and concentrations, ways have been found for extending this thermal method to temperatures up to 3000°K and, consequently, for measuring comparatively high values of heats of dissociation.

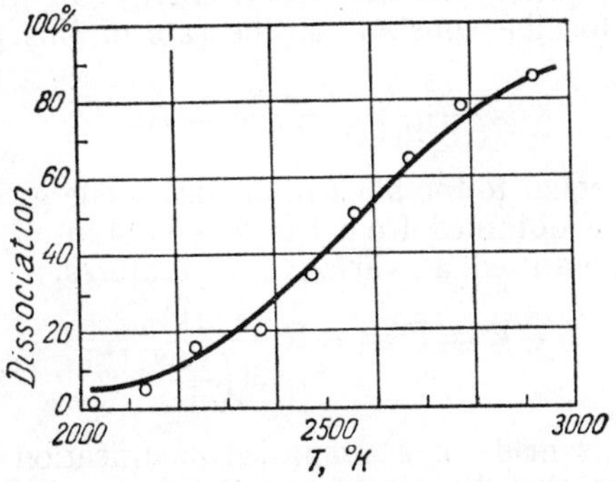

Fig. 124. Thermal dissociation of hydrogen (after Hendrie)

To illustrate, Fig. 124 gives the measured * (at various temperatures) values of the degree of dissociation of hydrogen $x = \frac{P_H}{P_{H_2} + P_H} \times 100\%$ (open circles). In this figure, the curve is plotted from the values of x obtained from the heat of dissociation of H_2.

Further possibilities for measuring large heats of dissociation are to be found in the *shock-wave method*, which is based on the relationship between the rate of propagation of a shock wave in a gas and the state of the latter, its temperature, pressure, and density. Correlating the measured and calculated rates of propagation of a shock wave in nitrogen, Toennis and Greene showed that of the two spectroscopically obtained values of the heat of dissociation of nitrogen, $D^0 = 170.22$ and 225.09 kcal/mol, only the latter value yields rates of propagation that coincide with the measured ones.

---

* In these experiments the concentration of the atomic component was determined by the deflection of a molecular beam in a nonuniform magnetic field.

All the foregoing methods are based on measurements of thermodynamical equilibrium in heat gases. Besides these there are thermal methods that might also be called *kinetic* inasmuch as they deal with measuring the rates of chemical processes. Of this group we shall consider only the *pyrolitic method*, which consists in measuring the rate of thermal decomposition of the substances concerned.

Obviously, we can here speak only of the decomposition of molecules into radicals, i.e., of the monomolecular process of type $R_1R_2 = R_1 + R_2$. The activation energy E that enters into the expression for the constant of the rate of this process

$$k = -\frac{1}{(R_1R_2)}\frac{d(R_1R_2)}{dt} = Ae^{-\frac{E}{RT}} \qquad (49.4)$$

is in most cases equal to the bond dissociation energy of $R_1 - R_2$ (D). Thus, D may be obtained from the rate constant of monomolecular decomposition measured at various temperatures:

$$D = E = -R\frac{d\ln k}{d\left(\frac{1}{T}\right)}. \qquad (49.5)$$

Frequent use is made of a simplified modification of this method based on the fact that the pre-exponential factor A in (49.4) is, in most cases, of the order of $10^{13}\,sec^{-1}$. Putting $A = 10^{13}\,sec^{-1}$ and measuring k at a certain (single) temperature, one obtains the dissociation energy of the bond

$$D = E = RT\ln\frac{10^{13}}{k}. \qquad (49.6)$$

This simplified method was first used by Butler and Polanyi to determine the dissociation energy of the C—I bond in various organic iodides. It later found wide application in many studies.

Spectroscopic methods comprise another important group of experimental methods for determining the heats of dissociation of molecules. Of this group, the most precise method is that based on a determination of the convergence limit of bands in the absorption spectrum of a given gas (v progressions, p. 398). As follows from the theory of molecular electronic spectra the frequency ν_{con}, which corresponds to the convergence limit of the bands, is in the following relationship to the excitation energy E and the heat of dissociation of the excited molecule D′:

$$h\nu_{con} = h\nu_{el} + D' = E + D'. \qquad (49.7)$$

Using this expression, one can determine the dissociation energy of an excited molecule to the accuracy with which the values of ν_{con}

and E are determined. And to find the dissociation energy of a molecule in the ground state it is necessary to have additional information on the origin of the terms that correspond to the ground and excited states of the molecule. Here, various cases are possible. We shall examine three.

Case a. The ground and excited terms of the BC molecule originate from terms of the B and C atoms which are in the ground state.

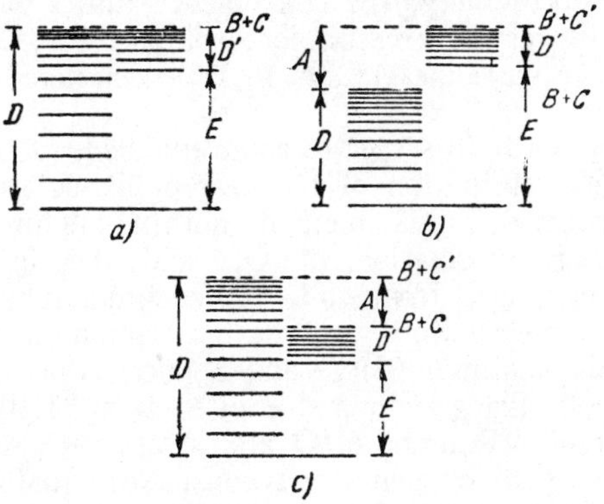

Fig. 125. Different cases of the photodissociation of diatomic molecules

In this case, as a result of the dissociation of the excited molecule we get two atoms in the ground state (Fig. 125 a); the sum E + D' will be equal to D (the heat of dissociation of the molecule in the ground state):

$$D = E + D' = h\nu_{con}. \tag{49.8}$$

Case b (Fig. 125 b). The ground term of the BC molecule originates from the ground terms of atoms B and C; the excited term, from the ground term of atom B and the excited term of atom C. In this case, the dissociation of an excited molecule yields B + C', while the dissociation of the molecule in the ground state yields B + C. The sum E + D' here should equal the sum D + A, where A is the excitation energy of atom C, i.e.,

$$D = E + D' - A = h\nu_{con} - A. \tag{49.9}$$

In this case, to determine the dissociation energy in the ground state from the convergence limit of bands, it is necessary, consequently, to know the excitation energy of one of the atoms.

Case c. The ground term of the BC molecule originates from the terms of atom B in the ground state and from the excited atom C;

the excited term, from the terms B and C, which are in the ground state. In this case, obviously (Fig. 125c),

$$D = E + D' + A = h\nu_{con} + A. \quad (49.10)$$

Here, as in the preceding case, we must know A in order to find D.

It should be noted that cases a and b, particularly the latter, are the most frequently encountered and, for this reason, the most important practically. Unfortunately, the convergence limits of the bands are observed only in very few cases, for example, for Cl_2, Br_2, I_2, O_2, and certain other molecules. Case b is encountered for all these molecules.

In connection with this spectroscopic method, of interest is the history of the determination of the heat of dissociation of oxygen. Before the discovery of this method nothing definite was known about the heat of dissociation of O_2, and the figures given by different workers ranged from 45 to 400 kcal/mol. The experimentally determined convergence limit of the absorption bands of oxygen came out to 162 kcal/mol (Birge and Sponer). For some time it was believed that both the ground and excited term of the O_2 molecule originates from the ^3P terms of O atoms (case a). Accordingly, the dissociation energy of oxygen D was considered equal to $D = h\nu_{con} = 162$ kcal/mol. However, Herzberg demonstrated that the excited state of the O_2 molecule ($^3\Sigma_u^-$), unlike its ground state ($^3\Sigma_g^-$), does not originate from the ground terms of O atoms ($^3P + {}^3P$, cf. p. 327), but from the terms $^3P + {}^1D$ (case b). Therefore, a precise determination of the heat of dissociation of O_2 proved possible only after A was found: $A = {}^1D - {}^3P = 45$ kcal/mol (Frerichs). On the basis of this value, from (49.9) we find $D = 162 - 45 = 117$ kcal/mol. At the present time, as a result of a precise determination of the band convergence limit (Herzberg) we have D^0 (at 0° K) = 117.96 kcal/mol.

It is to be noted that the heat of dissociation of hydrogen ($D^0 = 103.24$ kcal/mol) was determined from observations of the convergence limit in the emission spectrum (v′ progressions). In this case, the convergence limit directly yields the dissociation energy of the H_2 molecule in the ground state (that originates from atomic terms which correspond to the ground state of H) as the difference

$$D = h\nu_{el} - h\nu_{con}. \quad (49.11)$$

As was pointed out earlier, the band convergence limit is actually observed in very rare instances. And the spectra of most gases are either a system of bands consisting of the initial members of progressions or are continuous. In the first case, to find the dissociation energy from the spectral data, use is made of an approximate *method of extrapolation* (Birge and Sponer), which is based on the fact that the maximum vibrational energy of a molecule is equal to its dissociation energy. The following approximate formula is ordinarily used:

$$D = \frac{h\omega}{4x} \tag{49.12}$$

(Sec. 37), which is obtained on the assumption that the vibrational energy of a molecule is expressed by the two-term equation (37.10) (p. 355). As has already been pointed out, this equation is suitable only for an approximate description of the vibrational structure of the spectrum. Still less suitable should it be for extrapolation. The extrapolation formula (49.12) should therefore yield only extremely approximate values of D. As experiment shows, in most cases it gives exaggeratedly high values, as may be seen from the data in Table 55, which gives the true values of the dissociation energies (D_{meas}) for a number of molecules and also the values calculated from (49.12) D_{extrap}, and the departures of these from the true values (in percentage). It is seen that, on the average, the extrapolated values exceed the true values by $\sim 20\%$.

One should expect greater accuracy in the extrapolation method when using a more precise expression for the vibrational energy, a three-term expression for instance:

$$E_{vib} = h\omega\left(v + \frac{1}{2}\right) - h\omega x\left(v + \frac{1}{2}\right)^2 + h\omega y\left(v + \frac{1}{2}\right)^3$$

or a four-term one.

Table 55

Heats of dissociation of some diatomic molecules obtained by the extrapolation method (in kcal/mol)

Molecule	D_{extrap}	D_{meas}	$\frac{D_{extrap} - D_{meas}}{D_{meas}} \times 100\%$
H_2	111	103.2	7
N_2	275	225.1	22
O_2	147	118.0	25
NO	179	150.0	19
OH	127	101.5	25
CO	258	256.1	1
HCl	123	102.2	20
HBr	111	86.5	17
Cl_2	57	57.2	0
Br_2	70	45.4	53

Indeed, using the extrapolation formula

$$D = \frac{h\omega}{4x}\left(1 + \frac{y}{x}\right) \tag{49.13}$$

derived from the three-term expression, we find for the heat of dissociation of the hydroxyl OH — the vibrational energy of which is expressed by the formula $E_{vib} = h\left\{3738.48\left(v+\frac{1}{2}\right) - 85.482\left(v+\frac{1}{2}\right)^2 + 0.7232\left(v+\frac{1}{2}\right)^3 - 0.04544\left(v+\frac{1}{2}\right)^4\right\}$ — 118 kcal/mol, i.e., a magnitude 16% in excess of the true value, whereas the value given in Table 55 obtained from (49.12) exceeds the true value by 25%.

The extrapolation method is applicable in the case of a vibrational structure of the spectrum. However, when the absorption spectrum is continuous throughout, then, as follows from what has been said about the nature of continuous absorption spectra (Sec. 41), one can calculate the *upper limit* of the dissociation energy from the long-wave limit of the spectrum. Experiment indicates that this method ordinarily has an accuracy of several tens per cent, rarely of units per cent. Continuous absorption spectra have been detected in the case of molecules of type HX, MX (X is a halogen), etc., and also in the case of a large number of polyatomic molecules, for instance N_2O, Cl_2O, COS, XCN, H_2O, H_2S, H_2O_2, SO_3, saturated hydrocarbons, alcohols, ethers, acids, etc.

Let us now consider the spectroscopic method based on a determination of the predissociation limit. In the case of diatomic molecules the predissociation limit (frequency ν_{pred}) almost always yields only the upper limit of the dissociation energy:

$$D \leqslant h\nu_{pred}. \tag{49.14}$$

However, when it is possible to observe a break-off in the rotational structure in several vibrational levels of the molecule and thus to establish the trend of the perturbation curve, the predissociation method is an extremely precise method for determining the magnitude of D. Such is the case for the molecules H_2, N_2, CO, P_2, and SO. In a number of cases (including four of the above five), difficulties arise because it is impossible to give an unambiguous solution to the problem of the state of the dissociation products of a predissociating molecule. For example, a strictly definite limit of dissociation (from ν_{pred} for several bands) of the P_2 molecule lies at 116.03 kcal/mol. Identification of this number with the heat of dissociation of P_2 is based on the assumption that in the region of predissociation the P_2 molecule decomposes into the atoms $P(^4S)$ and $P(^2D)$. Another possible value of the heat of dissociation of P_2 equal to 94.98 kcal/mol is obtained if we consider the atoms $P(^4S)$ and $P(^2P)$ to be the products of dissociation. The latter value must, apparently, be considered less probable.

In the case of polyatomic molecules, the sharp limit of predissociation probably rather closely coincides with the dissociation energy, as far as it is possible to judge from the few known examples. One such case is observed in the spectrum of NO_2, from which we have 70.8 kcal/mol for the dissociation energy corresponding to the process $NO_2 \rightarrow NO + O$, whereas thermochemical data yield $D^0 = 69.6$ kcal/mol. In the majority of cases, the predissociation limit in the spectra of polyatomic molecules is highly diffuse, and its determination yields only the upper limit D.

Of late, the mass-spectroscopic method of determining the bond energy has become widespread. This method consists in electron bombardment of the molecules of the gas under study, in measuring the minimum energy of the bombarding electrons at which appropriate ions — detected by their mass spectrum — make their appearance (*appearance potential* of ions of this kind) and in measuring the energy of these ions. Of greatest interest from the viewpoint of determining the bond energy is the following process:

$$R_1R_2 + e = R_1^+ + R_2 + 2e.$$

Knowing the energy of this process, E_0, and the ionisation potential of the radical R_1, we can obtain from equation

$$D = E_0 - eI_{R_1} \qquad (49.15)$$

the bond energy $R_1 - R_2$ (D). E_0 is found from the appearance potential of the R_1^+ ion, i.e., from the minimum energy of the bombarding electrons at which the formation of these ions is observed.

The ionisation potential of the radical R_1 in formula (49.15) may be measured directly by means of the electron impact method. When R_1 is an atom, the value of its ionisation potential can be obtained spectroscopically.

Stevenson, who first applied the above-described method for determining bond energies, proposed another method that dispenses with the ionisation potential of the resultant ion. To illustrate, let us consider the case of the H_3C—H bond, the energy of which was also obtained via the measured ionisation potential of the radical CH_3 (first method). Summing the equalities

$$RCH_3 = R^+ + CH_3 + e - E_{RCH_3}$$

$$R^+ + H + e = RH + E_{RH}$$

$$CH_4 + RH = RCH_3 + 2H + \Delta H_{CH_4} + \Delta H_{RH} - \Delta H_{RCH_3} - 2\Delta H_H$$

we get

$$CH_4 = CH_3 + H - D_{H_3C-H}$$

where

$$D_{H_3C-H} = E_{RCH_3} - E_{RH} - \triangle H_{CH_4} - \triangle H_{RH} + \\ + \triangle H_{RCH_3} + 2\triangle H_H. \quad (49.16)$$

Thus, by measuring the appearance potential of the R^+ ion under electron bombardment of RH and RCH_3, i.e., the quantities E_{RH} and E_{RCH_3} (it is taken here that the energy of R^+ is equal to zero), we find D_{H_3C-H} from the known heats of formation of methane ($\triangle H_{CH_4}$), the substances RH and RCH_3 ($\triangle H_{RH}$ and $\triangle H_{RCH_3}$), and atomic hydrogen ($\triangle H_H$), using (49.16). In the first experiments, Stevenson took ethane C_2H_6 (RH) and propane C_3H_8 (RCH_3), i.e., $R = C_2H_5$. From the measured values of $E_{C_2H_6} = 15.2$ eV, $E_{C_3H_8} = 14.5$ eV and from the known heats of formation ($-\triangle H_{CH_4} - \triangle H_{C_2H_6} + \triangle H_{C_3H_8} + 2\triangle H_H = 5.08$ eV) it follows that $D_{H_3C-H} = 4.4 \pm 0.2$ eV, which coincides with the value obtained by means of the ionisation potential of CH_3.

Let us briefly dwell on the theoretical determination of the energy of chemical bonds. Theoretically, the dissociation energy of a given bond, for instance the energy of the $R_1 - R_2$ bond in the molecule R_1R_2, may be calculated as the energy difference of the particles R_1 and R_2 and the molecule R_1R_2. The mean energy of the bonds is determined from the heat of atomisation, which is obtained as the difference between the energy of all the atoms of the given molecule and the energy of the molecule. Thus, the theoretical problem of determining bond energies reduces, in the final analysis, to calculating the energy of the molecules.

However, even in the case of the simplest diatomic molecules, this calculation, which consists in the solution of the quantum-mechanical problem of the interaction of a definite number of electrons and nuclei, encounters tremendous mathematical difficulties. Suffice it to say here that it was only in the 17th approximation that calculation of the H_2 molecule (a system consisting only of two electrons and two nuclei) gave a heat of dissociation of H_2 that coincided with the experimental value (see p. 288). The heats of dissociation of certain other simple diatomic molecules were calculated with less accuracy.

Substantial progress in this field should be expected with the development of computer techniques. The molecules O_2 and N_2 were the first to be attacked by computing machines. Meckler calculated the heat of dissociation of O_2, which came out only 2% less than the true value (116 in place of 118 kcal/mol). Using two computational methods (variational and electrostatic) for the heat of dissociation of nitrogen, Brüchner obtained 227.07 and

227.95 kcal/mol, which differ from the true value of 225 kcal/mol by roughly 1%.

Naturally, the calculation of triatomic and more complex molecules is a still more difficult problem. As yet there is not a single satisfactory solution Therefore, of interest are various semi-empirical methods of calculating complex molecules that in part utilise experimental data, in this way greatly simplifying the computations.

Bond dissociation energies. Table 56 gives the heats of dissociation of some diatomic molecules. These heats are of interest in that they serve as the initial data for determining the bond energies in other diatomic and polyatomic molecules.

Table 56

Heats of dissociation of certain diatomic molecules in kcal/mol at 0°K

H_2	103.24	O_2	117.96	N_2	225.09	F_2	38.5	HO	101.4
HD	104.05	S_2	98.5	P_2	116.03	Cl_2	57.10	CO	256.14
D_2	105.02	Se_2	65	As_2	90.8	Br_2	45.44	NO	152.3
H_2^+	61.07	Te_2	53	Sb_2	70.6	I_2	35.57	SO	123.6

In this table, the heats of dissociation of H_2, HD, D_2, H_2^+, N_2, CO, O_2, Cl_2, Br_2, and I_2 are exact values; the errors do not exceed hundredths of a kcal/mol. The heats of dissociation of nitric oxide and hydroxyl may be considered accurate to within ± 0.9 and ± 0.5 kcal/mol, respectively. The heats of dissociation of the other molecules given in Table 56 (S_2, Se_2, Te_2, P_2, As_2, Sb_2, SO) are dependent upon certain assumptions, the validity of which has as yet not been definitively proved.

It may be noted that the heat of dissociation of CO is connected with the heat of formation of gaseous carbon ΔH_C by the relation

$$D_{CO} = \Delta H_C + \frac{1}{2} D_{O_2} - \Delta H_{CO}$$

from which it follows that $\Delta H_C = 169.96$ kcal. ΔH_C is of fundamental significance for computing the bond energies in molecules of organic compounds.

The heat of dissociation of NO may be obtained from the heats of dissociation of N_2 and O_2 and the heat of formation of NO from the formula

$$D_{AB} = \frac{1}{2}(D_{A_2} + D_{B_2}) - \Delta H_{AB}. \qquad (49.17)$$

On the basis of (49.17), we can calculate the heats of dissociation of many other molecules. For example, from the well-known heats of formation of the halogen hydrides HX and the heats of dissociation of hydrogen and the halogen molecules we obtain the following heats of dissociation of HX molecules (at 0° K): 134.1 (HF), 102.2 (HCl), 86.5 (HBr), and 70.5 (HI) kcal/mol. In the same way, from the heats of formation of gaseous alkali-halogen salts MeX (Me stands for an alkali metal atom) and the heats of dissociation of halogens we get the most precise values of the heats of dissociation of MeX molecules.

The heats of dissociation are also used for calculating the energies of splitting of complex molecules into atoms (*heats of atomisation*). For instance, from the heat of formation of water vapour $\Delta H_{H_2O} = 57.11$ kcal (at 0° K) and the heats of dissociation of H_2 and O_2 (Table 56) we get 219.3 kcal for the heat of atomisation of H_2O. The heats of atomisation are of prime importance in determining the average bond energies (see below).

It may be noted that when the heat of formation of a substance AB is unknown, the following procedure is often resorted to to find the heat of dissociation. Pauling and Jost postulated the additivity of the energies of single covalent bonds; by this the energy of a normal covalent bond between unlike atoms A and B is equal to the arithmetical mean of the two energy values D_{A_2} and D_{B_2}. Later, however, it was found that this postulate had to be replaced by a similar geometrical-mean postulate. According to the latter, the energy of a normal covalent bond between atoms A and B is $(D_{A_2}D_{B_2})^{\frac{1}{2}}$. Here, the difference between the true energy of dissociation and the value obtained for the geometrical mean must be the less the smaller the difference between atoms A and B as regards electronegativity, i. e., the more covalent the bond in the AB molecule.

However, it will readily be seen that this method of determining the dissociation energy is suitable only for a rough evaluation of this quantity. Indeed, taking advantage of the data in Table 56 and calculating the heats of dissociation of NO and HO molecules from the formula

$$D_{AB} = \sqrt{D_{A_2}D_{B_2}}, \tag{49.18}$$

we get 163 kcal/mol for NO in place of 152, and 111 for HO in place of 101, i.e., values that exceed by 10% those given in Table 56. A still greater discrepancy is found in the case of halogen hydrides where the values of D calculated from (49.18) are less than the true values by 14 to 54%.

The bond dissociation energy in saturated molecules and radicals is a quantity that is of interest both from the viewpoint of the structure of these particles and for elucidating the kinetics and reactivity of the compound. This quantity may be calculated from the following equation:

$$D(R_1 - R_2) = \Delta H_{R_1} + \Delta H_{R_2} - \Delta H_{R_1 R_2} \qquad (49.19)$$

from the heats of formation ΔH of the appropriate molecules, radicals, and the particles formed in their decomposition. Table 57 gives the quantities thus obtained for some of the simplest molecules that decompose with rupture of a simple chemical bond.

Table 57

The energy of decomposition of molecules into two univalent radicals at 25° C (in kcal/mol)

	H	CH_3	C_2H_5	C_6H_5	NH_2	OH	CN	NO	NO_2	Cl	Br	I
H	104.2	103	98	102	104	119.2	114	—	—	103.2	87.5	71.4
CH_3	103	86	84	90	81	89	90	—	49	82	68	54
C_2H_5	98	84	80	88	—	90	—	—	56	80	65	51
C_6H_5	102	90	88	98	90	105	—	—	62	85.6	70.9	57
NH_2	104	81	—	90	60	63	—	—	—	—	—	—
OH	119.2	89	90	105	63	50	—	51	51	—	—	—
CN	114	90	—	—	—	—	112	—	—	85	75	63
NO	—	—	—	—	—	51	—	2.9	9.6	38.0	30.6	—
NO_2	—	59	56	62	—	51	—	9.6	13.7	—	—	—
Cl	103.2	82	80	85.6	—	—	85	38.0	—	58.0	52.5	50.3
Br	87.5	68	65	70.9	—	—	75	30.6	—	52.2	46.1	42.5
I	71.4	54	51	57	—	—	63	—	—	50.3	42.5	36.1

Of great interest is the dissociation energy of simple chemical bonds in the homologous series. From general reasoning that follows from ordinary concepts concerning the mutual interaction of atoms in molecules it may be concluded that as radicals become more complex in the molecules that form the given homologous series, for example, the aliphatic radical $R_n = C_n H_{2n+1}$ in the series $R_n - X$ ($X = H$, OH, halogen, C_6H_5, etc.), the energy of the $R_n - X$ bond must tend to a certain constant value. An analysis of experimental data referring to paraffin hydrocarbons (both normal and of isostructure) carried out by Voyevodsky yielded 77.6 kcal/mol as the limiting value of the $C_n H_{2n+1} - H$ bond energy. The decrease in bond dissociation energy when passing from methane to ethane and other heavier hydrocarbons is to be explained, according to Voyevodsky by the inductive effect of CH_3 groups. Proceeding from this assumption, Voyevodsky obtained for the $C - H$ bond dissociation energy the following equation

$$D_{C-H} = D(C_n H_{2n+1} - H) = 77.6 + 8.0 \sum 0.4^{k_i} \qquad (49.20)$$

where k_i is the number of C atoms in each of the three radical chains R_1, R_2, and R_3

$$R_1 - \overset{\overset{\displaystyle R_3}{|}}{\underset{\underset{\displaystyle H}{|}}{C}} - R_2.$$

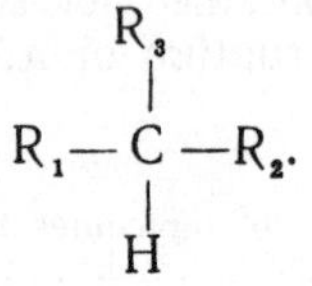

For example, in the case of

$$H_3 C - \overset{\overset{\displaystyle CH_3}{|}}{\underset{\underset{\displaystyle H}{|}}{C}} - CH_2 CH_3$$

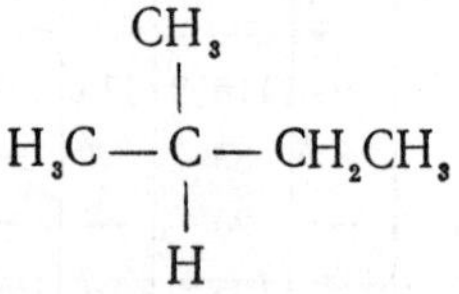

we have $k_1 = k_3 = 1$ and $k_2 = 2$. The energy values, obtained from (49.20), for the detachment of an H atom from various hydrocarbons are in good agreement with experiment.

A formula similar to (49.20) was derived by Voyevodsky also for the C—C bond dissociation energy in paraffin hydrocarbons.

With respect to known experimental data on the bond energies in homologous series we note that in the case of the series $R_n - H$, $R_n - CH_3$, $R_n - C_2 H_3$, $R_n - C_6 H_5$ the C—X bond energy diminishes, in accord with theoretical reasoning (see p. 505), with increase in the number of the series term (n) and tends to a certain constant value. Unlike these series, the energy of the C—OH bond in alcohols fluctuates about a certain mean value, which for normal alcohols is 89.4 kcal/mol. The same constancy of bond energy is observed in the homologous series of ethers $R_n - OR_m$, and also of alkyl nitrites $R_n ONO$, alkyl nitrates $R_n ONO_2$, and alkyl peroxides $R_n OOR_n$.

From the foregoing it may be concluded that the bond energies in the homologous series of different compounds retain approximate constancy if the participant in the bond is an oxygen atom (C—O bond in alcohols and ethers, O—O in peroxides, and N—O in nitrites and nitrates), while the C—C and C—H bonds exhibit a monotonic decrease to a certain constant value.

This decrease in the $R_n - X$ bond energy in the case of $X = H$ and CH_3 (and also in the case of $X = I$ and Br) and the practically constant bond energy in the case of $X = OH$ (alcohols) is correlated by Baughan, Evans, and Polyani with the particular stability of

R_n —OH molecules that is due to the considerable weight of the ionic structures $R_n - O^- H^+$ and $R_n^+ O^- H$.

If the decomposition of a molecule of a paraffin hydrocarbon $(C_n H_{2n+2})$ with rupture of the $C - H$ bond involves the expenditure of 100-80 kcal/mol and of the $C - C$ bond with 85 to 75 kcal/mol, then the corresponding decomposition of alkyl radicals $C_n H_{2n+1}$ takes about 40 kcal/mol and 25 kcal/mol respectively. This decrease in the $C - H$ and $C - C$ bond energies when passing from saturated compounds to radicals is caused by the fact that in the decomposition of the latter the expended energy is partially compensated for by the energy released as a result of the formation of a new bond, as is evident from the following scheme:

$$
\begin{array}{cc}
\text{H} \quad \text{H} & \text{H} \quad \text{H} \\
| \quad\ | & | \quad\ | \\
\text{H}_3\text{C} - \text{C} - \text{C} - \rightarrow \text{H}_3\text{C} - + \; \text{C} = \text{C}. \\
| \quad\ | & | \quad\ | \\
\text{H} \quad \text{H} & \text{H} \quad \text{H}
\end{array}
$$

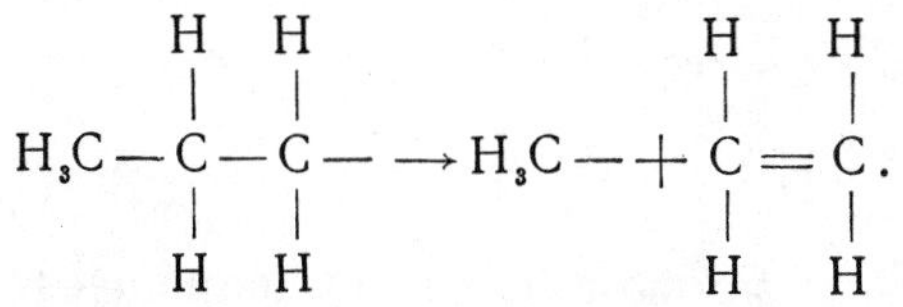

This compensation is absent in the decomposition of saturated compounds.

If as the result of the rupture of a simple chemical bond in the dissociation of saturated molecules there appear free univalent radicals, the rupture of a *double bond* leads to the formation of bivalent radicals, biradicals, or valence-saturated molecules. For instance, biradicals can form by rupture of the double $C = C$ bond in the ethylene molecule $H_2C = CH_2 \rightarrow 2CH_2$ or in the propylene molecule $H_2C = CH - CH_3 \rightarrow CH_2 + CH - CH_3$. It might even be that in the latter case there occurs, simultaneously with the rupture of the double bond, a displacement of the H atom in the biradical $CH - CH_3$ that leads to the formation of a new double bond, and the process follows the scheme $H_2C = CH - CH_2 \rightarrow CH_2 + H_2C = CH_2$. Due to partial compensation, the latter is more advantageous energetically than a process that leads to the appearance of two biradicals. Indeed, whereas the rupture of the $C = C$ bond in propylene (it leads to the formation of two biradicals) requires 146 kcal/mol, decomposition into CH_2 and $H_2C = CH_2$ requires an energy of only 85.6 kcal/mol, which is close to the dissociation energy of a single $C - C$ bond.

The compensation effect is naturally greater when it is possible for the molecule to decompose into two olefines. For instance, in the case of the decomposition of 2-butylene $CH_3CH = CHCH_3$ into two molecules of ethylene we have $CH_3CH = CHCH_3 = 2C_2H_4$, 23 kcal/mol or in the case of the decomposition of 2-pentene into ethylene and propylene $CH_3CH=CHCH_2CH_3=C_2H_4+C_3H_6$, 25 kcal/mol.

In addition to total rupture of a double bond we can also have a partial rupture, i.e., the transformation of a double bond into a single bond, as a result of which the molecule passes into the state of a biradical without decomposing, for instance, $H_2C=$
$$=CH_2 \rightarrow H_2\overset{|}{C}-\overset{|}{C}H_2.$$ The energy of this process (65 kcal/mol) was obtained as the energy expended on cis-trans-isomerisation of dideutero-ethylene that is accomplished via the intermediate biradical state:

$$
\begin{array}{ccc}
\overset{\displaystyle H}{|}\ \ \overset{\displaystyle H}{|} & \overset{\displaystyle H}{|}\ \ \overset{\displaystyle H}{|} & \overset{\displaystyle H}{|}\ \ \overset{\displaystyle D}{|} \\
C=C \rightarrow & -C-C- \rightarrow & C=C. \\
\underset{\displaystyle |}{\ }\ \ \underset{\displaystyle |}{\ } & \underset{\displaystyle |}{\ }\ \ \underset{\displaystyle |}{\ } & \underset{\displaystyle |}{\ }\ \ \underset{\displaystyle |}{\ } \\
D\ \ \ D & D\ \ \ D & D\ \ \ H
\end{array}
$$

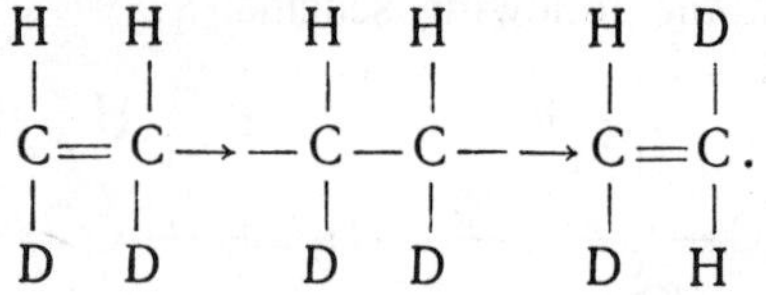

Biradical states are most frequently encountered experimentally among the aromatic compounds, in the case of which the energy of transition into the latter, i.e., the energy difference between the biradical and ground states of the molecule, is particularly small. For example, the excitation energy of the biradical state of the paraquinodimethane molecule

$$H_2C=\langle\!\!=\!\!=\!\!\rangle=CH_2$$

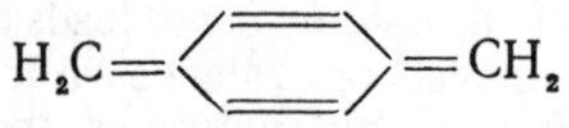

is only about 10 kcal/mol. Because of the low excitation energy of the biradical state, the concentration of biradicals of paraquinodimethane

$$H_2\overset{|}{C}-\langle\!\!=\!\!=\!\!\rangle-\overset{|}{C}H_2$$

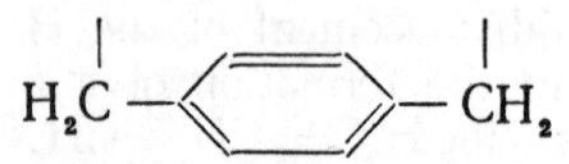

is very considerable already at room temperature.

Another example is the Chichibabin hydrocarbon

$$(C_6H_5)_2C=\langle\!\!=\!\!=\!\!\rangle=\langle\!\!=\!\!=\!\!\rangle=C(C_6H_5)_2,$$

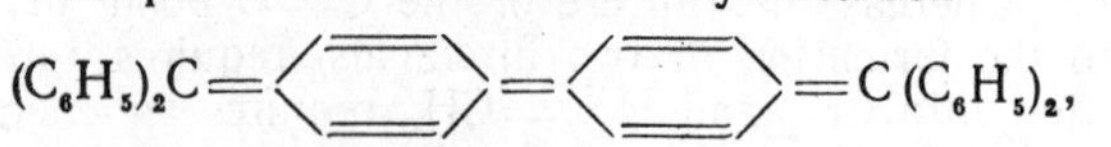

for which the excitation energy of the biradical state

$$(C_6H_5)_2\overset{|}{C}-\langle\!\!=\!\!=\!\!\rangle-\langle\!\!=\!\!=\!\!\rangle-\overset{|}{C}(C_6H_5)_2$$

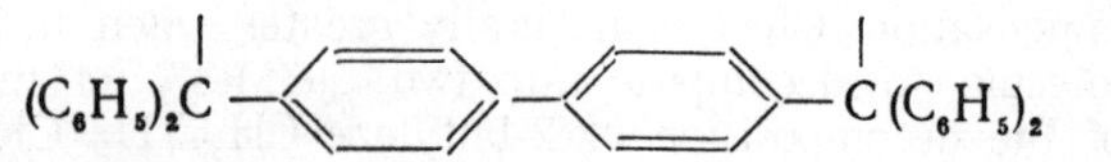

is estimated at several kilocalories. The ease with which biradicals are formed in these cases is due to the large energy gain in the formation of aromatic rings. In this sense, we can again speak of the compensation effect.

Transition to the biradical state frequently signifies a transition of the molecule from the ground singlet state to an excited *triplet*, which is one of the electron states of the given molecule. For this reason, in addition to thermal excitation, direct radiative excitation of the biradical state of the molecules is possible to the extent of probable intercombination transition from the singlet to the triplet state. Terenin demonstrated that the biradical triplet states of molecules play a very great part in photochemical reactions, particularly in the reactions of various dyes. And Terenin established that under the conditions of a photochemical reaction the biradicals can make their appearance both by means of a direct radiative transition to the triplet state and via an intermediate excited singlet state with subsequent transition to the triplet state upon collisions with molecules. In the case of radiative excitation of biradical triplet states the excitation energy can obviously be determined directly from the positions of the respective absorption bands in the spectrum of the given compound. This energy can also be obtained theoretically.

It may be added that in a number of cases the triplet biradical state has been detected by measuring the paramagnetic susceptibility of the compounds. This measurement is possible due to the considerable concentrations of excited molecules, which concentrations are in turn possible because triplet excited states are *metastable* and, hence, comparatively long-lived electronic states of molecules.

Proton affinity. Of considerable interest is the bond energy of various neutral particles (molecules and radicals) with the proton. It has been established, for example, that molecular ions of water H_2O^+, which initially form in an electric discharge in water vapour, interact with H_2O molecules, this yields hydroxonium H_3O^+ and hydroxyl OH. It will readily be seen that the thermal effect Q of the process

$$H_2O^+ + H_2O = H_3O^+ + OH$$

can be expressed as the difference of the heats of proton attachment to the H_2O molecule and to the OH radical, i.e., as the difference of *proton affinity* of H_2O and OH:

$$Q = P_{H_2O} - P_{OH}.$$

Proton affinity also determines the thermal effects of the formation of alkyl ions from protons and olefine molecules or complex alkyl ions from simpler ions and olefines.

Table 58 gives the values of proton affinity of free and hydrogenated atoms O, N, and C. These values are obtained for atoms and radicals from measured ionisation potentials and the heats of dissociation of the appropriate radicals.* The proton affinity of the NH_3 molecule was obtained indirectly.

Table 58

Proton affinity of free and hydrogenated atoms of oxygen, nitrogen, and carbon (in kcal/mol)

				C	138
		N	44	CH	158
O	115	NH	148	CH_2	183
OH	142	NH_2	185	CH_3	118
OH_2	169	NH_3	202	CH_4	122

The values of proton affinity of H_2O and CH_4 molecules have been measured by Frankevich and Talroze. In Table 58 we note a regular increase in proton affinity of the O and N atoms with their increasing degree of hydrogenation and the absence of an analogous regularity in the case of carbon. It is extremely probable that the sharp decrease in proton affinity in the transition from CH_2 to CH_3 is due to the absence of an unshared electron pair in methyl.

Other alkyl radicals, halogen atoms, olefines and other substances also display substantial proton affinity. Some of the relevant data are given in Table 59.

Table 59

Proton affinity of halogen atoms, alkyl radicals and the simplest olefines (in kcal/mol)

Halogens		Alkyl radicals		Olefines	
F	(120)	CH_3	118	C_2H_4	156
Cl	124.5	C_2H_5	144	C_3H_6	176 (H-C_3H_7)
Br	134.5	C_3H_7	156	C_3H_6	184 (iso-C_3H_7)
I	147	n $-$ C_4H_9	166	C_4H_8	196 (tert-C_4H_9)

Average bond energies and the rule of additivity of bond energies. The bond energies in the simplest molecules, such as H_2O, NH_3, CH_4 or Cl_2O, NCl_3, CCl_4, which contain the same bonds, may

* For example, the proton affinity of an oxygen atom is $P_O = D_{OH} + eI_H - eI_{OH}$, where D_{OH} is the heat of dissociation of OH, I_H and I_{OH} are the ionisation potentials of H and OH.

be calculated from the heats of formation of the molecules and the heats of formation of the component atoms. For example, by calculating the energy of formation of the methane CH_4 molecule from the H and C atoms (the energy of atomisation of methane) from the formula $A_{CH_4} = \Delta H_C + 4\Delta H_H - \Delta H_{CH_4} = 171.3 + 4 \times 52.1 + 17.9 = 397.5$ kcal/mol, for the mean energy of the C—H bond in CH_4 we find, in view of the identity of all four C—H bonds in the CH_4 molecule, $E_{C-H} = \frac{1}{4} A_{CH_4} = 99.4$ kcal/mol. In similar fashion, for the mean energy of the bonds N—H in NH_3 and O—H in H_2O we get $E_{N-H} = \frac{1}{3} A_{NH_3} = 93.4$ and $E_{O-H} = \frac{1}{2} A_{H_2O} = 110.8$ kcal/mol.

In the case of more complex molecules with different bonds, the mean energy of the bonds between respective pairs of atoms may be determined if we proceed from the fact that the bond energy of a given pair of atoms is approximately constant in different compounds. The most convincing experimental proof of this constancy consists in the possibility of a rather exact representation of the energy of atomisation of the various compounds (with single or with isolated * multiple bonds) in the form of a sum of the bond energies of the respective pairs of atoms *(additive formula)*. Let us consider, by way of illustration, the normal paraffins. Assuming the additive formula to hold, we represent the energy of atomisation of these compounds as the sum

$$A_{C_nH_{2n+2}} = 2(n+1) E_{C-H} + (n-1) E_{C-C}. \qquad (49.21)$$

On the other hand, A may be calculated from the experimentally known heats of formation of hydrocarbons of the class under study:

$$A_{C_nH_{2n+2}} = n\Delta H_C + 2(n+1)\Delta H_H - \Delta H_{C_nH_{2n+2}}.$$

The experimental values, calculated from this formula, of the energy of atomisation of normal paraffins are given in the second column of Table 60. In the third column are given the values of A obtained from the additive formula (49.21) for the following values of the mean bond energies: $E_{C-H} = 98.75$ and $E_{C-C} = 82.87$ kcal/mol.

As may be seen from the data of Table 60, already beginning with pentane there is complete agreement of the atomisation energies computed from the additive formula and obtained experimentally. It will be noted that the mean bond energy $E_{C-H} = 99.4$ kcal/mol (see above) obtained from the experimental value of the atomisation energy of methane differs by only 0.6 from the value of 98.75 kcal/mol taken in the additive formula.

---

* Isolated multiple bonds are bonds separated by more than one single bond.

Table 60

Atomisation energy of normal hydrocarbons of the paraffin series (in kcal/mol)

Hydrocarbon	A_{meas}	A_{calc}	$A_{meas}-A_{calc}$
CH_4	397.5	395.0	2.5
C_2H_6	675.3	675.4	—0.1
C_3H_8	955.3	955.7	—0.4
C_4H_{10}	1235.8	1236.1	—0.3
C_5H_{12}	1516.5	1516.5	0.0
C_6H_{14}	1796.8	1796.8	0.0
C_7H_{16}	2077.2	2077.2	0.0
C_8H_{18}	2357.6	2357.6	0.0
C_9H_{20}	2637.9	2637.9	0.0
$C_{10}H_{22}$	2918.3	2918.3	0.0
$C_{11}H_{24}$	3198.7	3198.7	0.0
$C_{12}H_{26}$	3479.1	3479.1	0.0

Correlating the mean energy of the C—C bond with the mean energies of single bonds of other atoms of the same period:

C—C	N—N	O—O	F—F
82.9	75.3	59.5	37.6

we note a decrease in bond energy from carbon to fluorine.

From the additive formula for the atomisation energy of normal alcohols

$$A_{C_nH_{2n+1}OH} = (2n+1)\,E_{C-H} + (n-1)\,E_{C-C} + E_{C-O} + E_{O-H} \qquad (49.22)$$

with the aid of the experimental values of the atomisation energy obtained from formula

$$A_{C_nH_{2n+1}OH} = n\Delta H_C + 2(n+1)\,\Delta H_H + \Delta H_O - \Delta H_{C_nH_{2n+2}OH}$$

and the above-obtained mean values of bond energies $E_{C-H}=98.75$, $E_{C-C}=82.87$, and $E_{O-H}=110.8$ kcal/mol, we get $E_{C-O}=85.5$ kcal/mol for the mean energy of the C—O bond in alcohols. A value of E_{C-O} close to this is obtained from the heats of formation of ethers (85.3) and also from the heat of formation of ethylene glycol CH_2OH-CH_2OH (85.9). Following are the mean energies of a single bond with oxygen for other elements as well:

C—O	N—O	O—O	F—O
85.5	75.5	59.5	45.8

Here E_{N-O} is obtained as $^1/_2 D_{NO}$ * and E_{F-O} as $^1/_2 D_{F_2O}$.

* E_{N-O} calculated as $^1/_2 A_{NO_2}$ comes out to 74.7 kcal/mol.

In similar fashion we can calculate the C—N bond energy. Such calculation from the heats of formation of CH_3NH_2, $C_2H_5NH_2$, $(CH_3)_2NH$, and HCN yields, on average, $E_{C-N}=69.0$ kcal/mol with an average spread of ± 0.7 kcal/mol. For different elements we get:

C—C	C—N	C—O	C—F
82.9	69.0	85.5	102.2

Here E_{C-F} is obtained as $^1/_4 A_{CF_4}$.

Let us also calculate the average energies of the bonds C—Cl, C—Br, and C—I. For E_{C-Cl} from the heats of formation of CCl_4, $CHCl_3$, CH_2Cl_2, CH_3Cl, C_2HCl_5, $C_2H_2Cl_4$, $C_2H_3Cl_3$, $C_2H_4Cl_2$, and C_2H_5Cl we get 79.2 kcal/mol, for E_{C-Br} from the heats of formation of CBr_4, $CHBr_3$, CH_2Br_2, CH_3Br, $C_2H_4Br_2$, C_2H_5Br, 66.6 kcal/mol, and for E_{C-I} from the heats of formation of CHI_3, CH_2I_2, CH_3I, $C_2H_4I_2$, and C_2H_5I, 52.4 kcal/mol. For the average bond energy of different elements with the chlorine atom we get:

C—Cl	N—Cl	O—Cl	F—Cl
79.2	37.9	49.6	61.0 .

Here E_{N-Cl} is obtained from the heat of formation of NOCl, E_{O-Cl} as $^1/_2 D_{Cl_2O}$ and E_{F-Cl} as D_{FCl}.

It will be noted that the energy of the C—C bond in trimethylene

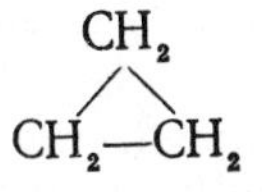

comes out appreciably reduced as compared with the hydrocarbons of the paraffin series. From the heat of formation of trimethylene (considering $E_{C-H}=98.75$ kcal/mol) we get $E_{C-C}=73.8$ in place of 82.9 kcal/mol.

Also reduced are the energies of the C—C and C—O bonds in the molecule of ethylene oxide

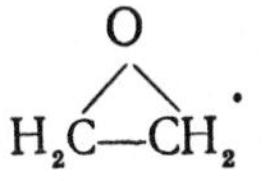

Considering $E_{C-H}=98.75$, from the heat of formation of ethylene oxide we get $E_{C-C}+2E_{C-O}=215.5$ in place of 253.9 kcal/mol. The decrease in the bond energies in both of the cases just considered (this signifies a rise in the energy of the molecule) is caused by a *deformation of valence angles* that is associated with ring structure. Let it be noted that in the case of cyclohexane C_6H_{12} where the deformation of the valence angles (tension) is absent, calculation of the average energy of the C — C bond yields a normal value, 82.9 kcal/mol.

Smaller, but quite clearcut, differences in the bond energies are observed also in passing from normal hydrocarbons to hydrocarbons of a different structure; this is directly evident from their heats of formation. For instance, the heat of formation of isobutane

$$
\begin{array}{c}
\text{H} \\
| \\
\text{H}_3\text{C}-\text{C}-\text{CH}_3 \\
| \\
\text{CH}_3
\end{array}
$$

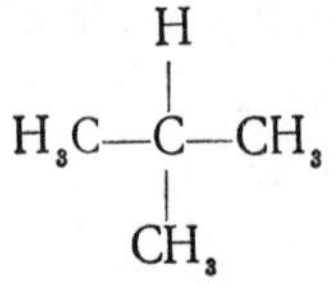

comes out to 1.6 kcal/mol more than that of normal butane $H_3C — CH_2 — CH_2 — CH_3$. In the same way, the heats of formation of the three isomers of pentane: normal pentane $H_3C — CH_2 — CH_2 — CH_2 — CH_3$, 2-methylbutane $CH_3CH_2CH (CH_3)_2$, and 2,2-dimethyl-propane (neopentane) $(CH_3)_4 C$ are 35.0, 36.9, and 39.7 kcal/mol, thus differing by 1.9, 2.8, and 4.7 kcal/mol.

Approximate constancy of bond energies is frequently observed also in the case of multiple bonds. For example, this constancy of energy of the double carbon-carbon bond occurs in the case of olefines, as may be seen from the data given below; calculating the energy of the $C = C$ bond from known heats of formation of olefines of normal structure and from the earlier accepted values of $E_{C-H} = 98.75$ and $E_{C-C} = 82.97$, we get, for the first twelve olefines, the following values of $E_{C=C}$: 143.4, 146.1, 145.8, 146.1, 146.1, 146.2, 146.1, 146 1, 146.2, 146.2, 146.2, and 146.2 kcal/mol. We see that beginning already with the second member of the series of normal olefines, $E_{C=C}$ is practically constant.

As in the case of paraffin hydrocarbons, the heats of formation of olefines of iso-structure turn out somewhat greater than those of the corresponding normal olefines. If this difference is due to the C — C bond, for example, in the case of pentenes, we will have: for 2-cis- and 2-trans-pentenes $CH_3CH = CHCH_2CH_3$ $E_{C=C} = 147.8$ and 148.7, for 2-methyl-1-butene $E_{C=C} = 149.8$, for 3-methyl-1-butene $E_{C=C} = 148.0$, and for 2-methyl-2-butene $E_{C=C} = 151.3$, whereas for normal pentene we had $E_{C=C} = 146.1$ kcal/mol.

An appreciably different mean energy of the $C = C$ bond is also obtained for the compounds of certain other classes. For instance, in the case of allene $H_2C = C = CH_2$ we have $E_{C=C} = 140.6$ kcal/mol.

Whereas the heats of formation of olefines are known to a high degree of accuracy for a large number of the members of the homologous series, due to a lack of such data for aldehydes, ketones, carbonic acids, and their alkyl derivatives, the mean energy of the $C = O$ bond in compounds of these classes may be determined only for the first two members of the homologous series of each of these classes. For this reason, one can only speak conditionally of the average energy of the C=O bond for these compounds.

The values of this energy obtained from known heats of formation of aldehydes RCHO, ketones R_1COR_2, and acids RCOOH are 173.0, 181.6, and 189.5 kcal/mol respectively. Despite the rather approximate nature of these values, variation in the average energy of the C=O bond when passing from aldehydes to ketones and to acids is, apparently, regular. The principal reason for this difference is to be sought in the *conjugation effect* (see below).

Bond energies in conjugated systems. When a hydrocarbon molecule has two or more double bonds, the energy of the carbon-carbon bonds depends upon their relative arrangement. We have already seen that the energy of the double bond C=C in allene $H_2C=C=CH_2$, which is a representative of hydrocarbons with cumulated double bonds, is considerably less (140.6 kcal/mol) than the energy of the C=C bond in olefines, where there is no cumulation of double bonds (146.2 kcal/mol). On the contrary, in compounds with conjugated double bonds, i. e., with double bonds separated by a single C—C bond, the energy of carbon-carbon bonds is always greater. For instance, in propylene $H_2C=CH-CH_3$ or in 1,4-pentadiene $H_2C=CH-CH_2-CH=CH_2$, in which the double bonds are isolated, the sum of the energies of single and double bonds $E_{C-C}+$ $+E_{C-C}$ is 229.0 and 228.8 kcal/mol, whereas in isoprene $H_2C=CH-$ $-CH=CH_3$ and 1,3-pentadiene $H_2C=CH-CH=CH-CH_3$, i. e., in molecules with conjugated bonds, this sum is 230.1 and 232.1 kcal/mol. In the symmetric benzene molecule with its most perfect system of conjugated bonds, the sum of energies of two carbon bonds is 242.6 kcal/mol.

The phenomenon of conjugation is not a specific peculiarity solely of carbon-carbon bonds and is observed also in the case of C=O and other multiple bonds; conjugation is also possible between a double bond and an unshared pair of electrons of some atom (for instance, an O atom or a halogen atom). These types of conjugation also lead to a strengthening of chemical bonds. An instance of conjugation of C=O bonds is glyoxal

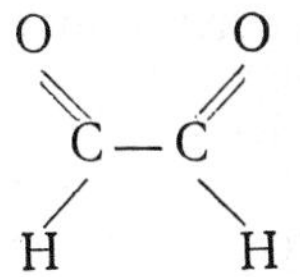

in which the energy of the C=O bonds is substantially higher than the energy of isolated C=O bonds in aldehydes (180.2 and

173.0 kcal/mol). We have a case of conjugation of the C=O bond with an unshared pair of electrons of hydroxyl oxygen in the carbonic acids, for which the average value of $E_{C=O}$ is 190 kcal/mol. This is appreciably greater than the value for carbonyl compounds. An outstanding instance of the strengthening effect of double-bond conjugation with an unshared pair of electrons (chlorine atom) is phosgene $Cl_2C{=}O$, for which $E_{C=O} = 183.7$ (cf. $E_{C=O} = 165.2$ kcal/mol for formaldehyde $H_2C{=}O$).

An examination of the experimental material referring to the energies of chemical bonds shows that the approximate constancy of binding energy of a given pair of atoms is best satisfied in the case of compounds with single bonds and also in molecules with similar structure, for example, in homologous series. But in the case of compounds of different classes containing both single and multiple bonds, the assumption of constant bond energies is extremely crude; this is clearly exemplified by data referring to C=O bonds.

It may be stated that the constancy of bond energies and the additive formula that follows therefrom are justified satisfactorily in those cases when the valence scheme of the molecule expressed by the accepted structural formula is *unique* or at least is predominant over other possible valence schemes. Only on this condition can the heat of atomisation of a molecule be represented (to a sufficient approximation) as the sum of energies of individual bonds, constant for the given pair of atoms, i. e., the additive formula

$$A = \sum E_i \tag{49.23}$$

where E_i is the energy of the ith bond in the molecule. However, in the case of several possible valence schemes (which is particularly characteristic of conjugated and aromatic systems), we can obviously write — in place of (49.23) and retaining the values of the bond energies —

$$A = A^0 + \Delta A \tag{49.24}$$

where $A^0 = \sum E_i^0$ and ΔA is a term that takes into account the variations in bond energies which violate the postulate of additivity and which, in the final analysis, are conditioned by the mutual interaction of the atoms in the molecules. The quantity ΔA, which is ordinarily called the *energy of conjugation* or the *resonance energy*, may be calculated to a certain degree of accuracy by means of quantum mechanics.

Another method of taking into account, empirically, the changes that the bond energy of a given pair of atoms undergo in different molecules consists in the following. Depending upon the class of compound to which the molecule belongs, some value is assigned to the bond energy of each pair of atoms. In this way, we distinguish the bonds C_{al}—H and C_{ar}—H, i.e., the bonds of C and H atoms in aliphatic and aromatic compounds, to the energies of which somewhat different values are assigned. The bonds C_{al}—C_{al}, C_{al}—C_{ar}, C_{ar}—C_{ar}, C_{al}—O, C_{ar}—O, etc., are further differentiated as having different energies as well.

This empirical method has been most consistently applied by Tatevsky, who used hydrocarbons of different structure and demonstrated that by introducing the concept of the types of C, C and C, H chemical bonds, which is determined by the position of the given bond among the other bonds in the molecule, and by assigning to the bond energy of each type a definite and characteristic value, it is possible (by means of an appropriate equation) to compute to a sufficiently high degree of accuracy the heats of atomisation and the heats of combustion of any hydrocarbon.

The additive formula, as a purely empirical formula (in the more simple and crude form that it is ordinarily used or in the more complex form proposed by Tatevsky that takes into account a variety of types, and even subtypes, of bond of a given pair of atoms), requires theoretical substantiation and a theoretical establishment of the range of its applicability. This problem reduces to the general problem of the molecule, a rigorous solution of which, however, encounters great mathematical difficulties.

In a number of cases the bond energies do not remain constant even very approximately. Thus, from the heat of the reaction $N_2 + O = N_2O$ we have for the energy of the N=O bond 39.9 kcal in place of the normal value close to 150 kcal. There is a large difference in the energies of the Hg—X (X = Cl, Br, I) bond in the molecules HgX_2 and in the radicals HgX: E_{Hg-X} calculated from the atomisation energy of HgX_2 molecules is 2 to 3 times the heats of dissociation of Hg—X radicals. As already pointed out (p. 303), this great lack of constancy of bond energies in these and analogous cases is to be explained by excitation of valence, i.e., by the variations of energy associated with changes in the valence state of the atoms.

Double-bond character. In concluding this section let us consider the problem of the relationship between the bond energy of a given pair of atoms and the distance between these atoms (*bond length*) in the molecules of different compounds. From calculations of the energy of chemical bonds in diatomic molecules it follows that between the energy of the bond (the heat of dissociation) and the equilibrium distance between the atoms there is an *inverse* relationship that finds expression in a decrease in the equilibrium distance with strengthening of the molecule. This relation is reflected in numerous empirical formulas connecting D and r. A similar relationship exists between the bond energy of a pair of atoms and the length of the respective bond in the case of polyatomic molecules as well.

Fig. 126 gives the earlier found C, C- and C, O-bond energies in different molecules as a function of the distance between the corresponding atoms in the molecule. These data for C, C-bonds refer to ethane $H_3C—CH_3$ (82.9 kcal/mol, 1.543 A), benzene C_6H_6 (121.3 kcal/mol, 1.387 A), ethylene $H_2C{=}CH_2$ (143.4 kcal/mol, 1.353 A), allene $H_2C{=}C{=}CH_2$ (140.6 kcal/mol, 1.309 A), and acetylene $HC{\equiv}CH$ (195.0 kcal/mol, 1.207 A); it is assumed that the additive formula holds for heats of atomisation of these compounds for $E_{C-H} = 98.75$ kcal/mol. The data for C, O-bonds refer to CO (257.2 kcal/mol, 1.131 A), CO_2 (192.2 kcal/mol, 1.163 A), and to methyl alcohol CH_3OH (80.2 kcal/mol, 1.427 A), for which it is taken that the additive formula holds for $E_{C-H} = 98.75$ and $E_{O-H} = 110.8$ kcal/mol. An analogous monotonic relationship is observed between the energy and the bond length in the case of other pairs of atoms as well. Attempts have likewise been made to establish analytical relations between E and r.

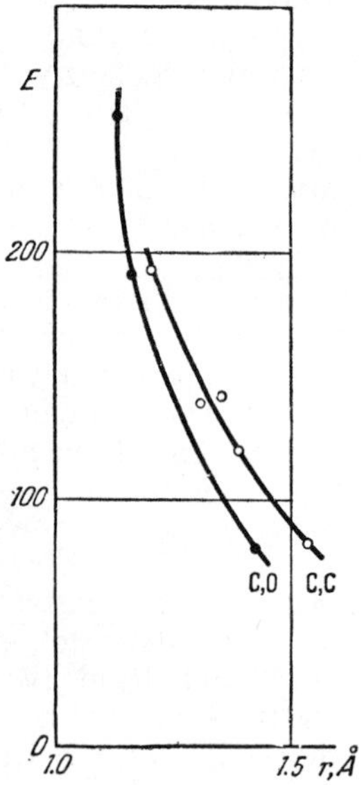

Fig. 126. Relationship between energy (E) and bond length (r) in different molecules

The curves in Fig. 126 are in close accord with the so-called double-bond-character curve introduced into the theory of chemical bonds by Pauling. The term "double-bond character" signifies the degree to which a bond between a given pair of atoms (carbon atoms, for instance) approaches a double covalent bond. In the case of two carbon atoms, the degree of the double-bond character of an isolated single C—C bond is assumed equal to zero and that of an isolated double bond, to unity. In the benzene molecule with its six identical carbon-carbon bonds, each of which may be considered 50% single and 50% double, the degree of double-bondedness is assumed equal to one half. Finally, in the case of graphite, the valence scheme of which may be represented (schematically) by the following structure:

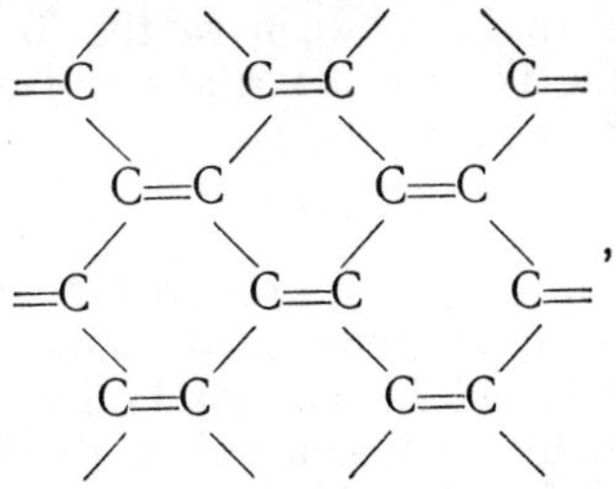

the degree of double-bondedness will, obviously, be equal to one-third because here, on the average, every third bond is double. The double-bond-character curve plotted from these four points is shown in Fig. 127; the abscissa is the degree of double-bondedness x, the

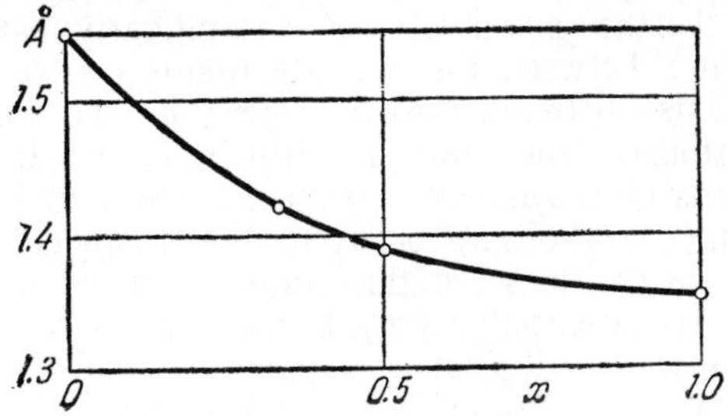

Fig. 127. Double-bond-character curve

ordinate is the distance between carbon atoms in ethane (1.543 A), graphite (1.42 A) benzene (1.387 A), and ethylene (1.353 A). According to Pauling, the double-bond-character curve may be approximately represented by the following formula

$$r = r_1 - \frac{3x}{2x+1}(r_1 - r_2)$$

where r_1 and r_2 are the distances between the given pair of atoms in isolated single and double bond, r is the distance between these atoms in the case of a bond intermediate between double and single. On the basis of the curve in Fig. 127 and similar curves plotted for other pairs of atoms, one can judge the nature of the respective bonds, and this is of great interest for elucidating the nature of bonds in general.

50. Vibrational Frequencies of Molecules

Relations between vibrational frequencies. The vibrational frequencies of molecules are the next important molecular constants after the dissociation energy and the energy of chemical bonds. As may be seen from (37.8) (p. 354), we have the following approximate relationship between the heat of dissociation of a diatomic molecule D and the vibrational frequency ω:

$$\omega^2 \sim D. \tag{50.1}$$

From this equation it follows that the greater D the greater should be the vibrational frequency. Experiment shows that this relationship is qualitatively fulfilled in practically all cases.

One of the most reliable and exact methods of experimental determination of the vibrational frequencies of molecules is the spectroscopic method, developed for the study of the structure of rotation-vibration (infrared) and electronic spectra, and also Raman spectra. Very important for analysing the vibrational structure of the spectra of complex molecules (due to the great comlexity of these spectra) is the possibility of theoretically establishing definite relationships between the separate frequencies of a given molecule (ω_i) and also between the frequencies ω_i and those of the corresponding diatomic molecules. To illustrate, we take the case of linear vibrations of a symmetric triatomic linear molecule YXY.

To establish a relationship between the frequencies of this type of molecule, one has to solve the problem of small vibrations of the molecule. Its potential energy U may be given approximately as

$$U(q_1, q_2, q_3) = f_1(q_1) + f_2(q_2) + f_3(q_3)$$

where q_1, q_2, and q_3 are the relative displacements of the atoms. The functions f_1, f_2, and f_3 represent the interaction energy of atoms Y and Y (f_1), Y and X (f_2), and X and Y (f_3). Disregarding the interaction of the end atoms (Y and Y) due to the great distance between them and expanding the functions f_i into a Taylor series in powers of q_i, we get (to a first approximation)

$$U(q) = U(0) + \frac{1}{2}\left(\frac{\partial^2 f_2}{\partial q_2^2}\right)_0 q_2^2 + \frac{1}{2}\left(\frac{\partial^2 f_3}{\partial q_3^2}\right)_0 q_3^2.$$

By virtue of the symmetry of the molecule, obviously,

$$\left(\frac{\partial^2 f_2}{\partial q_2^2}\right)_0 = \left(\frac{\partial^2 f_3}{\partial q_3^2}\right)_0 = k$$

and, hence,

$$U = U(0) + \frac{k}{2}(q_2^2 + q_3^2). \tag{50.2}$$

Then writing the expression for the kinetic energy of the vibrations,

$$T = \frac{1}{2}(mv_1^2 + Mv_2^2 + mv_3^2)$$

where v_1, v_2, and v_3 are the velocities of the atoms Y, X, and Y, m is the mass of the Y atom and M is the mass of the X atom, and introducing the relative velocities of the atoms

$$\dot{q}_2 = v_1 - v_2 \quad \text{and} \quad \dot{q}_3 = v_2 - v$$

and the velocity of the centre of gravity of the molecule

$$v_c = \frac{mv_1 + Mv_2 + mv_3}{M + 2m} \, (=0),$$

we can transform the expression for T to

$$T = \frac{1}{2}\left[\frac{m(M+m)}{M+2m}(\dot{q}_2^2 + \dot{q}_3^2) + \frac{2m^2}{M+2m}\dot{q}_2\dot{q}_3\right] + \frac{2m+M}{2}v_c^2. \quad (50.3)$$

Further, combining expressions (50.2) and (50.3) to form the Hamiltonian function

$$H = T + U$$

and finding the momenta p_2 and p_3 that correspond to the coordinates q_2 and q_3,

$$p_2 = \frac{\partial H}{\partial \dot{q}_2} = \frac{m(M+m)}{M+2m}\dot{q}_2 + \frac{m^2}{M+2m}\dot{q}_3.$$

and

$$p_3 = \frac{\partial H}{\partial \dot{q}_3} = \frac{m(M+m)}{M+2m}\dot{q}_3 + \frac{m^2}{M+2m}\dot{q}_2,$$

we obtain the canonical equations of linear vibrations of the molecule

$$\frac{m(M+m)}{M+2m}\ddot{q}_2 + \frac{m^2}{M+2m}\ddot{q}_3 + kq_2 = 0,$$

$$\frac{m(M+m)}{M+2m}\ddot{q}_3 + \frac{m^2}{M+2m}\ddot{q}_2 + kq_3 = 0.$$

Solving these equations by substitution of $q_2 = q_2^0 e^{2\pi i\omega t}$ and $q_3 = q_3^0 e^{2\pi i\omega t}$ we get (eliminating q_2 and q_3)

$$k = \frac{m}{M+2m}(M + m \pm m)(2\pi\omega)^2.$$

From the latter expression we find the frequencies ω_1 and ω_3:

$$\omega_1 = \frac{1}{2\pi}\sqrt{k\,\frac{M+2m}{mM}} \quad (50.4)$$

and

$$\omega_3 = \frac{1}{2\pi}\sqrt{\frac{k}{m}}. \quad (50.5)$$

It will be noted that the frequency of asymmetric vibrations ω_1 in which all three atoms participate depends on the masses of all the atoms, whereas the expression for the frequency of symmetric vibrations performed only by atoms Y involves only the mass of the latter.

From (50.4) and (50.5) we get the following relation between the frequencies ω_1 and ω_3:

$$\frac{\omega_1}{\omega_3} = \sqrt{\frac{M+2m}{M}}. \quad (50.6)$$

Using this relation it is possible to calculate one of the frequencies of the given molecule if the other frequency is known. The degree of accuracy of this calculation may be judged from the following data. Obtaining from (50.6) the relation of frequencies of the molecules CO_2 and CS_2, we get 1.92 and 2.52, whereas experiment yields 1.83 and 2.32, respectively. It is also possible to establish relationships between the individual frequencies similar to (50.6) for more complex molecules, thus greatly simplifying the analysis of their vibrational terms.

The ω_2 frequency of the YXY molecule that corresponds to bending vibrations cannot, of course, be derived from a consideration of linear vibrations due to central forces. To calculate this frequency, it is necessary to introduce a certain constant Δ, similar to the constant k and characterising the quasi-elastic forces that arise in the deformation (bending) of the molecule. Using the constant Δ, we can express the frequency ω_2 by the formula

$$\omega_2 = \frac{1}{2\pi}\sqrt{\Delta\frac{M+2m}{mM}}. \quad (50.7)$$

Experiment shows that as a rule the constant Δ is less than constant k by one or two orders of magnitude.

Let us consider the case of a symmetric triatomic molecule of triangular structure, such as H_2O, Cl_2O, SO_2. In this case, solution of the problem of small vibrations of the molecule leads to the following equation for frequencies ω_1, ω_2 and ω_3:

$$\left(\frac{m\lambda}{k'} - 1 - \frac{2m}{M}\sin^2\delta\right)\left[\left(\frac{m\lambda}{k'}\right)^2 - 2\left(\frac{k}{k'} + \frac{1}{2} + \frac{m}{M}\cos^2\delta\right)\frac{m\lambda}{k'} + \frac{2}{M}\frac{k}{k'}(M+2m)\cos^2\delta\right] = 0 \quad (50.8)$$

where k and k′ are constants of a quasi-elastic bond between the atoms Y, Y and Y, X, respectively; m and M are the masses of atoms Y and X, and 2δ is the angle $\angle$YXY. Equation (50.8) has three independent roots λ_1, λ_2, and λ_3, which yield three vibrational frequencies ω_1, ω_2, and ω_3 that are determined from the relations

$$\omega_i = \frac{1}{2\pi}\sqrt{\lambda_i}. \qquad (50.9)$$

The molecular vibrations corresponding to these three frequencies were displayed in Fig. 83 (p. 352). It will readily be seen that these vibrations pass into the vibrations of a linear molecule (Fig. 82) as the angle 2δ increases to 180°.

It will be noted that the triangular molecule YXY has three moments of inertia (three rotational degrees of freedom) and, hence, the number of its natural frequencies is $3N-6=3$. This is the number given by the previous calculation.

We shall illustrate the possibility of calculating the vibrational frequencies of a complex molecule from the frequency of a diatomic molecule in the case of halogen compounds of zinc, cadmium, and mercury. The Raman spectrum, the dipole moment and other properties of these molecules as well as electronographic measurements show that they are linear in the gaseous state and in nonaqueous solutions. Consequently, the frequencies of valence (linear) vibrations of these molecules (ω_1 and ω_3) may be expressed by the formulas (50.4) and (50.5). For the frequency of the diatomic molecule YX we have the expression

$$\omega = \frac{1}{2\pi}\sqrt{k_0\frac{M+m}{m\,M}}. \qquad (50.10)$$

From a comparison of (50.4), (50.5), and (50.10) it follows that

$$\omega_1 = \omega\sqrt{\frac{k}{k_0}\frac{M+2m}{M+m}} \quad \text{and} \quad \omega_3 = \omega\sqrt{\frac{k}{k_0}\frac{M}{M+m}}. \qquad (50.11)$$

In order to make use of formulas (50.11) it is necessary to know the relationship of the constants k and k_0. Comparing expressions (50.10) and (50.1), we can put k_0 proportional to the heat of dissociation of the YX molecule (D_0). Assuming a similar relationship in the case of triatomic molecules, we put constant k proportional to half the heat of atomisation of the YXY molecule.

Consequently, $\frac{k}{k_0}=\frac{1}{2}\frac{D}{D_0}$, and equations (50.11) transform to

$$\omega_1 = \omega\sqrt{\frac{D}{2D_0}\frac{M+2m}{M+m}} \quad \text{and} \quad \omega_3 = \omega\sqrt{\frac{D}{2D_0}\frac{M}{M+m}}. \qquad (50.12)$$

Since the vibrational frequencies of diatomic molecules ZnX, CdX, and HgX (X=Cl, Br, I) are known from their spectra,*

*

	ω, cm^{-1}		ω, cm^{-1}		ω, cm^{-1}
ZnCl	350.5	CdCl	330.5	HgCl	291
ZnBr	—	CdBr	230	HgBr	186
ZnI	223.5	CdI	178.5	HgI	126

just like the corresponding quantities D_0 and D (see Table 30, p. 303), it is possible, from (50.12), to calculate the frequencies ω_1 and ω_3 of molecules ZnX_2, CdX_2 and HgX_2. These values of ω_1 and ω_3, together with their measured values, are given in Table 61.

Table 61

Vibrational frequencies of molecules ZnX_2, CdX_2, and HgX_2 (X = Cl, Br, I), measured and calculated from the vibrational frequencies of diatomic molecules ZnX, CdX, and HgX (in cm^{-1}). The calculated values are given in parentheses

Molecule	ω_1, cm^{-1}	ω_2, cm^{-1}	ω_3, cm^{-1}
$ZnCl_2$	516 (507)	—	— (348)
$ZnBr_2$	413	—	—
ZnI_2	340	—	—
$CdCl_2$	427 (471)	—	— (367)
$CdBr_2$	315	—	—
CdI_2	265 (250)	—	137 (138)
$HgCl_2$	413 (413)	70	355 (355)
$HgBr_2$	293 (294)	41	220 (220)
HgI_2	237 (237)	33	155 (157)

It is seen that the calculated values are in satisfactory agreement with the measured values. In the case of HgX_2 the agreement is practically complete. Apparently, this is due to the high accuracy of D_0 and D in this case.

It may be noted that an analogous calculation of the frequencies of valence vibrations of the molecule CO_2 from $\omega_{CO} = 2168\ cm^{-1}$, $D_{CO} = 256.1$ and $\frac{1}{2} D_{CO_2} = 190.9$ kcal/mol yields $\omega_1 = 2350\ cm^{-1}$ and $\omega_3 = 1230\ cm^{-1}$ in place of the observed 2350 cm^{-1} and 1286 cm^{-1}. The worse agreement of quantities ω_3 should be attributed here to Fermi resonance (see p. 360).

Characteristic frequencies. Measurements of the vibrational frequencies of different molecules show that molecules containing a given pair of specifically bound atoms or a given group of atoms have close frequencies. This permits speaking of *characteristic frequencies* of individual groups (called *chromophoric groups*).

To illustrate, Table 62 gives the characteristic frequencies in the homologous series of mercaptans RSH, nitriles RCN, and amines RNH_2 (R is the alkyl radical). From this table it is seen that for homologous mercaptans we have a characteristic frequency close to

2570 cm^{-1}, for nitriles, 2240 cm^{-1}, and for amines, frequencies 3320 and 3370 cm^{-1}.

Table 62

Characteristic frequencies in homologous series (in cm^{-1})

	Mercaptans	Nitriles	Amines
CH_3	2572	2249	3372 3315
C_2H_5	2570	2243	3369 3310
C_3H_7	2575	2244	3377 3320
C_4H_9	2575	2240	3371 3319
C_5H_{11}	2573	2242	— 3320

Common to all homologous mercaptans is the presence of an SH group. It is therefore natural to assign a frequency of 2570 cm^{-1} to this group. This is confirmed by the fact that of the three frequencies of the H_2S molecule, one (2611 cm^{-1}) is close to the characteristic frequency of the mercaptans. That frequency 2240 cm^{-1} (which is characteristic of nitriles) belongs to the CN group is confirmed by the fact that all molecules containing this group have frequencies close to the characteristic frequency of nitriles (for example, ClCN has a frequency of 2206 cm^{-1}, BrCN, 2187 cm^{-1}, ICN, 2158 cm^{-1}, C_2N_2, 2149 cm^{-1}, etc.); finally, a frequency close to the characteristic frequencies of amines is observed in the case of NH_3 (3337 cm^{-1}).

Table 63 gives the characteristic frequencies of various atomic groups.

The fact that the frequencies which correspond to a given bond or a given atomic group have close values for different molecules is a simpie reflection of the approximate constancy of energy of the same bonds that follows from the approximate proportionality between the quasi-elastic constant k (which determines the vibrational frequency) and the bond energy.

Since the expressions for vibrational frequencies of molecules involve both the quasi-elastic bond constant and the masses of the vibrating atoms, the vibrational frequencies may be regarded only as conditional characteristics of the bond energies in a molecule. For example, due to the difference in mass of hydrogen isotopes the vibrational frequencies of the H_2O and D_2O molecules are equal, respectively, to $\omega_1 = 3693.89$ and 2758.06 cm^{-1}, $\omega_2 = 1614.50$ and 1210.25 cm^{-1}, $\omega_3 = 3801.78$, and 2883.79 cm^{-1}, i.e., they exhibit a very substantial difference, whereas the bond energies in the H_2O

Table 63

Characteristic frequencies of various atomic groups in cm^{-1} (after Herzberg)

Group	Bond-stretching vibration	Group	Bond-stretching vibration	Group	Bond-bending vibration
≡C—H	3300	—C≡C—	2050	≡C—H	700
=C—H	3020	>C=C<	1650		
⋗C—H	2960	⋗C—C⋖	900	=C<H H	1100
—O—H	3680	⋗C—F	1100	—C⋖H H H	1000
—S—H	2570	⋗C—Cl	650	>C<H H	1450
>N—H	3350	⋗C—Br	560	—C⋖H H H	1450
>C=O	1700				
—C≡N	2100	⋗C—I	500	C—C=C	300

and D_2O molecules are practically identical. This frequency difference is great also in other instances of bonds with the H and D atom. And in other cases, too, it always occurs to one degree or another. For this reason, it is not the frequencies but the quasi-elastic bond constants calculated from them that represent the true characteristic of the strength of chemical bonds in molecules.

SUBJECT INDEX

A

B

C

D

CATALOGUE OF DOVER BOOKS

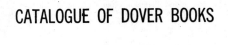

PHILOSOPHY OF SCIENCE AND MATHEMATICS

FOUNDATIONS OF SCIENCE: THE PHILOSOPHY OF THEORY AND EXPERIMENT, N. R. Campbell. A critique of the most fundamental concepts of science in general and physics in particular. Examines why certain propositions are accepted without question, demarcates science from philosophy, clarifies the understanding of the tools of science. Part One analyzes the presuppositions of scientific thought: existence of the material world, nature of scientific laws, multiplication of probabilities, etc.: Part Two covers the nature of experiment and the application of mathematics: conditions for measurement, relations between numerical laws and theories, laws of error, etc. An appendix covers problems arising from relativity, force, motion, space, and time. A classic in its field. Index. xiii + 565pp. 5⅝ x 8⅜.
S372 Paperbound **$2.95**

THE NATURE OF PHYSICAL THEORY, P. W. Bridgman. Here is how modern physics looks to a highly unorthodox physicist—a Nobel laureate. Pointing out many absurdities of science, and demonstrating the inadequacies of various physical theories, Dr. Bridgman weighs and analyzes the contributions of Einstein, Bohr, Newton, Heisenberg, and many others. This is a non-technical consideration of the correlation of science and reality. Index. xi + 138pp. 5⅜ x 8.
S33 Paperbound **$1.25**

THE VALUE OF SCIENCE, Henri Poincaré. Many of the most mature ideas of the "last scientific universalist" covered with charm and vigor for both the beginning student and the advanced worker. Discusses the nature of scientific truth, whether order is innate in the universe or imposed upon it by man, logical thought versus intuition (relating to math, through the works of Weierstrass, Lie, Klein, Riemann), time and space (relativity, psychological time, simultaneity), Hertz's concept of force, interrelationship of mathematical physics to pure math, values within disciplines of Maxwell, Carnot, Mayer, Newton, Lorentz, etc. Index. iii + 147pp. 5⅜ x 8.
S469 Paperbound **$1.35**

SCIENCE AND HYPOTHESIS, Henri Poincaré. Creative psychology in science. How such concepts as number, magnitude, space, force, classical mechanics were developed, and how the modern scientist uses them in his thought. Hypothesis in physics, theories of modern physics. Introduction by Sir James Larmor. "Few mathematicians have had the breadth of vision of Poincaré, and none is his superior in the gift of clear exposition," E. T. Bell. Index. 272pp. 5⅜ x 8.
S221 Paperbound **$1.35**

PHILOSOPHY AND THE PHYSICISTS, L. S. Stebbing. The philosophical aspects of modern science examined in terms of a lively critical attack on the ideas of Jeans and Eddington. Discusses the task of science, causality, determinism, probability, consciousness, the relation of the world of physics to that of everyday experience. Probes the philosophical significance of the Planck-Bohr concept of discontinuous energy levels, the inferences to be drawn from Heisenberg's Uncertainty Principle, the implications of "becoming" involved in the 2nd law of thermodynamics, and other problems posed by the discarding of Laplacean determinism. 285pp. 5⅜ x 8.
T480 Paperbound **$1.65**

THE PHILOSOPHICAL WRITINGS OF PEIRCE, edited by Justus Buchler. (Formerly published as THE PHILOSOPHY OF PEIRCE.) This is a carefully balanced exposition of Peirce's complete system, written by Peirce himself. It covers such matters as scientific method, pure chance vs. law, symbolic logic, theory of signs, pragmatism, experiment, and other topics. Introduction by Justus Buchler, Columbia University. xvi + 368pp. 5⅜ x 8.
T217 Paperbound **$2.00**

LANGUAGE, TRUTH AND LOGIC, A. Ayer. A clear introduction to the Vienna and Cambridge schools of Logical Positivism. It sets up specific tests by which you can evaluate validity of ideas, etc. Contents: Function of philosophy, elimination of metaphysics, nature of analysis, a priori, truth and probability, etc. 10th printing. "I should like to have written it myself," Bertrand Russell. Index. 160pp. 5⅜ x 8.
T10 Paperbound **$1.25**

MATHEMATICS AND SCIENCE: LAST ESSAYS (DERNIÈRES PENSÉES), Henri Poincaré. Translated by J. W. Bolduc. A posthumous volume of articles and lectures by the great French mathematician, philosopher, scientist. Here are nine pieces, never before translated into English, on such subjects as The Evolution of Laws, Space and Time, Space and 3 Dimensions, The Logic of infinity in Mathematics (discussing Russell's theory of types), Mathematics and Logic, The Quantum Theory and its Modern Applications, Relationship Between Matter and Ether, Ethics and Science and The Moral Alliance. First English translation of Dernières Pensées. New index. viii + 128pp. 5⅜ x 8½.
S1101 Paperbound **$1.25**

THE PSYCHOLOGY OF INVENTION IN THE MATHEMATICAL FIELD, J. Hadamard. Where do ideas come from? What role does the unconscious play? Are ideas best developed by mathematical reasoning, word reasoning, visualization? What are the methods used by Einstein, Poincaré, Galton, Riemann? How can these techniques be applied by others? Hadamard, one of the world's leading mathematicians, discusses these and other questions. xiii + 145pp. 5⅜ x 8.
T107 Paperbound **$1.25**

PHYSICS

General physics

FOUNDATIONS OF PHYSICS, R. B. Lindsay & H. Margenau. Excellent bridge between semi-popular works & technical treatises. A discussion of methods of physical description, construction of theory; valuable for physicist with elementary calculus who is interested in ideas that give meaning to data, tools of modern physics. Contents include symbolism, mathematical equations; space & time foundations of mechanics; probability; physics & continua; electron theory; special & general relativity; quantum mechanics; causality. "Thorough and yet not overdetailed. Unreservedly recommended," NATURE (London). Unabridged, corrected edition. List of recommended readings. 35 illustrations. xi + 537pp. 5⅜ x 8.
S377 Paperbound **$2.75**

FUNDAMENTAL FORMULAS OF PHYSICS, ed. by D. H. Menzel. Highly useful, fully inexpensive reference and study text, ranging from simple to highly sophisticated operations. Mathematics integrated into text—each chapter stands as short textbook of field represented. Vol. 1: Statistics, Physical Constants, Special Theory of Relativity, Hydrodynamics, Aerodynamics, Boundary Value Problems in Math. Physics; Viscosity, Electromagnetic Theory, etc. Vol. 2: Sound, Acoustics, Geometrical Optics, Electron Optics, High-Energy Phenomena, Magnetism, Biophysics, much more. Index. Total of 800pp. 5⅜ x 8.
Vol. 1 S595 Paperbound **$2.00**
Vol. 2 S596 Paperbound **$2.00**

MATHEMATICAL PHYSICS, D. H. Menzel. Thorough one-volume treatment of the mathematical techniques vital for classic mechanics, electromagnetic theory, quantum theory, and relativity. Written by the Harvard Professor of Astrophysics for junior, senior, and graduate courses, it gives clear explanations of all those aspects of function theory, vectors, matrices, dyadics, tensors, partial differential equations, etc., necessary for the understanding of the various physical theories. Electron theory, relativity, and other topics seldom presented appear here in considerable detail. Scores of definitions, conversion factors, dimensional constants, etc. "More detailed than normal for an advanced text . . . excellent set of sections on Dyadics, Matrices, and Tensors," JOURNAL OF THE FRANKLIN INSTITUTE. Index. 193 problems, with answers. x + 412pp. 5⅜ x 8. S56 Paperbound **$2.00**

THE SCIENTIFIC PAPERS OF J. WILLARD GIBBS. All the published papers of America's outstanding theoretical scientist (except for "Statistical Mechanics" and "Vector Analysis"). Vol I (thermodynamics) contains one of the most brilliant of all 19th-century scientific papers—the 300-page "On the Equilibrium of Heterogeneous Substances," which founded the science of physical chemistry, and clearly stated a number of highly important natural laws for the first time; 8 other papers complete the first volume. Vol II includes 2 papers on dynamics, 8 on vector analysis and multiple algebra, 5 on the electromagnetic theory of light, and 6 miscellaneous papers. Biographical sketch by H. A. Bumstead. Total of xxxvi + 718pp. 5⅝ x 8⅜.
S721 Vol I Paperbound **$2.50**
S722 Vol II Paperbound **$2.00**
The set **$4.50**

BASIC THEORIES OF PHYSICS, Peter Gabriel Bergmann. Two-volume set which presents a critical examination of important topics in the major subdivisions of classical and modern physics. The first volume is concerned with classical mechanics and electrodynamics: mechanics of mass points, analytical mechanics, matter in bulk, electrostatics and magnetostatics, electromagnetic interaction, the field waves, special relativity, and waves. The second volume (Heat and Quanta) contains discussions of the kinetic hypothesis, physics and statistics, stationary ensembles, laws of thermodynamics, early quantum theories, atomic spectra, probability waves, quantization in wave mechanics, approximation methods, and abstract quantum theory. A valuable supplement to any thorough course or text.
Heat and Quanta: Index. 8 figures. x + 300pp. 5⅜ x 8½. S968 Paperbound **$1.75**
Mechanics and Electrodynamics: Index. 14 figures. vii + 280pp. 5⅜ x 8½.
S969 Paperbound **$1.75**

THEORETICAL PHYSICS, A. S. Kompaneyets. One of the very few thorough studies of the subject in this price range. Provides advanced students with a comprehensive theoretical background. Especially strong on recent experimentation and developments in quantum theory. Contents: Mechanics (Generalized Coordinates, Lagrange's Equation, Collision of Particles, etc.), Electrodynamics (Vector Analysis, Maxwell's equations, Transmission of Signals, Theory of Relativity, etc.), Quantum Mechanics (the Inadequacy of Classical Mechanics, the Wave Equation, Motion in a Central Field, Quantum Theory of Radiation, Quantum Theories of Dispersion and Scattering, etc.), and Statistical Physics (Equilibrium Distribution of Molecules in an Ideal Gas, Boltzmann statistics, Bose and Fermi Distribution, Thermodynamic Quantities, etc.). Revised to 1961. Translated by George Yankovsky, authorized by Kompaneyets. 137 exercises. 56 figures. 529pp. 5⅜ x 8½. S972 Paperbound **$2.50**

ANALYTICAL AND CANONICAL FORMALISM IN PHYSICS, André Mercier. A survey, in one volume, of the variational principles (the key principles—in mathematical form—from which the basic laws of any one branch of physics can be derived) of the several branches of physical theory, together with an examination of the relationships among them. Contents: the Lagrangian Formalism, Lagrangian Densities, Canonical Formalism, Canonical Form of Electrodynamics, Hamiltonian Densities, Transformations, and Canonical Form with Vanishing Jacobian Determinant. Numerous examples and exercises. For advanced students, teachers, etc. 6 figures. Index. viii + 222pp. 5⅜ x 8½. S1077 Paperbound **$1.75**

Acoustics, optics, electricity and magnetism, electromagnetics, magneto-hydrodynamics

THE THEORY OF SOUND, Lord Rayleigh. Most vibrating systems likely to be encountered in practice can be tackled successfully by the methods set forth by the great Nobel laureate, Lord Rayleigh. Complete coverage of experimental, mathematical aspects of sound theory. Partial contents: Harmonic motions, vibrating systems in general, lateral vibrations of bars, curved plates or shells, applications of Laplace's functions to acoustical problems, fluid friction, plane vortex-sheet, vibrations of solid bodies, etc. This is the first inexpensive edition of this great reference and study work. Bibliography. Historical introduction by R. B. Lindsay. Total of 1040pp. 97 figures. 5⅜ x 8.
S292, S293, Two volume set, paperbound, **$4.70**

THE DYNAMICAL THEORY OF SOUND, H. Lamb. Comprehensive mathematical treatment of the physical aspects of sound, covering the theory of vibrations, the general theory of sound, and the equations of motion of strings, bars, membranes, pipes, and resonators. Includes chapters on plane, spherical, and simple harmonic waves, and the Helmholtz Theory of Audition. Complete and self-contained development for student and specialist; all fundamental differential equations solved completely. Specific mathematical details for such important phenomena as harmonics, normal modes, forced vibrations of strings, theory of reed pipes, etc. Index. Bibliography. 86 diagrams. viii + 307pp. 5⅜ x 8. S655 Paperbound **$1.50**

WAVE PROPAGATION IN PERIODIC STRUCTURES, L. Brillouin. A general method and application to different problems: pure physics, such as scattering of X-rays of crystals, thermal vibration in crystal lattices, electronic motion in metals; and also problems of electrical engineering. Partial contents: elastic waves in 1-dimensional lattices of point masses. Propagation of waves along 1-dimensional lattices. Energy flow. 2 dimensional, 3 dimensional lattices. Mathieu's equation. Matrices and propagation of waves along an electric line. Continuous electric lines. 131 illustrations. Bibliography. Index. xii + 253pp. 5⅜ x 8.
S34 Paperbound **$2.00**

THEORY OF VIBRATIONS, N. W. McLachlan. Based on an exceptionally successful graduate course given at Brown University, this discusses linear systems having 1 degree of freedom, forced vibrations of simple linear systems, vibration of flexible strings, transverse vibrations of bars and tubes, transverse vibration of circular plate, sound waves of finite amplitude, etc. Index. 99 diagrams. 160pp. 5⅜ x 8. S190 Paperbound **$1.35**

LIGHT: PRINCIPLES AND EXPERIMENTS, George S. Monk. Covers theory, experimentation, and research. Intended for students with some background in general physics and elementary calculus. Three main divisions: 1) Eight chapters on geometrical optics—fundamental concepts (the ray and its optical length, Fermat's principle, etc.), laws of image formation, apertures in optical systems, photometry, optical instruments etc.; 2) 9 chapters on physical optics—interference, diffraction, polarization, spectra, the Rayleigh refractometer, the wave theory of light, etc.; 3) 23 instructive experiments based directly on the theoretical text. "Probably the best intermediate textbook on light in the English language. Certainly, it is the best book which includes both geometrical and physical optics," J. Rud Nielson, PHYSICS FORUM. Revised edition. 102 problems and answers. 12 appendices. 6 tables. Index. 270 illustrations. xi +489pp. 5⅜ x 8½. S341 Paperbound **$2.50**

PHOTOMETRY, John W. T. Walsh. The best treatment of both "bench" and "illumination" photometry in English by one of Britain's foremost experts in the field (President of the International Commission on Illumination). Limited to those matters, theoretical and practical, which affect the measurement of light flux, candlepower, illumination, etc., and excludes treatment of the use to which such measurements may be put after they have been made. Chapters on Radiation, The Eye and Vision, Photo-Electric Cells, The Principles of Photometry, The Measurement of Luminous Intensity, Colorimetry, Spectrophotometry, Stellar Photometry, The Photometric Laboratory, etc. Third revised (1958) edition. 281 illustrations. 10 appendices. xxiv + 544pp. 5½ x 9¼. S319 Clothbound **$10.00**

EXPERIMENTAL SPECTROSCOPY, R. A. Sawyer. Clear discussion of prism and grating spectrographs and the techniques of their use in research, with emphasis on those principles and techniques that are fundamental to practically all uses of spectroscopic equipment. Beginning with a brief history of spectroscopy, the author covers such topics as light sources, spectroscopic apparatus, prism spectroscopes and graphs, diffraction grating, the photographic process, determination of wave length, spectral intensity, infrared spectroscopy, spectrochemical analysis, etc. This revised edition contains new material on the production of replica gratings, solar spectroscopy from rockets, new standard of wave length, etc. Index. Bibliography. 111 illustrations. x + 358pp. 5⅜ x 8½. S1045 Paperbound **$2.25**

FUNDAMENTALS OF ELECTRICITY AND MAGNETISM, L. B. Loeb. For students of physics, chemistry, or engineering who want an introduction to electricity and magnetism on a higher level and in more detail than general elementary physics texts provide. Only elementary differential and integral calculus is assumed. Physical laws developed logically, from magnetism to electric currents, Ohm's law, electrolysis, and on to static electricity, induction, etc. Covers an unusual amount of material; one third of book on modern material: solution of wave equation, photoelectric and thermionic effects, etc. Complete statement of the various electrical systems of units and interrelations. 2 Indexes. 75 pages of problems with answers stated. Over 300 figures and diagrams. xix +669pp. 5⅜ x 8. S745 Paperbound **$2.75**

MATHEMATICAL ANALYSIS OF ELECTRICAL AND OPTICAL WAVE-MOTION, Harry Bateman. Written by one of this century's most distinguished mathematical physicists, this is a practical introduction to those developments of Maxwell's electromagnetic theory which are directly connected with the solution of the partial differential equation of wave motion. Methods of solving wave-equation, polar-cylindrical coordinates, diffraction, transformation of coordinates, homogeneous solutions, electromagnetic fields with moving singularities, etc. Index. 168pp. 5⅜ x 8. S14 Paperbound **$1.75**

PRINCIPLES OF PHYSICAL OPTICS, Ernst Mach. This classical examination of the propagation of light, color, polarization, etc. offers an historical and philosophical treatment that has never been surpassed for breadth and easy readability. Contents: Rectilinear propagation of light. Reflection, refraction. Early knowledge of vision. Dioptrics. Composition of light. Theory of color and dispersion. Periodicity. Theory of interference. Polarization. Mathematical representation of properties of light. Propagation of waves, etc. 279 illustrations, 10 portraits. Appendix. Indexes. 324pp. 5⅜ x 8. S178 Paperbound **$2.00**

THE THEORY OF OPTICS, Paul Drude. One of finest fundamental texts in physical optics, classic offers thorough coverage, complete mathematical treatment of basic ideas. Includes fullest treatment of application of thermodynamics to optics; sine law in formation of images, transparent crystals, magnetically active substances, velocity of light, apertures, effects depending upon them, polarization, optical instruments, etc. Introduction by A. A. Michelson. Index. 110 illus. 567pp. 5⅜ x 8. S532 Paperbound **$2.45**

ELECTRICAL THEORY ON THE GIORGI SYSTEM, P. Cornelius. A new clarification of the fundamental concepts of electricity and magnetism, advocating the convenient m.k.s. system of units that is steadily gaining followers in the sciences. Illustrating the use and effectiveness of his terminology with numerous applications to concrete technical problems, the author here expounds the famous Giorgi system of electrical physics. His lucid presentation and well-reasoned, cogent argument for the universal adoption of this system form one of the finest pieces of scientific exposition in recent years. 28 figures. Index. Conversion tables for translating earlier data into modern units. Translated from 3rd Dutch edition by L. J. Jolley. x + 187pp. 5½ x 8¾. S909 Clothbound **$6.00**

ELECTRIC WAVES: BEING RESEARCHES ON THE PROPAGATION OF ELECTRIC ACTION WITH FINITE VELOCITY THROUGH SPACE, Heinrich Hertz. This classic work brings together the original papers in which Hertz—Helmholtz's protegé and one of the most brilliant figures in 19th-century research—probed the existence of electromagnetic waves and showed experimentally that their velocity equalled that of light, research that helped lay the groundwork for the development of radio, television, telephone, telegraph, and other modern technological marvels. Unabridged republication of original edition. Authorized translation by D. E. Jones. Preface by Lord Kelvin. Index of names. 40 illustrations. xvii + 278pp. 5⅜ x 8½. S57 Paperbound **$1.75**

PIEZOELECTRICITY: AN INTRODUCTION TO THE THEORY AND APPLICATIONS OF ELECTROMECHANICAL PHENOMENA IN CRYSTALS, Walter G. Cady. This is the most complete and systematic coverage of this important field in print—now regarded as something of scientific classic. This republication, revised and corrected by Prof. Cady—one of the foremost contributors in this area—contains a sketch of recent progress and new material on Ferroelectrics. Time Standards, etc. The first 7 chapters deal with fundamental theory of crystal electricity. 5 important chapters cover basic concepts of piezoelectricity, including comparisons of various competing theories in the field. Also discussed: piezoelectric resonators (theory, methods of manufacture, influences of air-gaps, etc.); the piezo oscillator; the properties, history, and observations relating to Rochelle salt; ferroelectric crystals; miscellaneous applications of piezoelectricity; pyroelectricity; etc. "A great work," W. A. Wooster, NATURE. Revised (1963) and corrected edition. New preface by Prof. Cady. 2 Appendices. Indices. Illustrations. 62 tables. Bibliography. Problems. Total of 1 + 822pp. 5⅜ x 8½.
S1094 Vol. I Paperbound **$2.50**
S1095 Vol. II Paperbound **$2.50**
Two volume set Paperbound **$5.00**

MAGNETISM AND VERY LOW TEMPERATURES, H. B. G. Casimir. A basic work in the literature of low temperature physics. Presents a concise survey of fundamental theoretical principles, and also points out promising lines of investigation. Contents: Classical Theory and Experimental Methods, Quantum Theory of Paramagnetism, Experiments on Adiabatic Demagnetization. Theoretical Discussion of Paramagnetism at Very Low Temperatures, Some Experimental Results, Relaxation Phenomena. Index. 89-item bibliography. ix + 95pp. 5⅜ x 8. S943 Paperbound **$1.25**

SELECTED PAPERS ON NEW TECHNIQUES FOR ENERGY CONVERSION: THERMOELECTRIC METHODS; THERMIONIC; PHOTOVOLTAIC AND ELECTRICAL EFFECTS; FUSION, Edited by Sumner N. Levine. Brings together in one volume the most important papers (1954-1961) in modern energy technology. Included among the 37 papers are general and qualitative descriptions of the field as a whole, indicating promising lines of research. Also: 15 papers on thermoelectric methods, 7 on thermionic, 5 on photovoltaic, 4 on electrochemical effect, and 2 on controlled fusion research. Among the contributors are: Joffe, Maria Telkes, Herold, Herring, Douglas, Jaumot, Post, Austin, Wilson, Pfann, Rappaport, Morehouse, Domenicali, Moss, Bowers, Harman, Von Doenhoef. Preface and introduction by the editor. Bibliographies. xxviii + 451pp. 6⅛ x 9¼. S37 Paperbound **$3.00**

SUPERFLUIDS: MACROSCOPIC THEORY OF SUPERCONDUCTIVITY, Vol. I, Fritz London. The major work by one of the founders and great theoreticians of modern quantum physics. Consolidates the researches that led to the present understanding of the nature of superconductivity. Prof. London here reveals that quantum mechanics is operative on the macroscopic plane as well as the submolecular level. Contents: Properties of Superconductors and Their Thermodynamical Correlation; Electrodynamics of the Pure Superconducting State; Relation between Current and Field; Measurements of the Penetration Depth; Non-Viscous Flow vs. Superconductivity; Micro-waves in Superconductors; Reality of the Domain Structure; and many other related topics. A new epilogue by M. J. Buckingham discusses developments in the field up to 1960. Corrected and expanded edition. An appreciation of the author's life and work by L. W. Nordheim. Biography by Edith London. Bibliography of his publications. 45 figures. 2 Indices. xviii + 173pp. 5⅝ x 8⅜. S44 Paperbound **$1.45**

SELECTED PAPERS ON PHYSICAL PROCESSES IN IONIZED PLASMAS, Edited by Donald H. Menzel, Director, Harvard College Observatory. 30 important papers relating to the study of highly ionized gases or plasmas selected by a foremost contributor in the field, with the assistance of Dr. L. H. Aller. The essays include 18 on the physical processes in gaseous nebulae, covering problems of radiation and radiative transfer, the Balmer decrement, electron temperatives, spectrophotometry, etc. 10 papers deal with the interpretation of nebular spectra, by Bohm, Van Vleck, Aller, Minkowski, etc. There is also a discussion of the intensities of "forbidden" spectral lines by George Shortley and a paper concerning the theory of hydrogenic spectra by Menzel and Pekeris. Other contributors: Goldberg, Hebb, Baker, Bowen, Ufford, Liller, etc. viii + 374pp. 6⅛ x 9¼. S60 Paperbound **$2.95**

THE ELECTROMAGNETIC FIELD, Max Mason & Warren Weaver. Used constantly by graduate engineers. Vector methods exclusively: detailed treatment of electrostatics, expansion methods, with tables converting any quantity into absolute electromagnetic, absolute electrostatic, practical units. Discrete charges, ponderable bodies, Maxwell field equations, etc. Introduction. Indexes. 416pp. 5⅜ x 8. S185 Paperbound **$2.00**

THEORY OF ELECTRONS AND ITS APPLICATION TO THE PHENOMENA OF LIGHT AND RADIANT HEAT, H. Lorentz. Lectures delivered at Columbia University by Nobel laureate Lorentz. Unabridged, they form a historical coverage of the theory of free electrons, motion, absorption of heat, Zeeman effect, propagation of light in molecular bodies, inverse Zeeman effect, optical phenomena in moving bodies, etc. 109 pages of notes explain the more advanced sections. Index. 9 figures. 352pp. 5⅜ x 8. S173 Paperbound **$1.85**

FUNDAMENTAL ELECTROMAGNETIC THEORY, Ronold P. King, Professor Applied Physics, Harvard University. Original and valuable introduction to electromagnetic theory and to circuit theory from the standpoint of electromagnetic theory. Contents: Mathematical Description of Matter—stationary and nonstationary states; Mathematical Description of Space and of Simple Media—Field Equations, Integral Forms of Field Equations, Electromagnetic Force, etc.; Transformation of Field and Force Equations; Electromagnetic Waves in Unbounded Regions; Skin Effect and Internal Impedance—in a solid cylindrical conductor, etc.; and Electrical Circuits—Analytical Foundations, Near-zone and quasi-near zone circuits, Balanced two-wire and four-wire transmission lines. Revised and enlarged version. New preface by the author. 5 appendices (Differential operators: Vector Formulas and Identities, etc.). Problems. Indexes. Bibliography. xvi + 580pp. 5⅜ x 8½. S1023 Paperbound **$2.75**

Hydrodynamics

A TREATISE ON HYDRODYNAMICS, A. B. Basset. Favorite text on hydrodynamics for 2 generations of physicists, hydrodynamical engineers, oceanographers, ship designers, etc. Clear enough for the beginning student, and thorough source for graduate students and engineers on the work of d'Alembert, Euler, Laplace, Lagrange, Poisson, Green, Clebsch, Stokes, Cauchy, Helmholtz, J. J. Thomson, Love, Hicks, Greenhill, Besant, Lamb, etc. Great amount of documentation on entire theory of classical hydrodynamics. Vol I: theory of motion of frictionless liquids, vortex, and cyclic irrotational motion, etc. 132 exercises. Bibliography. 3 Appendixes. xii + 264pp. Vol II: motion in viscous liquids, harmonic analysis, theory of tides, etc. 112 exercises, Bibliography. 4 Appendixes. xv + 328pp. Two volume set. 5⅜ x 8.
S724 Vol I Paperbound **$1.75**
S725 Vol II Paperbound **$1.75**
The set **$3.50**

HYDRODYNAMICS, Horace Lamb. Internationally famous complete coverage of standard reference work on dynamics of liquids & gases. Fundamental theorems, equations, methods, solutions, background, for classical hydrodynamics. Chapters include Equations of Motion, Integration of Equations in Special Gases, Irrotational Motion, Motion of Liquid in 2 Dimensions, Motion of Solids through Liquid-Dynamical Theory, Vortex Motion, Tidal Waves, Surface Waves, Waves of Expansion, Viscosity, Rotating Masses of liquids. Excellently planned, arranged; clear, lucid presentation. 6th enlarged, revised edition. Index. Over 900 footnotes, mostly bibliographical. 119 figures. xv + 738pp. 6⅛ x 9¼. S256 Paperbound **$3.75**

HYDRODYNAMICS, H. Dryden, F. Murnaghan, Harry Bateman. Published by the National Research Council in 1932 this enormous volume offers a complete coverage of classical hydrodynamics. Encyclopedic in quality. Partial contents: physics of fluids, motion, turbulent flow, compressible fluids, motion in 1, 2, 3 dimensions; viscous fluids rotating, laminar motion, resistance of motion through viscous fluid, eddy viscosity, hydraulic flow in channels of various shapes, discharge of gases, flow past obstacles, etc. Bibliography of over 2,900 items. Indexes. 23 figures. 634pp. 5⅜ x 8. S303 Paperbound **$2.75**

Mechanics, dynamics, thermodynamics, elasticity

MECHANICS, J. P. Den Hartog. Already a classic among introductory texts, the M.I.T. professor's lively and discursive presentation is equally valuable as a beginner's text, an engineering student's refresher, or a practicing engineer's reference. Emphasis in this highly readable text is on illuminating fundamental principles and showing how they are embodied in a great number of real engineering and design problems: trusses, loaded cables, beams, jacks, hoists, etc. Provides advanced material on relative motion and gyroscopes not usual in introductory texts. "Very thoroughly recommended to all those anxious to improve their real understanding of the principles of mechanics." MECHANICAL WORLD. Index. List of equations. 334 problems, all with answers. Over 550 diagrams and drawings. ix + 462pp. 5⅜ x 8. S754 Paperbound **$2.00**

THEORETICAL MECHANICS: AN INTRODUCTION TO MATHEMATICAL PHYSICS, J. S. Ames, F. D. Murnaghan. A mathematically rigorous development of theoretical mechanics for the advanced student, with constant practical applications. Used in hundreds of advanced courses. An unusually thorough coverage of gyroscopic and baryscopic material, detailed analyses of the Coriolis acceleration, applications of Lagrange's equations, motion of the double pendulum, Hamilton-Jacobi partial differential equations, group velocity and dispersion, etc. Special relativity is also included. 159 problems. 44 figures. ix + 462pp. 5⅜ x 8. S461 Paperbound **$2.25**

THEORETICAL MECHANICS: STATICS AND THE DYNAMICS OF A PARTICLE, W. D. MacMillan. Used for over 3 decades as a self-contained and extremely comprehensive advanced undergraduate text in mathematical physics, physics, astronomy, and deeper foundations of engineering. Early sections require only a knowledge of geometry; later, a working knowledge of calculus. Hundreds of basic problems, including projectiles to the moon, escape velocity, harmonic motion, ballistics, falling bodies, transmission of power, stress and strain, elasticity, astronomical problems. 340 practice problems plus many fully worked out examples make it possible to test and extend principles developed in the text. 200 figures. xvii + 430pp. 5⅜ x 8. S467 Paperbound **$2.00**

THEORETICAL MECHANICS: THE THEORY OF THE POTENTIAL, W. D. MacMillan. A comprehensive, well balanced presentation of potential theory, serving both as an introduction and a reference work with regard to specific problems, for physicists and mathematicians. No prior knowledge of integral relations is assumed, and all mathematical material is developed as it becomes necessary. Includes: Attraction of Finite Bodies; Newtonian Potential Function; Vector Fields, Green and Gauss Theorems; Attractions of Surfaces and Lines; Surface Distribution of Matter; Two-Layer Surfaces; Spherical Harmonics; Ellipsoidal Harmonics; etc. "The great number of particular cases . . . should make the book valuable to geophysicists and others actively engaged in practical applications of the potential theory," Review of Scientific Instruments. Index. Bibliography. xiii + 469pp. 5⅜ x 8. S486 Paperbound **$2.25**

THEORETICAL MECHANICS: DYNAMICS OF RIGID BODIES, W. D. MacMillan. Theory of dynamics of a rigid body is developed, using both the geometrical and analytical methods of instruction. Begins with exposition of algebra of vectors, it goes through momentum principles, motion in space, use of differential equations and infinite series to solve more sophisticated dynamics problems. Partial contents: moments of inertia, systems of free particles, motion parallel to a fixed plane, rolling motion, method of periodic solutions, much more. 82 figs. 199 problems. Bibliography. Indexes. xii + 476pp. 5⅜ x 8. S641 Paperbound **$2.00**

MATHEMATICAL FOUNDATIONS OF STATISTICAL MECHANICS, A. I. Khinchin. Offering a precise and rigorous formulation of problems, this book supplies a thorough and up-to-date exposition. It provides analytical tools needed to replace cumbersome concepts, and furnishes for the first time a logical step-by-step introduction to the subject. Partial contents: geometry & kinematics of the phase space, ergodic problem, reduction to theory of probability, application of central limit problem, ideal monatomic gas, foundation of thermo-dynamics, dispersion and distribution of sum functions. Key to notations. Index. viii + 179pp. 5⅜ x 8. S147 Paperbound **$1.50**

ELEMENTARY PRINCIPLES IN STATISTICAL MECHANICS, J. W. Gibbs. Last work of the great Yale mathematical physicist, still one of the most fundamental treatments available for advanced students and workers in the field. Covers the basic principle of conservation of probability of phase, theory of errors in the calculated phases of a system, the contributions of Clausius, Maxwell, Boltzmann, and Gibbs himself, and much more. Includes valuable comparison of statistical mechanics with thermodynamics: Carnot's cycle, mechanical definitions of entropy, etc. xvi + 208pp. 5⅜ x 8. S707 Paperbound **$1.45**

PRINCIPLES OF MECHANICS AND DYNAMICS, Sir William Thomson (Lord Kelvin) and Peter Guthrie Tait. The principles and theories of fundamental branches of classical physics explained by two of the greatest physicists of all time. A broad survey of mechanics, with material on hydrodynamics, elasticity, potential theory, and what is now standard mechanics. Thorough and detailed coverage, with many examples, derivations, and topics not included in more recent studies. Only a knowledge of calculus is needed to work through this book. Vol. I (Preliminary): Kinematics; Dynamical Laws and Principles; Experience (observation, experimentation, formation of hypotheses, scientific method); Measures and Instruments; Continuous Calculating Machines. Vol. II (Abstract Dynamics): Statics of a Particle—Attraction; Statics of Solids and Fluids. Formerly Titled "Treatise on Natural Philosophy." Unabridged reprint of revised edition. Index. 168 diagrams. Total of xlii + 1035pp. 5⅜ x 8½.
Vol. I: S966 Paperbound **$2.35**
Vol. II: S967 Paperbound **$2.35**
Two volume Set Paperbound **$4.70**

INVESTIGATIONS ON THE THEORY OF THE BROWNIAN MOVEMENT, Albert Einstein. Reprints from rare European journals. 5 basic papers, including the Elementary Theory of the Brownian Movement, written at the request of Lorentz to provide a simple explanation. Translated by A. D. Cowper. Annotated, edited by R. Fürth. 33pp. of notes elucidate, give history of previous investigations. Author, subject indexes. 62 footnotes. 124pp. 5⅜ x 8.
S304 Paperbound **$1.25**

MECHANICS VIA THE CALCULUS, P. W. Norris, W. S. Legge. Covers almost everything, from linear motion to vector analysis: equations determining motion, linear methods, compounding of simple harmonic motions, Newton's laws of motion, Hooke's law, the simple pendulum, motion of a particle in 1 plane, centers of gravity, virtual work, friction, kinetic energy of rotating bodies, equilibrium of strings, hydrostatics, sheering stresses, elasticity, etc. 550 problems. 3rd revised edition. xii + 367pp. 6 x 9. S207 Clothbound **$4.95**

THE DYNAMICS OF PARTICLES AND OF RIGID, ELASTIC, AND FLUID BODIES; BEING LECTURES ON MATHEMATICAL PHYSICS, A. G. Webster. The reissuing of this classic fills the need for a comprehensive work on dynamics. A wide range of topics is covered in unusually great depth, applying ordinary and partial differential equations. Part I considers laws of motion and methods applicable to systems of all sorts; oscillation, resonance, cyclic systems, etc. Part 2 is a detailed study of the dynamics of rigid bodies. Part 3 introduces the theory of potential; stress and strain, Newtonian potential functions, gyrostatics, wave and vortex motion, etc. Further contents: Kinematics of a point; Lagrange's equations; Hamilton's principle; Systems of vectors; Statics and dynamics of deformable bodies; much more, not easily found together in one volume. Unabridged reprinting of 2nd edition. 20 pages of notes on differential equations and the higher analysis. 203 illustrations. Selected bibliography. Index. xi + 588pp. 5⅜ x 8. S522 Paperbound **$2.45**

A TREATISE ON DYNAMICS OF A PARTICLE, E. J. Routh. Elementary text on dynamics for beginning mathematics or physics student. Unusually detailed treatment from elementary definitions to motion in 3 dimensions, emphasizing concrete aspects. Much unique material important in recent applications. Covers impulsive forces, rectilinear and constrained motion in 2 dimensions, harmonic and parabolic motion, degrees of freedom, closed orbits, the conical pendulum, the principle of least action, Jacobi's method, and much more. Index. 559 problems, many fully worked out, incorporated into text. xiii + 418pp. 5⅜ x 8.
S696 Paperbound **$2.25**

DYNAMICS OF A SYSTEM OF RIGID BODIES (Elementary Section), E. J. Routh. Revised 7th edition of this standard reference. This volume covers the dynamical principles of the subject, and its more elementary applications: finding moments of inertia by integration, foci of inertia, d'Alembert's principle, impulsive forces, motion in 2 and 3 dimensions, Lagrange's equations, relative indicatrix, Euler's theorem, large tautochronous motions, etc. Index. 55 figures. Scores of problems. xv + 443pp. 5⅜ x 8. S664 Paperbound **$2.50**

DYNAMICS OF A SYSTEM OF RIGID BODIES (Advanced Section), E. J. Routh. Revised 6th edition of a classic reference aid. Much of its material remains unique. Partial contents: moving axes, relative motion, oscillations about equilibrium, motion. Motion of a body under no forces, any forces. Nature of motion given by linear equations and conditions of stability. Free, forced vibrations, constants of integration, calculus of finite differences, variations, precession and nutation, motion of the moon, motion of string, chain, membranes. 64 figures. 498pp. 5⅜ x 8. S229 Paperbound **$2.45**

DYNAMICAL THEORY OF GASES, James Jeans. Divided into mathematical and physical chapters for the convenience of those not expert in mathematics, this volume discusses the mathematical theory of gas in a steady state, thermodynamics, Boltzmann and Maxwell, kinetic theory, quantum theory, exponentials, etc. 4th enlarged edition, with new material on quantum theory, quantum dynamics, etc. Indexes. 28 figures. 444pp. 6⅛ x 9¼.
S136 Paperbound **$2.65**

THE THEORY OF HEAT RADIATION, Max Planck. A pioneering work in thermodynamics, providing basis for most later work, Nobel laureate Planck writes on Deductions from Electrodynamics and Thermodynamics, Entropy and Probability, Irreversible Radiation Processes, etc. Starts with simple experimental laws of optics, advances to problems of spectral distribution of energy and irreversibility. Bibliography. 7 illustrations, xiv + 224pp. 5⅜ x 8.
S546 Paperbound **$1.75**

FOUNDATIONS OF POTENTIAL THEORY, O. D. Kellogg. Based on courses given at Harvard this is suitable for both advanced and beginning mathematicians. Proofs are rigorous, and much material not generally avaliable elsewhere is included. Partial contents: forces of gravity, fields of force, divergence theorem, properties of Newtonian potentials at points of free space, potentials as solutions of Laplace's equations, harmonic functions, electrostatics, electric images, logarithmic potential, etc. One of Grundlehren Series. ix + 384pp. 5⅜ x 8.
S144 Paperbound **$1.98**

THERMODYNAMICS, Enrico Fermi. Unabridged reproduction of 1937 edition. Elementary in treatment; remarkable for clarity, organization. Requires no knowledge of advanced math beyond calculus, only familiarity with fundamentals of thermometry, calorimetry. Partial Contents: Thermodynamic systems; First & Second laws of thermodynamics; Entropy; Thermodynamic potentials: phase rule, reversible electric cell; Gaseous reactions: van't Hoff reaction box, principle of LeChatelier; Thermodynamics of dilute solutions: osmotic & vapor pressures, boiling & freezing points; Entropy constant. Index. 25 problems. 24 illustrations. x + 160pp. 5⅜ x 8.
S361 Paperbound **$1.75**

THE THERMODYNAMICS OF ELECTRICAL PHENOMENA IN METALS and A CONDENSED COLLECTION OF THERMODYNAMIC FORMULAS, P. W. Bridgman. Major work by the Nobel Prizewinner: stimulating conceptual introduction to aspects of the electron theory of metals, giving an intuitive understanding of fundamental relationships concealed by the formal systems of Onsager and others. Elementary mathematical formulations show clearly the fundamental thermodynamical relationships of the electric field, and a complete phenomenological theory of metals is created. This is the work in which Bridgman announced his famous "thermomotive force" and his distinction between "driving" and "working" electromotive force. We have added in this Dover edition the author's long unavailable tables of thermodynamic formulas, extremely valuable for the speed of reference they allow. Two works bound as one. Index. 33 figures. Bibliography. xviii + 256pp. 5⅜ x 8. S723 Paperbound **$1.65**

TREATISE ON THERMODYNAMICS, Max Planck. Based on Planck's original papers this offers a uniform point of view for the entire field and has been used as an introduction for students who have studied elementary chemistry, physics, and calculus. Rejecting the earlier approaches of Helmholtz and Maxwell, the author makes no assumptions regarding the nature of heat, but begins with a few empirical facts, and from these deduces new physical and chemical laws. 3rd English edition of this standard text by a Nobel laureate. xvi + 297pp. 5⅜ x 8.
S219 Paperbound **$1.75**

THE MATHEMATICAL THEORY OF ELASTICITY, A. E. H. Love. A wealth of practical illustration combined with thorough discussion of fundamentals—theory, application, special problems and solutions. Partial Contents: Analysis of Strain & Stress, Elasticity of Solid Bodies, Elasticity of Crystals, Vibration of Spheres, Cylinders, Propagation of Waves in Elastic Solid Media, Torsion, Theory of Continuous Beams, Plates. Rigorous treatment of Volterra's theory of dislocations, 2-dimensional elastic systems, other topics of modern interest. "For years the standard treatise on elasticity," AMERICAN MATHEMATICAL MONTHLY. 4th revised edition. Index. 76 figures. xviii + 643pp. 6⅛ x 9¼.
S174 Paperbound **$3.00**

STRESS WAVES IN SOLIDS, H. Kolsky, Professor of Applied Physics, Brown University. The most readable survey of the theoretical core of current knowledge about the propagation of waves in solids, fully correlated with experimental research. Contents: Part I—Elastic Waves: propagation in an extended plastic medium, propagation in bounded elastic media, experimental investigations with elastic materials. Part II—Stress Waves in Imperfectly Elastic Media: internal friction, experimental investigations of dynamic elastic properties, plastic waves and shock waves, fractures produced by stress waves. List of symbols. Appendix. Supplemented bibliography. 3 full-page plates. 46 figures. x + 213pp. 5⅜ x 8½.
S1098 Paperbound **$1.55**

Relativity, quantum theory, atomic and nuclear physics

SPACE TIME MATTER, Hermann Weyl. "The standard treatise on the general theory of relativity" (Nature), written by a world-renowned scientist, provides a deep clear discussion of the logical coherence of the general theory, with introduction to all the mathematical tools needed: Maxwell, analytical geometry, non-Euclidean geometry, tensor calculus, etc. Basis is classical space-time, before absorption of relativity. Partial contents: Euclidean space, mathematical form, metrical continuum, relativity of time and space, general theory. 15 diagrams. Bibliography. New preface for this edition. xviii + 330pp. 5⅜ x 8.
S267 Paperbound **$2.00**

ATOMIC SPECTRA AND ATOMIC STRUCTURE, G. Herzberg. Excellent general survey for chemists, physicists specializing in other fields. Partial contents: simplest line spectra and elements of atomic theory, building-up principle and periodic system of elements, hyperfine structure of spectral lines, some experiments and applications. Bibilography. 80 figures. Index. xii + 257pp. 5⅜ x 8.
S115 Paperbound **$2.00**

THE PRINCIPLE OF RELATIVITY, A. Einstein, H. Lorentz, H. Minkowski, H. Weyl. These are the 11 basic papers that founded the general and special theories of relativity, all translated into English. Two papers by Lorentz on the Michelson experiment, electromagnetic phenomena. Minkowski's SPACE & TIME, and Weyl's GRAVITATION & ELECTRICITY. 7 epoch-making papers by Einstein: ELECTROMAGNETICS OF MOVING BODIES, INFLUENCE OF GRAVITATION IN PROPAGATION OF LIGHT, COSMOLOGICAL CONSIDERATIONS, GENERAL THEORY, and 3 others. 7 diagrams. Special notes by A. Sommerfeld. 224pp. 5⅜ x 8.
S81 Paperbound **$1.75**

EINSTEIN'S THEORY OF RELATIVITY, Max Born. Revised edition prepared with the collaboration of Gunther Leibfried and Walter Biem. Steering a middle course between superficial popularizations and complex analyses, a Nobel laureate explains Einstein's theories clearly and with special insight. Easily followed by the layman with a knowledge of high school mathematics, the book has been thoroughly revised and extended to modernize those sections of the well-known original edition which are now out of date. After a comprehensive review of classical physics, Born's discussion of special and general theories of relativity covers such topics as simultaneity, kinematics, Einstein's mechanics and dynamics, relativity of arbitrary motions, the geometry of curved surfaces, the space-time continuum, and many others. Index. Illustrations, vii + 376pp. 5⅜ x 8. S769 Paperbound **$2.00**

ATOMS, MOLECULES AND QUANTA, Arthur E. Ruark and Harold C. Urey. Revised (1963) and corrected edition of a work that has been a favorite with physics students and teachers for more than 30 years. No other work offers the same combination of atomic structure and molecular physics and of experiment and theory. The first 14 chapters deal with the origins and major experimental data of quantum theory and with the development of conceptions of atomic and molecular structure prior to the new mechanics. These sections provide a thorough introduction to atomic and molecular theory, and are presented lucidly and as simply as possible. The six subsequent chapters are devoted to the laws and basic ideas of quantum mechanics: Wave Mechanics, Hydrogenic Atoms in Wave Mechanics, Matrix Mechanics, General Theory of Quantum Dynamics, etc. For advanced college and graduate students in physics. Revised, corrected republication of original edition, with supplementary notes by the authors. New preface by the authors. 9 appendices. General reference list. Indices. 228 figures. 71 tables. Bibliographical material in notes, etc. Total of xxiii + 810pp. 5⅜ x 8⅜.
S1106 Vol. I Paperbound **$2.50**
S1107 Vol. II Paperbound **$2.50**
Two volume set Paperbound **$5.00**

WAVE MECHANICS AND ITS APPLICATIONS, N. F. Mott and I. N. Sneddon. A comprehensive introduction to the theory of quantum mechanics; not a rigorous mathematical exposition it progresses, instead, in accordance with the physical problems considered. Many topics difficult to find at the elementary level are discussed in this book. Includes such matters as: the wave nature of matter, the wave equation of Schrödinger, the concept of stationary states, properties of the wave functions, effect of a magnetic field on the energy levels of atoms, electronic spin, two-body problem, theory of solids, cohesive forces in ionic crystals, collision problems, interaction of radiation with matter, relativistic quantum mechanics, etc. All are treated both physically and mathematically. 68 illustrations. 11 tables. Indexes. xii + 393pp. 5⅜ x 8½. S1070 Paperbound **$2.25**

BASIC METHODS IN TRANSFER PROBLEMS, V. Kourganoff, Professor of Astrophysics, U. of Paris. A coherent digest of all the known methods which can be used for approximate or exact solutions of transfer problems. All methods demonstrated on one particular problem —Milne's problem for a plane parallel medium. Three main sections: fundamental concepts (the radiation field and its interaction with matter, the absorption and emission coefficients, etc.); different methods by which transfer problems can be attacked; and a more general problem—the non-grey case of Milne's problem. Much new material, drawing upon declassified atomic energy reports and data from the USSR. Entirely understandable to the student with a reasonable knowledge of analysis. Unabridged, revised reprinting. New preface by the author. Index. Bibliography. 2 appendices. xv + 281pp. 5⅜ x 8½.
S1074 Paperbound **$2.00**

PRINCIPLES OF QUANTUM MECHANICS, W. V. Houston. Enables student with working knowledge of elementary mathematical physics to develop facility in use of quantum mechanics, understand published work in field. Formulates quantum mechanics in terms of Schroedinger's wave mechanics. Studies evidence for quantum theory, for inadequacy of classical mechanics, 2 postulates of quantum mechanics; numerous important, fruitful applications of quantum mechanics in spectroscopy, collision problems, electrons in solids; other topics. "One of the most rewarding features . . . is the interlacing of problems with text," Amer. J. of Physics. Corrected edition. 21 illus. Index. 296pp. 5⅜ x 8. S524 Paperbound **$1.85**

PHYSICAL PRINCIPLES OF THE QUANTUM THEORY, Werner Heisenberg. A Nobel laureate discusses quantum theory; Heisenberg's own work, Compton, Schroedinger, Wilson, Einstein, many others. Written for physicists, chemists who are not specialists in quantum theory, only elementary formulae are considered in the text; there is a mathematical appendix for specialists. Profound without sacrifice of clarity. Translated by C. Eckart, F. Hoyt. 18 figures. 192pp. 5⅜ x 8. S113 Paperbound **$1.25**